Inside HELP®

Administration and Reference Manual for HELP (the *Hawaii Early Learning Profile*) Birth-3 years

Written and adapted by
Stephanie Parks, MA

Contributors
Marie Celeste, EdD
Lisa A. Dannemiller, PT, DSc, PCS
Gillian M. Donaldson, MA, CCC-SLP
Robin E. Gold, MS, OTR/L

VORT Corporation

www.VORT.com

Copyright © 1992, 2006 VORT Corporation.
Printed in the United States of America. All rights reserved.
ISBN:978-0-89718-097-9

Published by:
VORT Corporation
www.VORT.com

Publisher's Note

We are pleased to have the opportunity to publish this important resource. It is concise and compre-hensive, yet we cannot anticipate the circumstances under which a reader may apply its contents. Each child is unique and masters skills and develops at a rate and an age often different from other children. We therefore urge that you seek additional professional advice if you have any concerns about a child's health or development. We expressly decline liability for the techniques, activities, or results of conclu-sions you may reach about a child after reading and applying the contents of this book.

For Use by Professionals

These materials are intended for use by professionals working with the child and the family. The child's doctor must be consulted under all circumstances regarding the child's sleep position, if the child has special needs/health issues, or if there are any health or safety questions whatsoever.

Safety First!

Although precaution and safety notes are included for some activities, there may be some activities which are not appropriate for some children, and some which have the potential for misinterpre-tation. It is your professional responsibility to carefully review the appropriateness of the informa-tion and activities for each particular child, and to alter the activity and/or add additional safety precautions as needed. It is extremely important to use caution with the child and to supervise him carefully around sharp objects and utensils, appliances, small objects, scissors, hot water, etc. **Remind parents of these safety issues, and advise parents to *always* supervise their child.** For example, the U.S. Consumer Product Safety Commission (CPSC) urges caregivers to be sure that infant toys, such as rattles, squeeze toys, and teethers are large enough so that they cannot enter and become lodged in an infant's throat. Numerous toy and infant safety guidelines and brochures are available through their website: www.cpsc.gov.

> ### For the latest product information and samples,
> ### answers to Frequently Asked Questions (FAQs), and
> ### online ordering, please visit our Web site at:
> ### http://www.vort.com

A Quick Start to *Inside HELP*

• Structure of *Inside HELP* Developmental Domains and Strands

As shown on **pages i.4 - i.5**, *Inside HELP* is divided into seven major sections according to the following seven developmental domains:

    0.0 Regulatory/Sensory Organization
    1.0 Cognitive
    2.0 Language
    3.0 Gross Motor
    4.0 Fine Motor
    5.0 Social-Emotional
    6.0 Self Help

With the exception of 0.0 Regulatory/Sensory Organization, each of the domains is further divided into sequential sub-areas of development referred to as "Strands." Each strand represents an underlying concept in which the HELP skills and behaviors are sequentially ordered and hierarchical in nature; i.e., one skill leads to the next skill.

• Support for Infant and Toddler Legislation

See **pages i.8 - i.9** for a side-by-side comparison of the requirements of Part C, IDEA, and how *Inside HELP* can help you meet these requirements.

• Instructions for Using *Inside HELP*

See **pages i.15** through **i.35** for:
    Important Reminders (page i.15)
    Quick Tour of *Inside HELP* (page i.15)
    How to Use HELP
        Before the Assessment (page i.19)
        During the Assessment (page i.21)
        After the Assessment (page i.22)
    How to Determine and Report Levels of Development (page i.23)
    Using HELP to Achieve Outcomes (page i.28)
    Using HELP as an Ongoing Assessment (page i.29)
    Sample Structure of a Direct Assessment (page i.30)
    General Assessment Guidelines and Precautions (page i.32)
    Frequently Asked Questions – FAQs (page i.34)

• Use the Cross-Reference Index, page 374, to quickly locate individual skills
e.g., skill 1.01 is on page 6 of *Inside HELP*.

CONTENTS

Quick Tip #1
Use the header in the top corner of each page to quickly locate Strands and Domains, e.g., flip the pages to find Strand 5-1 on pages 60-68.

(Continued on page i.6)

Quick Tip #2

Use the Skills Cross-Reference Index on paeg 374 to quickly locate individual skills, e.g., skill 1.01 is on page 6 of *Inside HELP*.

ACKNOWLEDGMENTS

A project of this scope and nature could not have been accomplished without the teamwork, expertise, talents, assistance and encouragement of many people throughout the years of development. My deepest appreciation and gratitude is extended to:

Lisa Dannemiller, M.A. Ed., P.T., Gillian Donaldson, M.A., CCC-SPL, Robin Gold, and Marie Celeste, who as major contributors to this work, collaborated with me from the inception through completion —which continued well beyond my initial predictions!

The expert reviewers whose valuable advice, expertise, and many hours of dedication to the review process went beyond expectation: Kathy Katz, Ph.D., Lynn A. Balzer-Martin, Ph.D., O.T.R., Toby M. Long, Ph.D., P.T., and Eva K. Thorp, Ed.D.;

The pediatric team at the Prince William County Parent Infant Education Program whom I have had the wonderful opportunity to work with and learn from and who provided their valuable clinical talents, insights and suggestions during the field testing and revision process over last four years:
   Infant Educators: Laurie Andrews, Terri Del Colliano, Corrie Humberston and Mary Steensma;
   Social Workers: Joanne Kaufman, Jody Lyon and Mary Geisen;
   Pediatric Physical Therapists: Lisa Dannemiller, Kelly Hill, Betty Mallory and Trudy Roth;
   Pediatric Occupational Therapists: Susanne Breckenridge, Nancy Brockway, Robin Gold and
    Christie Roe;
   Speech Language Therapists: Gillian Donaldson, Peggy Fees and Elizabeth Nelson;

Gerry Desrosiers, my mentor and boss, for his design talents, and who provided me with the encouragement and freedom to conduct this work;

Neil Van Scott, my administrative assistant, for his technical support, constant good spirits, patience and respect for our efforts throughout the development of this work;

The hundreds of infants and toddlers with special needs and their families involved in field testing who taught us so much, helped shaped the direction of *Inside* HELP, and are the reason for the development of this work;

Meave Stevens-Dominguez, Ed.D., Early Childhood Training Unit, University of New Mexico and Eva K. Thorp, Ed.D. during her visiting assistant professorship at the University of Illinois, for their initial consultations and enthusiastic support during the early development of the strand framework;

Craig D. Chalfant for his artistic talents in his illustrations;

My postgraduate students at George Mason University who provided extremely helpful feedback and whose enthusiasm helped make the final completion even more exciting;

Tom Holt, president of VORT, for his help in the design of *Inside HELP,* and his patience and vision as the direction of this Manual evolved and expanded from its original outline;

And finally to my mother, LaVonne Berens, for her loving support, and to my daughter Kimberly, who once again will finally be getting her mother back.

S. P.

INTRODUCTION

Purpose

Inside HELP is a comprehensive administration and reference guide to be used in conjunction with all the HELP (Hawaii Early Learning Profile, Birth-3) curriculum and assessment materials: the *HELP Strands, HELP Checklist, HELP Charts, HELP Activity Guide, HELP at Home, HELP When the Parent has Disabilities,* and the *HELP Family-Centered Interview.*

   Inside HELP is intended to maximize the use of HELP as a curriculum-based assessment. It includes clear definitions, flexible contextually-based assessment guidelines, and credit criteria for each of the 685 developmental skills and behaviors appearing in all the HELP products (Birth-3). In addition, it provides guidelines for understanding and interpreting the child's skills and behaviors in the context of his caregiving relationships and environments, and recognizes families as *central* to the assessment process. As a curriculum-based assessment, HELP is directly linked with parent and professional curriculum activities and strategies to help promote the child's development and positive parent-child interactions.

Objectives of *Inside HELP*

Using *Inside HELP* with the *HELP Strands, Charts, or Checklist* will facilitate the professional's efforts to:
   * Identify and report qualitative descriptions of the child's developmental skills and behaviors along multiple lines of development;
   * Determine approximate developmental levels within and between major domains of development;
   * Identify strengths and needs within and between major domains of development;
   * Interpret how one area of development may be influencing another area of development;
   * Conduct a family-directed assessment of family concerns, priorities and resources as they relate to the development of their child;
   * Recognize factors in the child's physical environment that support development;
   * Recognize caregiver interactions that support and facilitate the child's development;
   * Develop child and family outcome statements with the family that are meaningful and functional to the child and family.

Designed to support Infant and Toddler Legislation (IDEA)

Professionals who work within early intervention programs will find *Inside HELP* especially valuable because it addresses many of the requirements for multidisciplinary, family-centered assessment in accordance with Part C, Individuals with Disabilities Education Improvement Act (see pages i.8 - i.9).

Sidebar:

• Maximizes use of HELP as a curriculum-based assessment tool

• Links HELP (Birth-3)
HELP Strands
HELP Checklist
HELP Charts
HELP Activity Guide
HELP at Home
HELP When the Parent has Disabilities
HELP Family Interview

• Qualitative descriptions

• Approximate developmental levels

• Identify strengths and needs

• Conduct family-directed assessment

• Recognize environmental factors

• Recognize caregiver interactions

• Develop child and family outcome statements

To be used as an interdisciplinary guide with young children who are delayed, have disabilities or are considered "at-risk"

• Supports legislation for Infants, Toddlers and their families

Inside HELP and Part C of IDEA

Using *Inside HELP* to Meet the Needs of Infants and Toddlers with Disability and their families in accordance with Part C of Individuals with Disabilities Education Improvement Act, P.L. 108-446- Dec. 3, 2004 / Section 636. Individualized Family Services Plan.

Part C of IDEA Requires ➡	Inside HELP provides...
"Sec.636. (a) **ASSESSMENT AND PROGRAM DEVELOP-MENT**: for each infant or toddler with a disability, and the infant's or toddler's family to receive-	• Assessment and intervention materials for infants and toddlers, birth to three years, and their families, including assessment and program adaptations for disabilities.
(1) a multidisciplinary assessment of the unique strengths and needs of the infant or toddler, and the identification of services appropriate to meet such needs;	• Assessment skills are applicable across multiple disciplines, e.g., special educators, speech-language pathologists, occupational therapists, physical therapists, psychologists. • Flexible definitions and assessment process helps identify the unique strengths and needs of the infant and toddler *within and across* 6 developmental domains using 40 conceptually-based "Strands".
(2) a family directed assessment of the resources, priorities, and concerns of the family and the identification of the supports and services necessary to enhance the family's capacity to meet the developmental needs of the infant or toddler; and	• Family Friendly explanations are included to help families understand what we are assessing and why. • "Parent Questions" are provided to help families 1) identify the unique strengths and needs related to the development of their child, and, 2) to help identify family concerns, priorities and resources related • *HELP Family-Centered Interview* is also available as a separate family directed assessment tool.
(3) a written individualized family service plan developed by a multidisciplinary team, including the parents...	• Addresses most components of IFSP as follows, in "CONTENT OF PLAN".
(d). **CONTENT OF PLAN.** – The individualized family service plan shall be in writing and contain-	• Comprehensive assessment information needed for a multidisciplinary team to develop an IFSP
(1) a statement of the infant's or toddler's present levels of physical development, cognitive development, communication development, social or emotional development, and adaptive development, based on objective criteria;	• More than 650 developmental skills and behaviors are available for assement within the areas of physical development (3.0 Gross Motor, 4.0 Fine Motor) cognitive (1.0 Cognitive) development, communication development (2.0 Language), social or emotional development (5.0 Social Emotional), and adaptive development (6.0 Self-Help). • Clear definitions and assessment criteria are provided for each skill and behavior.

Inside HELP and Part C of IDEA

Using *Inside HELP* to Meet the Needs of Infants and Toddlers with Disability and their families
in accordance with Part C of Individuals with Disabilities Education Improvement Act,
P.L. 108-446- Dec. 3, 2004 / Section 636. Individualized Family Services Plan.

Part C of IDEA Requires ⟶	Inside HELP provides...
(2) a statement of the family's resources, priorities, and concerns relating to enhancing the development of the family's infant or toddler with a disability;	• sample family-centered interview questions and meaningful family-friendly information to help families provide their own descriptions of their primary resources, priorities, and concerns related to enhancing the development of their child. • *HELP Family-Centered Interview* is also available as a separate family directed assessment tool.
(3) a statement of the measurable results or outcomes expected to be achieved for the infant or toddler and the family...	• examples of measurable, meaningful and functional child and family outcome statements that can be gleaned from developmental assessment skills.
(4) a statement of specific early intervention services based on peer-review research, to the extent practicable, necessary to meet the unique needs of the infant or toddler and the family, ...	• comprehensive, multidimensional information that is based upon expert peer review and research to help IFSP teams identify services necessary to meet the unique needs of the infant, toddler and family, e.g., - direct child assessment - transactional assessment of child's environment and caregiver interactions - information to help identify if and why a child displays significant delays in a particular Strand area of development.
(5) a statement of the natural environments in which early intervention services will appropriately be provided, including a justification of the extent, if any, to which the services will to be provided in a natural environment;	• Flexible use of assessment and curriculum materials, and, environments that are readily available, safe, and familiar to infants, toddlers, and their families

Curriculum assessment should be:
- An ongoing process
- Go beyond evaluation and observation
- Family-centered
- Pleasurable and meaningful
- Logically linked to intervention

Offers the most developmental skills and behaviors and intervention strategies

To be used as an administration and reference guide

Stresses the importance of interdependence and inter-relatedness between and within domains, strands, and the environment

Guiding Principles

The development and intended use of *Inside HELP* is based upon the following guiding principles:
- Curriculum assessment is a multidimensional ongoing process;
- Curriculum assessment should go beyond evaluation and observation of a child's skills and behaviors;
- Curriculum assessment should be family-centered;
- The curriculum assessment process should be pleasurable and meaningful for children and families;
- Disabilities should not interfere with a true assessment of a child's abilities;
- Assessment should be logically linked to intervention.

Issues Regarding Density and Multiple Lines of Development

One of the most unique features of HELP – applauded by both parents and professionals – is its density – the high number of quality, specific skills. No other currently available birth-to-three curriculum includes as many developmental skills and behaviors and intervention strategies as the HELP. This density provides families and clinicians considerable choice in the process of assessment and curriculum planning, and facilitates monitoring of the child's progress in small incremental steps.

The density and comprehensiveness of *Inside HELP* can appear overwhelming to the new user. Remember, however, that this manual is intended to be an administration and reference guide. As such, it is intended to be used as a resource for the professional to refer to on an "as needed basis" for clarification of specific skills when using HELP products, and for review or expansion of knowledge and skills in early childhood development and assessment. As you become familiar with the HELP skills and format of *Inside HELP*, the comprehensiveness and ease of use as a reference tool will become more apparent.

One final caution that cannot be overemphasized: Although the HELP is formatted along multiple lines of development through the use of developmental domains and strands, no domain, strand, or skill can be understood in isolation of other areas of development or in isolation of the environment. Separating development into domains and strands can be helpful for understanding and pinpointing underlying areas of strengths and needs, but children should never be viewed in separate, fragmented or isolated areas of development. The challenge for the clinician is to analyze the mutual impact and interplay of these multiple lines of development and then integrate findings with the family to determine integrated intervention strategies and functional outcomes. *Inside HELP* stresses the importance of interdependence and interrelatedness between and within domains, strands, and the environment.

History of HELP

The original HELP materials, the *Hawaii Early Learning Profile (HELP) Charts* and *HELP Activity Guide*, were developed by the multidisciplinary pediatric team of Setsu Furuno, Ph.D., Katherine A. O'Reilly, R.P.T., M.P.H., Carol M. Hosaka, M.A., Takayo T. Inatsuka, O.T.R., Toney L. Allman M.A., and Barbara Zeisloft M.S.,Sp., through a federal demonstration and training project, the Enrichment Project for Handicapped Infants, from 1971 to 1979. This project was conducted under the auspices of the School of Public Health, University of Hawaii, and was funded by the Bureau of the Education of the Handicapped.

Developed by a multidisciplinary pediatric team

Six-hundred and eighty-five (685) developmental skills and behaviors were selected by the multidisciplinary team from numerous available growth-and-development scales and standardized tests. The age ranges provided for the skills on the *Charts* and in the *Activity Guide* were "based on a synthesis of research and project data." There was "not always agreement in growth and development literature as to when a skill begins," and thus "age ranges" in months for when a skill typically emerges was included rather than one specific "month" level.

Six-hundred and eighty-five (685) developmental skills and behaviors

These 685 developmental skills provided the framework for developing curriculum activities for the *HELP Activity Guide* and *HELP Charts* within the six traditional domains: Cognition, Language, Gross Motor, Fine Motor, Social-Emotional and Self Help. All skills are not necessarily critical to the child's development, but were included because of their teachability and amenability to intervention.

Developmental skills provided framework for developing curriculum

The *HELP Charts* and *HELP Activity Guide* were field-tested by numerous programs for infants and toddlers with disabilities. The materials were also used and reviewed by programs in 35 states and 7 different countries for additional feedback.

Field-tested by numerous programs for infants with disabilities

Since the *HELP Activity Guide* and *HELP Charts*, additional HELP materials have been developed to meet the growing field of early intervention: *HELP at Home, HELP When the Parent has Disabilities, HELP Checklist,* the *HELP Family-Centered Interview*, and the *HELP Strands*. Each of these derivatives build upon and are cross-referenced to the 685 core HELP skills and behaviors.

Development of *Inside HELP*

Inside HELP was developed to provide: (1) flexible, clear, and valid definitions, (2) credit criteria, and (3) assessment procedures for each of the 685 core HELP skills and behaviors. This manual is intended to promote consistency and a common framework of reference among multidisciplinary professionals using HELP as a curriculum assessment for planning comprehensive programs for infants and toddlers with special needs and their families. This manual is **not** intended to provide standardized evaluation, or diagnosis.

Developed to provide:
1) flexible, clear and valid definitions
2) credit criteria
3) assessment procedures for each of the 685 skills and behaviors

The definitions, credit criteria, and assessment guidelines were derived from a variety of growth and development scales, standardized norm-referenced tests, infant curriculums, and extensive early intervention research papers, articles, and texts listed under References at the end of this manual. The guidelines presented in each strand "Preface" (e.g., Family Friendly definitions, Parent Questions, Transactional Assessment, etc.), were drawn from infant and family literature as well as from experience and collaboration with families and professional colleagues.

A core interdisciplinary team of pediatric therapists who work in the Prince William County Parent Infant Education Program contributed to the search of the literature process and development of this manual. A vision specialist who works with the Virginia Department for the Visually Handicapped provided her expertise and research in developing the adaptations for the visually impaired. When definitions, credit criteria, and assessment guidelines were vague or unclear in the literature, the team, in concurrence with at least two additional professionals from the applicable discipline, developed clarification and criteria through clinical judgment and experience. Each of the contributors to this work has a Masters degree and a minimum of 10 years of experience in the field. The pediatric physical and occupational therapists are NDT certified and have training and experience in sensory integration principles. The final draft was sent to four outside experts in the field for final critique and review.

Purpose of the HELP Strands

The *HELP Strands* is a curriculum-based developmental assessment booklet for direct use with individual children. It covers the same core 685 skills and six traditional developmental domains included in the original HELP materials, but it has been structured like *Inside HELP* to provide a more precise framework for assessment and planning – the traditional HELP domains have been divided into 58 developmentally sequenced *conceptual strands*. Each strand includes HELP skills which focus upon a specific underlying key concept and are hierarchical in nature; i.e., one skill leads to or builds the foundation for the next skill. Developmental levels, strengths, and needs <u>within</u> each domain can thus be more easily identified for curriculum assessment and individualized planning.

Skills listed on traditional developmental checklists and standardized tests, although generally listed in a developmental order according to age, are not generally hierarchical. For example, if a child "passes" one skill it does not necessarily mean that he is ready to learn the next skill. Conversely, if a child "fails" an item, this does not mean that he cannot accomplish or is not ready to learn a skill placed higher on the continuum. Without careful item analysis, it can be difficult to identify strengths and needs within a major area of development and difficult to identify "next steps" for planning. The *HELP Strands* were developed to address this need and to provide an additional option to the clinician for assessment and monitoring.

Features of the HELP Strands

- Regulatory/Sensory Organization (0.0) is a new section that has been added to the framework of the *HELP Strands*. It includes pertinent HELP skills selected from all domains which tap the child's self-regulation capacities (i.e., sleep cycles, regulation of moods, attention, and consolability), and, the child's capacities to perceive and organize various sensory experiences (i.e., sights, sounds, touch, taste, smell, vestibular [body movement through space and head position] and proprioception [awareness of body position in space]).
- Condensed definitions are included directly on the *HELP Strands* assessment form for quick reference.
- Some of the original HELP skills age ranges and wording have been updated to reflect current literature.

Strands provide a more precise conceptual framework for assessment and planning

Strands are hierarchical in nature; i.e., one skill leads to or builds the foundation for the next skill

New Regulatory/Sensory Organization section

Includes condensed definitions

• Completely cross-indexed: Each skill in the *HELP Strands* has the same skill identification number used in all of the HELP products. This allows for easy cross reference and linkage between all HELP materials (birth-3).

Development of the HELP Strands

Process for re-structuring core skills

The development and restructuring of the 685 core HELP skills into the *HELP Strand* format began in 1988. The first step included analyzing each of the HELP skills for its underlying concept regardless of the domain in which it was originally placed. This process was completed through clinical judgment, review of the early intervention literature, and collaboration with an interdisciplinary team of pediatric therapists and infant specialists. The skills were then sorted into respective multiple conceptual strands within the traditional six major domains and sequentially ordered by age. Several skills included more than one underlying concept and were thus placed in more than one strand.

Initial drafts of the *HELP Strands* (with definitions) were then developed and field-tested during the following three years with more that 200 infants and toddlers enrolled in the Prince William County, Parent Infant Education Program located in Manassas, Virginia. The infants and toddlers were aged birth (adjusted age for prematurity) to 35 months and were enrolled in ongoing early intervention services because of developmental delays, atypical development, and/or disabilities. Program staff conducting the curriculum assessments were experienced and licensed pediatric speech, occupational and physical therapists, and infant educators.

Field-tested with more that 200 infants and toddlers

The primary purpose of field testing was to test the adequacy of the initial sequencing of skills within strands based on a hierarchical structure. If a child "failed" more than two items in a row but then passed a higher item in spite of assessment adaptations for disabilities, the relevant skill items were more closely scrutinized. In some cases, the skill ended up "fitting" better conceptually and sequentially in another strand. In other cases, by the nature of the several-month age range span in which the skill typically emerges, the skill had simply been misplaced in the sequence. In some cases, through a search of more recent literature, it became evident that the age range references listed in the original *HELP Charts* needed to be revised, either to a higher or lower range. Some skills within strands such as 1-5 "Spatial Relationships," and 0.0 "Regulatory/Sensory Organization," although conceptually related, were not expected to have complete sequentiality because they include more than one underlying concept. This is noted when applicable in the applicable strand prefaces.

This ongoing process of refinement and reordering of skills within and between strands continued until the strands were considered as sequential and as hierarchical in nature as possible. The final *HELP Strands* were then reviewed by outside experts in the field for final confirmation.

HELP Revisions and Updates

Inside HELP and the *HELP Strands* were purposefully built upon the core original HELP skills to <u>provide consistency</u> and easy cross-referencing between <u>all</u> the HELP materials. As a result of literature searches, some relatively minor revisions were made, however, to some of the original HELP skill age ranges and wording (on products with © prior to 1994.) These changes were incorporated to reflect current literature and trends in the field.

Approximate Developmental Levels (see page i.23)

The HELP assessments, including the *HELP Strands*, are **not** norm-referenced or standardized, and will **not** yield a single age level or score. <u>The major purpose of HELP as a curriculum assessment is to identify curriculum outcomes, goals, strategies and activities.</u>

The *HELP Strands* can, however, be used to provide approximate or estimated developmental levels <u>within and between areas of development</u>, document that a child is not displaying skills and behaviors expected for his age, provide meaningful descriptions of a child's skills and behavior, and document when skills and behaviors are of poor quality, atypical, or dysfunctional.

Editorial and Formatting Notes

1. Skill ID#: As noted, specific identification #'s have been assigned to each of the HELP skills. This numbering system is consistent across all the HELP products to facilitate quick cross-referencing between products. This numbering system was developed with the first HELP materials, i.e., *HELP Charts* and *HELP Activity Guide* according to major domains, e.g., 1.0 Cognitive, includes skills 1.01, 1.02, 1.03, etc. The HELP skill ID#'s were originally (1979) assigned based upon the skill's placement on the *HELP Charts*, but the numbers do not necessarily reflect sequentiality. Skills within strands *are* in sequential order, and thus do not always appear in numerical order within a strand. A cross-reference index of the numerical order of skill ID#'s is on pages 374-377. If you are using the *HELP Charts* or *HELP Checklist*, pages 374-377 are intended to act as a quick reference for finding the page in *Inside HELP* for each of the skills.

2. Since there are no neutral words to designate male and female children, we were faced with the long standing editorial "she/he" issue. To avoid redundancy and confusion, all children are referred to as "he" throughout this manual. No gender bias is intended.

Skill ID numbering is consistent across all of the HELP products to facilitate quick cross-referencing

Note:
See page 378 for detailed information on each of the HELP (Birth-3) components supported by *Inside HELP*.

INSTRUCTIONS

Overview

Inside HELP is a comprehensive administration and reference guide to be used in conjunction with all the HELP (Hawaii Early Learning Profile: Birth-3) curriculum and assessment materials: the *HELP Strands, HELP Checklist, HELP Charts, HELP Activity Guide, HELP at Home, HELP When the Parent has Disabilities,* and the *HELP Family-Centered Interview.* You can find out more about each of these components on page 378 of this book.

IMPORTANT REMINDERS!

• No child is expected to display all HELP skills listed <u>nor</u> display all skills for an age range. Be sure to consider individual, environmental, or cultural differences per child.

• The age ranges reported in HELP are the ages at which a skill or behavior (for children who do not have disabilities) typically *begins* according to the literature. These age ranges are **not** when a skill begins *and* ends! Some skills are time-limited and emerge into more complex skills, while others are lifetime skills. Literature varies regarding the age at which a skill emerges, for example, one source may have reported 9 months, another source 10 months, and another source 12 months. HELP would list that skill at the 9-12 month age range.

• HELP is a curriculum-based assessment, **not** a standardized test. As such, there is no validity or reliability data available for HELP. It will **not** yield a definitive single age level or score. <u>The major purpose of HELP as a curriculum assessment is to identify curriculum outcomes, strategies and activities.</u>

• If your program requires standardized scores for eligibility purposes, HELP can be used *in conjunction* with a standardized test (see page i.34) to help pinpoint strengths and needs, and to help develop outcomes, strategies, and activities.

Quick Tour of *Inside HELP*

1. *Inside HELP* is divided into seven major sections corresponding to developmental domains. Each domain is assigned a Domain ID # ──────▶ for easy cross-reference among all HELP materials.

2. Domains are sub-divided into Strands. Each strand has a number ──────────▶ comprised of the Domain (e.g., **1-**) and the strand (e.g., **1-3** is Sound Awareness, the third strand under Cognitive). The Contents for *Inside HELP* corresponds directly to the structure of the Strands. **Note:** The upper corner or each page of *Inside HELP* shows the Strand number, e.g., **5-1**.

Examples

<u>Domains</u>
0.0 Regulatory/Sensory Organization
1.0 Cognitive
2.0 Language
3.0 Gross Motor
4.0 Fine Motor
5.0 Social Emotional
6.0 Self-Help

Domain sub-divided into <u>Strands</u>
<u>1.0 Cognitive</u>
　 1-1 Development of Symbolic Play
　 1-2 Gestural Imitation
　 1-3 Sound Awareness
　 1-4 Problem Solving

3. HELP skills are sequential and developmentally ordered within each strand, i.e., each skill leads to and builds the foundation for the next skill. Each skill uses the HELP skill ID# for easy cross-reference. ⟶

- The skills within Strands do not always appear in numerical order (because skill ID#'s are based on the original *HELP Charts* which were not broken down into Strands.)
- Age range indicates when a skill typically emerges, **not** when a skill begins and ends.

4. Definitions, example Observation Procedures (assessment procedures), and Credit Criteria are listed for <u>each</u> skill. ⟶

5. Each Strand has a Preface in *Inside HELP*. The strand Preface provides 10 key sections of assessment information <u>related to all skills within the strand</u>.

"Family Friendly" Interpretation of Strand Concepts, Assessment, and Purpose ⟶
A jargon-free definition and interpretation of the underlying strand concept. This includes a clear explanation of what you are assessing and why it is important to the child's development.

Professional FYI ⟶
Various information about the strand which may be helpful or important for the professional, e.g., the relationship of this strand to other strands or domains, special considerations, rationale for inclusion of certain skills, etc.

Parent Questions ⟶
Sample questions to facilitate a family-directed assessment of their child's unique strengths and needs as well as family concerns, priorities, and resources related to enhancing their child's development. These questions help identify family roles, beliefs, and values as they relate to the development of their child, and family preferences regarding the assessment process and content.

Skills are sequential within each Strand:
<u>1-2 Gestural Imitation</u> (strand)
<u>Skill#　Age　Skill Description</u>
　1.42a　7-8　Imitates familiar gesture
　1.42b　9-11　Imitates new gesture
　1.66　11-14　Imitates several new gestures
　1.84　14-17　Imitates invisible gesture

<u>Skill</u>
1.42a Imitates familiar gesture 7-8
Definition: The child makes a familiar visible gesture in imitation of a model. A familiar gesture is a movement that the child already uses frequently during daily activities...
Example observation opportunities: Observe gestures that the child typically makes during play or daily activities. These may be observed while assessing the child's play interactions...
Credit:
　+ imitates at least two familiar visible gestures

Each of the Preface sections has a unique icon for quick reference.
Examples

"Family Friendly" Interpretation
We will be observing how your child is learning to play with toys and other objects. Play is very important in a child's learning and development. Play helps children learn how to solve...

Professional FYI
1. This strand focuses on the child's interaction with objects and toys leading to the development of symbolic play. Social interactions and play with other children and adults, although closely related, is not highlighted...

Parent Questions
• Can you tell me a little about how he plays with some of the toys you mentioned?
• Are there certain toys that he does not seem to like?
• Has he ever played with the kind of toys we have here today?

Sample functional outcome statements ⎯⎯⎯➤
which may be generated by the family and related
to the strand concepts, skills and behaviors.
These are only *samples* to help move away from the
more rigid operational objectives that many of us
were trained to develop. The actual outcome statements you use are those *generated directly from the
family* through sensitive interview and active
listening techniques.

Sample functional outcome statements

My child will:
- Enjoy playing with toys;
- Play with his friends at daycare;
- Play with a toy for more than a few seconds;
- Play with his toys instead of always putting them in his mouth.

We will:
- Know what objects around home our child will enjoy playing with;
- Know more about the ways our child can learn through play.

Transactional Assessment of environment and caregiver interactions ⎯⎯⎯➤
This section offers examples of key factors in the
child's caregiving environment which can promote
or compromise the child's development. This section is also useful to review the professional's own
interactions and environment in the assessment
and interventions provided to children and
families.

Transactional Assessment

1. **Supportive:**
The child's caregiving environments usually:
- Have a variety of safe and develop-mentally appropriate play materials;
- Have safe spaces for the child to play;
- Keep play materials accessible to the child.

2. **Compromising:**
- The child's caregiving environments usual-ly do not have safe or developmentally appropriate toys or materials.

Identifying and Interpreting Needs ⎯⎯⎯➤
Help in sorting out why a child may display
a delay or atypical behavior in a particular strand.
This will help determine what types of interventions are most appropriate.

Identifying and Interpreting Needs

If a child is significantly delayed or
displays persistent atypical development
in this area, he may be having difficulty
with mental processes needed to engage
in meaningful play with objects. This
includes being able to:
1. Perceptually discriminate the qualities and functions of objects;
2. Mentally represent or internalize an action or object that is not present, i.e., representational thought.

Assessment Adaptations ⎯⎯⎯➤
Examples of adaptations for specific disabilities and
special needs to use when assessing skills and
behaviors in the strand.

Assessment Adaptations
- Motor impairments: *involve a pedi-atric therapist in the assessment of the child's play so that the therapist can adapt materials and positioning to meet the child's individual needs and promote interactions and mobility with toys. The following are some general adaptations:* Use play materials, battery-operated toys, and touch-sensitive switches that can be easily manipulated and adapted to accommodate the child's type of grasp. Larger or stabilized materials may help.

General child assessment procedures ⟶

Assessment procedures which are applicable to all skills in the strand. Although each skill also has specific assessment procedures, there are some procedures which are applicable to all the Strand's skills and are included in the Preface to avoid redundancy.

General child assessment procedures

a. Most items in this strand can be assessed simultaneously, i.e., observe the child's interactions with the objects and toys until he becomes repetitive in his play and is not displaying higher level interactions. Credit predominant play interactions accordingly.

b. Provide the child with some of the "example eliciting play materials" that are suggested under the procedure for each item in this strand.

Credit notes ⟶

Suggestions for documenting the presence or absence of particular skills and behaviors. Although specific credit criteria is included for each skill, there are general credit notes which are applicable to all skills in the strand and are thus included in the Preface to avoid redundancy.

+ - A Credit notes

+ child displays defined play interaction as a predominant interaction; not observed or reported.

+/- appears to be an emerging play scheme; displayed play scheme with adult prompting and modeling, but it is not considered a predominant scheme.

Assessment Materials ⟶

A list of materials and toys which are likely to elicit responses for assessment of skills within the strand. The materials listed are typically available in the child's natural environments. Notes are included to use materials which are culturally relevant, safe, and motivating.

A B Assessment Materials
Birth to approximately 1 year:
   Several easy-to-grasp toys which have different textures, sounds, and consistencies. Examples include: smooth plastic rattles; small blocks, some that have different pictures on the sides, such as alphabet blocks; soft textured squeak toy; crumpled piece of paper; dinner bell; plastic cup; toy cars; small doll.

How to Use HELP

Before the Direct Child Assessment Suggested Steps

1. Begin the family-centered interview process through home or center visits, and the telephone. During the interview:
   a. Explain the purpose of the assessment, what to expect, and options for how family members can participate as part of the assessment team.
   b. Get a general idea of the child's key milestones, e.g., how does he move around, what toys does he play with, how does he communicate.
   c. Identify family's primary concerns, priorities, expectations and preferences related to the assessment.

2. With written parental permission, collect, review, and collaborate with other professionals and the family about other information pertinent to the current assessment of the child and family, e.g.:
   a. Medical history, contraindications, and current conditions.
   b. Previous developmental evaluations, assessments, screenings.
   c. Other information family feels is important to the assessment.

3. Secure necessary releases and therapy prescriptions to conduct direct assessments.

4. Select the most appropriate HELP assessment recording form to use during the direct child assessment, i.e., *HELP Strands* or *HELP Checklist* (the Strands are recommended.) The *HELP Charts* can be used, but are more often used for communicating progress to families.

5. Highlight several skills above and below the child's approximate developmental age on the *HELP Strands* (or Checklist or Charts) within each developmental domain you anticipate assessing.

HELPful Tips

Use the *HELP Family-Centered Interview* or review and select Parent Questions from various strand Prefaces in *Inside HELP*.

From the collected information:
- Determine assessment team (i.e. disciplines), format (e.g., multidisciplinary, arena, or interdisciplinary), assessment content, methods, and adaptations
- Get a general idea of the child's current development to help target where to begin the assessment.

Some states require some therapists to have a prescription.

Use the *HELP Strands* if the child has specific disabilities or displays apparent "uneven" development.
Use the *HELP Strands* "loose leaf" format (Prod. No. 158-B) if more than one discipline will be assessing at one time.

The skills you highlight will be based upon the information gathered in steps 1 and 2 above.

6. Locate the skills you anticipate assessing in *Inside HELP* to prepare and plan for the direct child assessment.
   a. Review relevant strand Prefaces which correspond to selected skills.
   b. Review the definitions, credit criteria, suggested assessment procedures, and materials for each skill.
   c. Select and prepare for five-to-ten play and daily activity situations (from "Example Observation Opportunities") to include in the direct assessment. Choose activities which are likely to elicit several skills concurrently across developmental domains, e.g., playing with a ball or rattle, looking in a mirror, diaper changing.

7. You can record notes from this planning and review phase directly onto the *HELP Strands or Checklist*, or on separate note paper to take into the direct assessment.

If you are using *HELP Strands*, go directly to corresponding strand in *Inside HELP* to locate the specific skills.

If you are using *HELP Checklist* or *HELP Charts*, use the Skills Index on page 376 of *Inside HELP* to locate the highlighted skills you anticipate assessing.

You do not need to assess all skills or strands. Observation of one activity is likely to provide information about the child's development across many strands.

As you become more familiar with HELP, your preliminary preparation time and notes will be reduced.

HELP CAN ASSIST IN:

- Determining approximate or estimated developmental levels within and between major developmental domains
- Documenting whether a child is displaying skills and behaviors expected for his age
- Developing meaningful descriptions of a child's skills and behavior
- Documenting skills and behaviors that are of poor quality, atypical, or dysfunctional
- Interpreting how one area of development may be influencing another area of development.

During the Direct Child Assessment
Suggested Steps

1. Bring any notes you've prepared prior to the direct assessment (i.e., "Eliciting Situations" and Credit Notes) with the HELP assessment recording form you've chosen (i.e., *HELP Strands* or *HELP Checklist*) into the direct assessment.

2. Record the child's responses to eliciting situations and observations of parent-child interactions directly on the HELP assessment form or note paper.
   Suggested credit codes:
   +   skill or behavior is present
   -    skill is not present
   +/- skill appears to be emerging
   A   skill or behavior is atypical or dysfunctional
   N/A item is not applicable or not appropriate to assess due to disability or parent preference.
   O   circle any credit (i.e.,. +,-, or A) when the environment or caregiver interactions compromise the child's development in this area, and whenever family requests additional information or help in this area.
   Note: In domain 0.0 - Regulatory/Sensory Organization, there are two credit options for "Atypical" reactions or responses:
   A+ hyper responsive
   A- under responsive

3. Continue assessing until the child losses interest, tires, or cannot complete higher level tasks.
   If you are using the *HELP Strands*: (see i.23)
   a. If a child displays two or more skills in a row with good quality, you can generally assume that he has achieved earlier skills because of their hierarchical relationship.
   b. You can usually stop trying to elicit skills in a strand after the child has missed two skills in a row.
   Using the *HELP Checklist* or the *HELP Charts*, since skills are not always in hierarchical order, you may need to assess at least 4-5 skills above and below the child's apparent developmental level. Use clinical judgment.

4. Continue the family interview process.

HELPful Tips

You generally do not need to bring *Inside HELP* into the direct child assessment. Use it for a reference guide prior to and after the direct assessment.

Abbreviated definitions and credit notes are already included on the *HELP Strands*.

If more than one discipline is involved during the direct assessment, they can act as a consultant to the primary evaluator (professional and/or parent) by "coaching from the sidelines" to help elicit specific skills, and to record responses and interactions.

Some crediting is tentative at this point and will need to be confirmed after the assessment with the credit criteria listed for each skill in *Inside HELP*.

Record any needed adaptations directly on the HELP assessment you are using.

If a child "masters" a skill, you will still include it in your intervention plan if it is circled, for example, if the child can "Pull up to stand" but there are no sturdy furnishings at home for the child to use, you would circle this credit and could include interventions.

See "Sample Structure of a Direct Assessment," page i.30.

If permitted, use videotaping to help capture subtle responses and to confirm questionable credits after the assessment.

After the Direct Child Assessment
Suggested Steps

1. Team Collaboration: Review Observation and Credit Notes from the direct child assessment with all team members to ensure a comprehensive, interdisciplinary perspective.

2. Refer to "Credit Criteria" in *Inside HELP* to confirm any questionable credits you may have had during the direct assessment.
Note regarding use of A (Atypical): Atypical variation does not definitively indicate that the child is abnormal in his development. Variation in development is common. In addition, atypical motor or behavior patterns can be transient, especially during the first year.

3. Note any items which were not assessed that need to be followed up on or reassessed.

4. Determine any further specialized evaluations that may need to occur.

5. Determine approximate developmental levels across and within major domains. Be sure to note any adaptations used during the assessment to qualify credits and to help plan successful interventions.

6. Develop outcome statements with the family which reflect their concerns and priorities related to enhancing their child's development. The groundwork for developing outcome statements will have already occurred from initial contacts through the direct child assessment.
Outcomes may be long- or short-term, and may change frequently as the child and family concerns, priorities, and resources change.

7. Determine services and strategies to meet the unique needs of the child and family to achieve identified outcomes. These will be based upon several variables, e.g., family resources, concerns and priorities, child's strengths and needs, factors contributing to child's delays.

HELPful Tips

Remember, parents are an integral part of the team.

Review available videotaping.

If a child displays persistent atypical patterns, it is important to refer to a professional with expertise in that area of development; however, it is important not to unduly alarm families. Atypical patterns should be monitored and reassessed over a period of several months before assuming it is a more lasting area for concern.

For example, the child may have tired before you had an opportunity to assess a certain item, or certain eliciting situations or materials were not available.

For example, if the child displayed atypical muscle tone, further motor assessment by a pediatric therapist should be scheduled.

See "How to Determine and Report Levels of Development" page i.23, for detailed steps.

If you are using the *HELP Family-Centered Interview*, confirm and prioritize with the family the tentative outcomes you have outlined in the final column "Possible Final Outcome Statements."

Use the following sections from the Strand Preface to help determine services and strategies:
• Transactional assessment
• Identifying and Interpreting Needs for Intervention
• Assessment Adaptations

Address skills which were credited A, i.e., Atypical, and skills which were circled.

How to Determine and Report Levels of Development

IMPORTANT REMINDERS!

- No child is expected to display all HELP skills listed <u>nor</u> display all skills for an age range. Be sure to consider individual, environmental, or cultural differences per child.
- The age ranges reported in HELP are the ages at which a skill or behavior typically *begins* according to the literature. These age ranges are **not** when a skill begins *and* ends! Some skills are time-limited and emerge into more complex skills, while others are lifetime skills. Literature varies regarding the age at which a skill emerges, for example, one source may have reported 9 month, another source 10 months, and another source 12 months. HELP would list that skill at the 9-12 month age range.
- HELP is a curriculum-based assessment, **not** a standardized test. It will **not** yield a definitive single age level or score. <u>The major purpose of HELP as a curriculum assessment is to identify curriculum outcomes, strategies and activities.</u>
- If your program requires standardized scores for eligibility purposes, HELP can be used *in conjunction* with a standardized test (see page i.34) to help pinpoint strengths and needs, and to help develop outcomes, strategies and activities.

- *The following instructions and examples provide general "rule of thumb" guidelines for determining approximate developmental levels. There are no exact rules or formulas that will apply for every child or every assessment to derive developmental levels. Use clinical judgment and item analysis in this process (see the bottom of page i.34).*
- *Each Strand Preface in Inside HELP provides specific strand-related information for determining and reporting developmental levels under "General Assessment Procedures."*

Using the *HELP Strands* (see examples <u>1.</u> - <u>5.</u> below) to Determine Approximate Levels of Development

1. The highest skill in each strand.

The highest skill in each strand that the child can accomplish with good quality is, generally, the approximate developmental level of the child for that strand when he has accomplished at least two consecutive skills. If a child displays two or more skills in a row with good quality, you can generally assume that he has achieved earlier skills because of their hierarchical relationship within the strand. Conversely, after a child misses more than two skills or behaviors in a sequence, you can generally assume the child has not yet accomplished higher skills in that particular strand. See the examples below.

Example 1: Reporting for a 24 month-old child from Strand 1-4A. Object Permanence (Cognitive Domain):

Date	Credit	Skill#	Age	Skill
7/14/96	+	1.49	9-12	Finds hidden object under three superimposed screens
7/14/96	+	1.62	11-13	Hidden displacement one screen
7/14/96	+	1.78	13-14	Hidden displacement two screens
7/14/96	+	1.80	14-15	Hidden displacement three screens
7/14/96	+	1.81	14-15	Hidden displacement two screens alternately
7/14/96	−	1.94	17-18	Series of hidden displacements; object under last screen
7/14/96	−	1.113	21-22	Series of hidden displacements; object under first screen

Note: The Date and Credit are shown in italics to represent your assessment information for the child.

In example 1, the "approximate" developmental level for the child on Strand 1-4A is **14-15 months,** per the "general rule" cited in example 1 above. However, every child and assessment situation is unique. <u>There are exceptions to example 1 above which are outlined below in examples 2 through 5.</u>

2. The age range listed for the highest skill is not always the developmental range that you will report.

This situation can occur when:

   a. There is a wide age range listed for a skill, e.g., more than 3 months
   b. There is a several month gap between skills
   c. A child is older or developmentally higher than the age range listed for the last skill in a strand.

2a. If the age range of the skill which is the child's highest credit is greater than the age range of the next skill in that strand (which he could not accomplish), you would not report the child's developmental level as the full range reported for the skill accomplished.

Example 2a: Reporting for a 12 month-old child from Strand 1-4B. Means-Ends (Cognitive Domain):

Date	Credit	Skill#	Age	Skill
7/14/96	+	1.25	5-6.5	Reaches for second object purposefully
7/14/96	+	1.26	5-9	Works for desired, out-of-reach object
7/14/96	-	1.40	6.5-7.5	Retains two of three objects offered
7/14/96	-	1.45	8-10	Retains two and reaches for third object
		1.47	8-10	Retrieves object using other material
		1.46	8-11	Overcomes obstacle to obtain object

In example 2a above, the "approximate" developmental level for the child on Strand 1-4B would be **5-7 months** since the highest skill mastered in Means-Ends was #1.26 "Works for desired, out of reach object." This skill has an age range of 5-9 months. But since the child could not master higher skills in this strand with a lower age range, e.g., "Retains two of three objects offered," with an age range of 6.5-7.5, and "Retains two and reaches for 3rd object" with an age range 8-10 months, you would **not** report that the child displayed Means-Ends skills in the 5-9 month range. Instead, you could report e.g., "Johnny displayed Means-Ends skills at about the 5-7 month developmental level. He worked to attain an out-of-reach object, and purposely reached for a second object while holding one, but could not yet figure out how to obtain a third object."

2b. If there is a gap in age between skills within a strand, use clinical judgment to report the child's developmental level in that area, depending on the situation.

Example 2b: Reporting for a 17 month-old child from Strand 1-4C. Cause and Effect (Cognitive Domain):

Date	Credit	Skill#	Age	Skill
		1.30	5.5-8	Shows interest in sounds of objects
		1.24	5-9	Touches toy or adult's hand to restart activity
2/12/97	+	1.50	9-12	Guides action on toy manually
2/12/97	+	1.67	12-15	Hands toy back to adult
2/12/97	-	1.98	18-22	Attempts and then succeeds in activating mechanical toy

In example 2b, the "approximate" developmental level for the child on Strand 1-4C would be **"age appropriate"** since skill# 1.98 "Attempts and then succeeds in activating mechanical toy" is listed as typically emerging at any time within the 18-22 month range. The skill listed immediately before this, #1.67, "Hands toy back to adult" has an age range of 12-15 months. There is a three month gap between skills 1.67 and 1.98. If a 16- or 17-month old passed skill# 1.67 but not #1.98, you would **not** say that he displayed Cause and Effect skills at the 12-15 month level since this could imply a delay. Instead, you would report that the child displayed Cause and Effect skills which are typical for his age (i.e., age appropriate), and provide some examples.

2c. If a child accomplishes the highest level skill in a strand which has an age range less than the child's actual age, and if he displays higher level skills in other strands, use the higher ranged strand as your point of reference.

Example 2c: Reporting for a 10 month-old child (Gross Motor Domain):

Strand 3-1: Prone (lying on stomach)

Date	Credit	Skill#	Age	Skill
6/10/97	+	3.07	3-5	Holds head up 90 degrees in prone
6/10/97	+	3.26	4-6	Bears weight on hands in prone
6/10/97	+	3.43	6-7.5	Holds weight on one hand in prone

end of strand 3-1; so you would also consider other strands, such as, 3-2, 3-3, 3-4 below

Strand 3-2: Supine (lying on back)

Date	Credit	Skill#	Age	Skill
6/10/97	+	1.29	5-6	Brings feet to mouth
6/10/97	NA	3.35	5-6.5	Raises hips pushing with feet in supine
6/10/97	+	3.42	6-8	Lifts head in supine
6/10/97	+	5.27	6-12	Struggles against supine position

Strand 3-3: Sitting

Date	Credit	Skill#	Age	Skill
6/10/97	+	3.33	5-6	Holds head erect when leaning forward
6/10/97	+	3.34	5-8	Sits independently indefinitely but may use hands
6/10/97	+	3.51	8-9	Sits without hand support for 10 minutes

Strand 3-4: Weight bearing in Standing

Date	Credit	Skill#	Age	Skill
6/10/97	+	3.60	9.5-11	Stands momentarily
6/10/97	-	3.68	11-13	Stands a few seconds
6/10/97	-	3.71	11.5-14	Stands alone well

In example 2c, you would report "**age appropriate**" in Gross Motor. Do not report that child is at 6-7.5 month level in Prone unless he cannot accomplish higher skills in other Gross Motor strands.

3. Skills in Strand 1-5 Spatial Relationships, may not be in exact sequential order.

Several different spatial concepts are targeted in this strand. Therefore, although skills are sequenced according to age, these skills do not necessarily build upon each other. Hence, you cannot always assume that a child has achieved earlier skills in this strand when he displays higher skills, nor assume that he cannot achieve higher skills when he misses two consecutive skills. It is recommended that several items be assessed below and above the level at which the child seems to be developing.

4. In some cases you should not report developmental level.

    a. Sometimes a child may display persistent atypical or dysfunctional skills and behaviors that are not typical or appropriate at any age, e.g., pervasive repetitive behaviors, self destructive behavior, obligatory abnormal posturing. A description of these patterns is usually more appropriate than reporting levels.

    b. Some areas of development may be inappropriate to assess due to a child's disability, e.g. "Picture Concepts" for a child who is blind, or "Advancing Postural Control and Motor Planning" skills for a child who is non-ambulatory.

    c. Section 0.0 - Regulatory/Sensory Organization focuses upon the child's self-regulation capacities and his capacities to perceive and organize various sensory experiences. The purpose of this area is to look for patterns of preferences, capacities, and difficulties related to Regulatory/Sensory Organization. It is not appropriate to assign specific age ranges in this area. Instead, child responses can be described as "Typical," "Over-reactive" or "Under-reactive."

5. A delay can be "normal" for a child with a specific disability when compared to a child who does not have a disability.

For example, a delay in self-initiated mobility is normal for a child who is blind. The developmental ranges listed in HELP are based upon children who do not have disabilities. Be sure to review Assessment Adaptations for every strand in *Inside HELP* when assessing and reporting for children with disabilities.

Creating a Developmental Profile with the *HELP Strands* (back page of HELP Strands)

Since some children will display strengths and needs within and between developmental domains, the strand format can yield a profile of approximate developmental levels within and between domains.

1. In cases where there is a significant difference between strands within a domain, it is important to report these differences rather than report one broad age range for the entire domain.

    For example, when assessed in the Gross Motor domain, a six-month-old child displayed skills in the Prone and Supine strands at approximately the 0-2 month level and in the Sitting and Weight-Bearing strand at approximately the 5-6 month level. In this case, it is important to report these age level differences within a domain rather than reporting "scattered skills up to 6 months." This type of break-out, although appearing cumbersome at first glance, will actually provide the clinician with valuable interpretive and planning information which can save time in the long run.

    Example 1. Gross Motor Profile
    Important to report (differences) by strand
3-1 Prone	<u>0-2 months</u>
3-2 Supine	<u>0-2 months</u>
3-3 Sitting	<u>5-6 months</u>
3-4 Weightbearing and Standing	<u>5-6 months</u>

2. In other cases, you may not find significant age level differences between strands within a domain. In these cases and based on "informed clinical opinion," you can report an approximate age level for the entire domain.

    Example 2. Gross Motor Profile
    Using clinical judgment, can report one age range for domain, i.e. 3-5 months
    (or, if child is 5 months old, report "age appropriate")
3-1 Prone	<u>3-5 months</u>
3-2 Supine	<u>4-5 months</u>
3-3 Sitting	<u>4-5 months</u>
3-4 Weightbearing and Standing	<u>3-5 months</u>

Using the *HELP Checklist* (or *HELP Charts*) to Determine Approximate Levels of Development

1. On the *HELP Checklist* and the *HELP Charts*, skills are not always in hierarchical order, i.e., one skill is not necessarily related to the skill that is listed next. The "two in a row" rule outlined in Example 1 on page i.23, therefore, does **not** apply. If the child displays gaps within a domain, you will need to rely upon clinical judgment and item analysis, and report more estimated and broader ranges of development with a statement of gaps. As noted earlier, the *HELP Strands* are recommended for children who have specific disabilities or apparent "uneven" development.

2. Some of the original HELP skill age ranges and wording that appear on older (© before 1994) *HELP Charts, HELP Activity Guide* and the *HELP Checklist* have been revised. Be sure you are using current materials.

Using HELP to Achieve Outcomes

As a curriculum-based assessment, HELP makes the transition from assessment to intervention easier.

Suggested Steps

1. For each outcome listed:
   a. Determine which HELP skills and behaviors are most relevant for achieving that outcome. These will usually be the skills/behaviors which were rated <u>as emerging, not achieved, atypical, and/or achieved but circled because the family needs additional support in this area</u>.
   b. Be sure to integrate skills from **all** areas of development.
   c. If you are using the *HELP Strands,* you can usually assume that the "next step" in a strand will be the next skill in the strand that the child has not yet mastered.
   d. Review family resources which are most relevant for achieving outcomes. These should be readily available from the *HELP Family-Centered Interview.*

2. Use *Inside HELP* to refine or pinpoint the most appropriate intervention strategies.
   a. Review **Transactional Assessment** data to identify if interventions related to the environment and/or parent-child interactions are needed to achieve outcomes.
   b. Use **Assessment Adaptations** when appropriate as intervention strategies.
   c. Review **Identifying and Interpreting Needs for Intervention** for strands which the child displayed significant concerns or delays. This section can provide insight into underlying needs to help determine the most appropriate disciplines and strategies.

3. Use HELP curriculum materials to choose a variety of activities designed to support targeted skills to achieve outcomes. All HELP skills are cross-referenced to HELP curriculum materials. The HELP curriculum materials, although cross-referenced to specific skills, do not focus on teaching "to the test." Instead, HELP activities focus on the underlying concepts and behaviors that lead to functional skills and outcomes.

Examples

If the outcome is: "Danny won't become hysterical when his mother leaves the room," then the applicable HELP skill areas to target might be (depending upon child's development):
Cognition: Object (people) Permanence: remembering that the parent still exists even when out-of-sight.
Motor: crawling to search for parent from one room to another.
Auditory Localization: being able to find the parent when hearing her voice.
Language: Vocalizing rather than crying to attract parent's attention.
Social-Emotional: providing parents additional anticipatory guidance related to separation anxiety.
Applicable family resources could be:
"Family home has intercom system so Danny can hear parents from other rooms."
"Mother has had experience dealing with separation anxiety with Danny's older sister but it was not this extreme."

If the "child is unable to lift head in prone":
a. **Transactional Assessment**, e.g., if there are no interesting objects for child to look at, interventions may include adapting the environment.
b. **Assessment Adaptations**, e.g., if child has reflux, implement interventions in prone before feeding.
c. **Identifying and Interpreting Needs for Intervention**: If child has neuro-motor or musculo-skeletal problems which interfere with the development of controlled extension, a pediatric therapist should be involved in planning and implementing therapy activities.

HELP curriculum materials to help achieve outcomes include:
a. *HELP at Home*: ready-to-use activity sheets which you can individualize and copy for families.
b. *HELP Activity Guide*: in-program activities and strategies.
c. *HELP When the Parent has Disabilities*: suggestions for adapting child interventions to include family members who have a disability.

Using HELP as an Ongoing Assessment

HELP is an ongoing curriculum-based assessment. Since the developmental needs and priorities of young children and families change rapidly, assessment should be considered an ongoing cyclical process. Use HELP throughout your 0-3 intervention by completing or "filling-in" the *HELP Strands* (or Checklist or Charts) as skills and behaviors are mastered.

Sample: Using HELP Strands as an ongoing assessment and planning tool. Fill in frequently, adding new objectives and outcomes

Date	Credit	Skill#	Age	Skill
7/14/96	+	1.25	5-6.5	Reaches for second object purposefully
7/14/96	+	1.26	5-9	Works for desired, out-of-reach object
7/14/96	-	1.40	6.5-7.5	Retains two of three objects offered
8/22/96	+			
7/14/96	-	1.45	8-10	Retains two and reaches for third object
9/6/97	+			
10/2/97	+	1.47	8-10	Retrieves object using other material
10/2/97	+/-	1.46	8-11	Overcomes obstacle to obtain object

Targeted skills showing multiple assessments

Next skill to target

Sample Structure of a Direct Assessment

Process and Format: A sample structure for a direct child assessment appears below. However, the actual face-to-face assessment process and format will differ for each child and family and depend on family preferences and individual child variables, e.g., age of child, level of stranger anxiety, degree of involvement and role the family chooses to take, as well as the place, time, and duration of the assessment.

Duration: An initial direct assessment of the child can generally be expected to last from 45-90 minutes, but in some cases may only last 15-20 minutes. Remember, this is only the initial assessment, you may need to see the child more than one time in more than one setting to get a better picture of the child's strengths and needs. After the initial assessment and planning, continued assessment and planning will be an ongoing process.

Be sure to review "General Assessment Guidelines and Precautions," which follow on page i.32.

Suggested Steps

1. Free-play /warm up period:

10-15 minutes
Professional(s) sit unobtrusively on the "sidelines."
a. Provide a few developmentally appropriate play materials which are likely to elicit some of the skills and behaviors that you have targeted to assess before the direct assessment (see Instructions – page i.19).
b. Review purpose of assessment and "warm-up" period with family.
c. Invite family members to play with their child any way they choose.

2. Structured facilitation:

approximately 15-30 minutes
a. Transition to a more structured format as the child becomes comfortable. This part of the assessment is aimed at "fine-tuning" and filling in the gaps for skills which could not be observed incidentally during the free play and warm-up period.
b. Review the assessment activities and materials you selected before the direct assessment. Implement the activities which are most likely to elicit targeted Cognitive, Language, Fine Motor skills; e.g., table-top activities, drawing, looking at books, building with blocks, playing in a dramatic play corner, etc. Each activity is likely to yield information in several domains.
c. Observe how the child approaches and plays with materials and equipment before structuring eliciting situations directly with or through the parent.
d. Adapt toys and activities for specific disabilities and to ensure cultural sensitivity.
e. Continue interviewing the parent(s) with questions related to their child's typical skills and behaviors as well as their concerns and priorities. Use the

HELPful Tips

During "warm-up" and throughout the assessment, you may observe and identify:
• the style and level of family-child interaction
• additional structured activities you may want to incorporate
• some of the child's positional, movement, and toy preferences
• how the child solves problems
• child's spontaneous language.

Follow the child's cues when he is ready to transition from one activity and/or toy to another.

If more than one discipline is involved, they can act as a consultant to the primary evaluator (professional and parent) by "coaching from the sidelines" to help elicit specific skills, and recording the child's responses.

While you are targeting one skill, observers can simultaneously assess other skills; e.g., if you are facilitating Symbolic Play, the physical therapist can observe how the child moves from one toy to another; the occupational therapist may observe the type of grasp the child uses and his sensory responses to different textures sights and sounds; and the speech/language therapist may observe the child's spontaneous vocalizations, communication to others, and apparent understanding of directions.

HELP Family-Centered Interview or your notes from the Parent questions in strand Prefaces from *Inside HELP*.

Be sure to note any adaptations which were used to help assess skills.

Include parent responses to questions about their child's skills as part of the assessment.

3. Movement/motor activities:

approximately 10-15 minutes

Review the assessment activities and materials you selected before the direct assessment. Implement the activities which are most likely to elicit the targeted Gross Motor skills which have not yet been observed spontaneously. Provide mats, balls, and other large play equipment dependent upon the child's age and motor abilities, such as a tunnel, things to climb on, small slide, Tyke bike, or balance beam.

If it is necessary to directly test reflexes and postural responses, save this part of the assessment until toward the end, as this may be upsetting for the child.

If the child has or is suspected of having physical disabilities or motor dysfunction, have a pediatric PT or OT conduct and/or directly consult during assessment.

If the child is walking with good quality you can probably skip Section I. of Gross Motor strands and go directly to Section II., Strand 3-7 "Advancing postural control and Motor planning."

If the child is under 15 months or is not yet walking well, you can skip Section II. of the Gross Motor Strand.

If the child displays motor skills of good quality it may not be necessary to assess reflexes.

4. Feeding or Snack time:

approximately 10-20 minutes

Include washing up before and after snack to observe the child's participation in washing as well as his reactions to having his face washed. If the child is older, invite him to help clean up by wiping the table and throwing away some of the trash.
Most of the feeding assessment can occur by observing the parent feeding their child.

If oral motor dysfunction or feeding problems are present, schedule a separate assessment during the child's regular feeding time in his natural environmental with a pediatric speech or other therapist specializing in feeding.

Snack or meal time provides an excellent opportunity to observe the child's oral motor skills, independent feeding abilities, food and texture preferences, and any tactile reactions, posture during feeding, communication, and behavior.

5. Additional activities or closing time:

If the child is still alert and interested, additional assessment activities may be included to help fill in any gaps. If a therapist needs to do handling which may be disliked by the child, this could be scheduled toward the end.

The types and number of disciplines involved in initial assessment and planning will depend upon the present concerns about the child and family preferences and priorities. During an initial assessment, it may become evident that another discipline should also evaluate the child; this can be scheduled at a later time.

General Assessment Guidelines and Precautions

• Make assessments culturally relevant

It is important to assess and adapt items to reflect the child's relevant cultural and environmental experiences. Assessment should occur using the child's primary native language, both verbal and non-verbal, using toys and materials which are meaningful to the child. Some skills listed in the HELP may not be culturally relevant or appropriate to assess. Sample family interview questions have been included in the strand Preface to promote meaningful and culturally sensitive assessment and planning.

• Assess in natural environments

A complete picture of a young child's development can be difficult to achieve by unfamiliar observers in unfamiliar settings, especially with a shy or hesitant child. Although an initial assessment may need to be center-based, especially if more than one discipline is involved, whenever possible, also observe the child in multiple settings that the child is familiar with, e.g., home, day care. Most assessment items in this manual include example multiple naturalistic opportunities to observe the child's development during the course of typical daily activities, play and parent-child interactions which can be observed in a variety of settings.

• Include observations of the environment and caregiver interactions in your assessment

A child's development cannot be fully assessed or understood in isolation of the environment. Assessment of child skills and behaviors should include assessment of the child's physical environment and caregiver interactions which support development. For example, during the course of assessment it may be noted that the child is not pulling to stand. A child-focused assessment may generate specific motor therapy techniques to reach this goal. A transactional assessment, however, would consider factors in the environment which may be inhibiting the development of this skill. For example, if there are no sturdy, safe furnishings in the child's environments, it may be more appropriate to focus interventions on adapting the environment rather than specific therapy skills. The "Transactional Assessment" section in the Preface of each strand provides examples of key factors in the child's caregiving environment which can promote or compromise the child's development. Assessment of the physical environment and caregiver interactions can occur through observations of the child's primary environment, parent-child interactions during play and daily activities, and through sensitive parent interview.

Important note: No family or environment can be expected to display all of the given examples of sensitive interactions and supportive environments. Day-to-day stresses, being in an unfamiliar environment with professionals, cultural diversity, and other situational factors can influence how a caregiver interacts with the child at any particular time. The *Inside HELP* examples are only provided to help clinicians consider patterns of interactions and environments which can support and facilitate the child's development as intervention strategies are planned.

• Incorporate variety!

Since the HELP is an ongoing curriculum-based assessment, it is likely that items will be repeated with children as they are incorporated into curriculum activities and are periodically reassessed to measure progress. It is thus extremely important, especially in the Cognitive and Language areas to incorporate variety into the example Eliciting Procedures and use of materials to ensure generalization. Assessment and interventions should occur in multiple settings using a variety of materials and eliciting techniques.

• Be sure to identify medical limitations, precautions, and contraindications

It is very important to review the child's medical history and current medical status carefully, including vision and hearing if available, before assessment and intervention. Many conditions may require a medical clearance from the child's physician for assessment and intervention. Existing or prior medical conditions can restrict movements and positioning as well as influence the child's strength, endurance, quality and age of achieving motor milestones. Consult with the child's family, medical records, and physician regarding existing conditions or a history of: e.g., respiratory and/or cardiac difficulties; medications; surgeries; seizures; medical equipment: e.g., use of G-tubes; colostomy bag, oxygen, apnea monitor, or history of long-term IV.

If the child has poor strength and endurance, limit the number of activities assessed at any one time. Watch carefully for any signs of fatigue, and discontinue or modify the assessment at the first sign of physiological distress, e.g., shortness of breath, rapid breathing, changes in the child's skin or his behavior.

• Involve families in every step of the process

1. <u>Families should be invited to participate and make decisions during all phases of the assessment process.</u> Assessment content, process, and expectations should be adapted to respect and fit individual family priorities, beliefs, and values. For example, families should be afforded the opportunity to make choices and preferences regarding:
   - Their level of decision-making, participation, and involvement during the assessment;
   - Which family members to include in the assessment;
   - Which professionals and disciplines will participate in the assessment;
   - Assessment settings: times, places, duration;
   - Assessment content: priorities of skills and behaviors to assess, types of toys and materials to use;
   - Assessment methods: direct handling versus observation, types of encouragement;
   - Who should receive copies of reports which may be generated by the assessment.

2. <u>Parents are experts in their child's development</u> and can provide valuable and valid assessment information related to their child's skills and behaviors. Only families can assess their own concerns, priorities, and resources. As noted, example open-ended as well as specific skill-related interview questions are provided in the Preface of each strand. These are included to facilitate a family-directed assessment of their child's skills and abilities as well as of their concerns, priorities, and resources. Remember, family concerns, priorities, and resources can change frequently; a family-directed assessment is an ongoing process which occurs naturally throughout interventions.

3. <u>It is important to always explain what you are assessing and why.</u> Asking a child to draw a line, stack blocks, or find a hidden toy can be confusing and meaningless to a parent. "Family Friendly," jargon-free definitions and rationales for assessing various developmental skills and behaviors are included in the Preface of each strand. These examples and explanations should be further adapted for individual families.

• Involve a multidisciplinary team

Children with disabilities often have complex, multifaceted needs which require professionals from a variety of disciplines. There are generally three models in early intervention for involving multiple disciplines in the assessment: Multidisciplinary, Interdisciplinary, and Transdisciplinary. It is beyond the scope of this manual to describe the roles, functions, benefits, and weakness of each model, but all HELP materials can be used within each model. Whichever model is used, parents should always be considered a vital part of any team, and it is critical that team members work collaboratively to avoid fragmented views of a child's development and to ensure integrated curriculum assessment and planning.

Throughout *Inside HELP*, suggestions are made regarding which disciplines to include in an assessment and when to seek further evaluation. In addition, the "Identifying and Interpreting Needs for Intervention" and "Family Friendly Interpretation" sections in the Preface of each strand, and the clear definitions provided for each skill, promote interdisciplinary sharing and understanding of all areas of development, regardless of a discipline's area of expertise. In all cases, use your own clinical judgment to involve the necessary and appropriate disciplines.

• Adapt for disabilities

Assessment adaptations and modifications should be made to help ensure that a disability or delay in one are of development does not interfere with a true assessment of the child's capacities in other areas of development. In each strand Preface, Sample Adaptations are included to help assess a child's performance related to the underlying strand concept.

Frequently Asked Questions – FAQs

HELP covers so many items, where do I begin?

No other currently available birth-to-three curriculums include as many developmental skills, behaviors, and intervention strategies as the HELP. The density and comprehensiveness of HELP can, at first glance, appear overwhelming, especially to the new user. However, the comprehensiveness of HELP offers the clinician more variety and options for assessment and curriculum planning, and enables families and clinicians to plan and monitor progress in small, incremental steps. The following tips can help make using HELP more manageable.

Remember: HELP is not a "one-time" tool

HELP is an ongoing curriculum-based assessment which is not intended to be completed in one assessment session. There are a large number of skills, but they span three years and are intended to be addressed over a long period of time.

Not all skills are pertinent

All of the HELP skills and behaviors listed are rarely pertinent to any one child. Many will not be pertinent due to the child's age and developmental level, some skills may not be functional due to a child's disability, and other skills may not be necessary to assess because they are judged not to be important to assess for a particular child, e.g., ability to walk on a balance beam if the child displays no difficulty in motor planning or balance skills. As you consider these variables, the scope of skills appropriate to assess during initial observations and family interview can become narrower and more manageable.

Don't assess each skill, strand, or domain separately

Although each skill, strand, or domain has an underlying key concept or focus, it is typically unnecessary and inappropriate to assess each separately. Each observation of a child completing a task or involved in an interaction or daily activity yields information about a variety of skills and behaviors – simultaneously. For example, if you observe a parent asking the child to, "Throw the ball," and in response the child says, "ball" and throws the ball in a playful way to his parent, you could credit in receptive language his understanding of the words "ball" and "throw" in Strand 2-1, as well as his ability to follow a direction in Strand 2-2. In addition, you could credit his expressive vocabulary with the word "ball" in Strand 2-3, as well as his ability to produce single consonant vowel combinations in Strand 2-6. The gross motor and social interaction skills of throwing a ball can also be credited in the Gross Motor and Social-Emotional domains. Thus, a single response is likely to elicit information on several skills in several strands.

Get a general idea of where to begin before you begin

Parents can provide an enormous amount of information about their child to give you a general idea of level of functioning in most areas of development. This information can be gathered from family interviews over the phone, in person, and through application questionnaires.

In addition to family interviews, additional developmental information may be available from previous screenings or formal evaluations. Since many of the items on the HELP are similar to items contained in various screening and evaluation tools, this information is likely to be useful in identifying were to begin with the HELP

Can I use HELP to determine program eligibility?

This will depend primarily on your program's policies and the individual needs of the child. It is your professional responsibility to use instruments and qualified personnel that meet local, state, and federal requirements.

HELP is **not** standardized and thus should not be used if your program requires standardized instruments to determine developmental delay. In addition, since HELP cannot provide a single "score" or definitive developmental age, HELP should **not** be used to determine eligibility for children who may be experiencing mild developmental delays. In such cases, however, HELP can be used to compliment standardized instruments to support "informed clinical opinion" requirements, and it can be used as an initial and ongoing assessment to help identify the child's unique strengths and needs, services appropriate to meet those needs, and the resources, priorities, and concerns of the family.

If your program does not require standardized instruments, HELP can be used to help support your informed clinical opinion regarding eligibility for children with significant delays and atypical development. HELP can also be used as an initial and ongoing assessment to help identify the child's unique strengths and needs, services appropriate to meet those needs, and the resources, priorities, and concerns of the family. In addition, if a child is referred to your program with a previously diagnosed disability or special need which already meets program eligibility requirements, HELP can be used as an initial and ongoing curriculum-based assessment.

Which HELP assessment recording form(s) should I use?

HELP offers two primary formats for recording initial and ongoing assessments and collecting child data: the *HELP Strands* and the *HELP Checklist*. The *HELP Charts* are most typically used for communicating progress to parents, and not necessarily as the primary recording form.

The *HELP Strands* breaks the six major domains into sub-groups (strands) according to underlying skill concept; structured so that <u>one skill leads to the next skill</u>. The *HELP Strands* are thus usually better suited for children who have disabilities and/or more uneven development within a major domain. The *HELP Strands* are available in two formats: a loose-leaf format and a booklet format. The loose-leaf version pulls apart by major domain. If more than one discipline will be assessing at one time, use the loose-leaf format.

The *HELP Checklist* and *HELP Charts* list skills according to age and major developmental domains, but the skills are **not** sub-grouped within domain. Thus one skill does not necessarily lead to the next. The *HELP Checklist* can be used for children who have more even development or who do not have disabilities.

There is also a HELP form available for collecting family information – the *HELP Family-Centered Interview*. This form can be used from initial contacts with the family and throughout intervention to record and update family concerns, priorities, and resources.

Why are some age ranges on the HELP Checklist, Charts and Activity Guide different than the age ranges in Inside HELP and HELP Strands?

The original HELP products, i.e., the *HELP Activity Guide* and the *HELP Charts*, were developed in 1976-1979. Since that time, infant/toddler literature has expanded and more information has become available. Although most of the original HELP skill wording and age ranges remain the same, some skills needed to be revised to reflect current literature. These changes were made on the *HELP Strands* and in *Inside HELP* in 1992, and on the *HELP Charts* and *HELP Checklist* in 1994, and the *HELP Activity Guide* in late 1997. Check the © date on your copies to see if you have the latest versions.

Why are some HELP skills repeated in different strands?

Some skills are repeated in more than one strand because these skills involve more than one underlying key concept. For example, skill 4.29 "Reaches and grasps object" is listed in the Cognitive strand 1-5 "Spatial Relationships" and in Fine Motor Strand 4-3 "Reach/Approach." This skill is built upon the cognitive concepts related to depth perception and relationship of objects in space, as well as fine motor skills required for reaching. The definitions and credit criteria, therefore, will differ somewhat between strands for the same skill when it is repeated in different strands.

Is there an assessment kit available that has all the materials needed for the assessment?

No. HELP is not standardized and does not require standardized materials. The materials you use can be individualized to meet individual child preferences and needs. Whenever possible, use toys and materials in the child's natural environment which are functional and meaningful for the child (see i.18 – Assessment Materials).

Visit our Web site for the latest FAQ's: www.vort.com/faq.html

Inside HELP © 1992-1997 VORT Corporation

0.0 REGULATORY/SENSORY ORGANIZATION

1.01	0-1	Quiets when picked up
1.03	0-1	Responds to sounds
5.01	0-3	Enjoys and needs a great deal of physical contact and tactile stimulation
5.05	0-3	Molds and relaxes body when held; cuddles
1.02	0-6	Shows pleasure when touched and handled
1.05	1-2	Inspects surroundings
1.07	1-3	Listens to voice for 30 seconds
6.04	1-3	Stays awake for longer periods without crying - usually in p.m.
1.06	1-6	Shows active interest in person or object for at least 1 minute
1.15	3-6	Uses hands and mouth for sensory exploration of objects
5.08	3-6	Stops unexplained crying
5.15	3-6	Enjoys social play
1.22	4-6	Localizes tactile stimulation by touching the same spot or searching for object that touched body
5.18	4-8	Enjoys frolic play
1.34	6-12	Smells different things
1.35	6-9	Plays 2-3 minutes with a single toy
1.54	9-11	Listens to speech without being distracted by other sources
6.23	7-12	Drools less except when teething
6.25	9-12	Finger feeds self
6.27	9-12	Sleeps nights twelve to fourteen hours
6.29	10.5-12	Cooperates with dressing by extending arm or leg
1.68	12-18	Enjoys messy activities
1.69	12-18	Reacts to various sensations such as extremes in temperature and taste
1.99	18-24	Uses playdough and paints
5.60	18-24	Enjoys solitary play for a few minutes
5.61	18-24	Enjoys rough-and-tumble play
6.61	24-26	Handles fragile items carefully
1.127	24-29	Enjoys tactile books
1.120	24-36	Plays with water and sand
1.151	30-36	Identifies familiar objects by touch
1.152	30-36	Enjoys being read to and looks at books independently
5.93	30+	Participates in circle games; plays interactive games

Family Friendly Interpretation of Strand Concepts, Assessment, & Purpose

We will be observing how your child reacts to different sensations, such as touch, sound, and moving in space. Some children are extra sensitive and react strongly to certain sensations. For example, a child who is extra sensitive to touch may get very upset if he touches something furry or eats a certain texture of food. This is sometimes referred to as being "hypersensitive," "hyper-reactive" or "defensive." Other children may be unaware of, and thus not react to, certain sensations. For example, these children may not notice if something is too hot or if a piece of tape is stuck on their arm. This is sometimes referred to as being "hyposensitive" or "underreactive." A child may be extra or hyper-sensitive to some sights, sounds, textures or movements, but under- or hypo-sensitive to others.

A child's sleeping, feeding, and attention patterns, as well as his ability to plan body movements, to become calm, alert, and socialize, is often associated with how he experiences various sensations. For example, sometimes children who are very sensitive to touch or movement may be more irritable, have difficulty focusing their attention, or have trouble sleeping through the night.

Understanding how your child experiences and reacts to different sensations can help us determine the best activities and environments for nurturing your child's growth, learning, and development of happy relationships.

Professional FYI

The Regulatory/Sensory Organization strand has been added to the six original HELP domains. Sensory processing, reactivity and self-regulation are recognized as important foundation and influential forces to overall development in the areas of Cognition, Language, Gross Motor, Fine Motor, Social-Emotional and Self Help skills. Although considered important to development, Regulatory/Sensory Organization is often overlooked in traditional developmental checklists and curriculum-based assessments. It should not be considered as being independent from the

Professional FYI   (continued)

other six domains, but instead, it can be viewed as the foundation or "glue" for all other areas of development since it can directly affect the achievement and quality of most other behaviors and skills.

The Regulatory/Sensory Organization strand is comprised of key behaviors which screen for typical and atypical patterns of behaviors related to:

- The child's self-regulation capacities, i.e., sleep cycles, regulation of moods, attention, and consolability.
- The child's capacities to perceive and organize various sensory experiences, i.e., sights, sounds, touch, taste, smell, vestibular (body movement through space and head position) and proprioception (awareness of body position in space).

Effects on Development

Atypical regulatory and sensory responses can affect the child's development in each of the six developmental domains of the HELP. The following, often interconnected example problems, can be symptomatic of, or affected by, problems in regulatory and sensory organization and processing:

General

- Atypical muscle tone (usually low)
- Poor reflex integration
- Jerky movements
- Distractibility
- Difficulty "grading" movements, e.g., poor judgment of force, speed, aim.

Domain Specific

1.0 Cognitive
- Disorganization in play
- Delayed or absent symbolic play
- Poor gestural imitation

2.0 Language
- Delayed or atypical communication
- Difficulty following directions
- Poor articulation

3.0 Gross Motor
- Fear of movement or lifting feet from ground
- Poor postural control
- Difficulty with motor planning
- Poor equilibrium and righting responses

4.0 Fine Motor
- Visual spatial and perceptual problems
- Difficulty with eye-motor control
- Delayed or minimal manipulation of objects
- Poor accuracy of movements
- Difficulty with precise hand movements
- Difficulty sequencing fine motor movements, e.g., for block construction, drawing

5.0 Social
- Difficulty with transitions and shifts in activity
- Self-stimulation
- Extreme emotional shifts
- Poor impulse control
- Limited range of and/or extremes in emotional responses
- Difficulty forming attachments and social relationships

6.0 Self Help
- Poor oral-motor control
- Poor sleeping and feeding patterns
- Delayed or difficulty in sequencing steps needed to accomplish self help skills.

Considerations in Assessment and Planning

<u>Variation in children's reactions to sensory stimuli is common.</u> Variations can be normal and do not necessarily indicate that the child has a regulatory or sensory organization problem. In addition, atypical responses can be transient, especially during the first year. This is frequently evident in the premature or low-birth-weight infant. It is important not to unduly alarm families. If a child displays <u>several significant and persistent atypical responses</u>, however, it is important to refer to a pediatric therapist with experience in the principles of sensory integration for a more comprehensive sensory evaluation. The child should be reassessed over a period of several months before assuming that this is an area for lasting concern.

If a child is not evidencing difficulties in Regulatory/Sensory Organization and the parent does not report any suspect regulatory or sensory problems (from parent screening questions below), it is not always necessary to conduct an assessment in this area. Most of the items in this strand are also listed in the strands of the other six domains. However, it still may be useful for the clinician to conduct an assessment in this area because individualizing interventions to match the child's sensory preferences can enhance functional development in other domains.

This strand can be helpful in planning interventions because it can help us understand and identify a child's unique regulatory and sensory capacities, preferences, and needs. For example, which features of a toy engage a child best? Some children prefer strong visual features, such as bright colors; others may prefer stronger tactile or auditory features. Identifying sensory preferences and needs can assist us in designing interventions, adapting the environment, and adapting our interactions to be in tune with the child.

Parent Questions   (General Examples - see Skills for specific questions)

[For each question, may ask for more specifics from parents with questions such as, "Can you tell me a little more about that?" "Can you give me some examples?" "About how often?" "When does this usually occur?" "Are there some things you've tried that seem to help?"]

To help identify the child's unique strengths and needs related to regulatory and sensory organization:
- How would you describe your child's personality (e.g., easy going, difficult, fussy)?
- How are things going with your child's sleep habits?

[Additional questions - if not addressed above, or if parent expresses concerns]
- Is he sleeping through the night?
- How do you get your child to go to sleep at bed or nap time?
- What kinds of things have you tried to help him sleep better? Has anything seemed to help?
- Have you noticed if your child seems to get upset, startle, pull away, or stiffen up when he:
  - is cuddled or held?
  - sees or touches certain textures (furry things, silk, terry cloth, lotion) or toys?
  - is given a bath?...dried with a towel?...dressed or undressed?
  - is in certain positions, e.g., have you noticed if he fusses more on his tummy than on his back?
  - gets food or other messy things on his hands or face?
  - is around certain smells or odors such as perfume?
  - hears certain sounds?
  - is around bright lights?
- Does your child (or, for older children who are not mouthing, "did your child") mouth his toys?

- Does your child seem to especially like or dislike certain movements, e.g., rocking, lifting him up in the air, riding in a car?
- Have you noticed if he likes to rock himself; e.g., when he is alone in his crib?
- How does your child do during mealtimes? Are there some foods he loves or seems to crave; avoids touching or eating?
- How does your child react when he falls or gets hurt?
- Does your child seem to have any difficulties attending to a toy or person?
- Have you or your child's physician identified or been suspicious that your child has any food or environmental allergies?
- Are there any other important aspects of how your child reacts to touch, movement, sights or sounds that I have not asked you which you think are important to consider?
- (for older children) Are there certain movement toys he seems to really like or seems to avoid such as a "Sit 'n Spin™," a ride-on toy, swings, or rocking horse toys?

To help identify family resources, priorities and concerns related to the child's development in this area:
- Is there anything related to your child's sleep/feeding habits, ability to attend, or his reactions to touch, sights, sounds, movements or smells that you feel is especially important to understand or work on?
- What have you tried so far that seems to help? *[Use this question in conjunction with the needs identified above, e.g., "What have you tried so far that seems to help your child sleep through the night?"]*
- Is there anyone that can help with: e.g., consoling your child so you can get some sleep?

Sample *Functional* Outcome Statements which may be generated by the Family

[Will be dependent upon identified individual child and family needs, and should incorporate objectives and activities from other domains]

We will know:
- Pleasurable ways to hold and cuddle our child;
- How to adapt sights, sounds, and movements so they do not upset our child.

My child will:
- Not cry when he takes a bath;
- Explore toys with his mouth;
- Enjoy playing with creative materials such as sand, paint, and dough;
- Be able to pay attention when he is playing with a toy;
- Pay attention when we have story time;
- Not cry all the time.

Transactional Assessment

May assess through observation and interview.

Assessment of the Child's Environment

1. Supportive:
[Example environments which support/facilitate development in this area]
The child's caregiving environments usually:
- Offer a variety of interesting sights and sounds which support the child's sensory and regulatory capacities and needs;
- Offer the child opportunities to interact at his own pace with a variety of textures, to get "messy," and (if older) to engage in "rough and tumble" play;
- Provide fairly consistent and predictable routines;
- Match the child's unique regulatory and sensory needs, e.g., if the child is more sensitive and gets upset by crowds, are there quiet areas available?; if the child is difficult to alert or has difficulty attending, is there adequate controlled stimulation and novelty to attract sustained interest?; if the child is hypersensitive to particular sights or sounds, are these buffered for him?

[Example interview questions "Is it okay if your child puts some of his toys in his mouth?" "Does your child have any furry toys?; any soft rubbery toys?"; "Does your child try to finger feed himself? Has he tried feeding himself messier foods such as bananas?"
(If older) "Has your child ever played in sand?; with paints?; Play-Doh™?" "Has he ever played any rough-and-tumble-type games such as riding 'piggy back' or climbing on playground equipment?"]

2. Compromising:
[Example environments which may restrict, compromise, inhibit or be unsupportive toward development in this area]
The child's caregiving environments are frequently:
- Over- or under-stimulating to the child's unique sensory preferences and needs;
- Chaotic;
- Overly restrictive or permissive.

Assessment of Caregiver Interactions with the Child

1. Supportive:
[Example interactions which support/facilitate child's development in this area]
The child's caregivers usually:
- Are available to comfort the child;
- Provide predictable routines;
- Are able to read and respond sensitively to the child's unique responses to sensory stimulation during routine handling and play;
- Provide predictable interactions;
- Provide a variety of animate and inanimate stimuli which interest the child;
- Help attract the child's attention in a relaxed and child-focused manner.

2. Compromising:
[Example interactions which may restrict, compromise, inhibit or be unsupportive of the child's development in this area]

The child's caregivers frequently:
- Misinterpret and or respond inappropriately to the child's responses to sensory stimulation during routine handling;
- Are unavailable or do not try to comfort the child;
- Avoid holding, touching, or interacting with the child.

***[Important note**: Caregivers may have difficulty providing supportive interactions because it is the child who is a poor interactor. The child with regulatory or sensory problems may not be cuddly, may not give responsive eye contact, or may frequently pull away from caregivers. A parent may be exhausted, try too hard, or worry about "rocking the boat" when the child is quiet. Consequently, interactions that began as sensitive may appear compromising by the time of assessment.]*

Identifying and Interpreting Needs for Intervention

If a child displays several atypical reactions over repeated observations, he may be <u>having difficulty with regulatory and sensory organization</u>. Refer the child for a more comprehensive evaluation by a pediatric occupational or physical therapist who has experience in sensory integration principles.

However, before targeting regulatory/sensory organization as the <u>primary or only need</u> for intervention or referral, consider, rule out, or adapt for other factors that may be causing atypical

responses. These may include:
- <u>Allergies, food, environmental, or chemical sensitivities</u>.
- <u>Active ear infection, middle ear fluid:</u> may cause pain and may extend to affect vestibular mechanism.
- <u>Visual impairment</u>: mobility patterns and motor planning are strongly connected with vision.
- <u>Hearing impairment</u>: may be clumsy or awkward in movements because hearing impairment

Identifying and Interpreting Needs for Intervention   (continued)

affects the vestibular mechanism of the inner ear;
- • Neuromotor disabilities, especially atypical tone;
- • Cognitive disability, especially delayed object play skills (Strand 1-1);
- • Environmental/interactional - for example:
  - – Child is not held frequently or is held in uncomfortable positions;

- – Child is not allowed to mouth toys;
- – Caregivers get upset if child is messy;
- – Child has a lack of experience with textures and movements;
- – Child has a traumatic history.
- • Transient benign stressful situations that are likely to resolve, e.g., child is tired, hungry, ill.

Assessment Adaptations   (Examples)

- • Ear infections:
  - – Reassess when the child is free of middle ear fluid and infection; compare responses.
  - – Do not assess strong movement activities, i.e., #5.18 and #5.61, as these may be painful.
- • Visually impaired:
  - – Observe child's responses when he is in his familiar environment, using familiar materials. Most items can be observed while the child is sitting on the parent's lap.
  - – Introduce firm, solid materials before moving on to pliable, squashy, textured objects; e.g., watch how the child explores a block before introducing a Koosh™ Ball.
  - – The child may normally react to new or unexpected tactile and movement experiences with hyper-reactive responses that are not due to a true regulatory or sensory problem.
    1. Provide extra time for the child to become accustomed to new materials and movements before making judgment regarding his organization capacities.
    2. Describe all objects and movements before introducing them.
    3. Do not base assessment on initial reactions.
  - – Specific skill adaptations or considerations:
    #1.05 "Inspects surroundings"
    credit if child "inspects" through touch,

mouthing, apparent listening.
#1.15 "Uses hands and mouth for sensory exploration of objects"
mouthing may normally continue much beyond this age range.
#5.18 "Enjoys frolic play"
have parent demonstrate movement activities that child is familiar with.
#1.152 "Enjoys being read to and looks at books independently"
use tactile books, low vision books, books on audio tapes.
  - – Expect some atypical responses. These can be normal for a child who is blind.
- • Deaf:
  - – Omit #1.03 "Responds to sounds"
  - – Adapt #1.07 "Listens to voice for 30 seconds," by crediting child's visual attention to the person interacting with him.
  - – Expect some clumsy or awkward gross motor movements which may be normal for a child who is deaf.
- • Motor impaired and atypical tone:
  Adapt positioning and handling according to a pediatric occupational or physical therapist's recommendations.
- • Environmental:
  If the child has not had opportunities to touch or eat a variety of textures, allow extra time for the child to become acquainted with the stimulus; do not base assessment on initial reactions.

General Assessment Procedures & Processes   (apply to all items in this Strand)

1. **Assess the child's responses to all items *at and below* the child's age.** Although certain behaviors/responses may first become evident during a certain period, they continue and overlap as the child matures. For example, although a child is 18 months, it is important to observe earlier skills such as #1.02 "Shows pleasure when touched and handled" (0-6 mo.), and #1.15 "Uses hands and mouth for sensory exploration of objects" (3-6 mo.). Earlier items should, however, be assessed

according to other appropriate age expectations for the child's age; e.g., in skill #1.15 "Uses hands and mouth for sensory exploration of objects" (3-6 mo.), at 18 months, you would credit this item if the child explores objects with his hands but does not use his mouth for sensory exploration. If he is still mouthing, this can be noted to target for further assessment and intervention.

2. **This strand can be assessed while assessing other areas of development.** For example,

General Assessment Procedures & Processes (continued)

during snack time, while assessing oral motor and independent feeding, observe the child's responses to various food textures; during play, while assessing cognitive development, observe the child's ability to focus and attend to a toy.

3. **It is usually more meaningful and appropriate to describe the child's response to sensory stimulation as "typical," "over-reactive" hypersensitive or "hypo-reactive"** etc., rather than assessing by or assigning specific age ranges.

4. **It is important to look for patterns of preferences, capacities and difficulties** within and between different sensory and regulatory processes, i.e., tactile, auditory, movement, attention, consolability. A child may overreact to certain sensations and underreact to others, e.g., he may startle easily to certain sights or sounds but crave movement and handling; or he may overreact to light touch, but underreact to painful touch.

5. **There is an extra column on the strand assessment to note specific reactions to different stimuli.** Note the child's preferences and adverse reactions in the "Responses Observed" column.

6. **Cautions:**

a. Be sure to follow the child's lead and monitor his responses to sensory stimulation carefully. Watch for changes in the child's expression, respiration, color, skin temperature, and behavior. If he cries or otherwise expresses fear or distress, discontinue the eliciting situation, noting his reaction.

b. If the child has an ear infection do not assess #5.18 "Enjoys frolic play," or #5.61 "Enjoys rough and tumble play," as intense movement may be painful for the child.

+ - A Credit Notes:

+ if the child usually displays typical responses as defined.

A+ if the child predominantly displays over-reactive responses which affect positive interactions and developmental growth.

A- if the child predominantly displays underreactive responses which affect positive interactions and developmental growth.

A+- if the child displays a combination of responses which affect positive interactions and developmental growth.

O circle any credit (either - or +) if the environment and/or interactions do not support the child's unique regulatory or sensory needs.

N/A if the item is inappropriate to observe due to the child's disability or delay.

Assessment Materials

Furry toys or stuffed animals, "porcupine"-type squeeze toys, blocks, finger-paints, Play-Doh™, Theraputy™ (if available), water, sand or corn-meal, uncooked rice, foods of various textures and taste; stickers or tape; movement toys such as a Sit 'n Spin™, large ball, Tyke bike.

Quiets when picked up   0-1

Definition: The child is able to calm and recover from distress with external help from a sensitive care-giver, e.g., holding, rocking, swaddling, feeding, and/or placing the caregiver's hand on the child's chest over his hands.

Parent Questions: Does your child seem to fuss or cry a lot? What seems to help? About how long does it usually take for him to calm down?

Example Observation Opportunities: Observe as distressful situations naturally occur during observation periods. Advise parents at the beginning of sessions to feel free to pick up their child at any time if he seems upset. (Assure parents that they are not spoiling their child nor interfering with your session as needed.)

Credit: (see also Credit Notes in this strand's preface)

+ (if under 3 months) usually by report or observation, calms with some external caregiver support as defined.

A+ **hyper-reactive/irritable:** the child is usually irritable and takes more than 20 minutes to console and recover from distress, and/or, if over 6 months and continues to need extensive external support (e.g., holding, rocking) to calm.

A- **underreactive:** the child rarely or only weakly expresses distress.

O circle any credit if caregiver does not try or has difficulty identifying successful methods to console child, or waits until distress escalates before responding.

1.03 Responds to sounds   0-1

Definition: The child listens and enjoys a range of sounds, e.g., high- and low-pitched, soft and loud, rhythmical and irregular. During the first month responses to sudden sounds are reflexive bodily responses, e.g., startle, increase or decrease in respiration and/or activity, change in expression, or eyes widening. Later, he may smile, look for, or move his body in synchrony.

Example Observation Opportunities: Observe child's responses to sounds that occur naturally during the observation period, e.g., when you or parent talks to him in varying pitches; when the telephone rings, door slams, vacuum cleaner starts; during play with rattles, squeak toys.

Credit: (see also Credit Notes in this strand's preface)
+   child enjoys and attends to a wide range of sounds; if under 1 month, the child's reflexive responses diminish within a few moments of the sound and after several concurrent repetitions.
A+ **hyper-reactive:** child repeatedly and easily startles, cries, winces, becomes upset to certain sounds; over 6 months appears confused about the direction of sounds; covers ears.
A- **underreactive:** [_not_ related to hearing loss] minimal or little interest and responses to sounds; over 12 months child frequently selects toys and activities which make loud noises, or speaks very loudly much of the time.
O   circle any credit if caregivers have difficulty reading or interpreting child responses to sounds or the child's sound environment is over- or under-stimulating to child's needs.

(also in Strand 1-3 "Sound Awareness and Localization")

5.01 Enjoys and needs a great deal of physical contact and tactile stimulation   0-3

Definition: The child usually enjoys being touched and stroked. When touched, stroked, or held, he may smile, establish eye contact, or relax.

Parent Questions: How does your child respond when you stroke or touch him?

Example Eliciting Situations: Provide ample opportunities for parent to hold, touch and interact with the child during the observation period. Be sure to give parent "permission" to pick up or touch the child whenever he seems to need the parent. May also observe if child calms down; when parent picks him up or strokes him. If you are holding the baby, observe how he responds as you stroke and gently move his arms and legs. Also observe child's responses when lying on various surfaces, e.g., carpet, blanket, vinyl mat. [_If the parent does not pick child up or touch child often during the obser-vation period, probe through sensitive questioning if parent avoids close contact because child becomes fussy_]

Credit: (see also Credit Notes in this strand's preface)
+   usually appears comfortable with various forms of touch: relaxes, smiles, looks at adult or other-wise displays enjoyment when touched and held.
A+ **hyper-reactive:** child usually cries, fusses, arches, or pulls away when touched lightly; dislikes lying on textured surfaces; may accept firm touches
A- **underreactive:** seems unaware of touch or moderate pain; does not change posture or facial expression unless contact is extreme.
O   circle any credit if caregivers rarely touch child or have difficulty interpreting and responding sensitively to child's unique responses to touch.

(also in Strand 5-1 "Attachment")

5.05 Molds and relaxes body when held; cuddles   0-3

Definition: When content, the child usually conforms or shapes his body to fit closely to an adult cuddling him.

Parent Questions: Does your child usually like to be held and cuddled? About how often do you think babies should be held?

Example Observation Opportunities: May observe whenever parent is holding child when both are relaxed and content, e.g., during feeding, parent interview, rest, play. If the child is easily over-stim-ulated, explore less stimulating handling techniques, e.g., do not rock, talk, or look excessively at child while holding; try swaddling before holding. Note adaptations used in comment column.

Credit: (see also Credit Notes in this strand's preface)
+   can be characterized as "cuddly"; usually molds and relaxes body when held.
A+ **hyper-reactive:** usually cries, fusses, arches, pulls away when held.
A- **hypo-reactive:** usually feels or appears limp or passive when held; does not mold or adjust posture to adult.
O   circle any credit if caregivers rarely hold or cuddle child, or have difficulty identifying interac-tions and positions for holding which are comfortable for caregiver and child.

(also in Strand 5-5 "Social Interactions")

Shows pleasure when touched and handled   0-6

Definition: Routine handling involving movement is well tolerated by the child. He enjoys being picked up, gently rocked, or gently jiggled or bounced while being held by a trusted caregiver. He may smile, relax, vocalize, look or stop crying when appropriate movement is introduced.

Parent Questions: How does your child react when you pick him up...rock him in your arms...rock him in a cradle or infant seat...swing him gently in an infant swing?

Example Observation Opportunities: Provide ample opportunities for caregivers to move and interact with the child during the observation period. Observe the child's reactions to routine movement, e.g., being put down and lifted for a diaper change; changes of position as caregiver stands up or sits down. Also suggest some specific rocking in arms if this does not occur spontaneously.

Credit: (see also Credit Notes in this strand's preface)

+   usually enjoys and or remains calm when moved during routine activities, including rocking and gently swinging.

A+   **hyper-reactive:** displays strong aversion to reasonable movement; cries, fusses, or tenses body.

A-   **underreactive:** often seems unaware of movement, unless very fast and vigorous.

O   circle any credit if caregiver's handling is rough, abrupt, over-stimulating or irritating to child, e.g., fast movement transitions; insufficient support to body during movement.

Inspects surroundings   1-2

Definition: The child visually explores his environment. During alert periods, he may spend up to 10 minutes intermittently looking about, especially if there are attractive and novel visual stimuli within his visual field. During this period, the child attends for only a few seconds at a time, rests, and then looks about again.

Parent Questions: What does your child do when he is awake and lying in his crib or sitting in his infant seat? Have you noticed him looking at things around him? Are there certain things or places he seems to like looking at?

Example Observation Opportunities: Observe the child when no one is directly interacting with him and he is not engaged in looking a specific object or spectacle e.g., while you are collaborating with parents. Ideally, observe the child in an environment that has various large objects with contrasting colors and obvious contours, e.g., pictures or mirror on wall, television set, dark desk with desk lamp against light wall, dog walking nearby; avoid direct overhead or other bright lighting. The child can be in any resting or play position but if unable to observe, try observing when parent is holding child upright at shoulder or facing outward.

Credit: (see also Credit Notes in this strand's preface)

+   looks calmly at things in the environment for at least a few seconds at a time; in older infant, remains calm and focused while looking for a few minutes.

A+   **hyper-reactive:** is overly sensitive to bright lights; frequently cries or closes eyes in typical environments.

A-   **underreactive:** never looks at things in the environment unless there is movement and sound.

O   circle any credit if caregiving environments are usually over- or under-stimulating to child.

Listens to voice for 30 seconds   1-3

Definition: The child is able to attend and listen to people talking to him for at least 30 seconds. By 3 months, many infants can listen to and interact with an interesting partner for several minutes.

Parent Questions: Does your baby seem to enjoy it when you talk to him? What does he do?

Example Observation Opportunities: Observe caregiver and infant interactions in a variety of situations, e.g., during a diaper change, when feeding, soothing, playing. Observe how the caregiver attracts and engages child in conversations (e.g., varied facial and vocal expressions, exaggerated intonations) and how easy it is for the child to be engaged or over-stimulated. When the child is looking at you, initiate a "conversation," using short phrases with varied intonations. Observe if child displays preferences, e.g., high-pitched voices more than low-pitched.

Credit: (see also Credit Notes in this strand's preface)

+   the child is easy to engage and able to focus upon the speaker for at least 30 seconds many times during the observation period. He may look, smile, stop sucking, vocalize back or become still. He can attend to complex vocal patterns without looking confused or "tuning out."

Listens to voice for 30 seconds   1-3   (continued)

A+ **hyper-reactive:** is usually is distracted by common background sounds not normally noticed by others; may appear hyper-alert, but there is no shared attention or engagement with speaker; and/or child becomes quickly over-stimulated and may cry, hiccup, yawn, shut his eyes, avert gaze; change breathing patterns or color when someone talks to him.

A- **underreactive:** usually does not respond, e.g., no change in expression; not engaged with speaker; or responds only to exaggerated speech, e.g., speaker must use extreme changes in pitch, volume, facial expression to engage child [*not due to hearing*].

O circle any credit if caregivers do not, or only rarely, provide sensitive verbal interactions in sync with child's level of responsiveness.

Stays awake for longer periods without crying - usually in p.m.   1-3

Definition: As feeding and sleeping patterns become more established, the infant should have several alert, calm and responsive periods. Late afternoon or early evening may continue to be a fussy time.

Parent Questions: How would you describe your child's personality during the day? Does he seem to have some alert and calm periods? When do you notice that?

Example Observation Opportunities: Observe settings and interactions which promote the child's quiet alert states.

Credit: (see also Credit Notes in this strand's preface)

+ has regular sleep and feeding patterns; is frequently calm and can remained focused and responsive for 2 or more minutes at a time, e.g., sucking, looking, cuddling.

A+ **hyper-reactive: is** generally fussy and irritable when awake; does not have established feeding or sleep patterns; naps are brief, e.g., usually less than 20 minutes at a time; demands constant holding and attention.

A- **underreactive:** sleeps most of the time; is difficult to arouse and rarely becomes alert when awake; maintains flat or depressed affect when awake.

O circle any credit if caregivers are unsure of how to establish feeding or sleep schedules, and/or have difficulty identifying ways to engage child when awake.

Shows active interest in person or object for at least 1 minute   1-6

Definition: The child is able to remain calm and can focus on a variety of sights, sounds and people for at least a minute many times during the day. He may look, smile, adjust his posture, touch, display a responsive, interested facial expression, or otherwise interact with a person or object to show his focused attention.

Parent Questions: Are there certain toys or objects your child seems to enjoy looking at or playing with? How does he show you he's interested? What types of things do you do that seem to attract your child's attention? About how long does your child seem to look at or listen to you?

Example Observation Opportunities: Observe child's responses when he is content and people attempt to slowly engage him with verbal interactions and social games, e.g., smiling; saying "Hi" and waiting for a response; playing "Peek-a-boo"; and when child looks at various sights, including reasonably bright lights, various designs, facial gestures, and moving objects.

Credit: (see also Credit Notes in this strand's preface)

+ is usually able to sustain interest and focus attention on a variety of interesting people and objects, e.g., different visual designs, facial gestures, moving objects, for at least a minute (under 1 year), and for several minutes (if child is over a year.)

A+ **hyper-reactive:** usually becomes distressed when people are nearby, even if they are not touching him; becomes easily over-stimulated or distracted by people, bright lights, and or objects; is unable to focus; averts gaze; has irregular breathing; hiccups; brings hand to head; if child is over 9 months, prefers objects and toys to people; covers eyes; has fleeting attention.

A- **underreactive:** is generally unresponsive to most objects and people; maintains predominantly sober, uninterested, or depressed expression.

O circle any credit if caregivers have difficulty interpreting and responding to child's signs of over-stimulation or signals of engagement, or if interactions or environment are over- or under-stimulating to child.

(also in Strand 2-4A "Communicating with Others–Gesturally")

1.15   Uses hands and mouth for sensory exploration of objects   3-6

Definition: The child freely explores a variety of toys and textures with his hands and mouth.

Parent Questions: Have you noticed if your child dislikes touching or mouthing certain textured toys, such as his stuffed animal or a soft squeak toy?

Example Observation Opportunities: Offer the child a variety of easy-to-grasp toys which have different textures, one at a time. Examples include: smooth plastic rattle, small block, soft-textured squeak toy, furry stuffed animal, crumpled piece of paper. If the child is under 6 months, assist, if needed, to help the child bring the toy to his mouth, e.g., positioning in side-lying or hold cradled.

Credit: (see also Credit Notes in this strand's preface)

    +   freely explores a variety of textured toys through touch, and if under a year, with his mouth.

    A+ **hyper-reactive:** becomes upset, pulls away from and avoids touching or (if under a year) mouthing certain textures: note textures which elicit negative responses. Child may keep hands fisted unrelated to neuromotor problems.

    A- **underreactive:** over 1 year: touches or mouths everything in sight that interferes with functional play; does not seem to notice aversive touch-prickly objects; minimal or no reaction to pain; may bite self; or, does not explore objects through touch.

    O   circle any credit if caregivers do not have a variety of safe objects to explore, or if the child is under 1 year and caregivers punish child for mouthing.

(also in Strand 1-1 "Symbolic Play")

5.08   Stops unexplained crying   3-6

Definition: During the first few months, some infants may have "colicky" crying periods of up to 30-40 minutes several times per day for no apparent reason. By about 6 months, long periods of prolonged, unexplained crying usually resolves. The child now also has the capacity to self-console, i.e., the infant can calm without extensive help from an adult, e.g., by sucking; bringing his hands together.

Parent Questions: Does your child seem to cry or fuss a lot? Can you figure out why he's crying? About how long does he cry? How often? Does your child ever stop crying on his own, without your help? Have you noticed what he does to calm himself? Can you describe his cry? What types of things have you tried? Does anything seem to help?

Example Observation Opportunities: May observe anytime over multiple observations. If parent immediately responds to child's cries or fussiness, suggest waiting a minute or 2 to see if child uses any self-consoling techniques.

Credit: (see also Credit Notes in this strand's preface)

    +   frequently achieves and maintains a calm and organized state; can usually self-calm within 15 minutes by sucking on his fingers, rocking himself, bringing his hands together and/or listening to or looking at interesting people or toys.

    A+ **hyper-reactive:** constantly demands being held and/or having adult company; is frequently irritable and fussy; easily escalates from being content to intense cry; cannot self-console; needs extensive external help (e.g., holding, rocking, car rides for several hours each day) to console. When not crying, may appear hyper-vigilant, i.e., fleeting but constant attention to stimuli around him with a "wide-eyed, hyper" expression, seems "too alert." If the child is over a year, has severe and frequent temper tantrums.

    N/A if child never went through nor currently evidences extensive "colicky" periods.

    O   circle any credit if caregivers request help with identifying consoling techniques, or if caregivers usually give extensive external support at first whimper (e.g., bottle, holding, rocking, picking up) before child has chance to self-calm.

5.15 Enjoys social play   3-6

Definition: The child enjoys interactive play that involves playful movements and touch, e.g., parent nuzzling face in baby's belly to play "Peek-a-boo," patting baby's hands to play "Pat-a-cake," adult "walking" fingers across child's body to play "I'm gonna get you."

Example Observation Opportunities: When the child is in a playful mood, invite the parent to play interactive games the child is familiar with, giving examples if needed. Observe child's responses as well as how easy or difficult it is to engage the child; e.g., does the parent use a cautious approach not to upset child, or does the parent need to use high arousal techniques, such as larger or more vigorous movements? Is it difficult to arouse child or does he easily become over-stimulated or upset?

Credit: (see also Credit Notes in this strand's preface)
+ child is usually engaged and smiles, laughs, etc. during social interaction that includes playful movements and touch.
A+ **hyper-reactive:** child pulls away, averts gaze, cries; "falls" apart when activity changes; is overly fearful and clinging when others try to engage and play with child even after a long warm-up period.
A- **underreactive:** child has weak or minimal response; may seem "tuned out."
O circle any credit if caregivers play interactive games that do not match child's level of sensitivity or responsiveness (e.g., overexcites child or is too slow with many long pauses), or if caregivers cannot think of social games to play with child.

(also in Strand 5-5 "Social Interactions and Play")

1.22 Localizes tactile stimulation by touching the same spot or searching for object that touched body   4-6

Definition: When the child is touched by an object or person, he searches for the object he felt or localizes the body part touched.

Parent Questions: How does your child react to things which may be painful, for example, if he bumps his head or gets a shot at the doctor's?

Example Observation Opportunities: Incidental - may observe if child accidentally bumps into an object, such as his bottle or toy when he moves. Structured - unexpectedly touch the child on his shoulder or thigh with normal firm pressure when you are out of his direct line of vision (e.g., positioned behind him), or apply a sticker or ball of masking tape to a body part when he is not looking. If the child does not respond, try again when he is not engaged in an activity.

Credit: (see also Credit Notes in this strand's preface)
+ looks at or moves body part which is touched, or searches for the object or person that touched him.
A+ **hyper-reactive:** becomes very upset and or quickly pulls away from source of stimulation, which is not painful to others; may rub the spot that was touched.
A- **underreactive:** seems unaware unless it is very intense. In older infants: unaware of messiness around mouth or nose; does not react to pain as if it hurts; e.g., child may not react or may smile to scrapes, bumps, shots, or being hit by another child.

5.18 Enjoys frolic play   4-8

Definition: If in a playful mood, the child usually enjoys gentle "movement-in-space" games, e.g., being moved slowly back and forth or up and down by an adult holding him securely around his trunk.

Example Observation Opportunities: When the child is in a playful mood, ask the parent to hold him securely around his trunk, under his arms, face-to-face, to play some movement-in-space games. First, have the parent move the child slowly up and down two or three times. After a brief pause, have the parent playfully turn around in a circle two or three times. Finally, if the child is still tolerating the game, ask the parent to tip him down slightly toward the floor, face first. It may be helpful to demonstrate this with a doll first, modeling playful interactions, such as smiling and saying, "Whee, look at you! Up you go...now down!"

Credit: (see also Credit Notes in this strand's preface)
+ child tolerates or shows pleasure to movement in space in all planes.
A+ **hyper-reactive:** becomes distressed, gags or vomits, arches (note which movements elicit).
A- **underreactive:** shows no signs of being aware of movement in space; displays no change in affect, which remains sober, unless the movements are stronger, more sustained and quicker; child may seem to crave movement, spends significant time alone rocking self; may bang head rhythmically several times a day, not due to behavioral concerns.

1.34 Smells different things   6-12

Definition: The child is aware of routine odors in his environment, such as perfume, after-shave, food cooking, lemons. A child's sense of smell is typically well organized at birth.

Parent Questions: Have you noticed if your child likes to smell certain things? Does he ever seem to get upset by certain odors?

Example Observation Opportunities: May observe child's responses to typical environmental odors during a home-based observation, e.g., food cooking, after-shave; perfume; furniture polish.

Credit: (see also Credit Notes in this strand's preface)

+ no adverse responses to routine odors - by observation or report.

A+ **hyper-reactive:** obvious distressful change in behavior - by observation or report, e.g., fusses, becomes irritable or upset, becomes disoriented, pulls away, gags.

1.35 Plays 2-3 minutes with a single toy   6-9

Definition: The child can sustain his focus and play with an interesting toy for 2-3 minutes. His play at this stage includes examining the toy or object by looking at and manipulating in an exploratory manner. He may turn it around, pass it from hand to hand, and feel and probe its surface.

Example Eliciting Materials: Three to four easy-to grasp-toys that have different textures, sounds, and consistencies. The toys should be ones he's never seen or played with before. Examples include: smooth plastic rattle, small block with different pictures on the sides, such as an alphabet block, child-proof toy car with turning wheels, soft textured squeak toy, crumpled piece of paper, dinner bell, plastic cup, small doll with moveable parts.

Example Observation Situation: Toys should be offered one at a time, letting the child interact with them for a few minutes each. He may need a break in between each toy, so he is not always waiting for you to present another one instead of exploring the toy he has.

Credit: (see also Credit Notes in this strand's preface)

+ easily engages in playing with a toy and frequently sustains attention for 2-3 minutes incorporating a variety of play interactions.

A+ **overly distractible:** Beyond 9 months: unable to sit still and focus on an activity; attention seems to flit from one toy to another without exploring them; plays only briefly before wanting new activity; can't shift focus easily from one toy to another; may attend only to toys that provide high degree of visual, auditory and or tactile novelty; may be distracted by and perseverate on details in the toy or environment, e.g., picking fuzz from the carpet, persistent scratching of a freckle, only spinning the wheel of a car without seeming to notice the car as a whole; only flicking the eyelids of a doll without seeming to notice that the eyes are part of a doll.

A- **underreactive:** is very difficult to engage in toy; appears depressed and uninterested; may hold but not look at toy, or look at it but show no interest in exploring it; or may attend only to toys that provide high degree of visual, auditory and or tactile novelty; may become over focused in toy or toy part, ignoring adult overtures.

O circle any credit if caregivers do not provide age-appropriate safe objects or toys for the child to play with, and/or constantly intrudes or interrupt child's play.

(also in Strand 1-1 "Symbolic Play")

1.54 Listens to speech without being distracted by other sources   9-11

Definition: The child listens and can focus on the person who is talking to him without being distracted by common background sights or sounds.

Example Observation Opportunities: May observe during all aspects of assessment, i.e., during parent-child interactions within daily activities and play where typical background sounds and sights are present.

Credit: (see also Credit Notes in this strand's preface)

+ usually socially engages easily to friendly verbal interactions; is able to focus attention on the speaker and take in complex vocal patterns, e.g., varied pitch and volume; responds to speaker with eye contact, smiles; shows signs of some understanding of what adult is saying; e.g., looks at object named, lifts arms when parent asks if he wants to get up.

A+ **hyper-reactive:** attention is quickly diverted by even the smallest visual or auditory stimulus not typically noticed by others, e.g., lights, air conditioner, dishwasher in another room.

O circle any credit if caregivers provide minimal verbal interactions or if verbal interactions are over- or under-stimulating to the child, e.g., too loud, too long, too complex, without pauses to let chid respond, or with long blank pauses.

6.23

Drools less except when teething   7-12

Definition: By about 1 year, the child rarely drools unless he is teething, congested, or is stimulated by certain foods during feeding.

Example Observation Opportunities: May observe if child's chin and shirt are wet from excessive drooling. Use parent report if the child is congested or teething. Note if child usually maintains a closed-mouth posture. If child drools, record circumstances, e.g., during fine motor activities, prior to feeding, after feeding etc.

Credit: (see also Credit Notes in this strand's preface)

+   does not usually drool.

A+   excessive drooling <u>not</u> related to congestion or teething; may appear unaware of wetness around mouth.

(also in Strand 6-1 "Oral-Motor Development")

6.25

Finger feeds self   9-12

Definition: The child touches and eats a variety of textured foods.

Parent Questions: What are your child's favorite foods? Are there certain foods your child refuses to touch or eat?

Example Observation Opportunities: During snack time, offer the child a variety of textured foods with parental approval and observe his responses; e.g., soft banana, crunchy crackers, textured applesauce, cheese, peanut butter and jelly sandwich, and multi-textured foods, such as rice pudding or noodle soup.

Credit: (see also Credit Notes in this strand's preface)

+   touches and eats a variety of textured foods (soft, hard, mashed, pureed, mixed textured, slippery) without extreme reactions.

A+   **hypersensitive:** eats only soft food; frequently gags or vomits - not related to food allergies; refuses to touch or eat certain textures; spits out lumpy textured food;

A-   **hyposensitive:** craves strong tastes (e.g., spicy, salty) or textures (firm and crunchy); unaware of food remaining around mouth; may tend to overfill or stuff mouth.

O   circle any credit if child has not had experiences with varied textured foods.

(also in Strand 6-3 "Independent Feeding")

6.27

Sleeps nights twelve-fourteen hours   9-12

Definition: Sleep patterns by this age should be fairly regular. Nighttime sleep may average 12 to 14 hours with periodic brief awakenings. The child is able to fall asleep when tired, within about 20 minutes without extensive parental help.

Parent Questions: How are things going with your child's sleep habits? Is he sleeping through the night? How do you get your child to go to sleep at bed or nap time? What kinds of things have you tried to help him sleep better? Has anything seemed to help?

Credit by parent report:

+   usually sleeps through the night; falls to sleep within 20 minutes when tired without extensive external help.

A+   **hyper-reactive:** usually wakes up several times during the night and/or needs extensive external help to fall asleep, which usually takes more than 20 minutes*.

A-   **underreactive:** the child usually sleeps excessively, i.e., more than 14 hours per night and several hours during the day.

O   circle any credit if caregivers request help in identifying strategies to help the child sleep, or do not structure predictable sleep routines.

*Note if environmental conditions may be precipitating sleep disturbances, e.g., recent trauma, new infant in house, behaviorally related (e.g., parents have always quickly responded to child's whimpers, brought child into their room in middle of night, etc.).

(also under Strand 6-2 "Sleep Patterns and Behaviors")

6.29 Cooperates with dressing by extending arm or leg   10.5-12

Definition: The child is usually cooperative during dressing, sitting fairly still and helping by moving his arms or legs appropriately. He does not mind having clothing touch his skin.

Parent Questions: Does your child get upset when you dress him in certain types of shirts, pants or other clothing? Does he seem to prefer wearing many layers of clothing or wearing little or no clothing?

Example Observation Opportunities: Observe child's responses when his sleeves are pulled up to wash his hands; shirt is removed to put on a smock for painting; pants are removed to change a diaper.

Credit: (see also Credit Notes in this strand's preface)
+   displays no unusual responses to wearing clothing, or being dressed or undressed; guides arm and leg movements easily.
A+   **hyper-reactive:** prefers may layers of clothing, long-sleeve shirts even when temperature is warm or prefers little or no clothing, even when temperature is cool. Gets upset when dressed and undressed.

(also in Strand 6-2 "Dressing")

1.68 Enjoys messy activities   12-18

Definition: The child enjoys playing with messy materials, such as water play and food, e.g., pudding, Jello, applesauce. He uses his hands and fingers to poke, probe, smear, dab and spread them about. He is not overly concerned about touching them or being messy.

Parent Questions: Has your child ever played with any messy materials such as his pudding or applesauce during mealtime? *[If so]* Does he seem to like it? Does he ever seem upset about messy materials? Can you give me some examples? Do you mind if we see how your child reacts to touching different foods during snacktime or playing with Play-Doh™ and finger-paints today, *if we supervise him carefully*?

Example Observation Opportunities: <u>Incidental</u> - may observe during snack or mealtime if child plays with his food. Let him try some messy foods, such as pudding or Jello. <u>Structured</u> - demonstrate using soft Play-Doh™ or finger-paints, exclaiming how fun it is. Invite the child to join in. If this is his first experience, he may need reassurance from his parents.

Credit: (see also Credit Notes in this strand's preface)
+   plays with messy materials using hands.
A+   **Hypersensitive:** refuses to touch or may sometimes use one finger to hesitantly touch; avoids messy materials, may look upset or confused; if hands get messy, becomes overtly upset; frequently requests to have his hands cleaned even if only slightly messy.
A-   **Hyposensitive:** craves messy materials; more interested in the sensation than the material's purpose.
O   circle any credit if caregivers do not allow child to explore messy things or punish child if messy.

1.69 Reacts to various sensations such as extremes in temperature and taste   12-18

Definition: The child can feel the difference between warm and cold, and can taste the differences in various foods such as sweet and bitter. He uses adult-like facial expressions when presented with extremes.

Parent Questions: Does your child seem to notice the differences in how foods taste, such as sweet and sour? How can you tell? Does he ever get very upset about certain tastes? Have you noticed if he can tell the differences between things that are very warm or hot and things that are cold? For example, have you ever seen him pull away from water that was too warm, or drop an ice cube quickly because it was cold?

Example Observation Opportunities: <u>Incidental</u> - may observe child's facial or verbal responses during snack or meal time as child tastes foods and drinks of different tastes and temperatures. <u>Structured</u> - offer the child two shallow bowls to play with: one with a few ice cubes and one with warm water. Observe his facial and vocal expressions as you play with him, and describe how the ice is cold and the water is warm. During snack time, with parental permission, offer the child a cup of water and a cup of tart juice. Again, observe his differential facial and verbal expressions as he tastes each.

Credit: (see also Credit Notes in this strand's preface)
+   by observation or report if child reacts to differences in temperatures and tastes through his facial expressions, vocalizations, gestures, food preferences.
A+   **hypersensitive:** cries, gags to certain tastes or temperatures even if mild, e.g., will only drink warm milk; gags to mild fruit drinks.

Reacts to various sensations such as extremes in temperature and taste 12-18 (continued)

A- **hyposensitive:** appears unaware of extreme temperatures, e.g., parent reports child didn't cry or seem to notice when he was accidentally burned, or child picks up and holds an ice cube in the same manner he would a block; or child makes no responses to spicy or very sour or tart foods.

1.99 ## Uses Playdough and paints   18-24

Definition: The child freely interacts with Play-Doh™ and paints using his hands and fingers. The child pats, pokes, and squeezes the dough in an exploratory manner. During play, he may use the dough symbolically to represent the real object, e.g., ball, pretend food, snake, snowman; with some adult modeling or suggestion.

Example Observation Opportunities: Invite the child to join you and the parent to play with soft Play-Doh™. If this is a first experience, allow extra time for him to watch and approach the dough. Model different ways to manipulate the dough. Use the dough to make pretend objects; e.g., pretend to make a cake and ask the child to feed a puppet or add candles (using pegs). Introduce non-toxic, washable paints and finger-paints in a similar manner. Vary the texture of paints and dough with sand, water, or cornmeal.

Credit: (see also Credit Notes in this strand's preface)

+ freely explores dough and paints or other messy materials with his hands; uses material symbolically in play (if not delayed in play schemes due to cognitive delays, see Strand 1-1).

A+ persistently hesitant or refuses to touch; makes strong facial expressions.

A- seems to crave; eats, intensely squeezes dough, more interested in the texture than what he can "make" with the dough.

O circle any credit if caregivers are overtly upset if child gets even slightly messy, frequently wipe child's hands, or if child has never had experiences with any messy play materials.

5.60 ## Enjoys solitary play for a few minutes   18-24

Definition: The child is able to focus his attention on interesting play materials for several minutes at a time before moving on to another activity. His play is purposeful and involves several related interactions; e.g., the child pats a doll, hugs it and makes it walk, rather than only poking or manipulating the eyelids during the 2-3 minute unstructured play period. He usually does not need extensive structure or adult supervision during short periods of play.

Parent Questions: Tell me a little about how your child plays at home. Can he play alone? For about how long? What types of toys or other materials seem to hold your child's interest or attention the most?

Example Observation Opportunities: Observe over several observation periods as needed. Give the child a box with three or four toys and objects which elicit serial interactions and representational play, e.g., brush, two different cups, a few different-sized blocks, spoon, cloth, dowel, safe hand mirror, shoebox, doll, puppet, book. Invite him to play with the objects, but do not demonstrate or suggest how to play with them. Remain nearby with the parent, but minimize interactions with the child, e.g., may observe as you and the parent completing some paperwork.

Credit by parent report and observation:

+ sustained attention; engages in symbolic and purposeful play.

A+ **high distractibility:** child flits from one activity or object to another - needs constant adult supervision and high amount of structure to help attend; does not use toy according to function or use it symbolically, e.g., tears pages in book rather than looking at pictures.

A- **underreactive:** "tuned out," stares off in space; wanders aimlessly; spends long periods of time in more primitive, sometimes repetitive play, such as spinning wheels on a car or turning knobs on a radio.

A+- combination of all of above, dependent on setting, time of day, type of toys.

O circle any credit if caregiving environments do not offer age appropriate toys, and/or are chaotic or over-stimulating for child.

Enjoys rough and tumble play   18-24

Definition: The child enjoys various movement-in-space-activities, such as "piggy-back" rides, being lifted in the air to play "airplane," climbing on small playground equipment, riding a rocking horse or Tyke bike, jumping and bouncing on mattresses. Specific activities will be dependent upon his gross motor abilities.

Parent Questions: Determine if the child has had experiences with any rough and tumble activities such as those defined. Further probe regarding the child's reactions; are there some activities the child especially enjoys, some that he becomes upset with?

Example Observation Opportunities: Have the parent hold the child <u>securely</u> around his waist at arms length to play airplane. Demonstrate simultaneously with a doll, moving the doll fairly quickly up and down, then while up in the air, moving from side to side and turning yourself in a circle. If the child is enjoying the activity, continue to play by tipping the child backwards, down toward the floor. Keep the game playful and reassuring to the child through verbal praise and smiling throughout. Discontinue at any point if the child is not enjoying the activity or becomes upset. Also observe child's interest in and responses on movement toys, such as a "Sit 'n Spin™" toy, rocking horse, climbing equipment.

Credit: (see also Credit Notes in this strand's preface)

+   enjoys a variety of movement-in-space activities.

A+ **overreactive:** anxious when feet leave ground; cries or screams or strongly resists having head upside-down; avoids roughhousing and playground equipment; becomes carsick; has strong fear of heights; becomes overwhelmed by spinning, e.g., on a "Sit 'n Spin." *[Note: secondary effects, which may be evident in children who are hypersensitive to movement, include emotional lability, extreme fearfulness of new situations, excessively clingy and extreme separation anxiety, and rigid postures.]*

A- **hypo-reactive:** remains passive during movement activities or craves movement to exclusion of other activities and/or does not feel dizziness when other children do; likes to climb to high, precarious places; in constant movement, rocking, bouncing, running about.

Note if child displays secondary behavioral effects: frequent tantrums, over-stimulating himself to point of disorganization.

Also note if child has difficulty figuring out how to get on and off large equipment; e.g., once he is on a ride-on toy, he may ride it, but he must be placed on it because he cannot figure out how to plan his movements to get on it.

O   circle any credit if caregiving environments do not provide safe opportunities for rough and tumble play or movement toys.

 Handles fragile items carefully   24-26

Definition: The child can usually carry or handle fragile or breakable items without breaking or throwing them, although accidents may still occur.

Parent Questions: Is your child sometimes allowed to carry fragile or breakable things, such as a pet, flowers, or a glass? How does he do with this?

Example Observation Situations: During snack, invite the child to help carry his drink to the table; during painting activities, let him carry a half-full jar of paint to the easel; during dress up, let him play with jewelry.

Credit by observation and or report: (see also Credit Notes in this strand's preface)

+   usually respects and can handle fragile or breakable items with care (under adult supervision.)

A+ **overly aggressive:** purposefully breaks toys and other things with apparent anger and intent.

A- **underreactive:** frequently breaks toys unintentionally; cannot seem to judge how hard or soft to press when handling fragile items.

(also in Strand 6-7 "Household Responsibility")

Enjoys tactile books   24-29

Definition: "Tactile books" are books which have pop-up pictures, textured pieces glued on the pages, and other things for the child to interact with using his senses, e.g., scratch and sniff, rub, pat, pull a tab.

Example Observation Opportunities: If available, observe how a child interacts with a commercial or homemade tactile book during quiet one-on-one play. Demonstrate (as needed) the various interactions with the book.

Credit: (see also Credit Notes in this strand's preface)
- \+   explores freely.
- A+ **overly sensitive:** overly hesitant or upset to touch or smell.
- A- **underreactive:** unintentionally tears or breaks parts or pieces of book; cannot seem to judge how hard or soft to press, scratch, pull, etc.
- N/A if tactile books not available.

 Plays with water and sand   24-36

Definition: The child enjoys sand and water play. He freely puts his hands in water, usually accepts or enjoys his bath, and uses his hands to play with sand. During play, he may use sand and water to engage in imaginary play, e.g., making sand cakes, sand castles, having a tea party, making it rain on his castles (if not delayed in play schemes due to cognitive delays - see Strand 1-1.)

Parent Questions: Has your child ever played with sand, for example, in a sandbox or at the beach? Describe how he plays with sand. How is bath time going? Does your child, or has he ever, seemed to get very upset when you give him a bath? Has he ever played in a kiddie pool? Tell me how he plays.

Example Observation Opportunities: <u>Incidental</u> - observe child's reactions when playing in a sandbox or at a water or sand table; e.g., does he use his hands or does he avoid actually touching the sand by not sitting in a sandbox and always using "tools," to play with e.g., shovel, cups? <u>Structured</u> - provide the child a basin half filled with sand, cornmeal or rice. Provide the child with props, such as spoons, cups, dolls, and a toy car or dump truck. Let the parent play with the child (to observe the child's interactions and responses to the materials.) While the child is watching, hide one of the toys under the sand for him to find.

Credit: (see also Credit Notes in this strand's preface)
- \+   freely engages in sand and water play.
- A+ **hypersensitive:** avoids getting sand on hands or skin, uses tools (shovels, cups) if he plays with sand; appears strongly hesitant and makes strong facial expressions; cries or otherwise gets upset if sand is stuck to hands; very upset by bath (not because behavioral reasons).
- A- **underreactive:** seems to crave sand or water, e.g., persistently puts sand in mouth; squeezes sand intensely; more interested in the texture of materials than what he can do with it.
- O   circle any credit if caregivers are overtly upset if child gets even slightly messy; frequently wipe child's hands.

 Identifies familiar objects by touch   30-36

Definition: The child is able to discriminate and recognize familiar objects by touch, without seeing the object.

Example Observation Opportunities: (1) When the child is not looking, place a spoon in a cloth bag or box with a hole cut out on the side. Ask him to put his hand inside and tell you what is inside. Repeat with a small ball and a block. If the child is non-verbal, place two items in the bag and name an item for him to find and take out of the bag, or have duplicates of the item on a table for him to point to (what he feels.) Let the parent play this game first, using different objects to help the child understand the "rules" of the game. **(2)** During sand or cornmeal play, hide three small toys (spoon, car, block), which the child has been playing with in the sand, using the same procedure as in (1).

Credit: (see also Credit Notes in this strand's preface)
- \+   identifies at least two to three familiar objects by touch.
- A+ **hypersensitive:** refuses to put hand in or quickly yanks hand out.
- A- **hyposensitive/poor tactile discrimination:** seems confused; if he identifies the correct objects, it happens by chance rather than the child tactually exploring it before picking it; at other times, you may observe that the child always looks at his hands when he is manipulating objects, and he continues to mouth objects.

Enjoys being read to and looks at books independently 30-36

Definition: The child likes looking at various pictures books and attends when an adult reads simple picture-book stories. He understands and can follow along with the basic "plot" of short stories told (with or without a book.).

Parent Questions: Does your child have any favorite books he likes you to read him?...that he likes to look at on his own? About how long does he attend when you read him a story?...when he looks at his own books?

Example Observation Opportunities: Ask the parent to read the child a story using one of his favorite books. At this stage, storybooks should have colorful pictures, be short, have key phrases repeated within the story, and portray a simple plot and sequence of events which are relevant to the child, e.g., going to daycare or the doctor. Also observe child's attention to books during free play when an adult is not directly interacting.

Credit: (see also Credit Notes in this strand's preface)

+ can usually focus and attend to interesting books for at least 5 minutes at a time without extensive structure or reinforcement from an adult; i.e., adult does not need to "hold child down"; when adult reads to child, child attends to adult's questions, comments and pointing. (may also credit #1.140 "Listens to stories" in Strand 2-2.)

A+ **overly distractible:** typically has difficulty sitting for more than a minute to look at book; does not attend or focus; attention is fleeting; distracted by typical background sights and sounds; difficulty shifting focus from one page to next; cannot follow the "plot"; needs extensive external support.

A- **perseverates** on a small detail to the exclusion of attending to the whole picture or storyline; has difficulty shifting attention from one page to another or following the "plot."

O circle any credit if there are no books available to the child in caregiving environments.

Participates in circle games; plays interactive games 30+

Definition: The child enjoys and participates with peers in interactive games such as "Ring Around the Rosie," "Tag," "Hide and Seek," "London Bridge."

Parent Questions: Tell me how your child plays with other children; e.g., what types of games do they play, how does he seem to get along with others?

Example Observation Opportunities: May observe child in familiar peer settings, e.g., daycare, preschool. May also interview child's parents, daycare provider and/or teacher.

Credit: (see also Credit Notes in this strand's preface)

+ child usually interacts and plays well with two or three other peers in interactive games.

A+ **overly aggressive:** needs total control of the environment; runs the show; cannot respond to rules and limits even though it's clear he understands them; has difficulty sitting still for circle time; is aggressive or destructive in play; may bite or kick others; purposefully break toys.

A+ **hypersensitive:** does well in one-on-one interactions but becomes overwhelmed and falls apart in large groups or circle times; tends to shy away from new peers, distressed when others are nearby, e.g., sitting in a circle.

A- **underreactive:** does not participate in interactive way; is withdrawn – "tuned-out"; may wander aimlessly; may be preoccupied with inner thoughts.

O circle any credit if peer play environments are overly chaotic and unstructured.

N/A child has no opportunities to play with peers.

(also in Strand 5-5 "Social Interactions and Play")

1.0 - Cognitive Development
Introduction

Overview

Cognitive development has been divided into seven interrelated conceptual strands:

1-1 Development of Symbolic Play
1-2 Gestural Imitation
1-3 Sound Awareness and Localization
1-4 Problem Solving (Object Permanence, Means-Ends, and Cause and Effect)
1-5 Spatial Relationships
1-6 Concepts (Pictures, Numbers)
1-7 Discrimination/Classification (Matching and Sorting, Size, Associative)

Relationship to Other Domains: Key Issues

- The strands included under the Cognitive Domain focus on the development of mental processes related to thinking, remembering, and reasoning. These processes are developed and refined by the child's interactions with his physical environment as well as his social interactions with others.

- Thinking, remembering, and reasoning lay the foundation for and are also expressed through the child's language, social, self-help, and motor skills. A comprehensive assessment of cognition therefore includes observing how these cognitive processes are expressed through other developmental domains.

- Cognitive development is dependent on and strongly influenced by the child's perceptual capacities to: receive information through his senses (sight, touch, hearing, smell, movement), interpret that information, and then be able to use what he interprets to plan appropriate actions. Strands 1-3 "Auditory Awareness and Localization," 4-1 "Visual Responses and Tracking," and 0.0 "Regulatory/Sensory Organization" are key "windows" of the child's perceptual capacities that contribute to the mental processes related to thinking, remembering and reasoning. These areas must, therefore, be carefully assessed when trying to understand and plan for cognitive delays.

Important considerations and precautions

- Incorporate variety! Since HELP is an ongoing curriculum-based assessment, a child may be exposed repeatedly to HELP skill items during interventions and re-assessments. It is very important in the cognitive domain, therefore, to incorporate variety into the example assessment procedures and materials suggested in this manual in order to avoid "teaching to the test." Assessment procedures using a variety of toys and eliciting techniques, within multiple natural settings, are critical to ensure that the child has generalized the underlying cognitive concepts that are intended to be assessed by the individual skill items.

- Observing how a child approaches and accomplishes a task can be more important in curriculum planning than assessing what cognitive skills the child can complete. For example:
  – What sensory qualities and features of toys, objects, and activities attract and sustain the child's attention?
  – How much and what types of verbal and physical support and encouragement does the child need to engage and persist in playing with toys, solving problems, and completing cognitive tasks?
  – How does the child approach cognitive challenges? Does he seek an adult for help? Give up quickly? Or, does he persist and explore options through trial and error?
  – How does he react when he accomplishes or cannot accomplish a goal? Does he display a sense of pride or "fall apart?"

- Skills listed in Strands 1-2 "Gestural Imitation" and 1-4 "Problem-Solving," structurally end before 24 months, but development in these areas does not. Gestural imitation and problem solving skills will continue to develop and be incorporated in the remaining cognitive strands that extend beyond 2 years. Cognitive skills over the age of 18-24 months that are incorporated in other strands require the foresight and ability to mentally represent and internalize thought (which developed its foundations in Strands 1-2 and 1-4.)

  This has reporting implications if you are using the HELP Strands to help identify the child's approximate developmental age range. For example, if a 30-month-old child "ceils-out" of Strands 1-2 or 1-4, you would not report the child's problem solving or gestural imitation skills to be at the 17-23 month level, since this would imply a delay. Instead, in this example, you would arrive at the child's estimated developmental age from assessing the remaining strands which have higher level skills.

1-1 DEVELOPMENT OF SYMBOLIC PLAY

1.13	2.5-4	Begins play with rattle
1.15	3-6	Uses hands and mouth for sensory exploration of objects
4.39	5.5-7	Bangs object on table
1.35	6-9	Plays 2-3 minutes with a single toy
1.23	*7-9*	Plays with paper
1.36	6-11	Slides toy or object on surface
5.35	9-12	Engages in simple *relational* play
1.59	10-15	Demonstrates drinking from a cup
5.52		Imitates doing housework (and other *real-life activities*):
	15-18	a. Symbolic play with realistic props
	18-24	b. Symbolic play with similar but not real props
5.77	24-30	Dramatizes using a doll
1.130	24-30	Engages in simple make-believe activities
2.85	29.5-36	Talks intelligently to self
1.153	30-36	Plays house

Family Friendly Interpretation of Strand Concepts, Assessment, & Purpose

We will be observing how your child is learning to play with toys and other objects. Play is very important in a child's learning and development. Play helps children learn how to solve problems and helps them enjoy, understand, and get along in their world. When a child plays, he can learn about the various qualities of objects and what he can do with them. For example, that rubber things can bounce and that hard objects make noises when they drop. Children can also learn to imitate and practice different roles, activities and feelings during play. For example, when a child pretends to play house or diapers and hugs a doll, he is practicing a new role and learning to express feelings that he can't quite yet put into words.

Learning to play with toys seems to develop in a fairly predictable sequence, from simple to more complex:

1. At first, infants don't really care what they are playing with; they are more interested in their own actions. Their favorite interactions with toys are looking, mouthing, shaking, and banging. They will do one or more of these things with a toy or object no matter what it is! For example, if we give a child a block, he plays with it by mouthing it or banging it, rather than using it to build something. And then if we give him a doll, he'll do the same types of things – that is, mouth, shake or bang it instead of playing with it as a doll.

2. Children then begin to pay more attention to what they are playing with. They examine a toy more carefully to explore the toy's quali-

ties to figure out the best way to play with it. For example, at this stage, if we give a child a block he may first mouth and shake it, but then he ends up spending most of his time banging it on the table because this is the most interesting way to play with a small, hard object. Or, if we give him a crumpled piece of paper, he may taste, shake, and bang it, but then spend most of his time crumpling or tearing it. He realizes that crumpling or tearing is the most interesting thing to do with paper.

3. Next, children begin to play with toys and objects according to their true function or use. For example, the child understands that dolls are for hugging, boxes are for filling, balls are for rolling, cars are for pushing, and blocks are for building. At this stage, if we give the child some blocks, he may still first taste them, bang them or rub one against the table, but then he settles down to build with them or to put them in containers.

4. Finally, young children begin what is often termed "pretend" or symbolic play. At this stage, during play, they sometimes act out familiar activities that they have seen their parents do, for example, putting a baby doll to bed or having a tea party. The objects and toys they use in their play also begin to have a pretend quality to them. For example, a child may put a doll to bed in a shoe box, pretending the shoe box is a bed. Or he may make a "cake," using sand to be the cake mix and a stick to be the spoon to stir it.

Professional FYI

1. This strand focuses on the child's interaction with objects and toys leading to the development of symbolic play. Social interactions and play with other children and adults, although closely related, is not highlighted in this strand, since these interactions and play are heavily dependent on social-emotional development. A comprehensive assessment of a child's play behaviors should include social and interactive play, which is addressed in Strand 5-5 "Social Interactions and Play."

2. Reminder: Play is the context in which children learn. When planning interventions, it is more important to capitalize on play as the context for learning and socializing than focusing on play skills as outcomes or goals.

3. Descriptions and definitions for many of the skills listed in this strand have been expanded and changed somewhat from the original

HELP Activity Guide. This change reflects more recent findings and important behaviors in the development of play.

4. Although different play schemes appear to develop in a rather sequential order, the specific ages at which they emerge varies, as reported in the literature. There is also much overlap between stages of play; for example, a child may continue to use less mature interactions, such as mouthing, while learning to use objects according to their particular properties. In addition, some play schemes continue while others are replaced by more mature interactions. It is more important to identify the variety of play interactions the child has in his repertoire and to observe which ones seem to predominate in his current play than to be concerned with specific age levels.

Parent Questions (Examples)

To help identify the child's unique strengths and needs related to this developmental area:

• What are some of the toys and other household objects that your child likes to play with at home? *[It may be helpful to provide examples of objects a child might play with that the parent may not consider a "toy," e.g., paper, telephone, empty boxes, pots and pans]*

• Can you tell me a little about how he plays with some of the toys you mentioned?

• Are there certain toys that he does not seem to like?

• Has he ever played with the kind of toys we have here today?

• What do you think is the best way for us to assess your child's development in this area?

To help identify family resources, priorities and concerns related to the child's development in this area:

• What toys or other playthings would you like us to include in our assessment and planning?

• Is there anything about the way your child plays with toys and objects that you feel is especially important to understand/or work on?

• If you could think of one thing or toy that you'd like to see your child be able to play with better, what would that be? What have you tried so far that seems to help? Are there things you've tried that haven't seemed to help?

• Are you interested in getting information about our toy lending library?

Sample *Functional* Outcome Statements which may be generated by the Family

[Will be dependent upon identified individual child and family needs, and should incorporate objectives and activities from other domains]

My child will:
• Enjoy playing with toys;
• Play with his friends at daycare;
• Play with a toy for more than a few seconds;

• Play with his toys instead of always putting them in his mouth.

We will:
• Know what objects around home our child will enjoy playing with;
• Know more about the ways our child can learn through play.

Transactional Assessment

May assess through observation and interview.

Assessment of the Child's Environment

1. Supportive:
[Example environments which support/facilitate development in this area]
The child's caregiving environments usually:
• Have a variety of safe and developmentally appropriate play materials;
• Have safe spaces for the child to play;
• Keep play materials accessible to the child.

2. Compromising:
[Example environments which may restrict, compromise, inhibit or be unsupportive toward development in this area]
• The child's caregiving environments usually do not have safe or developmentally appropriate toys or materials.

Assessment of Caregiver Interactions with the Child

1. Supportive:
[Example interactions which support/facilitate child's development in this area]
The child's caregivers:
• Allow child to explore and play with toys and objects at his own pace;
• Sometimes imitate the child's play and then sometimes elaborate by showing him a new way to use or play with the toy;
• Are attentive to the child and his play when playing together;
• Sometimes talk about what the child is playing with and what he is doing;
• Let the child choose toys and activities for play.

2. Compromising:
[Interactions which may restrict, compromise, inhibit or be unsupportive of the child's development in this area]
The child's caregivers frequently:
• Physically try to make the child play the way they want him to;
• Make negative comments about the way the child plays;
• Control the choice of toys and duration of play activities.

Identifying and Interpreting Needs for Intervention

If a child is significantly delayed or displays persistent atypical development in this area, he may be having difficulty with mental processes needed to engage in meaningful play with objects. This includes being able to:
1. Perceptually discriminate the qualities and functions of objects;
2. Mentally represent or internalize an action or object that is not present, i.e., representational thought.

However, before targeting these cognitive processes as the primary area of need for intervention, consider, rule out, or adapt for other causes that may contribute to delayed or atypical play skills or interfere with a true assessment of the child's mental representational capacities. These may include:
• Motor impairments: e.g., delayed or atypical motor development can prevent a child from physically interacting with toys and objects;

• Visual impairments: interactions with objects and symbolic play rely heavily upon visually inspecting objects and observing how others interact and use them; more stereotypical or repetitive behaviors may be present;
• Regulatory and sensory organization problems: the child may perceive sights, sounds, touch and/or movements differently. This can cause responses that interfere with meaningful play, e.g., prolonged mouthing or avoiding mouthing and touch; not playing with certain toys, disorganized play, difficulty focusing, being more fearful etc. Refer to strand 0.0 "Regulatory/Sensory";
• Social-emotional problems: e.g., low motivation to play or engage (depressed affect); overly aggressive or anxious.
• Lack of experience exploring and interacting with objects due to severe environmental deprivation or disability.

Assessment Adaptations   (Examples)

[Note any adaptations needed to credit and help plan interventions]

- Motor impairments: *involve a pediatric therapist in the assessment of the child's play so that the therapist can adapt materials and positioning to meet the child's individual needs and promote optimal interactions and mobility with toys.* The following are some general adaptations:
  - Use play materials, battery-operated toys, and touch-sensitive switches that can be easily manipulated and adapted to accommodate the child's type of grasp. Larger or stabilized materials may help.
  - Position the child and materials in ways that optimize interactions and movement, e.g., the child may be able to interact better positioned in side-lying, a prone stander or adaptive seating.
  - Assist as needed to help the child reach for or grasp toys.
  - If the child has good language development but is severely restricted in his movements, let him tell you what to do with different toys and objects using speech or alternative form of communication. Pay special attention to the child's level of interest when he is observing others engaged in pretend play. This may be an added cue regarding his understanding of symbolic play.
  - Allow extra time for the child to interact and "take a turn."
- Visually impaired:
  - Use toys and objects that are reflective and/or have high color and texture contrast.
  - Provide extra time for the child to explore the materials. Physically guide and describe to demonstrate the functions of unfamiliar toys and objects.
  - Observe the child's play when he is in his familiar environments, using familiar materials. Use the child's own toys and objects.
  - Expect delays that may be normal for a child who is visually impaired and not necessarily a sign of impairment of cognitive thought; e.g., the child may mouth toys longer; may not imitate common socially instigated interactions and will have more difficulty with using non-similar and abstract objects in symbolic play as these are highly dependent upon visual experiences.
  - If the child is blind, do not assess nor plan interventions that teach him to use dissimilar or abstract objects to represent real objects. Use concrete materials and experiences. For example, when playing "house," use real foods and utensils, rather than plastic play foods.
- Regulatory and sensory organization problems: when possible, involve a therapist who is trained in sensory organization principles in the assessment of the child's play.
  - If the child is overreactive, help him to become relaxed and focused before assessing his play skills. For the young infant, it may be helpful to swaddle him or provide rhythmic vertical rocking. The older toddler may benefit from vestibular activities and a highly structured environment.
  - If the child is more passive and difficult to arouse, you may need to work harder to engage and get his attention e.g., with silly faces, novel toys. Respond to any signal, no matter how weakly the child sends it.
  - If the child is highly distractible, be sure the room is relatively free of other competing toys and activities. Offer only one or two toys at a time. Follow the child's lead. If for example, he prefers banging the blocks, imitate him. Then after he has experienced banging, try stacking a few or putting them into a container. If the child is not interested, don't force the activity; let the child move on to something else of interest.
- Social-emotional problems: some of the adaptations suggested for Regulatory/Sensory organization problems listed under #3 above, may be helpful. Consult with a psychologist or an infant mental health specialist for assessment and planning of therapeutic play interventions.
- Environmental: if the child has not had opportunities to interact with a variety of toys or materials, allow extra time for him to become acquainted with the ones you may bring to the assessment. If the child's experiences have been severely restricted due to severe environmental deprivation or disability, the child's initial assessment cannot be considered a true assessment of the child's cognitive abilities.
- Speech delayed: the only item requiring speech is #2.85 "Talks intelligently to self." If the child is delayed in speech, mark this item N/A (not applicable.)

General Assessment Procedures & Processes   (apply to all items in this Strand)

1. General Assessment Procedure:

   a. Most items in this strand can be assessed simultaneously, i.e., observe the child's interactions with the objects and toys until he becomes repetitive in his play and is not displaying higher level interactions. Credit predominant play interactions accordingly.

   b. Provide the child with some of the "example eliciting play materials" that are suggested under the procedure for each item in this strand. Invite him to play with the toys using simple verbal encouragement, such as, "Show me how you play with these toys" or "Show me what you do with these." Avoid telling the child what to do with the toys, because most responses are credited based upon the child's spontaneous interactions. It is, however, quite appropriate to make encouraging comments and gestures, such as smiling and nodding when he looks at you, as you comment, e.g., "Yes, you're brushing the doll's hair."

   c. Verbal prompting and demonstration can be provided after you have established the child's predominant spontaneous play interactions to try to elicit the next level of play. This can be helpful in planning the type of interventions that help him achieve higher levels of play. If the child displays the skill with verbal prompting or demonstration, credit this as emerging, i.e., +/-, and note the type of prompt used.

   d. <u>Remember</u>: Play should be assessed in a "playful" manner! Highly structured or rigid procedures should be avoided. <u>Observe</u> the child's play preferences, approach, spontaneity, and enjoyment, *rather than* <u>testing</u> play.

2. Describe the play behavior and the above "General assessment procedure" to the family and invite them to help observe

+ - A   Credit Notes:

and/or assess.

+   child displays defined play interaction as a predominant interaction.

-   not observed or reported.

+/-   appears to be an emerging play scheme; displayed play scheme with adult prompting and modeling, but it is not considered a predominant scheme.

A   atypical: pervasive and persistent rigid stereotypical or perseverate interactions with objects that are not due to immaturity (i.e., not because the child is learning a new skill or learning about a new toy); pervasive and persistent lack of curiosity, joyfulness or positive emotional engagement during play; extreme aggressiveness with toys and objects, e.g., purposely breaks things.

O   circle any credit if environment or interactions compromise or restrict child's play skills.

*As noted in the "Professional FYI" notes, play schemes overlap in a child's development. To determine the child's approximate stage of play, observe which play interactions are predominant in his play with a variety of play materials. It is also important to note, however, if the child is still using some less mature interactions in his play. For example, his predominant interactions with blocks may be functional, i.e., stacking, and putting into containers, but he may still sometimes revert to mouthing and banging them.

Note any adaptations used to credit.

Assessment Materials

[Reminder: it is important to use culturally-relevant play materials. Use the child's own toys or toys which the family suggests]

<u>Birth to approximately 1 year developmentally:</u>

Several easy-to-grasp toys which have different textures, sounds, and consistencies. Examples include: smooth plastic rattles; small blocks, some that have different pictures on the sides, such as alphabet blocks; soft textured squeak toy; crumpled piece of paper; dinner bell; plastic cup; toy cars; small doll.

<u>Approximately 1 to 3 years:</u>

Objects that encourage combining objects in play: e.g., brush, doll bed and doll, stick and xylophone; blocks or spoon and cup or bowl; pegs and pegboard, toy person and car; telephone receiver and base of telephone;

Objects that encourage serial interactions and representational play; e.g., brush, two different cups, a few different-sized blocks, spoon, cloth, dowel, *safe* hand mirror, shoe box, doll with moveable parts, puppet, doctor's kit, housekeeping props (sponge, pans, tea set, small broom etc.).

1.13   Begins play with rattle   2.5-4

Definition: The child plays briefly with a rattle or any easy-to-grasp object by holding, looking, and mouthing it. Although there may be some incidental waving or shaking, primary interactions characteristic of this stage are holding, looking, and mouthing.

Example Eliciting Materials: Rattle, teether or other safe objects with a slender handle.

Example Observation Opportunities: The toy will probably need to be placed in the child's hand at this stage. If the child keeps his hands predominantly fisted or has a strong grasp reflex, try positioning the child in side-lying or in a cradled position to help him relax. [*Refer to #1 under "General child assessment procedures" in the preface to this strand*]

Credit: (see also Credit Notes in this strand's preface)
+   displays at least two simple interactions with two different toys: holds, mouths, looks, waves, or shakes.

1.15   Uses hands and mouth for sensory exploration of objects   3-6

Definition: The child's primary interactions with objects at this stage are through "simple motor schemes." In addition to mouthing and holding, the child now incorporates the motor actions of shaking, patting and waving into his play, regardless of the toy or its true function. The child is more interested in the actions he can produce than in the object itself, but is beginning to differentiate what actions he uses according to the characteristics of the toy; e.g., he may shake a rattle more than a block because the rattle makes a sound.

Example Eliciting Materials: Several easy-to-grasp toys which have different textures, sounds, and consistencies. Examples include: smooth plastic rattle, small block, soft textured squeak toy, crumpled piece of paper.

Example Observation Opportunities: Toys should be offered one at a time, letting the child interact with them for a minute or two each. Place the toy in his hand, if needed. If the child has difficulty bringing his hand to his mouth, try positioning him in side-lying, or in an infant seat. (Refer to step 1 under "General child assessment procedures" in the preface to this strand.)

Credit: (see also Credit Notes in this strand's preface)
+   plays with at least three different objects by mouthing, holding, and, at least one: shaking, patting, hitting, or waving; displays some differential interactions dependent upon the type of toy, e.g., shakes a rattle more than a squeak toy; pats or hits squeak toy more than a teether. Note predominant interactions.
A   never mouths, and/or strongly resists or becomes upset when touching certain textures; or over 1 year and continues to mouth toys excessively.
O   if caregivers scold or prevent child from mouthing safe toys.

4.39   Bangs object on table   5.5-7

Definition: The child repeatedly hits a nearby surface with an object he is holding. The child is more interested in the motor action of banging than the object itself.

Example Eliciting Materials: Two or three easy-to-grasp toys which have different textures, sounds, and consistencies. Examples include: smooth plastic rattle, small block, soft textured squeak toy, crumpled piece of paper.

Example Observation Opportunities: Toys may be offered one at a time, placing them in the child's hand, if needed. Present the toys where there is a hard surface on which the child can bang the toys to provide "noisy" feedback. (Refer to step 1 under "General child assessment procedures" in the preface to this strand.)

Credit: (see also Credit Notes in this strand's preface)
+   sometimes bangs objects repetitively in play with a variety of objects; he may hit his leg, crib mattress, or other surface; note predominant interaction with objects.

1.35

Plays 2-3 minutes with a single toy   6-9

Definition: The child's play interactions are expanding and becoming more exploratory and differentiated. In addition to mouthing, shaking, waving, patting, and banging, he now also examines, pushes, pulls, turns over, pokes and tears objects. He can play with an interesting toy for 2-3 minutes and interacts with it according to the qualities of the particular toy.

Example Eliciting Materials: Three to four easy-to-grasp toys which have different textures, sounds, and consistencies. The toys should be ones he's never seen or played with before, but which also have the potential for functional use. Examples include: smooth plastic rattle, small blocks with different pictures on the sides, such as an alphabet block, soft textured squeak toys, crumpled piece of paper, dinner bell, plastic cup, small doll with moveable parts, brush, toy car, and a wash cloth.

Example Observation Opportunities: Refer to step 1 under "General child assessment procedures" in the preface to this strand.

Credit: (see also Credit Notes in this strand's preface)

+   uses a variety of interactions with toys according to the characteristic of the toy as defined; includes at least three: examining, pushing, rubbing, pulling, turning over, poking, or tearing; can focus on one or two toys for at least 2 to 3 minutes.

A   overly distractible or difficult to engage: see this item in Strand 0.0 "Regulatory/Sensory Organization."

1.23

Plays with paper   7-9

Definition: The child explores paper by crumpling, tearing or pulling it. This is another example of the child using more complex sensory motor interactions to explore objects as in #1.35 above.

Example Eliciting Materials: Any piece of paper that is easy for the child to grasp and explore, e.g., waxed paper, a piece of Mylar, tissue paper.

Example Observation Opportunities: Refer to step 1 under "General child assessment procedures" in the preface to this strand.

Credit: (see also Credit Notes in this strand's preface)

+   includes one or more complex motor schemes as the predominant interaction when playing with paper: crumples, tears, pulls.

1.36

Slides toy or object on surface   6-11

Definition: The child expands his play interactions to include "sliding" or rolling objects on a surface.

Example Eliciting Materials: Toy cars or other small, wheeled toys that move by friction.

Example Observation Opportunities: Refer to step 1 under "General child assessment procedures" in the preface to this strand.

Credit: (see also Credit Notes in this strand's preface)

+   incorporates sliding or rolling a predominant interaction with wheeled toys i.e., he may briefly shake, mouth and/or examine a car but then realizes its "rolling" function and spends more time rolling it than mouthing or examining it.

5.35

Engages in simple *relational* play   9-12

Definition: The child combines two different but related objects together during play, e.g., a brush to doll's head, stick to a xylophone, block in cup; spoon in bowl, toys in a box. At this stage, relating two objects together may only be crude approximations.

Example Eliciting Materials: Toys that can be combined and have relational qualities: e.g., xylophone, safe stick, spoon, bowl, a few blocks, thick peg, pegboard, doll, brush, telephone with a separate receiver.

Example Observation Opportunities: Give the child a box of objects that can be related as suggested above. Observe how the child plays with them. He may first explore each toy individually before combining any during play. (Refer to #1 under "General child assessment procedures" in the preface to this strand.)

Credit:

+   combines two different but related objects in any relational manner several times during play; he does not have to actually perform the social action; e.g., the brush or spoon can be purposefully placed on or next to the doll, but the child does not have to brush the doll's hair or feed the doll; the block can be placed in the cup or on top of another block, but he does not have to release or balance the block.

Demonstrates drinking from a cup   10-15

Definition: The child's predominant interactions with familiar objects are characterized as conventional or functional. At this stage, he applies appropriate social actions with objects according to their intended purpose, e.g., dolls are for hugging, cups are for filling or drinking out of, spoons are for stirring or eating, brushes are for brushing hair. At this stage, these functional social actions are carried out primarily with himself rather than with others, e.g., he uses a brush to brush his own hair but not his parent's or a doll's hair, but social actions may not predominate.

Example Eliciting Materials: Three or four familiar objects that elicit functional social interactions, e.g., brush, cup, plastic sunglasses, spoon, doll, wash cloth.

Example Observation Opportunities: Refer to step 1 under "General child assessment procedures" in the preface to this strand.

Credit: (see also Credit Notes in this strand's preface)

+   interacts with toys and objects according to their functional or conventional use.

Imitates doing housework and *other real-life activities*
Symbolic play with realistic props   15-18

Definition: The child sometimes imitates adult behavior in his play. This stage is the beginning of symbolic representation in play. Four key elements of symbolic play begin to emerge during this stage:

1. The child uses realistic "props" in his play, e.g., a miniature tea set to represent a real one, a child-sized broom to represent an adult's broom, a doll to represent a real baby.
2. Play activities include social interactions that are not part of his typical routine or role, e.g., pretending to "read" a newspaper, pretending to mop the "floor," pretending to feed a baby using a doll.
3. The child combines two simple actions in a sequence to act out a familiar activity, e.g., pretending to feed himself with a spoon and then feeding a doll, or pretending to stir some food and then taking a bite.
4. The child begins to direct some of his play with "passive" others; e.g., he pretends to feed his doll or teddy bear as well as himself.

Example Eliciting Materials: Several realistic props: e.g., doll, brush, napkin, wash cloth, cup, spoon, magazines, tea set, play food; toy cleaning materials (toy broom, dusting cloth). Non-realistic but similar props (in case child displays higher representational thought for #5.52 B): small and large, flat long blocks (for "roads"), shoe box (for a "bed"), dowel (for a "spoon" or "toothbrush"), circle shapes from a formboard or poker chips (for "cookies").

Example Observation Opportunities: Invite the child to play with the objects but do not demonstrate or suggest how to play with them. For example, if he offers a spoon toward you or the doll's mouth (to feed), it would be appropriate to encourage this play by commenting how good it tastes, but do not ask the child to then feed the doll. (Refer to step 1 under "General child assessment procedures" in the preface to this strand.)

Credit: (see also Credit Notes in this strand's preface)

+   play is sometimes characterized by using realistic props, acting out activities that are not part of his own daily routines; combining simple actions in a sequence and using passive others in his play as defined.

+/- needed verbal and gestural prompts.

Imitates doing housework and *other real-life activities*
Symbolic play with similar but not real props   18-24

Definition: The child continues to "act out" adult activities that are not part of his typical routine (as in #5.52A) with himself and dolls, but now his symbolic play reflects higher representational thought. He is now able to:

1. Use substitute objects to represent the real thing. (Substitute objects at this stage are nonrealistic but similar to the real thing, e.g., using a stick for a toothbrush, a napkin for a doll blanket, a shoe box for a doll bed, or lining up two blocks for a "road.")
2. Combine more actions and objects in a sequence, e.g., wets cloth and wipes table; puts doll in a car and pushes the car; stirs with spoon in cup and takes a drink or gives adult or doll a drink; drinks from one cup and gives doll a drink from another cup.

Example Eliciting Materials: Same as #5.52A
Example Observation Opportunities: Same as #5.52A
Credit: (see also Credit Notes in this strand's preface)
  +   in addition to the criterion for #5.52A, the child now also sometimes uses similar objects to represent the real thing and combines more actions and objects in a sequence as defined.
  +/- needed verbal and gestural prompts.

Dramatizes using a doll   24-30

Definition: The child's dramatic play with dolls, stuffed animals and puppets at this stage involve representational thought and ability to express emotional ideas. Play with dolls, stuffed animals or puppets now frequently incorporates:

1. Linking three or more actions to dramatize a meaningful, sequenced activity which has a beginning, middle and end; e.g., wets cloth, washes baby, and then dries baby doll; or, takes off doll clothes, diapers, and puts to bed.
2. Interacting with the doll as if it has emotions and can see, hear, feel, taste, or smell; e.g., shows stuffed dog his picture book, places doll in front of a mirror; soothes doll to sleep, lets puppet taste food and says "yum."
3. Making the doll perform actions with objects, e.g., putting spoon in doll's hand and moving the doll's hand to doll's mouth; making puppet talk on telephone; moving or talking for puppet as if puppet is talking.

Example Eliciting Materials: One or two dolls (or stuffed animals, puppets) that have moveable parts and doll play objects that encourage serial interactions and representational play, e.g., brush, a cup and spoon, two wash cloths, dowel, safe hand mirror, shoe box, small bowl of water.
Example Observation Opportunities: Refer to step 1 under "General child assessment procedures" in the preface to this strand.
Credit: (see also Credit Notes in this strand's preface)
  +   dramatizes with a doll as defined, i.e., linking three or more interactions with the doll in a meaningful sequence, acting as if the doll has senses, and making the doll perform actions.
(may also credit in Strand 5-3, "Expression of Emotions," if the child expresses emotional ideas during doll play, e.g., soothes doll to sleep, expresses anger to or through doll, hugs and kisses doll.)

1.130 **Engages in simple make-believe activities   24-30**

Definition: The child begins to act out make-believe activities through short discrete pieces of drama, such as playing doctor or having a birthday party. The child is the primary "actor" or participant in the make-believe activity. Characteristics of make-believe or pretend play at this stage include:

1. Using more abstract substitute objects to represent or symbolize the real thing, e.g., making a cake with mud or Play-Doh™, using a block as a spoon to eat the "cake," using a chair or table as the stove and a drawer as the oven, using a hat as a doll bed, using a crayon as a "shot."

2. Using the same abstract substitute object to represent more than one real thing, e.g., using a block as the spoon to feed himself and as a utensil to make the cake, using a crayon to give the doll a "shot" and using the crayon to look in doll's ears, using pieces of paper for food to cook, and using a piece of paper to be the pan to cook it on.

3. Demonstrating a "play plan" which has a theme with several sequenced steps; e.g., child says he's going to have a birthday party, makes a cake, pretends to eat the cake and then cleans up; or, child says he's going to "work," puts a hat on, gets in toy car and says "bye."

Example Eliciting Materials: Materials that promote thematic pretend play, e.g., soft playdough, small tin pan, blocks, pegs, doll; or, play doctor's bag with a stethoscope, BandAid, pegs, crayon, lotion.

Example Observation Opportunities: (Refer to step 1 under "General child assessment procedures" in the preface to this strand.) You may indirectly suggest using an abstract object to represent two different real things, if after several minutes he does not do so spontaneously; e.g., when the child picks up the peg or crayon to "check the baby's ears," suggest that "the baby needs a shot to feel better."

Credit: (see also Credit Notes in this strand's preface)
+   play incorporates a "play plan" and use of abstract objects to symbolize real objects as defined.

2.85 **Talks intelligently to self   29.5-36**

Definition: The child sometimes talks aloud to himself, toys, or imaginary "pets" to expand his play. He does this to express his ideas and emotions symbolically through words and to help develop a logical play plan. Examples: telling a doll to "sit," "be careful," or "no no" during a tea party to express his ideas about rules and limits; telling a doll, "me coming back" to express his emotions about separation and dependency; or to help him develop a logical play plan by saying, "I'm going to cook, " as he acts out a theme of cooking, or "I making house," as he builds with blocks.

Example Observation Opportunities: Elicit through parent report or may be observed anytime when child is engaged in dramatic play activities as in skills #1.130 (above) and #1.153 (which follows).

Credit: (see also Credit Notes in this strand's preface)
+   sometimes talks aloud to express ideas and plans during play as defined.
N/A not applicable because of speech delay.

1.153 **Plays house   30-36**

Definition: The child engages in elaborate make-believe activities, which are often displayed when "playing house." Playing house at this stage includes:

1. Incorporating themes (cleaning, cooking, getting ready to go out) that have several sequenced steps with an apparent plan;

2. Using similar, abstract and imaginary props to symbolize the real object, e.g., using his finger as a spoon to stir in the pan or just going through the motions of stirring using an "imaginary" spoon; brushing his hair without a brush.

3. Assigning simple roles to play house, e.g., he tells an adult, "I am the doctor, you are the baby," or "I am the mommy, you are baby."

Example Eliciting Materials: Props that promote playing house, e.g., blocks, dolls, draping a blanket over a table, small cardboard boxes, tub of sand with dishes; child-sized broom, mop, lawn mower; dress-up clothes; ride-on toy, small wagon, magazines, playdough.

Example Observation Opportunities: (Refer to #1 under "General child assessment procedures" in the preface to this strand.) Invite the child to play house with you and/or other family members as you begin to carry out a pretend activity. Be sure, however, to let the child "take the lead."

Credit: (see also Credit Notes in this strand's preface)
+   sometimes engages in elaborate make-believe activities that incorporate themes with at least four sequenced steps, using at least two imaginary or abstract objects, and assigning different roles as defined.

1-2 GESTURAL IMITATION

1.42a	7-8	Imitates familiar gesture
1.42b	9-11	Imitates new gesture
1.66	11-14	Imitates several new gestures
1.84	14-17	Imitates "invisible" gesture
1.96	17-20	Imitates several "invisible" gestures

Family Friendly Interpretation of Strand Concepts, Assessment, & Purpose

We will be observing how your child is learning to imitate or copy the actions and movements of others. This is sometimes termed "gestural imitation." Learning to imitate actions and movements is an important foundation for learning. Children learn to play, talk, dress and do many other life skills by watching how others do things and then trying to do them themselves.

Children learn to imitate in a fairly predictable sequence. At first, children learn to imitate gestures that are familiar to them because they already use the gesture during play. For example, if your child bangs toys during play,

banging is a familiar gesture for him. If you bang a toy, he may bang a toy to imitate.

Later, children learn to imitate gestures that are new to them because they do not make the gesture during play. An example of "new gesture" might be drumming fingers on a table if he does not usually do that. Finally, children learn to imitate what are generally termed "invisible gestures." These are gestures that are new and that the child cannot see himself perform. Examples of "invisible gestures" could be pulling an earlobe or wrinkling his nose.

Parent Questions   (Examples)

To help identify the child's unique strengths and needs related to this developmental area:
• Have you noticed your child imitating (mocking or copying) any gestures or body movements

you make, such as clapping his hands when you clap yours during "Pat-a-cake," "blowing kisses" when you throw him a kiss? or trying to wave "bye-bye?"

Sample *Functional* Outcome Statements which may be generated by the Family

[Will be dependent upon identified individual child and family needs and should incorporate objectives and activities from other domains]
My child will try to copy me when we play:

• "Peek-a-boo";
• "Pat-a-cake";
• "So Big."

Identifying and Interpreting Needs for Intervention

If a child is significantly delayed in this area, he may be having difficulty in motor planning, i.e., interpreting and/or planning how to imitate movements.

However, before targeting this as the primary area of need for intervention, consider, rule out, or adapt for other causes that can contribute to or interfere with his ability to imitate. These may include:
• Motor delays or impairments: the child may not

have the movement abilities to imitate certain gestures, or may imitate them inaccurately;
• Visual impairments: a child who is blind cannot see the gestures to imitate;
• Lack of attention or interest during the observation period. *[Be sure to give the child many different opportunities to imitate. A child may not play "Pat-a-cake," but will play "So big."]*

Assessment Adaptations   (Examples)

[Note any adaptations needed to credit and help plan interventions]

- Motor impairment: only use gestures which you are certain the child can physically accomplish. Consult with a therapist for individualized suggestions and positions that facilitate smoother movement patterns, e.g., adaptive seating or side-lying. Credit gestures which may be weaker or distorted due to motor impairments.

- Visually impaired. if the child is blind:
  - assess skill #1.42 a. "Imitates familiar gesture," using gestures that the child uses frequently which have a readily identifiable sound cue, e.g., banging a block or spoon on the table.
  - mark N/A for the remaining skills in this strand. It is not appropriate to assess or teach these skills, since the child does not learn through visual imitation.

General Assessment Procedures & Processes   (apply to all items in this Strand)

1. The assessment procedures listed for items in this strand are fairly structured. After becoming familiar with them, they can, however, **be incorporated incidentally during the child's play or other daily activities.** For example, after snack time, wipe the table with a napkin a few times and invite the child to help. If he does so, you may credit #1.42A or #1.42B, with confirmation by his caregiver that this is a familiar or new gesture.

2. After you have **modeled the gesture,** such as banging a block on the table, encourage the child to imitate with a phrase, such as, "Can you do that?" Do not, however, give verbal instruction that tells the child how to imitate; e.g., do *not* say, "Bang the block on the table." Praise all attempts so the child learns the intent of these games.

3. The items in this strand end around 20 months; however, **the child continues to develop and refine his imitative abilities in all areas of development.** This may be especially evident as the child uses his deferred imitation abilities to imitate adult interactions in his dramatic and imaginary play in Strand 1-1.

4. **Describe the skill and eliciting procedures to family members and invite them to help observe and/or assess.**

+ - A Credit Notes:

+ child usually displays imitation skills as defined during play and daily activities.

- not observed or reported.

+/- appears to be an emerging skill.

N/A not appropriate to assess due to disability.

Note any adaptations used to credit.

1.42a Imitates familiar gesture   7-8

Definition: The child makes a familiar visible gesture in imitation of a model. A familiar gesture is a movement that the child already uses frequently during daily activities. At this stage, the gesture is "visible," i.e., the child can see himself perform it. Examples of familiar visible gestures may include: patting, hitting, banging, shaking.

Example Observation Opportunities: Observe gestures that the child typically makes during play or daily activities. These may be observed while assessing the child's play interactions with objects (Strand 1-1). When the child is not using one of these gestures, model the gesture two or three times when he is watching you. Pause for several seconds and invite him to do the same thing. Repeat the game, using a different gesture that the child is familiar with. For example, if earlier you observed the child shaking and banging spontaneously during play, shake a rattle a few times and then give him a rattle. Later, bang the rattle on the table and invite him to imitate.

Credit: (see also Credit Notes in this strand's preface)

+ imitates at least two familiar visible gestures

Imitates new gesture   9-11

Definition: The child tries to imitate an unfamiliar visible or new gesture. An unfamiliar or new gesture is a gesture or simple combination of two gestures that the child does not currently use during interactions with people or objects, e.g., snapping fingers, banging two blocks together, drumming or scratching fingers on a table top, wiggling fingers in the air. The gestures are visible; i.e., he can see himself produce them. At this stage, his imitation may not be accurate, and he may not imitate them immediately but through gradual approximation.

Example Observation Opportunities: When the child is engaged in play using a familiar gesture, e.g., patting a doll, banging a block on the table, or clapping his hands, show him a gesture you've never seen him use; e.g., rub the doll, slide the block or bang two blocks together, or pat the table with both hands instead of clapping. Invite him to imitate. *[Confirm with the caregiver that this is an unfamiliar gesture]* Repeat a few times, pausing to encourage the child's imitative efforts. Continue with introducing a few more new gestures if the child remains interested and attentive.

Credit: (see also Credit Notes in this strand's preface)
+   imitates at least one new gesture; imitations do not have to be accurate but should be a good approximation. He may learn to imitate the gesture through gradual approximation during the eliciting procedure.

 Imitates several new gestures   11-14

Definition: The child can accurately and immediately imitate several different visible gestures which are unfamiliar to him, i.e., gestures he does not normally use. This is in contrast to #1.42B, in that his imitations are accurate, and he does not have to go through several trials of gradual approximation to imitate. He can also imitate several different new gestures rather than just one.

Example Observation Opportunities: Same as #1.42B.

Credit: (see also Credit Notes in this strand's preface)
+   imitates at least three new gestures immediately and accurately on the first try.
A   cannot immediately imitate a new gesture on first try; initial imitations, if they occur, are always delayed by at least several seconds.

 Imitates "invisible" gesture   14-17

Definition: The child imitates an unfamiliar gesture that he cannot see himself perform. At this stage, his imitations may be approximations. Examples of unfamiliar invisible gestures include: wrinkling nose; pulling earlobe; patting head or neck; poking cheek with finger.

Example Observation Opportunities: Confirm with the child's caregiver that some of the example invisible gestures are unfamiliar to the child. When the child is attentive, model an unfamiliar invisible gesture a few times. Pause and invite the child to imitate. Repeat with two or three more gestures during the same interaction if the child remains attentive, or later during the observation period.

Credit: (see also Credit Notes in this strand's preface)
+   imitates at least one invisible unfamiliar gesture; the imitation may not be accurate but does include the body part involved; e.g., if you wrinkle your nose, the child may widen his nostrils.

1.96   **Imitates several "invisible" gestures   17-20**

Definition: Same as #1.84 but now child can imitate several.

Example Observation Opportunities: Same as #1.84, "Imitates 'invisible' gesture."

Credit: (see also Credit Notes in this strand's preface)
+   imitates at least three invisible unfamiliar gestures, one of which is a fairly accurate and immediate imitation.
A   never immediately imitates a new gesture on first try; initial imitations, if they occur, are always delayed by at least several seconds.

1-3 SOUND AWARENESS, HEARING, AND LOCALIZATION

1.03	0-1	Responds to sounds
1.04	0-2.5	Responds to voice
1.10	2-3.5	Searches with eyes for sound
1.16	3-7	Turns eyes and head to sound of hidden voice
1.19	3.5-5	Localizes sound with eyes
1.41	7-10	*a. Finds hidden sound from below after turning head to side*
	9-13	*b. Finds hidden sound from below by looking directly*
	13-16	*c. Finds hidden sound from above after turning head to side*
	16-21	*d. Finds hidden sound from above by looking directly*
	36	*e. Finds hidden sound directly above and behind*

Family Friendly Interpretation of Strand Concepts, Assessment, & Purpose

We will be observing how your child responds to different sounds and if he can figure out where a sound is coming from. Locating or turning to the source of sound is sometimes termed "auditory localization" by professionals. The ability to locate sounds develops gradually. At first, a child learns to find a sound that is coming from his side. Later, he learns to locate sounds that come from below; for example, if a spoon hits the floor he looks down to the floor to find it. The most difficult sounds to locate are those that occur directly above or behind him when he is sitting or standing. Being able to localize sounds helps your child learn to associate sounds with objects and events, and helps him develop an awareness of where things are located around him (spatial awareness).

Professional FYI

- Delays or inconsistent response in this area may signal hearing loss in one or both ears, or may be a symptom of sensory processing problems, i.e., the child is able to hear the sounds but he hears or responds to them in a disorganized manner because he does not have the spatial awareness needed to locate them.
- The primary emphasis of this strand is auditory localization abilities. This strand provides only a cursory screening of the child's auditory acuity and it does <u>not</u> assess auditory discrimination, i.e., the ability to discriminate one sound from another.
- Although many children with hearing loss have no identifiable risk factors, one or more of the following factors does place the child at risk for hearing loss and thus should be followed more closely. Assess these risk factors through parent interview and review of medical records:

  - family history of childhood hearing impairment;
  - congenital infection, e.g., cytomegalovirus (CMV), rubella, herpes, toxoplasmosis, syphilis;
  - anatomic malformations of head and neck, e.g., cleft palate, abnormal appearance of outer ear, atypical appearance;
  - birth weight less than 1500 grams;
  - hyperbilirubinemia at such a high level that it required medical intervention;
  - meningitis, especially H. influenza;
  - severe asphyxia;
  - significant history or prolonged incident of middle ear fluid (more than three months;)
  - prolonged untreated ear infections.
- Skill #1.41 has been adapted and expanded from the original HELP Charts/Checklist to include localization skills at developmentally higher age ranges.

Parent Questions   (General Examples - see Skills for specific questions)

To help identify the child's unique strengths and needs related to this developmental area:

- How does your baby let you know that he seems to hear your voice or the sound of a toy?
- Does your child seem to like or dislike certain sounds or voices more than others? *If so,* Which sounds? How can you tell, or How does he let you know this?
- Does your child have any toys that make sounds, such a rattle, music box or squeak toy? Does he seem to deliberately shake or squeeze them to hear the sound? Does he move to the music of his music box or let you know that he wants to hear it again when the music stops?
- Has your child had any ear infections or fluid in his ears? *If so,* About how many? Was it treated by a doctor? What is the longest ear infection your child had that you can remember? Do you know if he has an ear infection or fluid now? Has a doctor treated the infection?
- Have you noticed if your child looks for sounds or voices that he can't see, such as turning his head when he hears the phone ring? *If so,* Can you give me some examples?

To help identify family resources, priorities and concerns related to the child's development in this area:

- Do you have, or have you ever had any concerns about your child's hearing?
- Has your child's hearing ever been tested?

[If concerns have been identified]

- Are you interested in getting information about community resources that can check your child's hearing?
- Does anyone in your child's family have a hearing loss which started in childhood?

Are there any other important aspects about your child's hearing or the way he reacts to sounds that you feel are important?

Sample *Functional* Outcome Statements which may be generated by the Family

[Will be dependent upon identified individual child and family needs, and should incorporate objectives and activities from other domains]

My child will:

- Know I'm nearby or coming to help him when he hears me talking;
- Be aware of sounds during play and daily activities: his sound-making toys, vacuum, telephone, tub water, blender;
- Enjoy hearing and playing with his rattle and squeak toys;

- Not startle or become upset with general household sounds, such as the telephone, door bell, door closing or opening;
- Associate the sounds he hears with the object;
- Be able to figure out where a sound is coming from.

We will know which types of sounds our child likes best.

Transactional Assessment

May assess through observation and interview.

Assessment of the Child's Environment

1. Supportive:

[Example environments that support/facilitate development in this area]

The child's caregiving environments usually:

- Provide a variety of interesting sounds that match the child's auditory preferences and needs, e.g., a variety of toys that make sounds, people who talk to him, play areas that are accessible to daily activities and routine sounds.

2. Compromising:

[Example environments that may restrict, compromise, inhibit or be unsupportive toward development in this area]

The child's caregiving environments are frequently:

- Over- or under-stimulating for the child's auditory interests and needs, e.g., loud television or stereo usually playing; or, child is typically isolated from daily activities and sounds.

Assessment of Caregiver Interactions with the Child

1. Supportive:
[Example interactions that support/facilitate child's development in this area]
The child's caregivers usually:
- Show and name the source of interesting sounds;
- Recognize when toys sounds are overstimulating and remove or adjust the sound accordingly;
- Make interesting sounds to attract their child's attention;
- Talk to their child using varied and animated expressions and voice tones;
- Identify and buffer environmental sounds that

are irritating to the child;
- Pause for the child to respond after saying a short phrase or making a sound with a toy.

2. Compromising:
[Example interactions that may restrict, compromise, inhibit or be unsupportive of the child's development in this area]
The child's caregivers frequently:
- Over-stimulate the child when showing him a sound toy, e.g., squeaks toy too close to face continuously without pausing;
- Provide minimal verbal interactions;
- Do not recognize or respond to child's responses to sounds.

Identifying and Interpreting Needs for Intervention

If a child displays delayed, inconsistent, or atypical development in this area, he may have a hearing impairment in one or both ears or may be having difficulty with sensory organization.
Refer the child for further medical and audiological evaluation if the:
  1. Parent has concerns about child's hearing;
  2. Child's responses to items in this strand are delayed, inconsistent, or absent.
Refer the child for further evaluation from a therapist trained in sensory organization principles if the child's hearing acuity is determined to be normal but the child does not localize sounds. He may appear confused and disorganized or display hypersensitivity to sounds, e.g., startles frequently even to soft sounds.
However, before targeting hearing or sensory processing as the primary need for referral and

intervention, consider, rule out, or adapt for other causes that may interfere with a true assessment of the child's hearing or localization abilities. These may include:
- Motor impairment, which makes it difficult for the child to turn his head to find a sound, or the child's motor responses may be distorted or delayed;
- Visually impaired: vision reinforces the location of sounds when a child turns to find it. Infants who are blind do not experience this automatic verification. Responses to sound may thus be delayed or not always present;
- Current ear infection or middle ear fluid;
- Competing environment, e.g., child is too intent looking at a novel toy or there are other competing sounds.

Assessment Adaptations   (Examples)

[Note any adaptations needed to qualify credit and help plan interventions]
- Motor impaired: *consult with a P.T. or O.T. to ensure maximal stability and ability to turn head.* Adaptive seating or positioning may be indicated. Provide extra time for the child to turn his head, or position the sound source so that it is out of the child's immediate sight but can still be located by eye searching only.
- Visually impaired: expect delayed or more subtle responses to sounds, as well as delays in localization abilities. Always let the child touch the sound stimulus and name it for him after the sound has started. Additional specific adaptations include:
  #1.10 "Searches for sounds with eyes." Omit and mark N/A.
  #1.16 "Turns eyes and head to sound of hidden voice": Credit orientation responses to sound, i.e., any head or

body adjustment toward the source of sound.
  #1.19 "Localizes sound with eyes." Credit if child responds to sounds selectively, e.g., may ignore some sounds and repeatedly respond in the same manner to others.
  #1.41 "Finds hidden sound from..." Expect significant delays in achievement, accuracy and response time.
- Hearing impairment: Sound localization for a person who has a hearing impairment in one or both ears is often difficult and is sometimes never acquired, even if sound is amplified with hearing aides. Instead of assessing and planning for localization skills, it will be more appropriate to assess and plan for awareness, attention and recognition of sounds and persistence in searching for the source of sound. Consult with the child's audiologist or speech-language therapist to

Assessment Adaptations (continued)

help select appropriate stimuli and functional goals and objectives. Mark N/A for items that require localization.

- Current ear infection or middle ear fluid: if the child has an ear infection or fluid, be sure to reassess when ears are clear.

General Assessment Procedures & Processes (apply to all items in this Strand)

1. Items in this strand are developmentally sequenced. **If a child passes an item in this strand, all items that precede it can be credited without specifically testing them.**
2. **Be sure to repeat the assessment procedures toward child's left *and* right ears on multiple occasions.** The child must respond without question at least twice with each ear to be certain of his localization abilities.
3. **Do not credit if the child is already looking at source of sound before the sound is made.**
4. **If a child has any identified risk factors listed in the Professional FYI, #3 above, periodic monitoring of the child's sound auditory awareness and localization skills should occur even if the child displayed appropriate responses on the initial screening.**
5. **Be sure to let the child see, play with or touch the source of sound after you have given him time to search for it.** Repeat the sound while he is attending.
6. **When assessing localization skills, it is important that the child is in a position that allows him to freely move his head to find the source.**
7. **When presenting a sound-producing toy, be careful to avoid giving visual cues to the object's location.** Make the sound while the

child is looking at something else, e.g., while looking at parent.
8. **Assess in a room that has minimal visual or auditory distractions.**
9. **Make the sound intermittently rather than continuously; e.g., shake rattle several times, pause a few seconds and shake again.**
10. **Describe the skill or eliciting procedures and invite family members to help observe and/or assess.** Help family members recognize their child's sound preferences and unique or more subtle responses to sounds.

+ - A Credit Notes:
+ child consistently responds as defined.
- no response or child was already displaying the response before the onset of sound.
A atypical response, e.g., cries, continues to startle after listening to the sound, appears very confused; takes more than several seconds to find, not due to motor or visual impairment.
N/A not able to assess due to child's disability.
O circle any credit if environment or interactions compromise or restrict child's optimal auditory awareness skills (refer to Interactional assessment above)
Note any adaptations used to credit.

Assessment Materials

Safe rattle, squeak toy, bell, closed can containing coins, pebbles or rocks; tissue paper to "rustle"; small wind-up music box; sound toys the family may have.

1.03 Responds to sounds 0-1

Definition: The child displays an awareness of sounds through generally reflexive responses. These responses may include one or more of the following: startle, increase or decrease in respiration and/or activity, change in expression, eyes widening or shifting, body tensing, frown.

Example Observation Opportunities: Incidental: Observe child's responses to sudden, fairly loud sounds that occur naturally in the environment throughout the observation period, e.g., telephone ring, door slam, knock on door, ball bouncing, vacuum cleaner, book or toy dropping on floor. Note responses to different sounds. Structured: (1) Observe the child's responses to two or three different musical sounds, e.g., bell, xylophone, maraca, drum, tambourine, music boxes. Make the sound 1 to 3 feet from the child's ear. (2) Observe the child's responses to two or three different sound-producing toys: different types of rattles, a Happy Apple or other chime ball.

Credit: (see also Credit Notes in this strand's preface)
+ clearly displays any of the defined responses to all sudden environmental, musical and toy sounds. Reflexive responses should diminish within a few moments of the sound.
A over 1 month continues to startle and/or cry to most sounds.
(also in Strand 0.0 "Regulatory/Sensory Organization")

1.04 Responds to Voice   0-2.5

Definition: The child displays one or more of the following responses when he hears someone begin to talk: facial expression brightens or becomes intent; looks for speaker; smiles; slowly turns toward voice; quiets; stops or increases sucking.

Example Observation Opportunities: Quietly observe while the parent talks to the child out of his direct line of vision. [Discuss or demonstrate using a higher-pitched voice and pausing to wait for child's response as needed] Note clarity of child's cues and how hard parent had to work to elicit if significant.

Credit: (see also Credit Notes in this strand's preface)

+   consistently displays one or more of the defined responses after hearing a voice.

1.10 Searches with eyes for sound   2-3.5

Definition: The child's responses to sounds at this stage, are less reflexive than in #1.03 "Responds to sounds." At this level, the child displays more intentional alerting and attention responses, such as moving his head toward the source of sound, searching with his eyes, and/or smiling.

Example Observation Opportunities: Same as #1.03.

Credit: (see also Credit Notes in this strand's preface)

+   displays definite eye searching, smiling, or moving head toward source of sound; he does *not* need to actually find the source of sound.

1.16 Turns eyes and head to sound of hidden voice   3-7

Definition: The child deliberately and successfully turns his head to find the person who is talking to him.

Example Observation Opportunities: Approach, or have parent approach, the child toward one side, within 1 to 3 feet of the child's shoulder. Use conversational level speech and call the child's name or say a "catchy" phrase, such as "Hi there!"

Credit: (see also Credit Notes in this strand's preface)

+   localizes and directly looks at speaker within a few seconds of hearing the phrase.

1.19 Localizes sound with eyes   3.5-5

Definition: The child localizes sounds that occur on a lateral plane about 1 to 3 feet from his ear. In contrast to #1.10 "Searches with eyes for sound," the child actually finds the source of sound, rather than just searching.

Example Observation Opportunities: When the child is not looking at the bell, shake it two to three times, 1 to 3 feet from his left ear. Wait a few seconds for his response. Repeat the procedure to child's right side. After letting the child see and touch the bell, repeat the procedure with two to three different rattle toys, and then a high-pitched squeak toy.

Credit: (see also Credit Notes in this strand's preface)

+   turns head to correct side to find the source of each sound (bell, two different toned rattle toys, high-pitched squeak toy,) that occurs on a lateral plane, 1 to 3 feet from the child's ear; this should be displayed with his left and right ear.

1.41a Finds hidden sound *from below, after turning head to side*   7-10

Definition: The child localizes sounds that occur from below on either side of him. At this stage he initially searches by first turning his head to the correct side and then looking downward.

Example Observation Opportunities: Incidental - may be observed when something is dropped on the floor within 1 to 3 feet, e.g., spoon, book, toy. Structured - when the child is *standing or sitting* in a seat or in an adult's lap, ring a bell when he is not looking to his left side at about his waist level. Wait a few seconds for his response. Repeat the procedure to child's right side. After letting the child play with the bell, repeat the procedure with two to three different rattle toys, and a high-pitched squeak toy.

Credit: (see also Credit Notes in this strand's preface)

+   turns head to side and then looks down to find source of each sound (bell, two different-toned rattle toys, high-pitched squeak toy) located to the side at or below his waist level.

1.41b   *Finds hidden sound from below by looking directly*   *9-13*

Definition: The child looks directly downward to find the source of sound that occurred from below on either side of him.
Example Observation Opportunities: Same as #1.41a.
Credit: (see also Credit Notes in this strand's preface)
+   looks directly down to locate the source of each sound; this should be displayed on the left and right.

1.41c   *Finds hidden sound from above after turning head to side*   *13-16*

Definition: The child localizes sounds that occur above him from either side, about 1 to 3 feet above his shoulder. He does so by first turning his head correctly to one side and then looking upward.
Example Observation Opportunities: Same as #1.41a, but present the sound out of sight, 1 to 3 feet above his left and then his right shoulder.
Credit: (see also Credit Notes in this strand's preface)
+   turns head to correct side and then looks upwards to find source of each sound (bell, two different-toned rattle toys, high-pitched squeak toy); this should be displayed on the left and right.

1.41d   *Finds hidden sound from above by looking directly*   *16-21*

Definition: The child looks directly upward to find the source of sound that occurred from above on either side, about 1 to 3 feet above his shoulder.
Example Observation Opportunities: Same as #1.41a, but present the sound out of sight, 1 to 3 feet above his left and then his right shoulder.
Credit: (see also Credit Notes in this strand's preface)
+   looks directly upwards to locate source of each sound, on each side.

1.41e   *Finds hidden sound directly above and behind*   *36*

Definition: The child localizes sounds that occur directly above his head and directly behind his back.
Example Observation Opportunities: Same as #1.41a, but present the sound 1 to 3 feet directly over his head at midline, and then, 1 to 3 feet directly behind his back at midline.
Credit: (see also Credit Notes in this strand's preface)
+   child looks directly upwards to locate source of each sound and turns around to locate source of each sound.

1-4 PROBLEM SOLVING

A. OBJECT PERMANENCE

1.09	2-3	Reacts to disappearance of slowly moving object
1.20	4-6	Finds a partially hidden object
1.32		Finds hidden object using:
	7-9	a. one screen
	8-10	b. two screens
	9-10	c. three screens
1.49	9-12	Finds hidden object under three superimposed screens
1.62	11-13	Hidden displacement one screen
1.78	13-14	Hidden displacement two screens
1.80	14-15	Hidden displacement three screens
1.81	14-15	Hidden displacement two screens alternately
1.94	17-18	Series of hidden displacements: object under last screen
1.113	21-22	Series of hidden displacements: object under first screen

Family Friendly Interpretation of Strand Concepts, Assessment, & Purpose

We will be playing some hiding and searching games with your child, by hiding a favorite toy under a cover and asking him to figure out where it went. These games help us understand how your child is learning the concept that objects still exist even if he cannot see, hear, or touch them. This is often termed "object permanence." Understanding that objects still exist is important because it helps a child learn to attend, remember, and solve problems. For example, when a child drops his bottle out of sight, if he wants to find it he must first remember that it still exists, and then problem-solve to figure out where it could be.

At first, babies respond to only what they can immediately see, touch or hear. When an object is removed, they seem to forget about it as if it no longer exists. As children begin to realize that objects still exist when out of sight, they begin to look for them or fuss to ask you to help find it. For example, if your child drops his bottle and still wants it, he remembers that his bottle still exists and may look down to the floor for it or

fuss to have you find it for him. At first, children need to see the object being hidden in order to find it. For example, if he drops his bottle and sees it roll under his blanket, he can find it as long as there are not any other places the bottle could be. As a child gets older, when he is looking for something that he did not actually see disappear, he may randomly search under several things to try to find it.

Finally, a child begins to use foresight and intuitive thought as well as persistence to figure out where a missing object is. At this stage, the child says to himself, "If it is not under here then it must be under there!" For example, at home if your child is playing and notices you going from one room to another, and then decides he wants to go to you, he has to figure out which room to go to find you. He does this by only searching in the rooms he saw you enter or at a higher level of thought, by only going to the room he last saw you go in. Earlier, he may have randomly looked for you in any room, even if he did not see you enter it.

Professional FYI

Related strands and skills: Strand 4-1, "Visual Tracking," and Strand 1-3, "Auditory Localization," have related concepts considered prerequisites for this strand for children who are not blind or deaf. Skill #1.33 "Plays Peek-a-boo," in Strand 5-5, is also closely related since it has an underlying concept of "people permanence." The onset of separation anxiety, Strand 5-1 is also a sign that the child has developed a sense of "people permanence".

Related concepts: When the basic understanding that objects continue to exist when out of perceptual contact is established in skill #1.32A, increasingly more difficult mental processes and abilities contribute to achieving higher level object permanence skills. These include the ability to persist, organize search efforts, hold in memory an increasing number of events, and logically deduce the location of objects through intuitive thought rather than random trial and error.

Parent Questions (Examples)

To help identify the child's unique strengths and needs related to this developmental area:

Children show us they are learning that objects still exist even when they can't see, hear or feel them in a variety of ways during daily activities. For example, a child may find his pacifier that drops out of his mouth, move to find a pet that has run into another room, or look for a toy that got covered up under the bubbles in his bath or sand in his sandbox.
• Can you think of a time when your child looked for something out of sight? How did he go about finding it?
• Can you think of any other examples that help us understand how your child is learning that objects still exist even if he cannot see, hear or touch them?

To help identify family resources, priorities and concerns related to the child's development in this area:
• If you could think of one thing that you wish your child could find on his own without always crying for help, what would that be?

Sample *Functional* Outcome Statements which may be generated by the Family

[Will be dependent upon identified individual child and family needs and should incorporate objectives and activities from other domains]
My child will be able to:
• Find the toys he drops;
• Find his pacifier when it drops;
• Know I'm nearby even though he can't see or hear me.

Transactional Assessment

May assess through observation and interview.

Assessment of Caregiver Interactions with the Child

1. Supportive:
[Example interactions that support/facilitate child's development in this area]
The child's caregivers sometimes:
• Give the child time to find things he's dropped before getting them for him;
• Play simple hiding games, such as "Peek-a-boo;"
• Let the child have the object he has searched for;
• Cue the child when moving out of sight, e.g., telling the child where they are going, talking to the child from another room;
• Respond supportively when the child cries because the caregiver is out of sight.

2. Compromising:
[Example interactions that may restrict, compromise, inhibit or be unsupportive of the child's development in this area]
• The child's caregivers hide things in a teasing manner, e.g., make the task purposefully too difficult, or take away the object just as he finds it.

Identifying and Interpreting Needs for Intervention

If a child is significantly delayed in this area he may be having difficulty in the cognitive skills of <u>understanding the permanence of objects, memory, and/or problem solving.</u>

However, before targeting cognition as the primary area of need for intervention, consider, rule out, or adapt for other causes that may interfere with a true assessment of the child's memory, object permanence or problem-solving skills. These may include:
• <u>Visual impairments</u>: people and objects seem to constantly appear and disappear into a void for infants who are blind. These infants do not have the immediate visual feedback to tell them that people and objects continue to exist unless they are holding them or listening to them. Substituting sound for objects, however, does not always provide enough information for the child, and auditory localization develops later in children who are blind;
• <u>Motor impairments</u>: the child may not be able to reach for or manipulate covers to find hidden objects;
• <u>Spatial problems</u>: if the child has difficulty with spatial relationships and/or sequencing he may understand that the object still exists but become confused during the searching process;
• <u>Interest</u>: the child may have no interest in the object being hidden and thus has little motivation to find or persist in finding it;
• <u>Difficulty attending to a task</u>: the child cannot focus long enough to attend to the task, or is highly distractible and cannot complete the task.

Assessment Adaptations (Examples)

[Note any adaptations needed to credit and help plan interventions]
- Visually impaired:
  - For child with low vision, use high-contrast color and textured objects and covers.
  - Blind: The specific skills listed in this strand are not appropriate to assess or teach. Mark, N/A. *Instead, consult with a vision specialist to design interventions that promote an understanding of object permanence through concrete experiences.* These may include keeping objects in predictable places (e.g., using mobiles, rattles on a wrist band, tying short strings on toys), and later learning to reach for people and sound-producing toys after the person or toy becomes quiet.
- Motor impaired:
  - Try different covers to see which ones the child can remove, e.g., use upside-down tall plastic cups or paper cones as covers with ample spacing in between so child can knock down the correct screen rather than having to manipulate the cover.
  - Allow extra time for the child to respond.
  - If the child is severely restricted in his movements, credit eye searching; if he has good language development, you can ask him to tell you where the toy is or you can ask him to look at the place he thinks it is.
  - Consult with a therapist for optimal positioning of the child and materials.
- Attentional difficulties: incorporate these items within typical play and daily activities rather than trying to assesses these items as a structured task. For example, for item #132B, during snack time, put the child's cookie under one of two napkins; for item #1.80, during car play, hide his favorite miniature car in your hand and then leave it under one of three boxes.

General Assessment Procedures & Processes (apply to all items in this Strand)

1. **Assessment considerations:**
   Formal assessment or planning for this strand is not always functional nor useful, especially if the child is not interested in or becomes frustrated by "hiding games." When possible, these items should be assessed unobtrusively during typical daily activities and play. Examples of naturalistic situations are suggested for items when possible. Likewise, if you are planning interventions related to object permanence, they should be taught through meaningful situations that promote generalization rather than through structured teaching, e.g., helping the child find a pacifier which has moved into the fold of a blanket, encouraging him to look for his cookie which dropped off the highchair tray, or helping him to remember in which pocket he placed his toy.

2. **Procedures if this strand is formally assessed:**
   a. Be sure the child is not pulling off screens as a game in and of itself. If he seems to be pulling off screens as the game rather than to obtain the object, discontinue the procedure and try at another time using a more novel and interesting object or using a more boring cover.
   b. The assessment procedures for items in this strand can be presented sequentially during one observation until the child fails to find the object in two successive items. If the child becomes frustrated by having objects he wants continuously hidden, give him a few minutes break to play with the toy or engage him in another activity before continuing. Be sure to keep the game playful and interactive; e.g., "Oh, you found it!" and clapping to cheer.
   c. If the child seems to prefer certain covers or gets used to finding an object under a certain cover, change the cover to ensure the child is finding the toy purposefully rather than finding it accidentally.
   d. ***Covers and Screens should remain stationary;*** do not move them around after placement.
   e. Positioning: The child can be in any position that provides enough support to optimize the child's reaching and visual tracking. If formally assessed, there should be a working surface in front of him, e.g., supported sitting with a tray, in prone stander at table.
   f. Prompting: To credit, you may give the child some verbal cues as needed to encourage him to "find the toy," but, do <u>not</u> give gestural cues, such as pointing or looking at the place where the object is hidden. If the child cannot find the toy after allowing sufficient time, help him find it by pointing to the correct place or lifting the cover. Although you should not credit this type of prompted response, this will help avoid frustration and promote a playful learning interaction.

3. **Describe the skill and eliciting procedures to**

Assessment Adaptations   (continued)

family members and invite them to help observe and/or assess. It is important, however, that caregivers do not interpret these activities as games that should necessarily be carried out at home in a structured manner. Explain that these games can be frustrating to a child and give alternative suggestions of how the concepts may be used more functionally during daily activities.

+ - A Credit Notes:

+   child usually displays skill or behavior as defined during play and daily activities.

-   not observed; child is more interested in the cover than the object it covered, or can only find with gestural prompts.

+/- appears to be an emerging skill, e.g., child finds object less than half the time or with "hints" from another.

N/A not appropriate to assess because of disability.

O   circle any credit if interactions compromise or restrict child's optimal skills in this area; e.g., adult did not give child enough time to find it, or began teasing the child by not letting him play with the found object, or moving the screens around.

Note any adaptations used to credit.

Assessment Materials

• Objects to hide: any small *safe* toy or object in which the child has shown interest, e.g., small doll, toy car, set of keys, cookie, cracker, pop beads.

• Covers:
– Formal assessment: three solid drab cloths (wash cloth, diaper, baby blanket), small plain box. Note: The covers should be boring to the child so that he is more interested in finding the object than playing with the cover.

– Incidental assessment: use covers which are available spontaneously in the environment, e.g., pockets on clothing, diapers, blanket, small pillow, napkin, box.

1.09 Reacts to disappearance of slowly moving object   2-3

Definition: When an object that the child is looking at slowly moves out of sight, he continues to look at the place it disappeared for a few moments.

Example Observation Opportunities: Incidental - if a child is watching a person or pet leave the room, watch to see if he continues to look at the door after the person has left. Structured - attract the child's attention to a doll, car, or ball. Push, roll or move it slowly while the child is watching until it is behind a barrier, such as a box or clipboard. Observe the child's reactions to the disappearance.

Credit: (see also Credit Notes in this strand's preface)

+   continues to look at the barrier for a few seconds after the object or person has disappeared behind it; the child should not be able to see OR hear the object or person.

1.20 Finds a partially hidden object   4-6

Definition: The child retrieves an object he has watched being hidden by a cover that hides at least 50 percent of the object.

Example Observation Opportunities: *[Note: To credit, hide a uniform object, i.e., an object that does not look like the complete object when partially covered, e.g., if a necklace chain or chain of pop beads were partially covered, the remaining chain would look like the full object. Example objects to use: toy car, doll, stuffed animal, hairbrush, pacifier]* Incidental - may observe if the child finds an object he dropped which becomes partially covered, e.g., his pacifier in the fold of his blanket, his toy that tumbles under his leg. May also observe when the child requests or retrieves objects that are partially hidden, e.g., his bottle sticking out of the diaper bag, his pacifier that is partially protruding from his parent's pocket. Structured - attract the child's attention to a doll, car or other non-uniform toy within easy reach. While he is watching, cover half the toy with a solid cloth. If the child accidentally covers the complete object as he attempts to pull the cover off, readjust the cover so that the object is visible.

Credit: (see also Credit Notes in this strand's preface)

+   removes cover or pulls the object out from under the cover. The child should show more interest in the toy than in the cover.

1.32

Finds hidden object using:
a. one screen *7-9*
b. two screens *8-10*
c. three screens *9-10*

Definition: When the child sees an object he wants covered up (entirely), he purposefully removes the correct cover on his first try to find it when:
a. only one cover is present;
b. two covers laying next to each other are available;
c. three covers laying next to each other are available.

Example Observation Opportunities: <u>Incidental</u> - observe the child's responses and efforts to find, e.g., a toy covered by a diaper; his bottle hidden by his blanket; a small toy you place in one of three pockets. <u>Structured</u> - attract the child's attention to an object. If he shows interest by reaching for it, immediately:

1. Cover it completely with a solid cloth while he is watching. Bunch up the cloth so that it does not mold around the object as a hint that it is there. Repeat with the same or a new toy. If he pulls the cover off to look at or play with the hidden object on each occasion, credit and proceed to b.

2. Place a second cover, which is a different color, a few inches next to the first screen used in procedure a. Each cover should be bunched up. Place a new (or the same object) under the second cover while child is watching. Repeat with the same or a new, more attractive object, two or three more times, alternating that cover the toy is placed under. If the child pulls both covers off at the same time, move them further apart. If the child pulls off the correct cover on each try, credit and proceed to #1.32C.

3. Add a third cover of a different color a few inches away from the second, again bunching each of them up. Place a new, more attractive object, or the same object if the child is still interested, randomly under one of the three screens, while the child is watching. If the child searches directly under the correct screen, continue to randomly place the toy under each of the screens for five or six more trials. Credit if the child searches under the correct cover on each trial.

Credit: (see also Credit Notes in this strand's preface)
On each of at least two occasions, the child:

+ <u>1.32a.</u> purposefully removes cover to find the toy he watched hidden, when there are no other covers available.
+ <u>1.32b.</u> purposefully removes correct cover on first try to find the toy he watched hidden, when two covers are available, and the object is randomly hidden alternately under different covers.
+ <u>1.32c.</u> purposefully removes correct cover on first try to find a toy he watched hidden, when three covers are available, and, the object is hidden under alternate covers.

1.49

Finds hidden object under three superimposed screens   9-12

Definition: The child finds an object he has watched being hidden under three covers which are layered one at a time on top of each other over the object.

Example Observation Opportunities: While the child is watching, layer three covers, one at a time, over an object that he has shown interest in. Be sure to choose and arrange covers so that they can be removed one at a time rather than accidentally with one swipe. For example, hide a cracker under a small box or in your closed hand, and then cover your hand or the box with a wash cloth. Then place a scarf on top of the wash cloth. Observe if the child pulls off the covers, one at a time in a searching manner. Repeat one or two times with the same or a new, more attractive toy.

Credit: (see also Credit Notes in this strand's preface)
+ on each of at least two occasions, the child removes covers one at a time to find a hidden object.
- removes covers all at the same time, e.g., in one swipe.

1.62   Hidden displacement one screen   11-13

Definition: Hidden displacement means that an object has been hidden while the child watches, but then it is moved and hidden in a different place *without* the child seeing it actually removed from the first hiding place. This is also referred to as "invisible displacement." In this item, only one extra screen or cover is available. The child finds an object under this cover even though he did not see the object placed there. He finds it by first looking in the place he last saw it, e.g., an adult's hand, and then realizing that since it is not there, it must be under the remaining cover and retrieves it.

Example Observation Opportunities: <u>Incidental</u> - may be observed if an adult takes something small away that the child wanted and as it is hidden in the adult's hand, the adult puts it in a purse, pocket or diaper bag. For example, a parent may take the child's pacifier away, hide it in her fist and then tuck it into a diaper bag while the child is watching. Observe if the child looks to the parent's hand and when seeing it is empty, goes over to the diaper bag and retrieves it. <u>Structured (4 step process)</u>:
1. While the child is watching, place an object he wants into a container that is laying on the surface in front of him; e.g., put a cracker into the palm of your hand or into a small open box which is laying on his highchair tray.
2. While the child is still watching, cover the container (e.g., your hand or the small box) with a cloth.
3. Empty the object from the container while it is still hidden under the cloth so that the child is *not* able to see you empty it; e.g., turn your palm or the box over while the cloth is still covering it so the cracker empties out onto the tray but remains hidden under the cloth. The cue for the child should be noticing the point from which your hand is removed. *[Note: the cloth should be "bunched" so that the hidden object does not bulge as a cue; 2. the object should not make a sound when it is emptied on the surface]*
4. Remove the now empty container (e.g., your fist or the box) from under the cloth (which is now hiding the object) and lay it next to the cloth. Invite the child to find the object.

Credit: (see also Credit Notes in this strand's preface)
+   on each of at least two occasions, looks or glances at the first container and then seeing that it is empty, goes directly to the cloth and removes it, or goes directly to the place the object is hidden instead of initially looking in the first container.

1.78   Hidden displacement two screens   13-14

Definition: Same as #1.62 "Hidden displacement one screen," but there is now an additional screen available. This screen is not used in any way; it only lays next to the first screen. This additional screen poses a higher problem-solving skill, as there is now an extra screen with which to contend.

Example Observation Opportunities: When the child successfully completes the structured procedure for #1.62, repeat the procedure, but this time add a second cloth of a different color or pattern next to the original cloth. Hide the object under the first screen through hidden displacement as defined in #1.62. Do not touch or hide the object under the second screen. Repeat the procedure with a new toy.

Credit: (see also Credit Notes in this strand's preface)
+   on each of at least two occasions, the child goes directly to the correct cover to find the object hidden through invisible displacement; ignores the second unused cover.

1.80   Hidden displacement three screens   14-15

Definition: The child finds an object hidden through invisible displacement when it is hidden under any one of three screens. Refer to #1.62 for definition of "hidden (or invisible) displacement."

Example Observation Opportunities: Same as #1.81, but add a third cover that is a different color or composition; e.g., if cloths or bowls were used for the first two covers, you may use an inverted cup. Repeat the procedure four or five times, hiding the object randomly under a different cloth through invisible displacement on each occasion.

Credit: (see also Credit Notes in this strand's preface)
+   on each of at least three occasions, goes directly to the correct cover when objects are hidden under one of three covers randomly by invisible displacement.

1.81   Hidden displacement two screens alternately   14-15

Definition: The child finds an object hidden through invisible displacement when it is hidden under any one of two screens. Refer to #1.62 for definition of "hidden (or invisible) displacement."

Example Observation Opportunities:
1. Show the child a small object of interest, such as an animal cracker, held in the palm of your open hand.
2. Place two different covers about a foot apart in front of the child. The covers can be either bunched up cloths of different colors or inverted bowls or boxes.
3. When the child is watching, hide the object in your hand by closing it.
4. Empty your hand under one of the covers. Be sure the object does not make a sound as it is placed on the surface.
5. Remove your empty hand and lay it between the two covers, holding it open. Invite the child to find the object.
6. If he finds it, repeat the procedure, but this time hide the object under the opposite cover.
7. If he goes directly to the correct cover, repeat the procedure and hide it under the first cover.

Credit: (see also Credit Notes in this strand's preface)
+   on each of at least three occasions, goes directly to the correct cover when objects are hidden under one of two covers alternately by invisible displacement.

1.94   Series of hidden displacements: object under last screen   17-18

Definition: The child systematically looks for and finds an object which has been hidden through invisible displacement under the last of three covers. He does so after watching an adult pass her hand holding the hidden object under each screen before leaving the object under the third cover. Refer to #1.62 for a definition of "invisible displacement."

Example Observation Opportunities: Follow this seven-step process:
1. Show the child a small object of interest, such as an animal cracker, held in the palm of your open hand.
2. Place three different covers about a foot apart in front of the child. The covers can be either bunched up cloths of different colors or inverted bowls or boxes.
3. When the child is watching, hide the object in your hand by closing it.
4. Move your hand in path from left to right, placing it under each cover. As you move your hand from screen to screen, pause to place your closed hand between each cover before going on to the next.
5. Empty your hand under the last cover. Be sure the object does not make a sound as it is placed on the surface.
6. Remove your hand from the last cover and show the child that it is empty as you invite him to find the object.
7. Repeat two or three times with a new object of interest, following the same path from left to right. If successful, move directly to skill #1.113 that follows.

Credit: (see also Credit Notes in this strand's preface)
+   on each of at least two occasions, the child looks under the last screen where the object was placed; he may find it by going directly to the last screen or by systematically looking under the first, second, and then the third.

1.113   Series of hidden displacements: object under first screen   21-22

Definition: *This item builds directly on item #1.94.* The child finds a hidden object which is left under the first of three screens when he has watched the adult's hand hiding the object move in a path under each of three screens. Since he expects the object to be under the third screen (from playing the game in #1.94), he searches there first. When it is not there, he retraces the path by searching under the middle cover before finding the object under the first.

Example Observation Opportunities: Immediately after administering skill #1.94, repeat the procedure but this time leave the object under the first screen, but continue to pass your closed hand under the middle and last screen as if you were still holding the object in your hand. After completing the path, show the child your empty hand and invite him to find the object. Repeat at least one more time.

Credit: (see also Credit Notes in this strand's preface)
+   on each of at least two occasions, searches systematically for the hidden object by looking under the last, then under the middle cover before finding it under the first cover.

1-4 PROBLEM SOLVING

B. MEANS-ENDS

1.25	5-6.5	Reaches for second object purposefully
1.26	5-9	Works for desired, out-of-reach object
1.40	6.5-7.5	Retains two of three objects offered
1.45	8-10	Retains two and reaches for third object
1.47	8-10	Retrieves object using other material
1.46	8-11	Overcomes obstacle to obtain object
1.53	9-12	Uses locomotion to regain object; resumes play
1.74	*9-12*	Pulls string horizontally to obtain toy
1.79	13-15	Pulls string vertically to obtain toy
4.64	12.5-18	Inverts small container to obtain tiny object after demonstration
4.66	13.5-19	Inverts small container spontaneously to obtain tiny object
1.95	17-24	Solves simple problems using tools
6.55	21-23	Opens doors by turning knob

Family Friendly Interpretation of Strand Concepts, Assessment, & Purpose

We will be observing how your child is learning to figure out the easiest way to get things, to get things done or to accomplish goals. Goals may include trying to figure out how to get things that are out of reach, how to carry many things at one time and how to get to something that has an obstacle in the way. Figuring out ways to get things and accomplish goals is a problem-solving skill that is sometimes termed "mean-ends." This term refers to how a child uses an action or "means" to achieve a goal, or the "ends."

For example, if a child wants a cookie which is out of reach on the table, he may lean forward to try to reach it, or pull the napkin it is lying on to bring it closer. If the child is older and more experienced in solving these kinds of problems, he may use his spoon to reach the cookie and slide it closer. How to move many things from one place to another in the easiest manner is another example of a problem a child may face and try to figure out. For example, if a child is trying to figure out how to carry several blocks at one time from his room to his play area, he may solve this problem by putting some blocks in his pockets, a box or by pulling out his shirt to act as a carrier. Overcoming obstacles is another example of problem solving in which children need to figure out a way to get what they want. When a child moves a box out of the way to get a toy, or turns a door knob to open the door, he is showing us that he is learning to figure out how to overcome obstacles.

Parent Questions (General Examples - see Skills for specific questions)

To help identify the child's unique strengths and needs related to this developmental area:

• Have you noticed how your child tries to get something that is out of reach?

• Have you ever tied a short ribbon to your child's highchair or stroller with a toy attached so you don't always have to pick up the toy every time your child drops it? *If so,* have you noticed if your child gets the toy by himself by pulling the ribbon?

• Has your child figured out how to open any doors at home?

• Have you noticed if your child can get things when they are placed up high on something,

e.g., on his dresser or the kitchen counter? How does he do this?

To help identify family resources, priorities and concerns related to the child's development in this area:

• What toys or objects do you think we should use that will be motivating for your child to try to get?

• Can you think of some things you wish your child could figure out how to get on his own instead of always fussing for you to get it?

• Would you like your child to learn how to open doors? *[Some families prefer not to work on this skill because of the danger this may pose]*

Sample *Functional* Outcome Statements which may be generated by the Family

[Will be dependent upon identified individual child and family needs and should incorporate objectives and activities from other domains]
My child will be able to figure out how to:
• Get his toys if they roll under the coffee table;

• Get his cracker when he drops it at the far end of his tray;
• Get his ball when it rolls behind furniture;
• Carry his pile of blocks from the floor to his room.

Transactional Assessment

May assess through observation and interview.

Assessment of the Child's Environment

1. Supportive:
[Example environments which support/facilitate development in this area]
The child's caregiving environments usually:
• Have a variety of safe objects and toys;
• Have safe spaces for the child to move about;
• Are child-proofed to accommodate the child's

emerging problem solving skills; e.g., cords to appliances and lights are kept out of reach; dangerous and fragile items are kept completely out of reach or in locked places as the child learns to climb on supports to reach high places and learns to open cabinets, doors.

Assessment of Caregiver Interactions with the Child

1. Supportive:
[Example interactions which support/facilitate child's development in this area]
The child's caregivers sometimes:
• Give the child time to try to figure out how to get things before automatically giving them to him;
• Encourage the child to figure out problems with praise and modeling, and by setting up interesting opportunities.

2. Compromising:
[Example interactions which may restrict, compromise, inhibit or be unsupportive of the child's development in this area]
• The child's caregivers frequently:
• Get the things their child wants before giving him time to try for himself;
• Frustrate or tease their child by putting the object further out of reach, just as he figures how to get it.

Identifying and Interpreting Needs for Intervention

If a child is significantly delayed in this area he <u>may be having difficulty in the cognitive processes related to "means-end," i.e., combining actions and using foresight to solve problems.</u>

<u>However,</u> before targeting cognition as the primary area of need for intervention, consider, rule out, or adapt for other causes that may interfere with a true assessment of the child's "means-ends" abilities. These may include:
• <u>Motor impairments</u> that may restrict the child's movements to reach, grasp or move to get objects;

• <u>Visual impairments</u>: the child may not be aware of objects that are out of reach because he cannot see them; he also does not have the visual experiences of watching to see how others solve problems;
• <u>Difficulties with spatial awareness or spatial relationships;</u> e.g., if the child does not pull a toy vertically with a string, he may be having difficulty understanding the effect of gravity; or difficulty with <u>object permanence</u> if the toy is out of sight.

Assessment Adaptations   (Examples)

[Note any adaptations needed to credit and help plan interventions]

- Motor impairment: *[consult with a therapist for specific positions and adaptations which meet the individualized child's needs]*
    - Examples of adaptations may include:
        - #1.25 *Reaches for second object purposefully*: If the child has difficulty reaching, keep the second toy very close to the child. Credit if he gestures with his empty hand or looks to his empty hand. Or show him the second toy and ask, "Which hand should I put it in," again watching for any gestures he may use.
        - #1.26 *Works for desired, out-of-reach object*: Place the desired toy near the child, according to the child's movement abilities. Credit any movements the child makes that indicate he is attempting to obtain it.
        - #1.47 *Retrieves object using other material*- Try using an inverted shoe box top for the support instead of a cloth which may be easier to pull, rather than having to grasp it.
        - #1.46 *Overcomes obstacle to obtain object*- The child with severe motor limitations faces "obstacles" anytime he wants objects. This item may be adapted to be more functional, e.g., communicates desire for an object. Assessment and interventions would be directed at identifying appropriate communication methods.
        - #1.53 *Uses locomotion to regain object*; resumes play. Position the object in a place that is accessible according to child's motor level; e.g., if the child can roll one or two turns, place the toy only a foot away. If the child has no method for mobility, place the second object out of reach on a support for him to pull. If the child is severely motor impaired, this item may be inappropriate to assess or teach during the early years (later this may be taught with the child's form of mobility, such as a walker or wheelchair). Instead, adapt by accepting child's communicative efforts to obtain object.
        - #1.74 *Pulls string horizontally to obtain toy* and #1.79 *Pulls string vertically to obtain toy*: tie a large plastic ring on the end of the string for the child to hold or slip his hand through; use shorter strings so the child does not have to move his arm as much.
        - #1.95 *Solves simple problems using tools*: ask parents if there are any devises they have developed or found that help the child obtain out-of-reach objects. Experiment with various tools to see which ones the child can effectively use. If the child is severely restricted in his movements, a communication board can be considered his "tool" for obtaining what he wants.
    - Items that cannot be adapted and are not considered functional for the child to learn, should be marked N/A and not considered when identifying child's approximate cognitive level.
- Visually impaired:
    - Expect delays of skills in this strand since the child does not have the visual cues needed for solving these problems. Delays, however, do not necessarily reflect cognitive problems since age ranges assigned are based on sighted peers.
    - Auditory cues may be used as a motivator, but remember that ear-hand coordination usually does not occur until late in the first year, and sound may not hold the same attracting qualities that vision does at this age. Use sound toys that make a continuous sound: e.g., music box, beeper ball.
    - For items #1.47, #1.74, and #1.79: let the child explore the toy, orienting him to the supports or strings attached, before moving it out of reach. If the child has not specifically been taught these skills, he should not be expected to display them on initial assessment. Provide hand-over-hand modeling and verbal description to teach him how the supports and strings relate to the object and how to bring the object closer.
    - Items #4.64 and #4.66 will also be inappropriate to assess unless the child has specifically been taught this concept through hand-over-hand modeling and verbal description.

General Assessment Procedures & Processes   (apply to all items in this Strand)

1. **Always make sure that child is strongly interested in an object before trying to elicit his problem-solving response.** This can usually be established by watching to see if he will reach for the toy before placing it out of reach.

2. **Be sure to let or help the child play with toys after he's worked so hard to get them.**

3. Many items can be observed naturally within the context of play while assessing Strand 1-1 or during other daily activities. **Observe how the child approaches and tries to solve problems during any part the assessment.** Instead of automatically helping the child obtain an object, discuss with parent how you will be observing how he tries to figure out how to do and get things.

4. **Describe the skill and eliciting procedures to family members and invite them to help observe and/or assess.**

+ - A Credit Notes:

  +   child usually displays skill or behavior as defined during play and daily activities.

  -   not observed or reported.

  +/- appears to be an emerging skill.

  N/A not applicable due to child's disability.

  O   circle any credit if environment or inter-actions compromise or restrict child's optimal skills in this area.

Note any adaptations used to credit.

Assessment Materials

- Plastic toy links (e.g., Link-a-doos™), cord, or ribbon attached to a lightweight toy such as a punch ball or stuffed animal. *Caution: never leave child unsupervised with long strings or ribbon as they can become entangled and choke. Advise caregivers of this precaution.*

- Small easy-to-grasp toys, such as nesting cups, blocks, rattles, very soft squeak toy.

- Supports to pull toys on, such as a cloth place mat, diaper, or small pillow.

- "Tools" to obtain objects (large soup spoon, child's small plastic rake, T-stick, foot stool, basket.)

- Cheerios™ and clear narrow neck container

1.25 Reaches for second object purposefully   5-6.5

Definition: The child reaches for a second toy when he is already holding one. He realizes that although he is already holding something, it is still possible to obtain another object. He may reach for the second toy with either hand and does *not* have to actually attain the second one.

Example Observation Opportunities: Incidental - may observe anytime child attempts to reach for a small toy when he is already holding something in one hand. Structured - when the child is holding a small toy, attract his attention to another nearby toy. You can hold out the second toy or place it in front of him, tapping the toy on the surface to attract his attention as needed. Use safe objects or toys that can be held in one hand, e.g., cubes, teethers, rattle. The child should be well-supported in sitting or lying on his back.

Credit: (see also Credit Notes in this strand's preface)

  +   makes purposeful attempts to reach for the second toy and holds on to the first one.

  -   attempted to obtain toy, only if toy was offered directly to child's empty hand.

1.26 Works for desired, out-of-reach object   5-9

Definition: The child "works" for a toy out of reach by reaching repeatedly or by reaching and then stretching or wiggling forward. His reaching efforts reflect clear intention, purpose, and persistence to obtain a desired object.

Example Observation Opportunities: Incidental - may observe anytime the child tries to get something out of reach, e.g., his pacifier or bottle when it drops out of reach; a cracker at snack time; his toy that rolled away; a bubble during bubble play that floats and lands nearby; a bath toy that floats out of reach. Structured - attract the child's attention to an interesting toy, such as a roly-poly. Invite him to play with the toy. The object should be placed about 6 inches from the child's fingertips of his outstretched arm. Observation can occur when child is in prone, side-lying or supported sitting at a table or tray. Be sure to let the child play with the toy after he has worked to get it, even if unsuccessful.

Credit:

  +   makes purposeful movements according to his level of motor development to obtain a toy just out of reach; he may reach repeatedly, pivot, roll, stretch, wiggle or crawl. He does not have to obtain the object but must persist in his reaching efforts for several seconds.

1.40   Retains two of three objects offered   6.5-7.5

Definition: If a third object is offered when the child is already holding two objects, one in each hand, he suddenly, without much thought, drops one them while reaching to obtain the new object. At this stage, he is not purposefully trying to figure out a method to hold all three.

Example Observation Opportunities: Offer the child three small easy-to-grasp objects, one at a time. Or offer him an object when you notice he is already holding two. The third object should be more inviting than the two he is holding. The child should be positioned so he can feel secure to freely reach, in supported sitting, on parents lap, or lying on his back.

Credit: (see also Credit Notes in this strand's preface)
  +   when holding two objects, drops one of them to obtain the third.

1.45   Retains two and reaches for third object   8-10

Definition: The child tries to figure out a method to hold a third object when he is already holding two objects, one in each hand. This is in contrast to #1.40, since the child demonstrates intentional thought rather than immediately dropping a toy to obtain another. His purposeful attempts may include reaching with his mouth, purposely laying one block down *before* reaching for a third, banging the third object with one he's holding, or adapting his grasp to try to hold a third. At a higher level of thought, he may try transferring one object to another hand or storing it somewhere (e.g., in his mouth or crux of his arm).

Example Observation Opportunities: Same as #1.40.

Credit: (see also Credit Notes in this strand's preface)
  +   demonstrates any of the defined purposeful attempts to obtain and hold all three objects, even if he is unsuccessful.

1.47   Retrieves object using other material   8-10

Definition: The child purposefully pulls a cloth or other support to bring a toy that is resting on it closer to him.

Example Observation Opportunities: <u>Incidental</u> - may observe spontaneously if the child, for example, pulls a napkin or cloth place mat to obtain a cookie; pulls a small blanket or cloth diaper to obtain his bottle or toy; pulls a shoe box closer to obtain a small toy which is at the opposite end. <u>Structured</u> - the child should be sitting at a table with adequate support so his hands are free to move. Lay a place mat, cloth, or small pillow on the table before him. Let him play with the support before showing him the toy if he is interested. Attract his attention to a toy or a cookie. As he starts to reach for it, lay it on the cloth, out of reach. Invite him to get the object but do not allow him to climb out of the chair. Observe the methods he uses to try to get the object; if he looks to an adult for help, give him verbal encouragement that he can try. If he gives up or begins to show signs of frustration, move the support several inches toward him so he can see how it works, and then return to its original position. Invite him to try again. Repeat with a different object.

Credit: (see also Credit Notes in this strand's preface)
  +   on at least two occasions intentionally pulls the support for the purpose of obtaining the object; may have one initial demonstration.
  -   pulls cloth to play with the cloth and ignored the object.

1.46   Overcomes obstacle to obtain object   8-11

Definition: The child figures out a way to obtain a toy which is accessible but behind an obstacle, such as a box. Depending upon his motor abilities, type of obstacle and the location of the object, he may reach over, move around, or push the obstacle aside.

Example Observation Opportunities: <u>Incidental</u> - may observe anytime child is faced with an obstacle that is in the way of a desired object, e.g., a small pillow in front of his toy or bottle; a toy behind a box or laundry basket; his spoon or cookie behind his cup, a toy behind a mound of sand; a ball that rolled behind his parent's leg. <u>Structured</u> - show the child an interesting toy. When he starts to reach for it, place it behind a small pillow, wide box, or basket. The object should remain visible but unreachable, and the obstacle should be lightweight and easy to move if the child does not have mobility skills. Repeat with a different, more motivating toy if the child does not attempt to get the first toy.

Credit: (see also Credit Notes in this strand's preface)
  +   figures out a way to obtain a desired object that is blocked from immediate reach due to an obstacle; he may move around the obstacle, push it out of the way, or reach over it.

Uses locomotion to regain object; resumes play   9-12

Definition: The child uses some form of locomotion to obtain an object he needs in order to play. For example, if he is playing with a hammer toy and the hammer is out of reach, he crawls to get the hammer and brings it back to play with the toy. The type of locomotion will depend upon the child's motor skills. He may roll, crawl, creep, climb or walk.

Example Observation Opportunities: Incidental - may observe spontaneously during play when the child moves to get, e.g., a block that rolled out of reach and puts it in his can; a toy hammer to bang on a xylophone; a brush to use with a doll. Structured - when the child is engaged in relational play with two objects, as suggested above, "accidentally" move one out of the child's reach. If the child has no method for mobility, place the second object out of reach on a support for him to pull.

Credit: (see also Credit Notes in this strand's preface)
   + on at least two occasions, moves from one place to another to get an object to play with.

Pulls string horizontally to obtain toy   *9-12*

Definition: The child pulls a string horizontally which is attached to an object out of reach to bring the object closer. The "string" can be any handle-like attachment that the child uses for the purpose of bringing the object closer. This skill assesses the child's understanding of the general principle that if two objects are connected in space, movement of one will influence movement of the other.

Example Observation Opportunities: Incidental - may observe anytime during play or daily activities when child pulls a string, strap or handle for the express purpose of obtaining the object on the end, e.g., pulling a shoestring to get the shoe; pulling the strap of a purse or diaper bag to obtain the purse or the bottle he sees in the diaper bag; pulling the string on a pull toy if he pulls it to play with the toy. Structured - when the child shows interest in a toy that is out of reach by reaching toward it, e.g., a stuffed animal or doll, tie a thick cord or ribbon around the toy while the child is watching. Place the toy out of reach with the cord a few inches from the child's hand. The object should be in clear view. If the child does not attempt to pull the string, demonstrate how pulling the string pulls the object closer a few inches. Return the toy to its original position, with the cord placed near his hand, and observe to see if he pulls the cord to get the toy. *Provide caregivers with precautions never to leave child unattended with strings.*

Credit: (see also Credit Notes in this strand's preface)
   + pulls string horizontally to obtain a desired object; observed on at least two occasions with two different objects and two different types of "string," e.g., cord, ribbon, shoestring. May credit if one demonstration was provided.
   - pulls string, but does not show interest in the object on the end.

Pulls string vertically to obtain toy   13-15

Definition: The child pulls a string upwards for the express purpose of obtaining an object attached at the end of the string. The object should be lightweight and desired by child.

Example Observation Opportunities: Incidental – may observe spontaneously if child pulls plastic toy chain links purposefully to obtain attached toy dangling from highchair. Structured – the child should be sitting well supported, in his highchair with a tray, or, on his parent's lap, facing you. Encourage him to watch you lower a lightweight toy toward the ground using an attached cord or a toy chain links. Place the cord or links within reach and ask the child to "get the toy". If the child does not pull the attachment, encourage him to lean over to see the toy, and/or demonstrate pulling the attachment to bring the toy upwards part way and invite him to try again.
   /!\ Safety Check: Remind caregivers never to leave their child alone with strings, nor to attach toys or pacifiers using strings, ribbons, or elastic to highchairs, playpens, cribs, or strollers because this is a serious strangulation hazard.

Credit: (see also Credit Notes in this strand's preface)
   + pulls string vertically to obtain a desired object; observed on at least two occasions with two different objects and two different types of "string," e.g., cord, ribbon,. May credit if one demonstration was provided.
   - pulls string, but does not show interest in the object on the end.

4.64 Inverts small container to obtain tiny object after demonstration   12.5-18

Definition: The child is learning to figure out that the best way to obtain a tiny object in a bottle is to turn the bottle over. At this stage, he may try to get the object out by poking his finger in the top of the bottle or by shaking the bottle. Then, after watching an adult turn the bottle over, he is able to do so.

Example Observation Opportunities: <u>Structured</u> -

Materials: The container should: (1) be clear or opaque so the child can see the object inside, (2) have a narrow neck which is too small for the child to put his hand in and the object cannot be easily shaken out, (3) be easy to grasp in one hand. Example containers: empty, small clear-plastic shampoo or other hairdressing bottle, medicine bottle, or clear plastic baby bottle. Tiny objects can be a piece of dry cereal or cookie bit, or a breath mint pellet.

Procedure: Encourage the child to put a tiny object, such as a Cheerio, into the container or bottle. If he has difficulty or would prefer eating the Cheerio, have him watch you put it in. Then give him the bottle and ask him to take it out. After some trial-and-error time, demonstrate turning the bottle over to retrieve the object. Put it back into the bottle and ask him to try again. If he tries to "drink" out of the container to retrieve the object, say something like, "Yuk, not in your mouth, turn the bottle over with your hand," while you demonstrate again.

Credit: (see also Credit Notes in this strand's preface)

+   purposefully turns bottle over to obtain object after adult demonstration.

4.66 Inverts small container spontaneously to obtain tiny object   13.5-19

Definition: Same as #4.64 "Inverts small container to obtain tiny object after demonstration," but child does not need a demonstration. He may still initially try to poke his finger in the top or shake the bottle, but then discovers that turning the bottle over is most effective method.

Example Observation Opportunities: Same as #4.64, but do not demonstrate or give verbal direction. If you have just administered #4.64 and the child needed a demonstration, assess this item at another session. It is important to use a container from which the object cannot be shaken out, or the child will learn this as the best method to obtain it.

Credit: (see also Credit Notes in this strand's preface)

+   on at least two occasions purposefully turns bottle over to obtain without demonstration or verbal instruction. He may initially poke his finger into the container and shake it.

(also in Strand 1-5 "Spatial Relationships".)

1.95 Solves simple problems using tools   17-24

Definition: The child purposely uses an unrelated object as a "tool" or a means to obtain a desired object or goal. For example, using a stick as the "tool" to get his ball that rolled under sofa, or using his toy wagon as his "means" to move a pile of blocks from one place to another. This skill demonstrates a child's ability to use foresight and invent new methods to obtain his goal.

Example Observation Opportunities: <u>Incidental</u> - may observe spontaneously anytime during play or daily activities, e.g., using a stool to obtain a toy or food placed out of reach on a counter; using a stick, toy rake, T-stick, spatula or large soup spoon to get a toy that has rolled under a chair; using a spoon to reach a cookie at the far end of a feeding tray; using a box, wagon or pulling his shirt out, to act as a carrier to move several blocks from one location to another. <u>Structured</u> - attract the child's attention to a desired out-of-reach object which has a "tool" nearby (using any of the situations provide above). If needed, point out the "tool," but wait to see if child spontaneously uses it to obtain the object. If not, demonstrate how to use it.

Credit: (see also Credit Notes in this strand's preface)

+   uses "tools" as a means to obtain goals as defined; may credit if child is not completely successful as long as he displays purposeful intent; without verbal instruction or demonstration.

+/- uses "tool" after demonstration.

6.55 Opens doors by turning knob 21-23

Definition: The child has figured out that he can get to the other side of a door by turning the door knob.

Example Observation Opportunities: May observe if child uses knobs to open doors when, e.g., leaving the assessment room; opening the door to a toy oven; opening the door to a toy storage cabinet.

Credit: (see also Credit Notes in this strand's preface)
+ tries to open doors by turning their knobs; he does not always have to be motorically successful but should display cognitive intent, i.e., he is turning the knob for the express purpose of opening the door rather than simply playing with the knob.

N/A Caregivers prefer that this item not be taught or assessed at this time.

(also in Strand 6-7 "Household Independence")

1-4 PROBLEM SOLVING

C. CAUSE AND EFFECT

1.11	2-3	Inspects own hands
1.14	3-4	Enjoys repeating newly learned activity
1.21	4-5	Continues a familiar activity by initiating movements involved
1.30	5.5-8	Shows interest in sounds of objects
1.24	5-9	Touches toy or adult's hand to restart an activity
1.50	9-12	Guides action on toy manually
1.67	12-15	Hands toy back to adult
1.98	18-22	Attempts and then succeeds in activating mechanical toy

Family Friendly Interpretation of Strand Concepts, Assessment, & Purpose

We will be observing how your child is learning to make things happen and how to make things work. For example, when he smiles at you and you smile back, he is learning he can make you smile by smiling! Or, when he hits his roly-poly toy and it jingles, he is learning that he can make the toy work by hitting it. This type of problem-solving is often termed "Cause and Effect."

Learning "cause and effect" seems to develop in a fairly predictable sequence, from simple to more complex:

1. At first, a child does not realize that the actions of objects or people are separate and act independently from him. He thinks he causes things to happen simply by moving his body. At this stage, he is learning the effect of his actions primarily through accident. For example, at this stage he may accidentally wave his arms and cause his roly-poly toy to make a sound. Then he keeps waving them to keep the sound going but does so without really understanding how the sound is produced.

2. Next, the child starts to learn that objects can indeed make actions and sounds independent of his own movements, and that he can make something happen rather than that things just happen by accident. At this stage, he deliberately does things to objects to cause an effect; e.g., he purposefully bangs a toy on the table to make a sound, or hits an action toy when it stops to try to make it move again.

3. Later, the child learns that if he can't directly make something happen or make something work, he can use other people as resources. For example, when he sees he cannot make a mechanical duck wobble the way he saw it wobble when an adult turned it on, he hands it back to the adult.

4. Finally, the child learns that there can be other ways or underlying causes that can make things work. For example, he begins to figure out that the key on the wind-up duck is the way to make it wobble. At this stage, if we give him the mechanical duck, he'll try to turn the key instead of immediately giving it to an adult.

Professional FYI

This strand focuses primarily on "cause and effect" as the child applies causality with objects and toys. The concept and importance of learning cause and effect, however, is broader and evident across developmental domains as the child learns that his actions and behaviors affect others. This may be especially apparent in Strands 1-1 "Development of Symbolic Play," 2-4 "Communicating with Others," and throughout the Social-Emotional domain (5.0).

Parent Questions   (Examples)

To help identify the child's unique strengths and needs related to this developmental area:

• What are some of the toys and other household objects that your child seems to like to play with best?

• Has he ever played with action toys that have things, such as switches, buttons, strings or levers?

• Can you tell me a little about how he plays with (naming various toys and objects parent as suggested)?

• Has your child ever played with any of the toys we have here today?

• *For older child:*

Has he figured out how to turn on your radio or TV? What about turning lights off and on?

To help identify family resources, priorities and concerns related to the child's development in this area:

• Does your child have any toys that you wish he could play with better?

• Are you interested in:
   – Learning about our toy lending library?
   – Obtaining resources for (adaptive) switch toys?

Sample *Functional* Outcome Statements which may be generated by the Family

[Will be dependent upon identified individual child and family needs and should incorporate objectives and activities from other domains]
• My child will figure out how to make his action toys work.

• We will know how to adapt toys so our child can play with them.

 ## Transactional Assessment

May assess through observation and interview.

Assessment of the Child's Environment

1. Supportive:
[Example environments which support/facilitate development in this area]
The child's caregiving environments:

• Have a few safe toys which are accessible and promote learning "cause and effect," e.g., busy boxes, mobiles, windup toys, roly-poly toys.

Assessment of Caregiver Interactions with the Child

1. Supportive:
[Example interactions which support/facilitate child's development in this area]
The child's caregivers encourage their child:
• To try to figure out how to make toys work by pointing out the activating mechanism of toys and letting him explore it through trial and error;
• To "take a turn" during interaction games, such as bouncing on knees and "Pat-a-cake";
• Request adult help when needed.

2. Compromising:
[Example interactions which may restrict, compromise, inhibit or be unsupportive of the child's development in this area]
The child's caregivers frequently:
• Ignore their child's bids for help when frustrated with a toy;
• Tease the child by removing the toy as he attempts to explore and activate it;
• Make negative statements to the child when he is have difficulty figuring out how to make things work.

 ## Identifying and Interpreting Needs for Intervention

If a child is significantly delayed in this area, he may be having difficulty in the cognitive processes related to learning causality.

However, before targeting cognitive skills as the primary need for intervention, consider, rule out, or adapt for other causes that may contribute to or interfere with a true assessment of the child's cause and effect abilities. These may include:
• Motor impairment which prevents the child from manipulating objects;
• Hearing impairment which prevents the child from hearing the effects of his actions;
• Visual impairment which prevents the child from seeing the visual effects of his actions;

• Social-emotional:
  – If the child has not developed a sense of himself as a separate person (Strand 5-2,) he will have difficulty learning that causal events happen separate from himself.
  – If the child has not had successful experiences in eliciting positive interactions from others, he may have difficulty learning that his actions can cause an effect on his world; e.g., if he cried, no one came to help him; when he smiled, no one smiled back.
• Attentional: the child may not be interested in the assessment toys or may have difficulty attending long enough to explore what he can do with the toy.

Assessment Adaptations   (Examples)

- Motor impaired: *consult with a therapist to ensure optimal positioning of the child and toys.* Use roly-poly toys and electronic switch toys that require minimal movement. If the child is severely restricted in his movements, through careful and patient observation, you may observe and credit deliberate eye pointing or searching for the causal mechanism. Allow extra time for the child to respond.

- Hearing impaired: use toys that create interesting visual effects. For skill #1.30 "Shows interest in sounds of objects," substitute with toys that create different visual spectacles, such as a transparent rattle or bottle filled with some glitter and oil.

- Visually impaired: use toys which the parent reports the child plays with frequently. Use toys that create interesting auditory effects: toy radios, roly-polys that make sound. Be sure to also provide much verbal description of the "effects" he is producing. If the child is blind, mark N/A for skill #1.11 "Inspects own hands." It is appropriate, however, to assess if the child "inspects" his hands tactually (but he may not do so for a few more months).

- Social-emotional: give the child a variety of toys. Allow him time to show preference since he may be very cautious. Warmly support him in his choices without being overstimulating.

General Assessment Procedures & Processes   (apply to all items in this Strand)

1. **It is important to use objects and activities which are interesting and motivating to the child.** Several examples are listed for each item; however, others may need to be used if the child does not show interest.

2. **It can be difficult to discern if the child is making a deliberate intentional response** or "procedure" to activate, restart or maintain the action of a toy or activity for items #1.14 "Enjoys repeating newly learned activity" and #1.21 "Continues a familiar activity by initiating movements." This can be especially true for a child with atypical muscle tone. Each child may use unique "procedures." Observe carefully for a consistent and differential response.

3. **Several items in this strand can be observed concurrently with one eliciting procedure.** For example, by simply observing how the child responds to a wind-up toy when it stops moving, you can observe the last four items in this strand.

4. **Describe the skill and eliciting procedures to family members and invite them to help observe and/or assess.**

＋ - A   Credit Notes:

+ child usually displays skill or behavior as defined during play.

- not observed or reported.

+/- appears to be an emerging skill; learned during the assessment after demonstration.

O circle any credit if environment or interactions compromise or restrict child's optimal skills, in this area.

Note any adaptations used to credit.

Assessment Materials

- Two or three sound producing toys: e.g., squeak toys, small disposable aluminum pie tin, rattles, toy plastic keys or discs on a chain.

- Roly-poly toy, such as the "Happy Apple" or a chime ball.

- Toys that create an interesting action: banging two blocks together; spinning a top or tipping a roly-poly; blowing a few bubbles.

- One or two toys that have a mechanism to activate it: e.g., battery-operated switch toys, a variety of wind-up toys that produce an action (toy radio, animal that walks); pop-up toys, handle of a Jack-in-the-Box, pulling the string of a "See and Say" toy.

Inspects own hands   2-3

Definition: The child sometimes brings one or both hands into view to watch and explore the movements he can make when he moves his hands and fingers. He is learning that he can cause an interesting spectacle when he moves his hands or fingers. The child may inspect his hands for up to a minute several times a day, but should easily "break out of it" to look at a new person or interesting object.

Parent Questions: Have you noticed your child watching his hands as he waves or wiggles them in front of his face? When do you see him do this? About how often?

Example Eliciting Situations: Hand-watching usually occurs at this age when a child is alone and content lying on his back in a quiet environment. May observe anytime during observation period if setting is conducive.

Credit: (see also Credit Notes in this strand's preface)

    +   if under 5 months and child sometimes watches the movements he can make with his hands, even briefly.

    A   if over 5 months and spends a significant amount of time hand-watching or prefers hand-watching to interacting with people.

(also in Strands 4-3 and 5-2)

 Enjoys repeating newly learned activity   3-4

Definition: The child repeats a body movement or gesture to keep an interesting event going. For example, if his foot accidentally kicks into a chime ball that jingles when it moves, he repeats his kicking action to make the jingle sound happen again.

Example Observation Opportunities: <u>Incidental</u> - may observe when the child kicks or waves his arms to activate his cradle gym. <u>Structured</u> - position a roly-poly toy, such as the "Happy Apple" or a chime ball, within "bumping distance" of the child's arm or foot. If he does not accidentally hit the toy after several seconds, gently guide his arm or leg to hit the toy, remaining quiet so the child can hear or watch the toy's movement. Pause to observe if he repeats the same or similar body movement several times to recreate the toy's action.

Credit: (see also Credit Notes in this strand's preface)

    +   systematically waves arms, kicks legs or makes some other repetitive body movement or gesture several times to prolong the visual or auditory spectacle of a toy; this should be observed on several occasions.

    -    child was already kicking or making the body movement before the toy was available.

1.21 **Continues a familiar activity by initiating movements involved   4-5**

Definition: The child makes a specific body movement, gesture or vocalization to "restart" an activity that has stopped. For example, if the parent is rocking or bouncing the child on her lap and then suddenly stops, the child rocks or bounces his body in an attempt to get his parent to start bouncing again.

Example Observation Opportunities: Identify with the parent what interactive "games" the child is familiar with, e.g., "Peek-a-boo," blowing on tummy, tickling tummy, "So Big," bouncing on knees, raising him in the air. Start one of these games and if the child enjoys it, after a couple repetitions, stop the game. Observe to see if the child makes a specific body movement, gesture or vocalization to restart the game. If so, restart the game immediately. Again, after a few repetitions, stop to see if he will repeat the <u>same</u> body movement or vocalization. Continue this one or two more times.

Credit: (see also Credit Notes in this strand's preface)

    +   makes the same specific body movement, gesture, or vocalization during three consecutive pauses to restart a game.

    -    child was already making the body movement, gesture, or vocalization before the game stopped.

(also in Strand 2-4A "Communicating with Others Gesturally")

Shows interest in sounds of objects   5.5-8

Definition: The child is learning that he can cause objects to make sounds by performing different actions with them, e.g., shaking, waving, banging, hitting or squeezing. Initially he produces the sound by accident. Then, when he realizes he caused the sound, he repeats the same action and may continue to try more. For example, if given a soft squeak toy to hold, he may incidentally hit the toy against his tray. When he hears the squeak, he hits the toy against the surface a few more times to deliberately reproduce the sound. Then he may try hitting it on his leg or squeezing it to see if he can reproduce the sound.

Example Observation Opportunities: Give the child two or three sound-producing toys, one at a time, to explore for a few minutes. Example toys: squeak toy, small disposable aluminum pie tin, rattles, toy plastic keys. Observe if the child purposely uses actions with the toy to produce sounds. If you are unsure if the child is truly using his actions deliberately to produce sounds, give him a toy that does not make sounds to see if he interacts in the same way, e.g., a stuffed animal.

Credit: (see also Credit Notes in this strand's preface)
+   investigates ways to make sounds with objects; uses these procedures or actions more with toys that make sounds than with toys that do not make sounds, e.g., bangs hard noisy toys more frequently than soft, quiet toys.

Touches toy or adult's hand to restart an activity   5-9

Definition: The child is beginning to understand that the actions of objects can occur independently of himself. When the action of a mechanical or wind-up toy stops, he touches either the toy or an adult's hand to try to make it start again.

Example Observation Opportunities: Start the action of a wind-up or mechanical toy in clear view of the child and leave your hand nearby. When the action stops, observe the child's responses to see how he tries to make the toy or activity restart. Repeat the action two or three times, pausing each time for the child to make a response. If the child does not show interest, try at least two more objects. Examples of toys to create an interesting action: pulling the string of a "See and Say" toy; spinning a top or roly-poly; turning a wind-up musical toy one or two turns.

Credit: (see also Credit Notes in this strand's preface)
+   deliberately touches toy or adult's hand to restart action of a toy, but makes no effort to activate the toy himself.

Guides action on toy manually   9-12

Definition: The child tries to restart an action or mechanical toy by manually putting the toy through the motions. For example, after watching a wind-up duck move forward and then stop, he pushes the duck manually rather than trying to wind it back up; after watching a toy pop-up from a busy box, pushes the button to make it pop up again. At this stage, children know that objects can produce actions independently of themselves. They understand non-mechanical causal actions, such as pressing the key on a keyboard to produce sounds. They have not yet, however, learned that other, more indirect mechanisms, can cause the action, e.g., that winding a key, pushing a button or using a switch for a mechanical toy is directly related to restarting the toy.

Example Observation Opportunities: When the child is watching, activate an interesting action toy (which can also be moved manually) that has a switch, button, key, or other mechanism to make the toy move. Observe the child's attempts to restart the toy. Examples may include: battery-operated switch toys; pop-up surprise box; variety of wind-up toys. When the toy stops, invite the child to play with it.

Credit: (see also Credit Notes in this strand's preface)
+   tries to recreate the toy's action by manually putting the toy through its motions rather than using the attached switch, key, or button.

1.67 **Hands toy back to adult   12-15**

Definition: The child hands an action toy back to the adult to restart it if he cannot restart it himself. The child is learning that he can rely upon adults as helpful resources and that other people can cause things to occur or produce results that he cannot.

Example Observation Opportunities: Same as #1.50. If the mechanism is easier to activate, such a button, he may activate the toy himself incidentally or purposefully. Try a more difficult toy to ensure the child is learning that adults can act as "agents" when his efforts fail.

Credit: (see also Credit Notes in this strand's preface)
+ hands or pushes toy back to an adult as gesture to request help (not simply because he no longer is interested in the toy); he may initially try to put the toy manually through its actions or explore the mechanism that starts the action, but when he realizes he cannot produce the same effect, he seeks adult help.

1.98 **Attempts and succeeds in activating mechanical toy   18-22**

Definition: The child understands that there is a "causal mechanism," such a switch, button, or wind-up key that activates a mechanical toy. He thus uses the mechanism to restart the toy, first through an adult demonstration and later by direct problem-solving.

Example Observation Opportunities: Activate a toy without the child seeing how you did so and then let him watch the toy's actions. When the toy stops, invite him to make it go again. If after plenty of exploration time, the child does not activate the mechanism, show him how to do it. Again after the toy stops, invite him to try. *Use objects according to fine motor abilities.* Examples include battery-operated switch toys, or a variety of wind-up toys that produce an action (toy radio, animal that walks); pop-up toys, handle of a "Jack-in-the-Box." Be careful not to use wind-up toys that reactivate accidentally by simply touching the toy, or the child will learn this as the effective method. Repeat with two different toys.

Credit: (see also Credit Notes in this strand's preface)
+ at 18-20 months, if the child attempts to activate two different toys using the mechanism, after an adult demonstrates how to do so.
+ at 20-22 months, if the child looks for and activates the mechanism (e.g., switch, key) on two different action toys without demonstration; if he does not have the manipulative abilities to successfully activate the switch, may still credit if child looks for and attempts to activate it.

1-5 SPATIAL RELATIONSHIPS

4.14	2.5-3.5	Looks from one object to another
4.29	4.5-5.5	Reaches and grasps object
1.31	5.5-7.5	Anticipates visually the trajectory of a slowly moving object
1.37	6-8	Follows trajectory of fast moving object
4.48	9-11	Takes objects out of container
1.50.1	*9-12*	*Rotates objects to find functional side*
1.51	9-12	Throws objects
1.58	10-11	Takes ring stack apart
4.60	12-13	Puts three or more objects into container
1.76	12-13	Looks at place where ball rolls out of sight
4.61	12-16	Builds tower using two cubes
1.79	13-15	Pulls string vertically to obtain toy
1.64	*13-15*	Stacks rings
1.75	12-18	Makes detours to retrieve objects
4.66	13.5-19	Inverts small container spontaneously to obtain tiny object
1.88	15-18	Brings objects from another room on request
1.105	18-24	Rights familiar picture
1.128	24-27	Finds detail in favorite picture book
1.147	30-36	Completes three- to four-piece puzzle

Family Friendly Interpretation of Strand Concepts, Assessment, & Purpose

We will be observing how your child is learning about how objects relate to each other in space. Child development specialists often termed this "spatial relationships." This applies to how your child understands the location, orientation, or direction of movement of objects in respect to himself or other objects.

For example, your child is learning about the spatial relationships of objects when he:

1. puts objects in and takes them out of containers; this is termed the concept of "container and contained" relationships;
2. puts one object on top of another; this is termed the concept of "equilibrium";
3. turns over bottles to make something fall out, drops objects to watch them fall, or pulls up something by a string to make it rise; this referred to as "understanding the effects of gravity";
4. turns his play mirror over so he can find his reflection; this shows he is learning that "objects have three dimensions," i.e., a front, back, top, and bottom;
5. reaches for objects which are nearby, but he does not bother to reach if they are too far away; this shows he is learning about "depth perception."

Professional FYI

Most of the skills in this strand integrate skills from other cognitive strands i.e., play schemes, in Strand 1-1, and problem-solving skills in Strand 1-4. In addition, most items are dependent upon fine motor skills, especially visual tracking, reach, grasp, and release skills. Thus, several strands can be assessed concurrently.

The challenge for the clinician, however, will be to "tease-out" where the child's strengths and needs lie if there are gaps between or within strands. For example, if a child does not anticipate the trajectory of a slowly moving object in skill #1.31, is it because he does not have the beginning understanding of object permanence, or is it because he has not developed the underlying spatial concept of reconstructing the trajectory by watching the direction the ball has traveled? Or if a child cannot place rings on a ring stack, is it because he does not understand the spatial relationship concepts of how objects fit together? Or is it because the child does not have the required the visual-motor skills or manipulative skills to do so, or is it because the child is delayed in play skills and is not at the level of combining objects in play?

Auditory awareness and localization, Strand 1-3, is also closely related to this strand. Auditory localization facilitates awareness of where objects and events are located in his environment.

A "new" item, which is not in the original HELP, has been added to this strand, i.e., "Rotates objects to find functional side." This was added because the original HELP did not include any skills which were specifically targeted to assess the important spatial concept of three dimensionality.

Parent Questions   (Examples)

To help identify the child's unique strengths and needs related to this developmental area:
- Can you tell me how your child plays with things, such as blocks and boxes?
- Sometimes children get into a "throwing stage." Has your child started to throw or drop things, such as toys, out of his crib or playpen?

- Can you think of a time when you asked your child to get something from another room and he was able to get it?
- Has your child ever played with a ring-stack toy similar to the one we have here today? Tell me how he usually plays with it.

Sample *Functional* Outcome Statements which may be generated by the Family

[Will be dependent upon identified individual child and family needs and should incorporate objectives and activities from other domains]
My child will be able to:
- Play with his ring-stack toy;

- Bring things from other rooms when I ask him to get them;
- Stack things on top of each other;
- Fill and dump containers during sand and water play.

Transactional Assessment

May assess through observation and interview.

Assessment of the Child's Environment

1. Supportive:
[Example environments which support/facilitate development in this area]
The child's caregiving environments usually have a few toys and objects which:
- Are safe, accessible and developmentally

appropriate;
- Promote learning about spatial relationships, e.g., containers and objects to put in them; things to stack; toys to rotate; toys which have pieces to put together.

Identifying and Interpreting Needs for Intervention

If a child is significantly delayed in this area, he may be having <u>difficulty in understanding one or more concepts related to spatial relationships</u>, i.e., container and contained; equilibrium; gravity; part-whole; and/or three dimensionality.

However, before targeting spatial relationships as the primary area of need for intervention, consider, rule out, or adapt for other causes which may interfere with the child's understanding of spatial relationships. These may include:
- <u>Visual impairment</u>: understanding the relationships of objects in space is highly dependent upon seeing them and watching how others interact with and use objects;

- <u>Motor impairment</u>: most of the items in this strand require motor movements which the child may be unable to make, i.e., grasping, releasing, manipulating, and moving from one place to another;
- <u>Other cognitive delays</u>: delays in play schemes and problem solving have a direct effect on the completion of many tasks in this strand, refer to Professional FYI notes for this strand;
- <u>Sensory organization problems</u>: this strand will be strongly influenced by sensory organization problems. If the child does not display significant delays in other cognitive strands, but does so in this strand, it may be appropriate to refer to a therapist trained in the principles of sensory organization.

Assessment Adaptations   (Examples)

[Note any adaptations needed to credit and help plan interventions]

- Visual impairment:
  - Children who are blind may typically have more difficulty with spatial skills, and develop these skills later than children who have vision because the concept of spatiality relies heavily upon visual cue. Age for expected emergence should thus be adjusted by several months.
  - If specific spatial concepts have not been taught through physical guidance and verbal descriptions, it will be inappropriate to judge the child's capacities to understand spatial relationships during an initial assessment.
  - The following items should be marked N/A for children who are blind (#4.14, #1.31, and #1.37 may be adapted by substituting sound toys, but localization of sound may develop much later):

    #4.14 "Looks from on object to another"

    #1.31 "Anticipates visually the trajectory of slow moving object"

    #1.37 "Follows trajectory of fast moving object"

    #1.76 "Looks at place ball rolls out of sight"

    #1.75 "Makes detours to retrieve objects"

    #1.128 "Finds detail in favorite picture book"

    #1.147 "Completes three- to four-piece puzzle"

  - The following items may be adapted – keeping in mind the factors noted above:
    1. Item #4.29 "Reaches and grasp object:" Use bright or reflective familiar toys that make a continuous sound while the child is reaching for it, e.g., a rattle, music box. Let the child hold and play with each toy <u>before</u> encouraging him to reach.
    2. Item #4.61 "Builds tower using two cubes:" Provide plenty of time for the child to explore and manipulate the blocks so he can become familiar with their size and weights. Use larger blocks rather than inch cubes, or items, such as small boxes or books. Stack two or three blocks and help him tactually explore the model.
    3. Item #4.66 "Inverts small container spontaneously to obtain tiny object:" tiny objects should make a sound in the container when the

child shakes it. It will also be inappropriate to assess unless the child has specifically been taught this concept through hand-over-hand modeling and verbal description.
    4. #1.79 "Pulls string vertically to obtain toy:" Let the child explore the toy, orienting him to the string attached before moving it out of reach. If the child has not specifically been taught this skill, he should not be expected to display it on initial assessment. Provide hand-over-hand modeling and verbal description to teach him how the string relates to the object and how to bring the object closer.
    5. #1.105 "Rights familiar picture:" substitute using familiar objects which have a highly differentiated top and bottom, e.g., bottle, cup, doll, car.

- Motor impairment:

  Consult with a physical and/or occupational therapist for optimal positioning of the child and materials, as well as adapted equipment. Examples of adaptations may include:
  - If the child has delayed or atypical grasp, use materials that accommodate the child's current grasping abilities, e.g., use larger blocks, tie a large plastic ring on the end of the string for the child to hold or slip his hand through; use shorter strings so the child does not have to move his arm as much.
  - If the child is delayed or has difficulty with bilateral or midline skills, assist by helping to stabilize objects; e.g., help him hold the container steady when dropping objects into or taking them out of containers; hold and tilt the base of the ring-stack toy when placing or removing rings.
  - For item #4.29 "Reaches and grasps object": credit if the child displays reaching efforts even if he does not accurately obtain them; side-lying may facilitate reaching efforts.

- Other cognitive delays: be sure the child has attained the underlying concepts in object permanence, means-ends and play schemes before expecting the child to accomplish spatial relationship skills which are dependent upon these concepts at equivalent levels.

General Assessment Procedures & Processes   (apply to all items in this Strand)

1. The items in this strand **may not be in exact sequential order**. As noted, various spatial concepts are assessed through these strands that may not necessarily build upon each other. Thus, we cannot always assume in this strand, as we can in many other strands, that a child has accomplished items preceding those observed, nor can we assume that if he cannot achieve one item, then he cannot achieve others, which are at higher age ranges. *It is thus recommended that several items be assessed below and beyond the level which the child seems to best "fit."*

2. **Describe the skill and eliciting procedures to family members and invite them to help observe and/or assess.**

+ - A **Credit Notes:**

+   child usually displays skill or behavior as defined during play and daily activities.

-    not observed or reported.

+/- appears to be an emerging skill.

O   circle any credit if environment or interactions compromise or restrict child's optimal skills, in this area.

Note any adaptations used to credit.

Assessment Materials

- Two or three colorful squeak toys, dangling plastic keys, small, brightly colored ball to look at.
- Interesting toy on a string that can be lowered to the floor.
- Toys that encourage a child to find the functional side, e.g., baby-proof small mirror, cups, bottles, blocks which have a stimulus on one side.
- Container, at least 3 inches in diameter, e.g., plastic butter or Cool Whip tub, shoe box, or plastic cup or bowl.
- Small objects to put into containers, e.g., blocks, large wooden stringing beads, thick pegs.
- Things to stack: use blocks sized according to his

fine motor abilities; sponges or flat blocks may be easier.
- Transparent container with a small opening, e.g., empty trial-sized shampoo bottle, medicine bottle, or plastic baby bottle.
- One or two tiny, *safe* objects to put in the bottle, e.g., a piece of dry cereal or cookie bit, or a thick peg.
- Ring-stack toy that has only three or four rings on the stick. The stick should be uniform with a flat base rather than a graduated stick with a rocking base.
- Two to three familiar picture cards or photographs.

4.14   Looks from one object to another   2.5-3.5

Definition: When two interesting objects positioned next to each other are presented, the child looks at each object alternately, switching his glance rapidly between the two. (Note #4.03, Strand 4-1, "Regards colorful object for few seconds," is a prerequisite)

Example Observation Opportunities: <u>Incidental</u> - may observe when child is watching his mobile. <u>Structured</u> - when the child is content and alert, present two equally interesting objects to the child about a foot away from his chest, positioned 6 to 8 inches apart. Example objects: various colorful squeak toys, dangling plastic keys, small brightly colored ball. Keep your face toward his side to prevent distraction but close enough to observe the child's eye movements. Do not let the toys make any sound. Let him observe for about a half minute. Repeat with a different set of toys.

Credit: (see also Credit Notes in this strand's preface)
+   switches his glance several times to look directly at each of two objects.

4.29   Reaches and grasps object   4.5-5.5

Definition: The child reaches for and grasps a small object held within his easy reach. He may initially under-reach before adjusting to accurately reach and grasp. The child is developing an awareness of depth perception and awareness of objects in space.

Example Observation Opportunities: The child's reaching attempts can be observed throughout the observation period as objects are positioned within reach. Observe if the child reaches for objects which are nearby more frequently than those which are clearly out of reach. This helps assess his understanding of the position of objects in space and depth perception. If an adult is immediately available, however, his reaching efforts toward out-of-reach objects may be more of a gesture to signal he wants the toy. Try to observe this when adults are not in his immediate sight.

Credit: (see also Credit Notes in this strand's preface)
+   reaches for nearby objects more frequently than distant objects when an adult is not immediately present; he may initially under-reach but then adjusts to obtain the object.
(also in Strand 4-3 "Reach/Approach")

1.31   Anticipates visually the trajectory of a slowly moving object   5.5-7.5

Definition: When the child is watching an object moving slowly in a path and then it briefly disappears behind a barrier, he looks to the other side of the barrier waiting for the object to reappear. He is learning to anticipate the movement of objects in space. (Note- Prerequisite skills: #4.17 "Follows with eyes 180 degrees" and, #1.09 "Reacts to the disappearance of a slowly moving object.")

Example Observation Opportunities: Incidental - may observe when child is watching a ball or pet moving across the room, if at some point the ball or pet briefly moves behind a barrier, such as a large box or chair. Structured - attract the child's attention to a quiet pull toy on a string. Invite him to "watch the toy move." Pull it slowly horizontally in front of him. After he has tracked the toy for about a foot, let it move behind a barrier, such as a book or clipboard held upright. Continue to pull the toy at the same pace until it continues moving out the other side of the board. When the toy is briefly hidden behind the barrier, observe the child's eye's carefully to see if he watches the toy disappear and switches his glance to the side where the toy should reappear. Repeat the procedure several times.

Credit: (see also Credit Notes in this strand's preface)
+ tracks a slowly moving object to the point of disappearance and then switches his glance to the other side of the barrier at the point of expected reappearance. May credit if he needed a few initial trials to learn the "game."

1.37   Follows trajectory of fast moving object   6-8

Definition: When an object falls to the floor, the child looks to the floor to find it. He is learning to anticipate the movement an object will take in space even if he cannot see the object travel (if it is hidden behind a barrier as it falls).

Example Observation Opportunities: Incidental - may observe if the child drops something from his highchair or crib and looks directly to the floor to find it. The object should be soft so it does not make a sound (as a cue) when it hits the floor, e.g., dropping a cracker, empty bottle, or a small stuffed animal on a carpeted floor. Structured - show the child an attractive, lightweight object while he is sitting on a chair in his parent's lap facing you. The object could be a crumpled piece of paper, a brightly colored sponge, or small stuffed animal. Present it a few inches above his line of vision as you name the object and invite him to watch it. While he is looking at it, drop the object so it lands on the floor out of direct sight, keeping your hand in the same position. Observe to see if he looks to the floor.

Credit: (see also Credit Notes in this strand's preface)
+ directly leans to look for an object that drops quietly to the floor; he does not have to actually find it if it rolled out of his visual range.
+/- looks for object that makes a sound when it drops to the floor.

4.48   Takes objects out of container   9-11

Definition: The child takes a few objects out of a container by turning the container over to dump them, or by reaching in and taking the objects out. This skill demonstrates his awareness of "container and contained" relationships between objects.

Example Observation Opportunities: Incidental - may observe during mealtime if child takes finger foods out of a bowl or cup or purposefully turns the container over; during play if he takes toys out of a box or blocks out of a container; during diapering if he pulls his diaper out of a box. Structured - when the child is sitting on the floor (if he has good sitting balance) or seated at a support, let him watch you put two or three interesting objects or toys into a container. Invite him to play with them. Use containers that are fairly shallow, such as a plastic butter or Cool Whip tub, shoe box, or plastic cup or bowl. The size of objects should accommodate child's grasping abilities e.g., blocks, large wooden stringing beads, thick pegs, squeak toys. After a few minutes of play, invite him to place the objects back in the container if this is not observed spontaneously.

Credit: (see also Credit Notes in this strand's preface)
+ removes objects from a container by purposefully dumping the container over or taking them out.
+/- puts hand into container and manipulates objects but does not remove any.

Rotates objects to find functional side   9-12

Definition: The child turns objects around to purposefully find the most functional side. This demonstrates the child's growing awareness of the three-dimensional aspects of objects.

Example Observation Opportunities: <u>Incidental</u> - may be observed when the child spontaneously turns an object around to find the functional side, e.g., during play when he turns his cup over to take a drink; when he takes his bottle and turns it around to drink; when he turns over a mirror toy to find his reflection. <u>Structured</u> - show the child an object that has a definite functional side. As he begins to reach for it, quickly turn it around so that the functional side is not immediately visible. Observe how he responds to this new view and if he deliberately turns the object to find the functional side. Example eliciting objects: baby bottle (present it horizontally, with the nipple facing you); a rubber duck or other animal that can stand up (present it on the table lying down); a child-sized mirror that has a mirror on only one side; a plastic cup (presented face down or on its side).

Credit: (see also Credit Notes in this strand's preface)
+ turns at least two toys around purposefully to find functional side.

Throws objects   9-12

Definition: The child repeatedly drops or throws objects intentionally to the floor. He is learning to appreciate the visual and auditory effects that occur through gravity when objects drop.

Example Observation Opportunities and Materials: May be observed incidentally when child is exploring any small toy or object during play and daily activities. This can often be reported or observed when child throws his toys, pacifier, bottle, etc. out of his playpen, crib or highchair. If you are unsure whether he drops or throws because he dislikes the object, offer it back to him; he should eagerly take it back.

Credit: (see also Credit Notes in this strand's preface)
+ sometimes purposefully drops or throws things repeatedly, watching them as they land on the floor; pays more attention to the effect his action has on the toy than to the effect he has on his caregivers.

Takes ring stack apart   10-11

Definition: The child can remove large rings from the stick of a ring-stack toy. He is learning about "parts of a whole" and their spatial relationships.

Example Observation Opportunities: Show the child a ring-stack toy that has only three or four rings on the stick. If the child has fine motor delays or difficulty with manipulating and grasping, use larger rings or rings that have larger holes (e.g., canning jar rings, plastic shower curtain rings). If he does not remove one spontaneously, take one off and invite him to take a turn. Help stabilize or tilt the base, if needed, due to motor delays.

Credit: (see also Credit Notes in this strand's preface)
+ deliberately removes at least one ring from the ring stack; the ring may be removed by pulling it off upright, or turning the base on its side to slide the ring off the stick.

Puts three or more objects into container   12-13

Definition: The child puts small objects into a container and then removes them. He is experimenting with "container and contained" relationships.

Example Observation Opportunities: Observe while the child is playing with a container and several small objects. Use containers, such as a pot, large plastic butter or Cool Whip tub, small box, or plastic cup or bowl. The size of objects should accommodate child's grasping abilities, e.g., blocks, large wooden stringing beads, thick pegs, squeak toys.

Credit: (see also Credit Notes in this strand's preface)
+ enjoys putting objects in and out of containers.

(also in Strand 4-4 "Development of Voluntary Release" but with different credit criteria.)

1.76   Looks at place where ball rolls out of sight   12-13

Definition: The child goes directly to the place he has seen an object roll and disappear, e.g., if a ball rolls under a skirted sofa, he goes to the place it disappeared to look for it. He is able to anticipate where the object must be from watching the directional movement the object traveled in space. (Note: Skill #1.32A "Finds hidden object using one screen" strand 1-4A, is a prerequisite skill.)

Example Observation Opportunities: <u>Incidental</u> - may observe if child's pet, bottle or ball moves under a sofa or bed. <u>Structured</u> - play a game of rolling a ball back and forth, helping the child as needed to push the ball back. When the child is watching, "accidentally" push the ball so that it goes under, behind, or through a barrier, hidden out of direct sight, e.g., a couch, play tunnel, large box turned on its side. Invite the child to help find it.

Credit: (see also Credit Notes in this strand's preface)
  + goes directly to the place an object that rolled out of sight was last seen; if the child does not have mobility skills may credit sustained eye pointing or gesturing if this is observed a few times.

4.61   Builds tower using two cubes   12-16

Definition: The child places an object on top of another to stack them. He is learning how objects relate to each other in equilibrium.

Example Observation Opportunities: Observe while the child is playing with blocks or other objects that promote stacking, e.g., stacking cups, boxes. Use objects that accommodate the child's grasp and release skills. If the child does not try, build a tower, knock it down and invite the child to make a tower so he can play this "knock-down" game. Distract to a new activity if the child starts to throw blocks.

Credit: (see also Credit Notes in this strand's preface)
  + places one object on top of another, releasing his hand from the second object.
(also in Strand 4-6B "Block Construction" but with different credit criteria)

1.79   Pulls string vertically to obtain toy   13-15

Definition: The child pulls a string upwards for the express purpose of obtaining an object attached at the end of the string. The object should be lightweight and desired by child. He is learning to appreciate the effects of gravity.

Example Observation Opportunities: <u>Incidental</u> - may observe spontaneously if child pulls string or ribbon (which is tied at one end to his highchair) to obtain toy that is dangling from the other end of the string. <u>Structured</u> - the child should be sitting well-supported in his highchair with a tray or on his parent's lap facing you. Encourage him to watch as you lower a small lightweight toy that is attached to a heavy cord to the floor. Lay the cord on his tray or across his lap and tell him to get the toy. Remind him that the toy is still there by encouraging him to lean over to look at it. The cord can be weighted to lay on the tray or his lap by tying a wooden bead or ring on the end. If he does not pull the cord up spontaneously, demonstrate pulling the cord to pull the object up halfway while the child is watching. Invite him to try. *Provide caregivers with precautions never to leave child unattended with strings.*

Credit: (see also Credit Notes in this strand's preface)
  + pulls string vertically to obtain desired object; on at least two occasions with two different objects and two different types of string, e.g., cord, ribbon. May credit if one demonstration was provided.
  - pulls string, but does not show interest in the object on the end.
(also in Strand 1-4B "Means-Ends")

1.64   *Stacks rings*   *13-15*

Definition: The child can replace a few rings on the stick of a ring-stack toy. He is continuing to learn about "parts of a whole" and their spatial relationships as he combines parts of a toy together.

Example Observation Opportunities: <u>Incidental</u> - may observe spontaneously during play with a ring-stack toy. <u>Structured</u> - show the child a ring-stack toy that has only three or four rings on the stick. The stick should be uniform with a flat base rather than a graduated stick with a rocking base. Pull the rings off the stick and then place one back on. Invite the child to try placing the remaining rings on the stack. Adapt as needed to accommodate for the child motor abilities, refer to skill, #1.58 "Takes ring stack apart."

Credit: (see also Credit Notes in this strand's preface)
  + places at least two rings on the stick of a ring-stack toy. The adult may hold the base of the ring stack to stabilize or tilt, if needed.

1.75 **Makes detours to retrieve objects   12-18**

Definition: The child takes the easiest route to get to an object. For example, if a ball rolls under and out from a chair, he walks around to the back of the chair rather than trying to follow the path of the ball.

Example Observation Opportunities: <u>Incidental</u> - may observe if child's pet runs under a chair or table to the other side, or if child's bottle, toy car, or ball rolls under a table or chair during play. <u>Structured</u> - during ball or toy car play, "accidentally" push the car or ball under a barrier, such as a chair or low table so that it rolls to the opposite side of the barrier. Invite the child to retrieve it.

Credit: (see also Credit Notes in this strand's preface)
+   takes the easiest route to get to an object rather than following the path it may have taken.

4.66 **Inverts small container spontaneously to obtain tiny object   13.5-19**

Definition: The child figures out how to get an object out of a narrow-necked bottle by turning it over. This skill combines the spatial relationship concepts of "container and contained" with understanding the effect of gravity on objects in space.

Example Observation Opportunities: <u>Structured</u> -
<u>Materials:</u> The container should: (1) be clear or opaque so the child can see the object inside; (2) have a narrow neck that is too small for the child to put his hand in and so that the object cannot be easily shaken out; (3) be easy to grasp in one hand. Example containers: empty, small clear-plastic shampoo or other hairdressing bottle, medicine bottle, or clear plastic baby bottle. Tiny objects can be a piece of dry cereal or cookie bit, or a breath mint pellet. *Supervise carefully.*
<u>Procedure:</u> Encourage the child to put a tiny object, such as a Cheerio, into the container or bottle. If he has difficulty or would prefer eating the Cheerio, have him watch you put it in. Then give him the bottle and ask him to take it out.

Credit: (see also Credit Notes in this strand's preface)
+   on at least two occasions, purposefully turns bottle over to obtain object without demonstration or verbal instruction. He may initially poke his finger into the container and shake it.
(also in Strand 1-4B "Means-Ends")

1.88 **Brings objects from another room on request   15-18**

Definition: The child indicates his understanding of the whereabouts of familiar objects that are not in the same room by going to or naming the expected location of the requested object. This indicates the child's ability to form a mental representation of an object in its usual space even when he cannot see it.

Parent Questions: Have you noticed if your child can typically remember where to find something around home if you ask him to get something? Can you give me some examples?

Example Observation Opportunities: May observe incidentally when the child purposefully goes to the typical place an object is kept to retrieve a requested or desired object not in sight; e.g., to his closet to get his shoes; to his bookshelf in his room to get a book; to his room to retrieve a diaper; to his room to get his bear to take to daycare. The requested object should be one that you are certain is in his receptive vocabulary, and one that is kept in a consistent location. This skill also requires the child to remember a direction for a few minutes until the object is retrieved and requires that the child not get distracted along the way. Repeat the request as needed.

Credit: (see also Credit Notes in this strand's preface)
+   indicates the location of at least two objects that are in a different room. He may have a reminder of the object he is retrieving along the way. Depending on the child's motor and language abilities, the child may move to get the object, name the place it can be found, and/or point directly to expected location as the adult carries him.

Rights familiar picture   18-24

Definition: The child spontaneously rotates a familiar picture to its correct orientation when it is handed to him upside down.

Example Observation Opportunities: Incidental - may observe if the child spontaneously turns a picture book around if he picks it up upside down, or moves to the other side of a book if someone facing him is looking at it. Structured - show the child some familiar pictures cards or photographs, one at a time as you name them and then let him hold and look at each picture. After the second or third picture, show and then hand him a picture upside down without naming it. Observe to see if he turns the picture in the correct orientation before naming it and exclaiming how it was upside down. Use pictures that have a distinct top and bottom, e.g., a standing person, tree, or car, but *not* a ball, or apple.

Credit: (see also Credit Notes in this strand's preface)

+   rotates pictures to their correct orientation.

 Finds details in favorite picture book   24-27

Definition: The child looks and points to details in pictures, e.g., a bird in the tree, buttons on the clown suit, curled tail on a mouse. The child is becoming aware of the "parts" as well as the "whole" of a picture and how these spatially relate to each other.

Example Observation Opportunities: Use a picture storybook which is a favorite of the child's (if available). Observe to see if the child points out details as he explores the pictures. Interject some interesting story lines, occasionally asking him to find a detail in the picture.

Credit: (see also Credit Notes in this strand's preface)

+   points to at least two details in a picture, upon request or spontaneously.

 Completes three- to four-piece puzzle   30-36

Definition: The child can complete a puzzle of a familiar object, animal or person which has three or four related pieces. The child is continuing to learn about "parts" of the "whole" in a picture and how these spatially relate to each other.

Example Observation Opportunities: Show the child a completed three- to four-piece puzzle of a familiar object animal or person. Use puzzles which have clear, distinct relational pieces to make a whole picture, e.g., a dog that has a head, body and tail pieces rather than a puzzle of an orange. Name or invite the child to tell you what it is. Let him help remove and then explore the pieces before asking him to try to put it back together.

Credit: (see also Credit Notes in this strand's preface)

+   completes a three- to four-piece puzzle. He may do so through trial and error but should not have any gesture cues.

1-6 CONCEPTS

A. PICTURES

1.44	8-9	Looks at pictures 1 minute when named
1.60	10-14	Enjoys looking at pictures in books
1.82	14-15	Pats picture
1.107	19-27	Matches objects to picture
1.117	21-30	Points to five to seven pictures of familiar objects/people
1.129	24-28	Recognizes familiar adult in photograph

Family Friendly Interpretation of Strand Concepts, Assessment, & Purpose

We will be showing your child some pictures to see if he recognizes different pictures of familiar objects and people. Learning to recognize pictures is an important cognitive skill that helps children learn that pictures can represent real objects and people. The first pictures children learn to recognize are often those that look exactly like the real thing, such as large clear-colored pictures or photographs.

Professional FYI

The concept of this strand involves similar mental processes associated with learning that objects symbolize real things (e.g., in Strand 1-1 "Development of Symbolic Play,") and that words are symbols for thoughts and things (in the Language domain 2.0.)

None of the skills in this strand require expressive language. Related picture skills that require a child to name pictures are located in Strand 2-3 "Expressive Vocabulary." The last two skills (#1.117 and #1.129) require a basic level of receptive language, but the earlier skills are not dependent upon language per se, as the child needs only to recognize the picture as a symbol for objects by looking, patting, or matching.

Parent Questions (Examples)

To help identify the child's unique strengths and needs related to this developmental area:
- Tell me what your child does when you show him pictures in a book or photo album.
- Are there certain pictures, photos, or books that your child seems to like best? Can you give me some examples?
- These are the pictures we might be showing your child. Is he familiar with the kinds of toys and objects they represent? Are there other pictures you think we should include?

To help identify family resources, priorities and concerns related to the child's development in this area:
- What pictures and picture books would you like us to include in our assessment and planning?
- Are there certain times during the day or week that you have time to look at books with your child?
- Are you interested in borrowing some picture books from our toy lending library?

Sample *Functional* Outcome Statements which may be generated by the Family

[Will be dependent upon identified individual child and family needs and should incorporate objectives and activities from other domains]

My child will:
- Enjoy looking at books with us;
- Learn some of the names of simple pictures he sees in his ABC book.

Transactional Assessment

May assess through observation and interview.

Assessment of the Child's Environment

1. Supportive:
[Example environments which support/facilitate development in this area]

The child's caregiving environments usually:
- Have interesting picture books that the child is free to explore.

Assessment of Caregiver Interactions with the Child

1. Supportive:
[Example interactions which support/facilitate child's development in this area]
The child's caregivers frequently:
• Name pictures that are seen spontaneously in the environment, e.g., on food containers,

pictures on walls;
• "Read" picture books with their child, naming pictures and giving the child time to respond;
• Let their child freely explore pictures at his own interest and pace.

Identifying and Interpreting Needs for Intervention

If a child is significantly delayed in this area he may be having difficulty in <u>understanding that pictures are symbols for real objects and people</u>.

However, before targeting cognitive development as the primary area of need for intervention, consider, rule out, or adapt for other causes that are not related to his symbolic capacities. These may include:
• <u>Lack of interest</u> in the pictures presented or in the activity;

• <u>Poor attention</u>;
• <u>Visual impairment</u>;
• <u>Motor impairment</u> that interferes with child's ability to physically match or point to pictures;
• <u>Receptive language delay</u>: the child recognizes pictures for objects but does not understand the word labels.

Assessment Adaptations   (Examples)

[Note any adaptations needed to credit and help plan interventions]
• <u>Lack of interest</u> in the pictures presented or in the activity. Reassess at another time or try more interesting pictures.
• <u>Poor attention</u>: keep this activity brief. Capitalize on identifying pictures that occur naturally during the child's activities, e.g., identifying pictures on the cookie box during snack time, or pictures which are hanging on the wall.

• <u>Visual impairment</u>:
  – Low vision: use photographs or high contrast, good quality pictures.
  – Blind: omit assessment of this strand; mark N/A.
• <u>Motor impairment</u>: accept eye pointing to indicate recognition; be sure the child and pictures are positioned comfortably and visibly.
• <u>Receptive language delay</u>: skill #1.117 - expect a delay until receptive language skills improve.

General Assessment Procedures & Processes   (apply to all items in this Strand)

1. **Be sure that the pictures are positioned in clear view of the child.**
2. **You may also assess the following related skills from other domains while assessing this strand:**
   Fine Motor (Strand 4-7A)
     #1.83 "Helps turn pages"
     #1.89 "Turns two or three pages at a time"
     #1.116 "Turns pages one at a time"
   Language (Strand 2-3B)
     #2.56 "Names two pictures"
     #2.61 "Names three pictures"
     #2.70 "Names five pictures"
     #2.83 "Names eight or more pictures"
   Spatial (Strand 1-5)
     #1.105 "Rights familiar picture"
     #1.128 "Finds detail in favorite picture book"
   Matching (Strand 1-7A)
     #1.139 "Matches identical simple

   pictures of objects"
     #1.145 "Matches similar pictures of objects"
3. **Describe the skill and eliciting procedures to family members and invite them to help observe and/or assess.**

+ - A   Credit Notes:
  +   child usually displays skill or behavior as defined.
  -   not observed or reported.
  +/- appears to be an emerging skill.
  A   atypical: usually perseverates on a detail of a picture without any regard for the whole picture.
  N/A unable or inappropriate to assess due to disability.
  O   circle any credit if environment or interactions compromise or restrict child's optimal skills, in this area.
Note any adaptations used to credit.

Assessment Materials

- Colored pictures and books with pictures of familiar objects and animals: Pictures can be from a child's simple picture book, picture cards, or magazine. They should be clear and life-like and culturally sensitive, preferably at least 3 by 5 inches. Let the parent identify pictures which are familiar and common to the child i.e., items he has seen, used, and heard named. Examples: baby, shoe, cup, bottle, apple, car, cup, spoon, banana, cup, key, brush, sock and shoe.
- Clear black and white outline drawings of familiar objects, e.g., cup, shoe.
- Two or three photographs of people and pets the child sees frequently, e.g., family, friends, caregivers, family or neighbor dog. The child's parents may have photos available or this item may be assessed through parent interview.

1.44 Looks at pictures 1 minute when named   8-9

Definition: The child looks with interest at realistic pictures of familiar people and objects sometimes for up to a minute.

Example Observation Opportunities: Show the child two or three realistic pictures or simple photographs of familiar people and objects, one at a time. The pictures should be colored, clear, and contain only one main object. Name, describe, and point to each picture as the child looks. Wait until the child's interest wanes before going on to the next.

Credit: (see also Credit Notes in this strand's preface)
- + looks intently at a few pictures, sometimes for up to a minute.
- − plays with the picture without ever really looking at it.

1.60 Enjoys looking at pictures in books   10-14

Definition: The child looks with interest at pictures in a book or magazine.

Example Observation Opportunities: May be observed when the child is looking a book by himself or with an adult. Use one of the child's favorite books if available. An adult may encourage him to look by pointing, naming and/or describing the pictures. Wait until the child's interest wanes before turning the page. If the child is more interested in flipping the pages, let him do so before expecting him to focus on the pictures.

Credit: (see also Credit Notes in this strand's preface)
- + shows interest in one or more of the pictures in a book. He may show interest by looking intently, smiling and/or patting at the picture. At some point he should show more interest in the picture than the book in general.

1.82 Pats picture   14-15

Definition: The child pats at or touches pictures and photos as if to see if they are real.

Example Observation Opportunities: May use single picture cards or pictures in a book. Refer to eliciting procedures in skills #1.44 and #1.60 above.

Credit: (see also Credit Notes in this strand's preface)
- + pats or touches pictures while looking at them.

1.107 Matches objects to picture   19-27

Definition: The child can match a picture with the real object. He understands that pictures represent three-dimensional objects.

Example Observation Opportunities: Incidental - during snack time, let the child choose which box his cracker came from when one of the boxes has a picture of the cracker on it; during playtime, ask the child to put a toy back in the box it came from when a few boxes, which have pictures of corresponding toys on them, are available; during story time, ask the child to find the picture of the toy, doll, or stuffed animal that he is holding. Structured - give the child a common object to play with, such as a car, block, toothbrush or comb. Show him three or four pictures of objects from different categories, one of which is a picture of the object he is playing with; e.g., if he has a comb, show him pictures of a comb, apple, shoe, dog. The picture should be in color but does not have to be exactly like the object; e.g., it may be a different color or size. Point to the object he is holding and invite him to find the picture of it without naming it. If he does not seem to understand the game, show him the answer and try again with two or three more objects.

Credit: (see also Credit Notes in this strand's preface)
- + matches at least two different objects to their corresponding pictures, one at a time, when there are at least three from which to choose.

Points to five to seven pictures of familiar objects/people   21-30

Definition: The child recognizes outline pictures (black and white drawings) as symbols for real objects. He can identify several different pictures of common objects and people when asked and when three or four other pictures are available.

Example Observation Opportunities: Gather about 10 picture cards which have realistic outline drawings of objects familiar to the child. The pictures may be one to a card or have four to six pictures per card. Example pictures: dog, spoon, baby doll, leaf, bottle, car. *[Confirm with parent that child is familiar with the objects]* Show the child four to six pictures at a time. Allow time for him to look at and name them spontaneously. When he is looking at them, ask him to "find" (point, touch or pick up) the one you name. Repeat for at least five pictures, or up to 10 if the child has any misses during the first five. If he becomes disinterested in the game, return to this item at a later time.

Credit: (see also Credit Notes in this strand's preface)
+   identifies at least five outline pictures of objects when named or by spontaneously naming them.

Recognizes familiar adult in photograph   24-28

Definition: The child can identify or name familiar people in a photograph. He has a clear understanding that pictures of people represent real people.

Example Observation Opportunities: May observe as child looks through family album, pictures around his home environment, or pictures in his parents wallet. The picture does not have to look exactly like the person, e.g., may have different hairstyle, glasses, mustache.

Credit: (see also Credit Notes in this strand's preface)
+   names the pictures of at least three familiar people.

1-6 CONCEPTS

B. NUMBERS

1.123	24-30	Understands concept of one
1.135	25-30	Gives one out of many
1.150	30-36	Understands concept of two

Family Friendly Interpretation of Strand Concepts, Assessment, & Purpose

We will be observing how your child is learning the underlying principles of counting. Although children do not have a true understanding of number concepts until much later, they can at this age begin to associate the number "one" with one object, and then later the number "two" with two objects.

Parent Questions   (Examples)

To help identify the child's unique strengths and needs related to this developmental area:
• Does it seem like your child understands when you tell him to take just "one" of something? Can you give me some examples? *[Continue with "two" if appropriate]*

Sample *Functional* Outcome Statements which may be generated by the Family

[Will be dependent upon identified individual child and family needs and should incorporate objectives and activities from other domains]
My child will:

• Understand what I mean when I tell him to "take one";
• Be able to count two objects.

Transactional Assessment

May assess through observation and interview.

Assessment of the Child's Environment

1. Supportive:
[Example interactions which support/facilitate child's development in this area]
The child's caregivers:
• Sometimes talk about one-to-one correspondences as natural situations occur during play and daily activities, e.g., "You have one cracker, there are many crackers in the bowl," "Let's get one more block for this tower,"
"One step, two steps!"

2. Compromising:
[Example interactions which may restrict, compromise, inhibit or be unsupportive of the child's development in this area]
The child's caregivers:
• Expect their child to be able to count beyond appropriate developmental level.

Identifying and Interpreting Needs for Intervention

If a child is significantly delayed in this area, he may be having difficulty in <u>understanding one-to-one correspondence</u>.

However, before targeting cognitive development as the primary need for intervention, consider, rule out, or adapt for other causes that are not related to his understanding of one-to-one correspondence. These may include:
• <u>Motor impairment</u>, which prevents child from carrying out the related request.

Assessment Adaptations   (Examples)

[Note any adaptations needed to credit and help plan interventions]
• <u>Motor impaired</u>: accept any form of gestural or eye pointing to indicate which hand is holding, e.g., two objects.

General Assessment Procedures & Processes   (apply to all items in this Strand)

1. **Describe the skill and eliciting procedures to family members and invite them to help observe and/or assess.**

 + - A Credit Notes:

+   child usually displays skill or behavior as

defined during play and daily activities.
-   not observed or reported.
+/- appears to be an emerging skill.
O   circle any credit if environment or interactions compromise or restrict child's optimal skills in this area.

Assessment Materials

• Several similar objects, e.g., blocks, balls, cookies, crayons, cars.

1.123   Understands concept of one   24-30

Definition: The child can identify a set of "one" from a set of more than one.

Example Observation Opportunities: <u>Incidental</u> - during story time use a picture book that is about number concepts. Ask the child which picture has "just one," for example, dog (when there is a corresponding picture with two of the same objects). During snack time, ask the child which hand has just one spoon; when he's eating a cookie, ask him how many cookies he has; during play, ask which box has just one block (crayon, peg, car etc.). <u>Structured</u> - place a block or other small object in one hand, and two or more blocks in your other hand. Ask the child, "Which hand has *one* block?" After he's indicated his selection, let him play with the blocks. A little later, repeat with different objects.

Credit: (see also Credit Notes in this strand's preface)

+   selects a set of one from more than one on two occasions, or if he answers correctly when asked, "how many."

1.135   Gives one out of many   25-30

Definition: The child gives or takes one of something from a group of similar objects on request.

Example Observation Opportunities: <u>Incidental</u> - during snack time: when the child has a bowl with several bits of food (e.g., Cheerios), ask him to give you or his parent "one"; ask the child to take "just one" from a bowl of several (e.g., one piece of apple, one cracker); during play, ask the child to give his parent one block when he has several; to take one crayon out of the box of crayons; to get one book off the shelf which has several. <u>Structured</u> - after the child has been playing with several small blocks (pegs or other objects), ask him to "put one block, only one," into a container or on a piece of paper. Gesture to the place he is to put it. Wait several seconds before commenting or taking the block away to make sure he does not continue to place more blocks in the container.

Credit: (see also Credit Notes in this strand's preface)

+   gives or takes one out of many on request on at least two occasions.

1.150   Understands concept of two   30-36

Definition: The child gives or takes "two" of something from a group of similar objects on request.

Example Observation Opportunities: <u>Incidental</u> - during snack time: when the child has a bowl with several bits of food (e.g., Cheerios), ask him to give someone "two"; ask the child to take "two" from a bowl of several (e.g., crackers, apple pieces). During play, ask the child to give his parent two blocks when he has several; to take two crayons out of the box of crayons; to get two books off the shelf which has several. <u>Structured</u> - after the child has been playing with several small blocks (pegs or other small objects) for awhile, e.g., when assessing stacking of cubes or pegboards), ask him to "put two blocks," into a bowl (box, or on a piece of paper). Gesture to the place he is to put it. Wait several seconds before commenting or taking the blocks away to see if he continues to place more.

Credit: (see also Credit Notes in this strand's preface)

+   gives or takes two out of many on request, on at least two occasions, or says, "one, two" in one-to-one correspondence while taking or pointing to two objects.

1-7 DISCRIMINATION/CLASSIFICATION

A. MATCHING AND SORTING

1.70	12-18	Shows understanding of color
1.85	15-19	Matches objects
1.108	19-24	Sorts objects
1.136	26-30	Matches shapes–circles, triangles, squares
1.137	26-29	Matches colors–black, white
1.139	27-30	Matches identical simple pictures of objects
1.144	29-33	Matches primary colors
1.145	30-36	Matches similar pictures of objects
1.146	30-36	Sorts shapes–circle, triangle, square [toys]
1.156	33 +	Sorts colors and points to several colors when named

Family Friendly Interpretation of Strand Concepts, Assessment, & Purpose

We will be giving your child different sets of objects and pictures to see how he is learning to match and sort them by different qualities, such as color and shape. This is an important thinking skill that involves comparing similarities and differences. For example, if your child is helping you sort his socks from a laundry basket, and finds a red sock to match the red sock he is holding, he is showing you that he is learning to match things by their color.

Professional FYI

The original HELP skill #1.70 "Shows understanding of size and color," has been modified for this strand to read "Shows understanding of color." Size concepts are located in the next Strand (1-7B).

The items related to matching shapes are closely associated to the matching skills required for formboard skills located in the Fine Motor domain, Strand 4-6B. These items, however, are not dependent upon fine motor skills.

Parent Questions   (Examples)

To help identify the child's unique strengths and needs related to this developmental area:
• Have you noticed if your child seems to recognize the difference between basic colors, such as red, blue, and yellow? Can you give me some examples?
• Have you noticed if your child seems to recognize the difference between basic shapes, such as circles, squares, or triangles? How can you tell?
• Has your child ever played with any shape toys or puzzles? Can you tell me a little about how he plays with them?

Sample *Functional* Outcome Statements which may be generated by the Family

[Will be dependent upon identified individual child and family needs and should incorporate objectives and activities from other domains]
My child will be able to:
• Recognize basic colors;
• Play with his shape sorting toys;
• Put his toys back in their correct places, e.g., putting his crayons back in the can with the rest of his crayons and putting his cars back in the box where we keep his cars.

Transactional Assessment

May assess through observation and interview.

Assessment of Caregiver Interactions with the Child

1. Supportive:
[Example interactions which support/facilitate child's development in this area]
The child's caregivers sometimes:
• Name the colors of objects, foods, and toys for the child while he is interacting or looking at them;
• Name the basic shapes of blocks and puzzle pieces for the child while he is interacting or looking at them.

Assessment of Caregiver Interactions with the Child   (continued)

- Point out similarities and differences in the environment as they occur naturally during daily activities; e.g., "That lady has a hat on just like my hat," "Mommy's car is blue, that car is red."

2. Compromising:
[Example interactions which may restrict, compromise, inhibit or be unsupportive of the child's development in this area]
The child's caregivers:
- Expect their child to know his colors and shapes before he is developmentally ready.

Identifying and Interpreting Needs for Intervention

If a child is significantly delayed in this area he may be having difficulty in <u>discriminating the differences and similarities of objects</u>.

However, before targeting cognitive development as the primary need for intervention, consider, rule out, or adapt for other causes that are not related to his ability to <u>discriminate similarities and differences</u>. These may include:
- <u>Visual impairment or color blindness</u>;

- <u>Motor impairment,</u> which prevents the child from manipulating objects to match and sort;
- <u>Poor tactile discrimination</u>: learning about the differences and similarities of shapes occurs by touching and looking. If the child has poor tactile discrimination, he may have more difficulty matching and sorting shapes;
- <u>Lack of interest</u> in or attention to the activity.

Assessment Adaptations   (Examples)

[Note any adaptations needed to credit and help plan interventions]
- <u>Visual impairment</u>:
   - If the child can match and sort black and white or other dark and light colors, but never primary colors, as in #1.156 "Sorts colors and point to several colors when named," he may have color blindness (achromatopsia). Refer to a vision specialist.
   - If the child is blind, omit all items requiring color and picture discrimination; mark N/A.
   - If the child is blind, expect delays in skills related to shapes unless the child has had ample experiences and specific teaching of these in matching and sorting.
   - If the child has low vision, omit item #1.145 "Matches similar pictures of objects." Make sure that the pictures in item #1.139 "Matches identical objects" are clear, of high contrast, and exactly alike.
- <u>Motor Impairment</u>: if the child is severely

restricted in his movements, sort and match for him and let him tell you verbally or through eye gaze where an object should go. Expect delays in discriminating shapes if the child has not been able to explore shapes tactually in his environment due to motor impairments unless the child has had specific training experiences in discriminating shapes visually. Use of selected software may be very appropriate.
- <u>Poor tactile discrimination</u>: emphasize the visual differences and similarities; consult with a therapist trained in sensory processing for activities to promote tactile discrimination.
- <u>Lack of interest</u> or attention to the activity: try to incorporate matching and sorting into the daily activities and play that the child is able to attend to. Capitalize on natural situations that arise to assess and plan, e.g., letting the child sort his crayons during coloring; matching his paint brush in the correctly colored paint cup; showing him how pictures on his cereal boxes are similar and different. Examples are listed for most items.

General Assessment Procedures & Processes   (apply to all items in this Strand)

1. **Describe the skill and eliciting procedures to family members and invite them to help observe and/or assess.**

+ - A Credit Notes:

+   child usually displays skill or behavior as defined during play and daily activities.

-   not observed or reported.

+/- appears to be an emerging skill; seemed to

learn during assessment.
N/A not appropriate to assess due to disability.
O   circle any credit if environment or interactions compromise or restrict child's optimal skills in this area.
Note any adaptations used to credit.

Assessment Materials

- Objects to match and sort by shape: two or three of each shape: circle, square, triangle. Use formboard shapes, shape blocks or shapes cut out of poster board. The shapes should be approximately the same size and color.
- Objects to match and sort by color: Three to four each of similar objects that are black and white, e.g., three black and three white blocks, cars, paper scraps, or socks.
- Three to four each of similar objects that are blue, red, and yellow, e.g., blocks, cars, pegs,

socks, Play-Doh™, paint.
- Similar, exact, and dissimilar pictures to match:
    Two sets of three pictures of familiar objects, two of which are exactly alike.
    Two sets of three pictures of familiar objects, two of which are similar but not exactly alike, and the third dissimilar, e.g., two picture of two different types of dogs and one picture of a bird.
- Three shallow containers, e.g., pie pans.

1.70 Shows understanding of color   12-18

Definition: The child is beginning to display an awareness of colors when he interacts with objects. Examples of this early awareness may be seen as he prefers his red ball or toy car over his blue ones, looks at the colors of his crayons before selecting one, or sometimes groups his red blocks together, ignoring his blue ones.

Example Observation Opportunities: May be observed incidentally when child is playing with similar materials that have different colors. Examples: looking at the colors of crayons before selecting one; piling his red blocks in a cup while discarding or ignoring his blue ones; looking intently at your colored shirt and then looking at his own.

Credit: (see also Credit Notes in this strand's preface)
+   shows any signs of awareness of color when interacting with or looking at objects as defined.

1.85 Matches objects   15-19

Definition: The child places three to four objects in a related group during play.

Example Observation Opportunities: <u>Incidental</u> - observe if the child groups items in a relational way spontaneously during his play; e.g., while playing with dolls and cars, the child moves his cars to one side and doll items to another group. <u>Structured</u> - give the child three or four related objects within a group of five or six objects, two of which are not related, e.g., four blocks, one car, and a spoon; four doll items (brush, bottle, doll, doll clothes), one plastic ring and a block. If he does not spontaneously group them, hold up one block, and ask, "Can you show me a toy that looks like mine?" Repeat with a few more toys.

Credit: (see also Credit Notes in this strand's preface)
+   moves three or four related objects or toys in a group at anytime during play, demonstrating his apparent understanding of their relationship to one another, or matches two to three objects, one at a time with a model on request.

1.108 Sorts Objects   19-24

Definition: The child can sort a pile of assorted objects into three separate piles of identical objects.

Example Observation Opportunities: <u>Incidental</u> - during mealtime, suggest or observe if the child sorts different foods on his plate; e.g., if given a mixed fruit cup, or if he sorts his meats from his vegetables when they become mixed up during the course of the meal. During clean-up after play, give the child three boxes to sort his toys in, e.g., one box for his crayons, one for his blocks, and one for his paper. <u>Structured</u> - give the child three empty containers and a mixed group of toys or objects. The group of objects should include three each of different objects, e.g., blocks, cars, clothes pins. Invite the child to put them in the containers. If the child starts to randomly place them in the containers, make a comment, such as, "Oops, the cars go here, not with the blocks," to help him learn the game and let him try again. Repeat with a different set of mixed objects.

Credit: (see also Credit Notes in this strand's preface)
+   sorts a mixed group of objects into three separate piles of identical objects; with at least two different sets of objects to sort.
+/- sorts a mixed group of objects into two piles after verbal cues and modeling.

Matches shapes - circles, triangle, square   26-30

Definition: When shown a circle, triangle or square shape, the child can identify another shape that matches the model.

Example Observation Opportunities: Gather two or three of each shape: circle, square, triangle. Use formboard shapes, shape blocks or shapes cut out of poster board. The shapes should be approximately the same size and color. Give the child a circle and a triangle shape and let him explore them as you name and describe them; e.g., "Circle! The circle is round. Triangle! See the points!" Hold up another circle and ask him to show or give you the one he has that looks just like yours. If he does not seem to understand the game, have another participant play so he can watch and repeat the procedure. After he gives or shows the circle, give him a square shape so that he is now holding a square and triangle. Hold up your triangle and repeat your request for him to show you his. Continue this procedure with the square and repeat with each of the shapes in a game-like fashion. If the child maintains interest in this game and is successful, proceed to assess #1.146 "Sorts shapes..." that follows later in this strand.

Credit: (see also Credit Notes in this strand's preface)
+   matches each of three shapes at least twice consecutively; i.e., initially may not match because does not understand the game. After he learns the game he should be able to match each shape twice.

Matches colors - black, white   26-29

Definition: When shown a black or white object, the child can identify another similar object of the same color.

Example Observation Opportunities: <u>Incidental</u> - may be observed during painting activities, the child puts his brush with black paint on it into the black can of paint when another colored can of paint is available; during dressing, the child takes a white sock when another colored sock is available to match the white sock he already has. <u>Structured</u> - gather three or four similar objects that are black and white, e.g., three black and three white blocks, cars, paper scraps, or socks. Give the child one black and one white object and let him explore them as you name and describe the color. Hold up a similar black object and ask him to pick up or show you the one he has that looks just like yours. If he does not seem to understand the game, have another participant play so he can watch, and repeat the procedure. After he shows you the black object, hold up a similar white object and repeat your request for him to show you his. Continue this procedure with another set of black and white objects in a game-like fashion. If the child maintains interest in this game and is successful, proceed to assess #1.144 "Matches primary colors" that follows later in this strand.

Credit: (see also Credit Notes in this strand's preface)
+   matches black and white objects at least twice consecutively; i.e., initially may not match because does not understand the game. After he learns the game, should be able to match each color twice.

Matches identical simple pictures of objects   27-30

Definition: The child matches a picture he has with another picture exactly like the one he is holding.

Example Observation Opportunities: Give the child a simple picture of a familiar object. After he's had time to explore it, hold up two pictures, one of which is exactly like the one he is holding. Ask him to look at, touch, point to the picture "just like his" as you point to his picture. Do not name the picture until after the matching process. If he does not seem to understand the game, show him the answer and try again with several more pictures. Randomly hold the correct picture in different hands. *[May use picture stickers to make matching cards]*

Credit: (see also Credit Notes in this strand's preface)
+   matches at least three out of four identical pictures.

Matches primary colors   29-33

Definition: When shown a blue, red, or yellow object, the child can identify another object of the same color to match.

Example Observation Opportunities: Same as #1.137 "Matches colors-black, white," but substitute primary-colored objects for black and white objects. May also include incidental observations during play with Play-Doh™; e.g., when finished child puts yellow dough back in the can with other yellow dough, blue dough back in the can with other blue dough, etc.

Credit: (see also Credit Notes in this strand's preface)
+   matches each primary color at least twice consecutively; i.e., initially may not match because does not understand the game. After he learns the game he should be able to match each color twice.

Matches similar pictures of objects   30-36

Definition: The child matches a picture he is holding with another picture that is similar but not exactly alike, e.g., matches a picture of a German Shepherd dog to a picture of a Collie when it is paired with a picture of a bird.

Example Observation Opportunities: Give the child a simple picture of a familiar object. After he's had time to explore it, hold up two more pictures, one of that is similar, but not exactly like the one he is holding, e.g., different shirts, houses, cats, cups. Ask him to look at, touch, point. to the picture you are holding that is "like his" as you point to his picture. Do not name the picture until after the matching process. If he does not seem to understand the game, show him the answer, naming the picture and try again with several more pictures. Randomly hold the correct picture in different hands. [May use picture stickers or pictures from a store catalogues to make matching cards of similar pictures]

Credit: (see also Credit Notes in this strand's preface)

+ matches at least three out of four similar pictures.

 ## Sorts shapes - circle, triangle, square [toys]   30-36

Definition: The child is able to sort a pile of assorted shapes (circles, triangles, squares) into three separate piles according to shape.

Example Observation Opportunities: Place a pile of shapes (three of each: circle, square, triangle) in front of the child. Use formboard shapes, shape blocks, or shapes cut out of poster board. The shapes should be approximately the same size and color. Let him explore the shapes as you name and describe them. Then place three shallow containers in front of the child and ask him to put the shapes away. If he makes an error, wait to see if he corrects it himself before helping him. If the child continues to put them back randomly, make a comment, such as "Oops, the circle goes in this can, not with the square."

Credit: (see also Credit Notes in this strand's preface)

+ sorts at least two out of three each of circles, squares, and triangles with some initial guidance to help learn the game.

 ## Sorts colors and points to several colors when named   33 and above

Definition: The child is able to sort a pile of mixed colored objects into three separate piles according to color. He also knows the names of at least three colors and can point to them when named.

Example Observation Opportunities: <u>Incidental</u> - may observe if child sorts according to color his blocks, crayons, pegs, socks, etc. spontaneously as part of his play. May observe child naming or pointing to named colors during paint/crayon/paper play; play with colored Play-Doh™, or when choosing which ball (shirt, hat, etc.) he wants. <u>Structured</u> - gather about 10-15 similar objects of three different colors (generally primary colors unless parent advises child knows another color). Examples: four red, four blue, and four yellow blocks (or, socks, cars, thick pegs, etc.). Place them in a mixed pile in front of the child. After the child has had time to explore them, give him three shallow containers and ask him to put them away. Demonstrate with one color each as you comment about the colors. If the child starts to put an object in the wrong box, comment on how it does not match and point to the correct box. Provide this cue only one or two times to help the child understand the intent of the game. During the process, ask the child to put the "red one in the box" (repeating for each color, to assess if he recognizes the colors by name).

Credit: (see also Credit Notes in this strand's preface)

+ sorts into three groups according to color at least three of four same-colored objects per group, and identifies at least three colors by naming or pointing to them on request; may have initial guidance learning the intent of this game.

1-7: DISCRIMINATION/CLASSIFICATION

B. SIZE DISCRIMINATION

1.70	12-18	Shows understanding of size
1.72	12-19	Nests two then three cans
1.109	19-24	Assembles four nesting blocks
2.76	25-30	Uses size words
1.148	30-36	Stacks rings in correct order
1.149	30-36	Points to larger or smaller of two spoons
1.157	33+	Identifies longer stick
1.158	33-36	Begins to pick longer of two lines

Family Friendly Interpretation of Strand Concepts, Assessment, & Purpose

We will be giving your child different sets of toys, such as nesting cups to see how he is learning to compare them by size. Understanding about size differences is an important discrimination skill that helps children learn how to solve daily problems. For example, as a child learns to discriminate sizes he can figure out that small blocks balance on large blocks, but large blocks do not balance very well on top of small blocks; or that he can fit something small into something large but cannot fit something large into something small.

Professional FYI

The original HELP skill #1.70 "Shows understanding of size and color" has been modified for this strand to read "Shows understanding of size" because color concepts were addressed in the previous Strand (1-7A).

Parent Questions   (Examples)

To help identify the child's unique strengths and needs related to this developmental area:
• Have you noticed if your child is beginning to notice or compare the sizes of different toys objects? Can you give me some examples?

• Has your child ever played with a ring-stack toy?...nesting cups? Can you tell me a little about how he plays with them?

Sample *Functional* Outcome Statements which may be generated by the Family

[Will be dependent upon identified individual child and family needs and should incorporate objectives and activities from other domains]

My child will be able to:
• Recognize basic size differences;
• Play with his nesting cup and ring-stack toys.:

Transactional Assessment

May assess through observation and interview.

Assessment of Caregiver Interactions with the Child

1. Supportive:
[Example interactions which support/facilitate child's development in this area]
The child's caregivers sometimes:
• Talk about the different sizes of objects, foods, and toys for the child while he is interacting or looking at them;
• Point out similarities and differences in size that occur naturally during daily activities, e.g., "That is the big ball, I have the little ball."

Identifying and Interpreting Needs for Intervention

If a child is significantly delayed in this area he may be having difficulty in <u>discriminating size differences</u>.

However, before targeting cognitive development as the primary area of need for intervention, consider, rule out, or adapt for other causes that are not related to his ability to <u>discriminate sizes.</u>

These may include:
- <u>Visual impairment</u>: the child does not have the visual cues to help him discriminate size differences;
- <u>Motor impairment</u>, which prevents the child from manipulating different-sized objects;
- <u>Lack of interest</u> in or attention to the activity.

Assessment Adaptations   (Examples)

[Note any adaptations needed to credit and help plan interventions]
- Visual impairment:
  – Use toys and objects that are very familiar to the child. If he has not had experience with the tasks, he may need hand-over-hand instruction on the initial tries. Size differences should be more pronounced.
  – Specific item adaptations:
    #1.149 "Points to larger or smaller of two spoons," ask the child to give you the larger or smaller spoon rather than pointing to it. Use a tiny spoon and a large serving spoon.
    #1.158 "Begins to pick longer of two lines," use tactile lines, e.g., different-sized cord glued to cardboard; one line should be twice the size of the other.

- <u>Motor impairment</u>: if the child is severely restricted in his manipulative abilities, play with the ring-stack and nesting cup toys while the child watches you; encourage him to tell you verbally or through eye gaze, where an object should go. Use objects that are very different in size as the child will need to rely upon visual cues.
- <u>Lack of interest</u> or attention to the activity: try to incorporate size discrimination activities into the child's activities and play that he can focus on best. Capitalize on natural situations that arise to assess and plan, e.g., asking the child take the big spoon to help you stir; to get his big ball to play ball. Additional examples of natural situations are listed for most items.
- <u>Speech delays</u>: adapt item #2.76 "Uses size words," by letting child point to the correct object when you ask, e.g., "Touch the <u>big</u> box."

Assessment Materials

- Three empty round containers that differ significantly in size: e.g., coffee can, soup can, small tomato paste can *[tape edges of cans for safety]*; or, if using a set of commercial nesting cups use the largest, smallest and middle-sized.
- Four boxes of graduated sizes that fit easily inside each other. These may be commercial nesting boxes, jewelry boxes, square Tupperware containers.
- Ring stack which has a uniform stick with three to five rings of graduated size.

- Items to compare long and short, e.g., cardboard paper towel insert and a cardboard toilet paper insert; "long" drum stick with a short drum stick; long and short paint brush; long and short pieces of ribbon; paper and crayon to draw long and short lines.
- Items to compare big and little, e.g., big and little cookies; large stirring spoon and tiny children's spoon; big rubber ball and a small ball; big block and small inch cubes.

Shows understanding of size   12-18

1.70

Definition: The child is beginning to discriminate sizes when he interacts with similar objects that vary in size. Examples of this early awareness may be seen as he puts a small cup into a larger one; puts a small block on top of a large block; and uses two hands to pick up a large box but only one hand to pick up a tiny box.

Example Observation Opportunities: May be observed spontaneously when child is playing with similar materials which have significant size differences. Examples: putting a small nesting cup in a large one (which may at first be through trial and error); placing a small shoe on or near a doll's foot when a large shoe is also available; choosing a large cookie over a small one; examining the differences when he puts large hats versus small hats on himself or a doll; selecting a small spoon from a large stirring spoon to eat pudding; placing a small block on top of a much larger one.

Credit: (see also Credit Notes in this strand's preface)
  +   shows an awareness of size when interacting with objects as defined.

1.72   ## Nests two then three cans   12-19

Definition: The child places a small round container, such as a cup or can into a larger one; later he learns to put three containers of varying size into one another.

Example Observation Opportunities: <u>Incidental</u> - may be observed during a "tea party," or after snack time if child helps clean up and nests two or three different-sized cups. <u>Structured</u> - use three empty round containers that differ significantly in size, e.g., coffee can, soup can, small tomato paste can; or if using a set of commercial nesting cups, use the largest, smallest and middle-sized. First show the child the largest and smallest, nested. While he is watching, take out the smallest and give him both cans. Let him explore them in any way. If he does not spontaneously nest them give a verbal prompt such as, "Put them back together." You may also have a nested model available, but do not demonstrate putting them together. If successful, repeat, using three cans.

Credit: (see also Credit Notes in this strand's preface)
+   at 12-15 months, if child nests two round containers of different sizes, no demonstration; may initially use trial and error.
+   at 16-19 months, if child nests three round containers of different sizes, no demonstration; may initially use trial and error. The child may put the little one into the middle-sized can first, or the middle-sized can into the large one before nesting the smallest one.

 1.109   ## Assembles four nesting blocks   19-24

Definition: The child nests four boxes of graduated sizes into each other.

Example Observation Opportunities: Use four boxes of graduated sizes that fit easily into each other. These may be commercial nesting boxes, jewelry boxes, square Tupperware™ containers. Present the four boxes nested as you comment how they all fit together. While the child is watching, remove each box but do not line them up in order of size. Invite the child to put them back together, letting him explore them and practice through trial and error.

Credit: (see also Credit Notes in this strand's preface)
+   nests four graduated sized boxes in correct order; may do so after initial trial and error practice.

 2.76   ## Uses size words   25-30

Definition: The child understands and can say one or two words to describe the size of something. "Big," "little," "tiny," "long" are typical first size words.

Example Observation Opportunities: Observe other size words that the parent uses with the child during interactions; e.g., parent may typically say "teeny" instead of "little." Use these words as the basis for assessment. <u>Incidental</u> - show the child either one unusually large object (e.g., large therapy ball; giant stuffed animal) or two objects that are similar but differ in size, one at least twice the size of the other (e.g., 1/4 graham cracker and a whole cracker; a safe, small rubber ball and a large basketball; baby spoon and soup spoon; doll shoe and an adult shoe). Let child explore the different-sized objects (two at a time) and note if he spontaneously says a size word to comment or request. <u>Structured</u> - if the child does not say a size word spontaneously during play, try saying, " I have two (name of object) which one do you want?" If the child only points or says, "this one," further request with an inviting expression, "Do you want the big or little one?...tell me."

Credit: (see also Credit Notes in this strand's preface)
+   says at least one size word meaningfully to comment on the size of the object; if the child is speech delayed credit if he points to the objects that is described by size.

(also in Strand 2-3 "Expressive Vocabulary")

Stacks rings in correct order   30-36

Definition: The child stacks graduated-sized rings on a stick, or graduated-sized blocks on top of each other in correct order.

Example Observation Opportunities: Introduce one or both of the following dependent upon the child's preferences:

1. Present a ring stack that has a uniform stick with three to five rings placed on it from largest to smallest. The rings should be clearly different in size. Comment how the big ring is on the bottom and the little one on top. Remove the rings and invite the child to stack them just like yours was stacked. Do not line the rings up in graduated order before the child. Allow the child to explore through trial and error. If he does not place them according to size, make a comment to put the "big" one on first but do not provide gesture cues.

2. Present a tower of three to five blocks or boxes that become progressively smaller. Comment how the big block is on the bottom and the little or tiny block is on top. Knock the tower down and invite the child to build it again.

Credit: (see also Credit Notes in this strand's preface)
+ stacks rings or builds blocks in correct order of size; minimal or no trial and error.

Points to larger or smaller of two spoons   30-36

Definition: The child understands the words and meaning of "large" and "small," and/or "big" and "little".

Example Observation Opportunities: During snack time ask the child e.g., to take the "big" cookie when a little one is also available; the small spoon when a large stirring spoon is also available; the little cup when a large one is also available.

During play ask the child e.g., to get the big ball when it is next to a small ball; the big doll when it is next to a tiny doll; the large block when it is mixed with several inch cubes.

Credit: (see also Credit Notes in this strand's preface)
+ selects or names at least two sizes correctly when two comparative objects are present: big, little, large or small.

Identifies longer stick   33+

Definition: The child understands the comparative meaning of the word "longer" when applied to three-dimensional objects.

Example Observation Opportunities: During music time, ask the child to "toot" through the long tube (cardboard paper towel insert) when a short tube (cardboard toilet paper insert) is also available; to take the "long" stick to hit the drum when a short stick is also available. During craft play, ask the child to use the "long" brush when a short brush is also available; to use the long crayon when a broken crayon is also available; to pick up the long playdough snake when a short one is also available. During dress up, ask the child to select the long ribbon to tie on the doll when a short one is also available.

Credit: (see also Credit Notes in this strand's preface)
+ selects the longer of two objects when asked if the object is at least 2 inches longer than the comparison.

Begins to pick longer of two lines   33-36

Definition: The child understands the comparative meaning of the word "longer" as it applies to lines.

Example Observation Opportunities: During gross motor play, ask the child to walk along the "longer" line, made with tape on the floor. One line should be about 1.5 times the size of the other. During paper and crayon activities, draw a 6-inch line and about a 4-inch line. Ask the child to touch, draw on or push a miniature car on the "longer" line. Use the word "longer," not "bigger."

Credit: (see also Credit Notes in this strand's preface)
+ selects the longer of two lines when asked.

1-7 DISCRIMINATION/CLASSIFICATION

C. ASSOCIATIVE

1.104	18-22	Matches sounds to animals
1.118	22-24	Matches sounds to pictures of animals
1.125	24-28	Demonstrates use of objects
1.126	24-28	Identifies clothing items for different occasions
1.142	28-34	Identifies objects with their use
1.143	28-34	Identifies body parts with their function
2.94	33-36	Begins to respond to opposite analogies

Family Friendly Interpretation of Strand Concepts, Assessment, & Purpose

We will be asking your child questions which help us understand how he is learning that certain ideas or things are related to each other. For example, if you said to your child, "We are going to the swimming pool, what do you want to wear?" and he picked out his swimming suit, he would be associating or recognizing the relationship between certain clothing items with certain activities. Or if we ask, "What do you drink from?" when a cup and a shoe are available, and your child points to the cup, he is showing us he is associating the functions of objects with the objects themselves. This is an important thinking skill, which involves not only understanding the meaning of words and ideas, but also understanding how certain things are associated or connected with other things.

Parent Questions   (Examples)

To help identify the child's unique strengths and needs related to this developmental area:

• These are some toy animals and pictures of animals that we'll be showing your child. We will be assessing if he is beginning to associate different animal sounds with different animals. Is your child familiar with these animals? How is he familiar with them? Are there other animals that would be better for us to use that he is more familiar with? Can your child imitate any animal sounds?

• These are some objects that we'll be showing your child. We will be assessing if he is beginning to associate the different uses of these objects with the object. Is your child familiar with these objects? Are there other objects that would be better for us to use that he is more familiar with?

• Have you noticed if your child seems to associate certain types of clothes with certain activities, e.g., associating his bathing suit with going to the pool; his dress-up clothes for going to religious services; his pajamas with going to bed? Can you give me some examples?

• What body parts does your child seem to know?

Sample *Functional* Outcome Statements which may be generated by the Family

[Will be dependent upon identified individual child and family needs and should incorporate objectives and activities from other domains]
My child will understand:

• The uses of common objects;
• Which type of clothes to wear for different occasions: sleep, raining, snow, swimming.

Transactional Assessment

May assess through observation and interview.

Assessment of Caregiver Interactions with the Child

1. Supportive:
[Example interactions which support/facilitate child's development in this area]
The child's caregivers sometimes:
• Talk about and demonstrate the functions of objects with their child during daily activities;
• Talk about what types of clothing to wear on different occasions;
• Talk about the functions of body parts.

Identifying and Interpreting Needs for Intervention

If a child is significantly delayed in this area he may be having difficulty in <u>understanding associative concepts</u>.

However, before targeting cognitive development as the primary need for intervention, consider, rule out, or adapt for other causes that are not related to his ability to <u>understand associative concepts</u>. These may include:
- The child is <u>not familiar with assessment materials</u>;
- <u>Motor impairment</u>, which prevents child from carrying out the related request.

Assessment Adaptations   (Examples)

[Note any adaptations needed to credit and help plan interventions]
- <u>Motor Impaired</u>: Accept any form of gestural or eye pointing to indicate which hand is holding, e.g., two objects.
- <u>Blind</u>: Use only real tangible objects which are familiar to the child; omit item #1.118 "Matches sounds to pictures of animals."
- <u>Speech delayed</u>: omit #2.94 "Begins to respond to opposite analogies."

General Assessment Procedures & Processes   (apply to all items in this Strand)

1. **Describe the skill and eliciting procedures to family members and invite them to help observe and/or assess.**

+ - A Credit Notes:

+   child usually displays skill or behavior as defined during play and daily activities.

-    not observed or reported.
+/- appears to be an emerging skill.
N/A not able to assess due to disability.
O   circle any credit if environment or interactions compromise or restrict child's optimal skills in this area.
Note any adaptations used to credit.

Assessment Materials

Toy animals, animal pictures and common objects that the parent confirms are familiar to the child, e.g., shoe, comb, key, crayon, car, ball, cup.

1.104 Matches sounds to animals   18-22

Definition: The child is able to associate familiar animal sounds with the correct animal.

Example Observation Opportunities: <u>Incidental</u> - may be observed during story time when looking at books with animal pictures; during play with plastic or stuffed animals; at home if pets are available; during "circle time" singing "Old MacDonald." <u>Structured</u> - give the child three realistic animal toys the parent has reported he is familiar with. Play alongside him, commenting occasionally about the name of the animal. If he does not spontaneously make animal sounds, ask, for example, "What does the cow say?" and later, "Which animal says "moo?" If he does not respond, answer your question aloud for one of the animals to ensure he understands the game. Or play a tape of real animal sounds if available and let the child choose from two pictures or toy animals, which animal he hears.

Credit: (see also Credit Notes in this strand's preface)
+   matches at least two animal sounds correctly. He may do so by spontaneously making the sound upon seeing the animal; pointing to the correct animal when someone else makes the sound; or on request when asked, "What does the (animal) say?"

1.118 Matches sounds to pictures of animals   22-24

Definition: The child is able to associate two or three animal sounds with the correct animal picture.

Example Observation Opportunities: Same as #1.104 "Matches sounds to animals," but only use pictures.

Credit: (see also Credit Notes in this strand's preface)
+   matches at least two animal sounds to the correct animal pictures. He may do so by spontaneously making the sound upon seeing the animal picture; pointing to the correct animal picture when someone else makes the sound; or on request when asked, "What does the (pictured animal) say?"

Demonstrates use of objects 24-28

Definition: The child associates objects with their functions and can demonstrate what an object is used for when asked.

Example Observation Opportunities: Incidental - during daily activities and play, occasionally ask the child "What can we do with this cup?" Repeat with items, such as a comb, telephone, car, pan, dress-up hats, ball, etc. Structured - gather a few common objects the child has used or seen used. Examples: shoe, cup, crayon, spoon, telephone, comb, car. Present one object at a time and ask him to show you (or tell you, if child has good verbal skills) "What do you do with a (name of object)?" If he misses the first one, show him the answer to help him understand the "game." Repeat with several objects.

Credit: (see also Credit Notes in this strand's preface)
+   demonstrates or tells the function of at least three objects.

Identifies clothing items for different occasions 24-28

Definition: The child associates appropriate clothing with activities and particular occasions; e.g., boots and raincoats are worn on a rainy day; pajamas are worn to bed, swimsuits are worn to the pool.

Example Observation Opportunities: During doll or dress-up play with the child, set up situations for the child to select appropriate clothing to match the activity. For example, "It's time for baby to go to sleep, what should she wear?" and let the child pick between pajamas and a dress; when going outside, say, "It's cold, what should you wear?"

Credit: (see also Credit Notes in this strand's preface)
+   identifies at least two clothing items with appropriate occasions.

1.142 Identifies objects with their use 28-34

Definition: The child associates the functions of common objects with the correct object.

Example Observation Opportunities: Incidental - during doll play, ask the child what the doll can drink from, eat with, put on her feet, etc.; during snack time ask what he drinks from; during dressing ask what he puts on his feet; during free play ask which toy he can throw or kick, ride on, write with. Structured - show the child four common objects which he has used before (or pictures of objects if he understands picture concepts). Examples: shoe, cup, crayon, spoon, children's scissors, book, car. Ask him to give you (or, point to, touch, name) the object that "We drink out of," "Wear on our feet," "Write with," "Cut with," etc. If he misses the first one, show him the answer to help him understand the "game".

Credit: (see also Credit Notes in this strand's preface)
+   identifies at least three out of four familiar objects by their function.

1.143 Identifies body parts with their function 28-34

Definition: When the function of a body part is described, the child names or points to the correct body part on himself, another, or a doll.

Example Observation Opportunities: During doll play or while playing a "guessing game," ask the child questions, such as, "What do we see with?" "...hear with?" "...smell with?" "...eat with?" "....chew with?" Show the right answer (if needed) the first couple of times to help the child understand the game.

Credit: (see also Credit Notes in this strand's preface)
+   points to or names at least one body part when the function is described.

Begins to respond to opposite analogies 33-36

Definition: The child gives the opposite of a word when a word is presented in a leading phrase, such as, "The fire is hot, ice is...?"

Example Observation Opportunities: Play a "guessing game" with the parent and child, after prepping the parent on how to respond. Present a leading opposite analogy phrase, and let the parent answer so the child understands how to play the game. Then proceed with several other phrases, inviting the child to finish the sentence. Example leading phrases: "The stove is hot, the refrigerator is...," "Men are big, babies are...," "Milk is cold, soup is....," "Bugs are little, elephants are...," "Daddies are men, mommies are...," "Water is wet, a towel is...," "This floor is hard, cotton is..."

Credit: (see also Credit Notes in this strand's preface)
+   responds correctly to at least one opposite analogy.

2.0 - LANGUAGE
Introduction

Overview
Language is divided into two sections and associated strands:

I. Receptive Language
  - 2-1 Understanding the Meaning of Words
  - 2-2 Understanding and Following Directions

II. Expressive Language
  - 2-3 Expressive Vocabulary
  - 2-4 Communicating with Others
    - A. Gesturally
    - B. Verbally
  - 2-5 Learning Grammar and Sentence Structures
  - 2-6 Development of Sounds and Intelligibility
  - 2-7 Communication through Rhythm

Section I consists of two strands. Strand 2-1, "Receptive language," relate to the child's advancing ability to <u>understand the meaning</u> of information, ideas, and feelings expressed by other's verbal and nonverbal communication. Strand 2-2, "Understanding and following directions," is also dependent upon the child's movement and motor planning abilities. Neither of these two receptive strands is dependent upon expressive language.

The expressive language strands under Section II relate to the child's ability to <u>express or exchange</u> information, ideas and feelings through verbal and nonverbal symbols within a "rule-governed" system of communication. In contrast to receptive language, meaningful expressive language *is* usually dependent upon receptive language.

Effective communication is the result of each of these strands working together. A child may, however, have more difficulty in one area than in others, causing difficulties in effective communication. Although strongly interrelated and interdependent, separate stands can help pinpoint, better understand, and plan for areas of strengths and needs within communication and language.

Relationship of Language with Other Domains
Language is part of a broader communication system which incorporates and is interdependent with cognitive and social-emotional development. Communication is also dependent upon sensory organization and motor development. A comprehensive assessment of communication must include careful consideration and assessment of the interplay of language with cognitive and social-emotional skills as well as sensory and motor development. It is important to look at isolated strands of development to assess patterns of strengths and needs but the challenge and key to planning effective language interventions is to then integrate all areas of development for effective communication.

<u>Dependence on Sensory Organization</u>
The ability to process language and sounds in a variety of contexts is dependent upon adequate sensory organization or processing (Strand 0.0). The child needs to perceive and organize vision, touch, sound, and movement in order to regulate attention and to process and understand what people are communicating without becoming overloaded. Sensory organization is also needed to plan and sequence the sounds in a word, words in a sentence, and movements to follow directions in an organized manner.

<u>Relationship with Cognition</u>
Cognition plays an important role in understanding that words and gestures are symbols for objects, events, and relationships. Examples of cognitive interplay include:
- During play (Strand 1-1), children learn to use objects in their play to represent or symbolize objects, events, and relationships similar to the way children learn to understand and use words as symbols for objects, events and relationships. For example, in play a doll begins to represent a live baby, and in language the word or sign for doll or baby represents the real doll or real baby. In addition, combining objects in play and later carrying out a series of actions and gestures in a "play plan" appears to parallel learning to understand multi-word sentences spoken by others, and later speech production of two word combinations.
- Learning to imitate familiar and unfamiliar gestures (Strand 1-2) is related to learning to use conventional gestures to communicate, because the child learns to use conventional gestures by observing and imitating others. In addition, being able to imitate unfamiliar, invisible gestures may help the child learn to say new words as he imitates new oral motor movements.
- Auditory awareness and localization abilities (Strand 1-3) have obvious implications on language. The child must hear and process sounds in order to understand and produce speech.
- Object permanence (Strand 1-4A) also plays an important role in language. The concept that objects continue to

exist when not perceptually present impacts upon the child's ability to understand or use words to represent objects, events and relationships which are not immediately present.

- The concepts of "cause and effect" and "means-ends" (Strands 1-4B and 1-4C), play an important role in the child's efforts and motivation to communicate and exchange information with others. These cognitive concepts help the child learn that his verbal and nonverbal behaviors can affect others and are a means to achieve goals.
- Concept, classification and discrimination skills (Strands 1-6 and 1-7) are needed to understand and generalize relational, associative and categorical words or symbols such as "more" and "big."

Relationship with Social-Emotional Development

Similar parallels and interplays exist in the social-emotional domain. Communication involves expressing emotions and feelings and is dependent upon the child understanding that he is a distinct and important person who can affect others to get his needs met (Strands 5-1, 5-2, and 5-3). In addition, learning the power of social interactions, as well as learning social rules and expectations, help guide the child in his social relationships (Strands 5-4 and 5-5). This is similar to learning the rules which govern language, such as "taking a turn" in a verbal or gestural exchange.

Dependence on Motor Development

Language development is also dependent upon gross and fine motor control, muscle tone, and motor planning (Domains 3.0 and 4.0). The quality and level of overall motor development can affect the postures and movements used in gestures, facial expressions, signs, and speech production during communication. The quality of speech production is also strongly dependent upon oral motor control (Strand 6-1), which may also be strongly influenced by gross motor development and sensory processing.

Assessment Considerations Applicable to All Strands in the Language Domain

Hearing loss: Understanding and verbalizing meaningful words is strongly dependent upon the ability to hear. If a child is delayed in language, hearing impairment must first be ruled out before assessing and planning language skills. HELP does not assess hearing per se, but hearing is addressed further in Strand 1-3 "Auditory awareness and localization." Children who have significant ear infections or chronic middle ear fluid may have transient hearing impairments which can also impede auditory processing and language development.

The following parent interview questions are applicable to all strands in the Language Domain

- Do you have, or have you ever had, any concerns about your child's hearing?"
- Has your child's hearing ever been tested?"
- Has your child had any ear infections or fluid in his ears? *If so*, About how many? Was it treated by a doctor? What is the longest ear infection your child had that you can remember? Do you know if he has an ear infection or fluid now?" Has a doctor treated the infection?

Simultaneous assessment of Language Strands

Although each strand has an underlying key concept, it is usually unnecessary and inappropriate to assess each strand separately. Language sampling and observation of language during play, daily activities, and other areas of assessment will yield findings in various language strands concurrently. Thus, a single response in one strand area is likely to allow you to credit items in several language strands as well as other areas of development. For example, if you asked the child to "throw the ball" when a ball and doll are available, and in response the child says, "ball" and throws the ball to you in a playful way, you could credit in receptive language his understanding of the words "ball" and "throw" in Strand 2-1, as well as his ability to follow a direction in Strand 2-2. In addition, you could credit his expressive vocabulary with the word "ball" in Strand 2-3 as well as his ability to produce single consonant vowel combinations in Strand 2-6. The gross motor and social interactive skills of throwing a ball can also be credited in the gross motor and social-emotional domains.

Language assessment must be culturally relevant

It is important to assess and adapt language items to reflect the child's relevant cultural and environmental experiences and language. Assessment of language abilities should occur using the child's primary native language, both verbal and nonverbal, using objects and pictures that are meaningful to the child. Specific family interview questions have been included to help assure meaningful assessment and planning.

Assess in natural environments and through family interview

A true assessment of a young child's language can be difficult to achieve by unfamiliar observers in unfamiliar settings, especially with a shy or hesitant child. Sample naturalistic opportunities are included for most skill items to observe the child's language during the course of typical daily activities, play, and parent-child interactions.

Many items may need to rely on accurate parent reporting of their child's typical language. Accurate parent reports will depend heavily on *your* ability to ask meaningful and clear, specific questions. Parent interview questions, specific to many of the language items, are included within the procedures for the respective language skill.

Incorporate variety!

Since HELP is an ongoing curriculum-based assessment, it is likely that items will be repeated with infants as they are incorporated into curriculum activities and are periodically reassessed to measure progress. To ensure generalization, it is extremely important, especially with language, to incorporate variety into the example assessment procedures and objects and pictures used. Assessment and interventions should occur in multiple settings, using a variety of materials and eliciting techniques.

General Assessment Adaptations applicable to all strands in language

Hearing impairment:

To accurately obtain and interpret an assessment of the child's communication abilities, the assessment should be conducted with a professional who is trained and experienced in working with children who have hearing impairments. The environment must be arranged to provide optimal auditory and visual stimuli while reducing distracting stimuli. The facilitator should use the child's preferred method of communication to communicate effectively with the child and to assess and credit skill items. If the child has hearing aids, he should be tested for proper functioning prior to assessment, and his hearing aids should be worn during the observation period.

When assessing a child who is learning to use sign language be sure:
- to sign as well as talk using short simple messages;
- to use matching facial expressions;
- to sign with clear view of the child;
- to use frequent repetition of signs;
- the child understands what you are requesting; the child may need several examples of the expected response to understand what is expected; use modeling and signs or other prompts.

A hearing impairment specialist should work closely with all of those involved in intervention planning and implementation of appropriate communication goals.

Motor impairment:

If the child has a severe neuromotor disability, speech and communication may be severely compromised. Assessment and planning should occur with a pediatric speech-language therapist and physical or occupational therapist to help identify optimal positions and movements for promoting communication, and to help identify alternative or augmentative communication systems when appropriate.

Regulatory/Sensory Disorders:

All aspects of communication and language may be affected by regulatory and sensory organization problems. If a child evidences difficulties in this area (refer to Strand 0.0 "Regulatory/Sensory Organization"), it is very important to involve a therapist trained and experienced in sensory organization in evaluation and intervention planning.

Medical conditions:

Motor impairments, cardiac or respiratory disorders, or other medical conditions can interfere with endurance and breathing patterns used in vocalizations and speech. Always consult with the child's physician and a speech-language therapist for evaluation and intervention planning.

Cultural adaptations:

Assess the child using his primary language if assessment is for the purpose of identifying speech and language impairments; credit words, gestures and dialects that are used in the family and culture. Use culturally relevant toys, dolls, objects, foods, and pictures. A member of the assessment team should be a person who shares the same culture as the family, or who is bicultural/bilingual and is trained and experienced in communicating with young children.

2-1 UNDERSTANDING THE MEANING OF WORDS

A. OBJECTS, EVENTS, AND RELATIONSHIPS

1.12	2-3	Watches speaker's eyes and mouth
2.16	5-7	Looks and vocalizes to own name
1.38	6-8	Looks for named family members or pets when named
1.48	8-12	Listens selectively to familiar words
1.55	9-12	Knows what "no no" means and reacts
2.26	9-14	Shows understanding of words by appropriate behavior or gesture
1.93	16-19	Understands most noun objects
1.92	16-21	Recognizes and points to four animal pictures
1.102	18-20	Points to several clothing items on request
1.112	20-24	Understands personal pronouns, some action verbs and adjectives
1.124	24-28	Identifies rooms in own house
1.134	24-27	Understands complex/compound sentences
1.132	24-30	Selects pictures involving action words
1.140	27-30	Listens to stories
1.141	27-30	Understands many action verbs
1.155	30-33	Understands more adjectives
2.75	24-36	Formulates negative reasoning
1.159	33-36	Understands all common verbs, most common adjectives, some prepositions

B. BODY PARTS

1.91	15-19	Identifies one body part
1.111	19-22	Identifies three body parts
1.119	22-24	Identifies six body parts
1.131	24-28	Knows more body parts
1.154	30-36	Points to six body parts on picture of a doll

Family Friendly Interpretation of Strand Concepts, Assessment, & Purpose

We will be observing how your child is learning to understand the meaning of the words he hears when others talk to him. For example, if I said, "See the ball," and your child looked at his ball, this would be a good clue that he understands the meaning of the word "ball" even though he may not be able to say it. Learning the meaning of words is an important language skill which requires your child understand that words are symbols for objects or events. Professionals often call this "receptive language." Before a child learns to say a word, he needs to hear the word spoken many times so he can learn the meaning of the word. Children usually understand many more words than they can say.

The first words that children learn to understand are words for objects and events which they hear, see, and touch every day. For example, words such as "bottle," "ball," "eat" and the names of familiar people are common first words children understand, because they see and experience and hear the names for them every day. Later, children learn to understand the meanings of words which they hear frequently but are not concrete; i.e., they can't actually see or touch the word. These words are usually words which describe actions and objects, such as "big," "under," or "down."

Professional FYI

Early sensory, cognitive, social, emotional and interactional competencies lay the foundation for helping a child understand the meaning of words. If the child is under 6 months or is evidencing delays in this area, assess birth-6 month skills and behaviors in the regulatory/sensory organization, cognitive and social-emotional domains which are considered pre-linguistic development.

The early skills in this strand focus on understanding specific concrete objects and people which can be named by substantive words, e.g., "mommy," "car." These substantive words generally parallel the development of expressive vocabulary in Strand 2-3. Skills after about 2 years include relational words (verbs, adjectives, adverbs) that derive their meaning from the objects and events they describe. These relational words generally parallel the development of expressive skills in the latter part of expressive Strands 2-3, "Expressive Vocabulary" and in 2-5 "Learning grammar and sentence structures."

Parent Questions   (General Examples - see Skills for specific questions)

To help identify the child's unique strengths and needs related to this developmental area:
- What are some toys or other objects that your child sees or plays with almost every day that he seems to understand when you name them ? *[Repeat with foods, utensils, clothing, people, pets and body parts]*
- Can you give me an example of how your child lets you know when he understands what you are saying to him?
- Does your child seem to know the names of any body parts such as "eyes" or "nose"?
- Is your child familiar with the pictures, toys and objects I've brought today?

- Can you think of others you think we should use in our assessment?
- What languages does your child hear at home?...at daycare?

To help identify family resources, priorities and concerns related to the child's development in this area:
- Are there any words that you think are especially important for your child to learn to understand during the next six months?
- You mentioned several words that your child seems to understand. Was there anything special that you did that seemed to help him learn these words?

Sample *Functional* Outcome Statements which may be generated by the Family

[Will be dependent upon identified individual child and family needs, and should incorporate objectives and activities from other domains]

My child will:
- Know his name;
- Know the names of his favorite toys and foods;

- Know the names of some body parts;
- Understand me when I ask him to do something;
- Stop when he is told "no";
- Enjoy story time.

Transactional Assessment

May assess through observation and interview.

Assessment of the Child's Environment

1. Supportive
[Example environments which support/facilitate development in this area]

The child's caregiving environments have a variety of opportunities to interact with interesting people, toys, objects, and pictures.

Assessment of Caregiver Interactions with the Child

1. Supportive
[Example interactions which support/facilitate child's development in this area]
The child's caregivers usually:
- Use a variety of intonations, gestures and facial expressions to help engage and encourage their child's attention and understanding of words;
- Name the people, objects, toys, body parts and pictures that the child is looking at or interacting with;
- Describe what the child and other people are doing using clear, simple language;

- Position themselves so their child can see their facial expressions and gestures.

2. Compromising
[Example interactions which may restrict, compromise, inhibit or be unsupportive of the child's development in this area]
The child's caregivers:
- Rarely talk to their child;
- Often overuse directives and commands rather than word labels or descriptions, e.g., saying "no" or "don't get it," rather than "Get your ball."

Identifying and Interpreting Needs for Intervention

If a child is significantly delayed in this area he may be having difficulty in <u>interpreting and understanding words or signs as symbols for people, objects, events and relationships.</u> As noted in the Introduction to Language, page 87, this may be due to hearing, cognitive, social-emotional, sensory organization or auditory processing problems.

<u>However,</u> before targeting one of these issues as the primary area of need for intervention, also consider and rule out, or adapt for other causes that may interfere with a true assessment of the child's ability to <u>interpret and understand words as symbols for people, objects, events and relationships.</u> These may include:

• <u>Limited exposure to enriching language experiences</u> and/or language models in primary caregiving environments.

• <u>Pictures or objects used in assessment were not familiar or meaningful to the child,</u> e.g., child may never have played with a ball or seen a bottle.

• <u>Situational:</u> e.g., the child may comprehend language but not respond in the ways we expect him to because he is not interested in the assessment materials, is "not himself" in a new setting or with new people, is not feeling well, or the setting has too many distractions.

• <u>Child has not learned the cognitive concept of recognizing pictures as symbols for real people and objects.</u>

• <u>Motor disability or delays</u> which interfere with child's ability to indicate when he understands a word; e.g., he may not be able to point, pick up, go get, etc.

• <u>Visual impairment:</u> the child will have difficulty understanding words which are dependent upon visual characteristics and observing gestures, e.g., "pretty," "red," "over there."

• <u>Poor body awareness, which</u> is a prerequisite for learning the names of body parts on himself.

Assessment Adaptations (Examples)

[Note any adaptations needed to credit and help plan interventions]

• <u>Visually impaired</u>
  – When assessing the child's understanding of words which label objects, give him two or three different familiar objects to explore thoroughly before asking him to indicate a named object. Do not expect him to point to the named object. Instead, ask him to "Find," "Play with," or e.g., "Give Mommy the…"
  – Use only familiar tangible objects that represent the real object; e.g., do not use imitation foods or objects which the child has not had frequent experience with; use the child's own clothing rather than pictures or adult clothing. Exception: if the child has toy animals that he has had much experience with, these may be used instead of animal pictures.
  – Substitute familiar, real, tangible objects for pictures. If assessing the child's understanding of action words, adapt by encouraging the child to "act out" the simple command containing verbs and actions with a doll; e.g., orient the child

to a doll and appropriate props (cup, bed) and ask, "Let baby go to sleep," "Help baby drink."
  – Use adjectives the child can touch or hear rather than adjectives that rely upon vision, e.g., "big," "loud," or "wet," rather than "pretty" or "red."
  – Children who are blind may have delays in body awareness. Unless specifically taught through hand-over-hand modeling, expect a delay in learning the names of body parts.
  – There may be a delay in understanding the personal pronoun "I." This appears to be related to the child's greater difficulty in establishing social identity.

• <u>Hearing impaired:</u> *[Also refer to Assessment Adaptations on page 89, in the Introduction to Language]* Because the signs for body parts are the actual pointing to the body parts, you cannot assess the child's understanding of the signs for body parts by signing the request. Assess through parent interview and observations during play that may indicate the child's understanding of body parts.

• <u>Motor impaired:</u> accept eye pointing if the child can not gesturally indicate his responses.

General Assessment Procedures & Processes   (apply to all items in this Strand)

[Refer to the Introduction, "Assessment Considerations Applicable to All Strands in Language," page 88]

1. Many items can be credited by parent report. It is not uncommon for parents initially to be unsure of all the specific words their child understands. After parents have been given time to respond to the broader general and open-ended questions previously listed, **it can be helpful to probe through categories and daily activities**; e.g., during meal and snack times "What foods and eating/drinking utensils does your child seem know the names for?"; during play "What toys does your child seem to understand the names for?"; during dressing "What clothing and body parts does your child seem to understand the names for?" *[Important note: With each question, emphasize and clarify that the child does not have to say the word to credit.]*

2. **Receptive skills are generally considered prerequisite to meaningful expressive skills.** If the child says words spontaneously and meaningfully you may credit his receptive understanding as well as his expressive vocabulary in Strand 2-3. Be sure, however, that the child is not saying the word in imitation and that he can say the word in different contexts to ensure he has full understanding of the word.

3. Be careful to **avoid giving the child any gesture hints** when assessing his understanding of target words.

4. **Alternate the placement of objects or pictures** when presenting them to the child to avoid having him select items based on their placement, e.g., always choosing the picture or object in your right hand.

5. If the child does not respond, or responds incorrectly, **show him the correct answer.** Let him hold and explore the correct picture or object, if interested, regardless of whether he responded correctly.

6. **Describe the skill and eliciting procedures to family members and invite them to help observe and/or assess.**

+ - A Credit Notes:

+   child usually displays understanding of target words as defined during play and daily activities by observation and/or caregiver report.

-   not observed or reported.

+/- appears to be an emerging skill; e.g., child seemed to learn the word during observation period or parent reports that skill is sometimes observed.

O   circle any credit if caregiver's interactions compromise or restrict child's optimal skills in this area; e.g., do not label objects, give unclear directions, etc., refer to interactional assessment above.

Note any adaptations used to credit.

 Assessment Materials

[Same as materials used for Strand 2-3, Expressive Vocabulary]

- Doll or puppet wearing simple common clothing items: shoes, hat, shirt, pants.
- Six common objects which the parent has identified or confirmed as familiar to the child, e.g., shoe, bottle, spoon, baby doll, toy car, cup, keys.

- An assortment of clear, colored pictures or photos which depict several actions which are meaningful to the child, e.g., "washing," "eating," "sleeping," "brushing," "walking," "running," "laughing," "crying." The pictures should be at least 3 by 5 inches and the depicted action should be the primary focus.

A. OBJECTS, EVENTS, AND RELATIONSHIPS

 1.12 Watches speaker's eyes and mouth   2-3

Definition: The child watches the eyes and mouth of an interesting person who is talking to him. Infants can discriminate many speech sounds by 3 months.

Example Observation Opportunities: Observe caregiver and infant interactions in a variety of situations, e.g., during a diaper change, when feeding, soothing, playing. Observe if the child sometimes watches the speaker's eyes and mouth. When the child is looking at you, initiate a "conversation," using short inflectional phrases.

Credit: (see also Credit Notes in this strand's preface)

+   looks at the speaker's eyes and mouth many times during the observation period; can attend to a variety of vocal patterns without looking confused or "tuning out."

2.16   Looks and vocalizes to own name   5-7

Definition: The child recognizes his name. When others call his name, he usually looks toward that person and/or may vocalize.

Parent Questions: Does your child seem know his name when you call him? How can you tell? Do you call your child by any other names? Which name do you and family members use most?

Example Observation Opportunities: May observe anytime during feeding, play, diapering. Observe when a familiar person calls the child's name when he is not already looking at the speaker. The key is to be sure that the child is turning to his name, not just the sound of a new voice.

Credit: (see also Credit Notes in this strand's preface)
+   usually differentially turns to or looks to the person who called his name or nickname. He does <u>not</u> have to vocalize for credit. May also credit other clear indicators of understanding; e.g., an older child may vocalize "huh" or purposely ignore and move in another direction to avoid doing something.

(also in Strand 5-2 "Development of Self")

1.38   Looks for family members or pets when named   6-8

Definition: The child knows the names of family members and pets he sees frequently. Note: The parent should define who the "family" is, e.g., a close friend living with them or daily care provider may be considered family.

Parent Questions: Who are the people and the pets your child sees almost every day that he might consider "family?" What do you call yourself to your child? Mama? Mommy? Does your child seem to know it is you when he hears "Mama"? How can you tell? Repeat for various family members and pets.

Example Observation Opportunities: Observe child's responses when he hears the names of family members or pets. The named person may be absent or present. Examples: Someone calling a pet to eat, or saying the pet's name to child when the pet is nearby; calling a sibling who is out of the room; asking where is "Daddy?"; asking the child to show the toy he is holding to "Mommy."

Credit: (see also Credit Notes in this strand's preface)
+   shows recognition of at least three names of family members or pets by looking at or pointing to the person/pet named if present. If a named person or pet is not present, he may look in the direction that the person or pet is expected to return, and/or show anticipatory excitement. If there are less than three family members or pets available in the child's environment, note and credit accordingly.

1.48   Listens selectively to familiar words   8-12

Definition: The child understands some single familiar words when used in context as a single word or as a key word within a short phrases, e.g., in the phrase, "Where's your bottle?" the child recognizes the word "bottle" and looks toward it or holds it out to his parent. "Familiar" words are words that are directly meaningful to the child. They are words he has heard many times in the context of familiar routines, e.g., understanding the meaning of "juice" and "cookie" during mealtime, or "bye bye" when someone leaves. At this stage, a particular word may represent one specific item but may not be generalized to other similar objects which he has not seen; e.g., the word "cup" refers to the child's cup only.

Parent Questions: What are some of the words your child seems to understand even though he cannot say them yet? *[Inquire through various categories as needed, e.g., toys, foods, greetings]*

Example Observation Opportunities: May observe anytime during daily activities, play and parent child interactions; e.g., when parent asks "Where's your bottle?" "You have a ball" or "See the baby," especially if extra emphasis is added to the key word. Pay special attention to the child's responses to phrases that provide contextual but <u>not</u> gestural cues, e.g., child looks at bottle when it is present and named, but the speaker did not point to it or hand it to him while naming it.

Credit: (see also Credit Notes in this strand's preface)
+   displays specific and consistent signs of recognition without gestural cues for at least three to five words; signs of recognition may include: looking, touching, gesturing toward, holding out to give, anticipatory excitement, or displaying a consistent specific change in facial expression. Note words credited.
+/- understands one to two words said in phrases.

1.55 Knows what "no no" means and reacts   9-12

Definition: The child understands "no no" as meaning "stop what you are doing" or "stop what you are getting ready to do." He may demonstrate his understanding by briefly stopping the activity he is engaged in but will probably then continue. Some children may respond as though their feelings have been hurt and may actually cry. At this stage, his understanding is still very limited, however, and he does not have the impulse control to hesitate more that briefly. "No" means "not this second" rather than "never" or "not now."

Parent Questions: How does your child react when you tell him "no?" *[Observe what terms the parent uses to tell her child "no." For example, the parent may say "Hey!" or "Uh-Uh!." Use these terms as the basis of assessing child's understanding of "no no"].*

Example Observation Opportunities: Incidental - observe child's responses if parent says "no" (or other similar term) when for example, the child starts to put non-edible in mouth, pull someone's hair, throw a toy, get into parent's purse or diaper bag. *[Note: The unfamiliar examiner should avoid saying "no" to the child. Instead, in a "no" situation it is preferable to distract child to a new toy or activity]*

Credit: (see also Credit Notes in this strand's preface)
+   briefly inhibits or displays other signs of understanding "no," e.g., crying, puckering lip.
O   circle any credit if caregivers overuse "no"; do not show child acceptable or alternative behaviors and do not set any limits even in dangerous situations.

(also in Strand 5-4 "Learning Rules and Expectations")

2.26 Shows understanding of words by appropriate behavior or gesture   9-14

Definition: Same as #1.48, earlier in this strand, but the child also understands familiar words when said outside of the typical context or routine in which he learned them; e.g., he may point to his shoe when named during mealtime rather than only during dressing.

Parent Questions: Same as #1.48.

Credit: (see also Credit Notes in this strand's preface)
+   displays specific and consistent signs of recognition for at least six familiar words without always needing familiar contextual or gestural cues. Signs of recognition may include: spontaneously naming, looking, pointing, reaching for, holding out to give, moving toward object, picking up or touching it. Note words credited.

1.93 Understands most noun objects   16-19

Definition: The child understands the names of most common objects in his environment such as the names of foods, utensils, clothing, toys, furniture. He understands them when said as single words and in multi-word phrases. At this stage, he understands their meaning in typical contexts and out of typical contexts, e.g., he may point to his shoe when named during mealtime rather than only during dressing. Another important feature of the child's comprehension at this stage, is his ability to understand that a word can represent different objects rather than just one specific object, e.g., the word "cup" means not only his cup but all cups he sees in his environment.

Parent Questions: What are some of the words your child seems to understand even though he cannot say them yet? *[Probe through various categories as needed, e.g., toys, foods, clothing, etc.]*

Example Observation Opportunities: At different times throughout the observation period, ask or observe when others incidentally ask the child to get, touch, show, or give various familiar objects which are within his immediate sight. Note which words the child understands, their category (e.g., food versus toy, toy versus clothing), generalization of the word meaning to other objects (e.g., "ball" can mean a red ball, a large ball, a blue ball), and if he understands them out of routine context.

Credit: (see also Credit Notes in this strand's preface)
+   displays an understanding of at least 10-15 objects from a variety of categories, generalizing the words to other similar objects and out of routine contexts as defined; he may point, name spontaneously, give, pick up, or look directly at the named object.

Recognizes and points to four animal pictures   16-21

Definition: The child understands the names of at least four different familiar animals.
Parent Questions: What are some animals that your child might recognize from seeing them in books, on TV, or outdoors? Does he have any pets or toy animals that he plays with?
Example Observation Opportunities: <u>Incidental</u> - observe to see if the child points to or otherwise indicates familiar animals when the animal is named, e.g., during story time, while taking a walk out of doors, while playing with animal toys. <u>Structured</u> - show the child an animal picture book with at least four familiar animals on a page or present four separate large pictures at the same time. Ask the child to "find" or "touch" each one. Have available at least six familiar animal pictures. If child has difficulty with pictures, try toy or real animals if available; e.g., family may have pet fish, dog, cat, bird, rabbit etc.
Credit: (see also Credit Notes in this strand's preface)
+ identifies at least four real, pictured or toy animals, by pointing to them on request or spontaneously naming them.

Points to several clothing items on request   18-20

Definition: The child understands the names of at least four familiar clothing items.
Parent Questions: "What are some clothing items that your child seems to understand the names for?" *[Probe with examples, such as diaper, bib, hat, and boots in addition to standard clothing names, such as shirt and shoes]*
Example Observation Opportunities: May observe when asking child to touch or get a clothing item during dressing or diapering; to dress or undress a doll during doll play; when giving or taking his coat upon arrival or departure; or when the child looks at clothing item when you name and admire it.
Credit: (see also Credit Notes in this strand's preface)
+   points to, spontaneously names or otherwise indicates understanding at least four clothing items without gesture cues.
+/- understands names of one to three clothing items.

Understands personal pronouns, some action verbs and adjectives   20-24

Definition: The child can understand many pronouns and some action verbs and adjectives. These include:
• most pronouns (I, you, me, he, she, it, yours, mine) when used in context in short phrases;
• a few action words which he hears often in familiar phrases, e.g., "let's *dance*," "*open* the box," "Time to *eat*;
• a few familiar adjectives, e.g., "hot," "big."
Example Observation Opportunities: <u>Incidental</u> - observe the child's responses (gestures, facial expressions, and actions) when others give short directions in context with<u>out</u> gestures. Examples: Say, "Give the block to *me*," when the child is holding a block and appears no longer interested in playing with it; "Baby wants to *eat*," when the child is involved in doll play and there is a toy spoon or bottle available; "*Your* hands are *dirty*," after playing in paints or playdough; "Get the *big* block," if one block is at least twice the size of another; "Touch *your* nose," and then, "touch *my* nose" during mirror play; "Lets *dance*," when music is playing but the child is not already dancing; "May I have a *bite*?" when the child is eating a cookie.
Credit: (see also Credit Notes in this strand's preface)
+   demonstrates understanding of at least two verbs, two adjectives and each of the pronouns: you, your, me, my, and I, without gesture cues in several contexts.

Identifies rooms in own house   24-28

Definition: The child understands the names of primary rooms in his own home, such as kitchen, bathroom, his bedroom, living room. He understands the names of whatever labels family members use, e.g., the den may be labeled "family room" or "TV room."

Parent Questions: Does your child seem to know any of the names of the rooms in your home? Which ones? How can you tell? What names do you call the rooms at home where your child spends most of his time?

Example Observation Opportunities: If assessing at child's home, ask the child (or observe when the child is asked incidentally) to take or retrieve something from at least two different rooms at various times. May also simply ask him where different rooms at home are. Use room names that he is familiar hearing. If not observing in routine environments, may assess when child is playing with a doll house if the rooms have distinctive features, e.g., sink, toilet, beds.

Credit: (see also Credit Notes in this strand's preface)
+   identifies at least two names of familiar rooms by pointing to or going to the correct room when asked.

 Understands complex/compound sentences   24-27

Definition: The child is able to understand many sentences which have logical multi-word combinations such as, "You may have your cookie when you come to the table," or "Pick up your doll and put it in the bed."

Example Observation Opportunities: Observe child's responses to complex and compound sentences which are directed toward him naturally throughout the course of observation (with only minimal or incidental gestures); e.g., child puts toys away and goes to table when an adult says, "When you put you blocks away, we'll have some juice and cookies"; or if child retrieves his coat or goes to the door when an adult says, "We're finished playing, it's time to go home. Use sentences that do not necessarily require the child to follow a direction as these require motor planning that is not the intent of this strand.

Credit: (see also Credit Notes in this strand's preface)
+   by clinical judgment, child seems to understand many logical sentences said in context; there may be some errors because the child may not always attend to each word in a sentence; e.g., the child may get *his* sweater when the parent requests, "Please get *my* sweater so I can hang it up," because he did not focus on the pronoun "my."

 Selects pictures involving action words   24-30

Definition: The child can identify pictures of a few familiar action verbs such as "sleeping," "eating," "crying," "brushing," "washing."

Example Observation Opportunities: Have available several clear pictures which illustrate common actions, one action per picture, e.g., child brushing teeth, eating a cookie, drinking from a cup, sleeping in a bed, washing hands at a sink, blowing bubbles, throwing a ball. Ask the child to "touch," "take," or "look at" the example; e.g., the boy who is *eating* (brushing, crying, etc.) just before you actually show him the pictures to avoid pre-selection. Then show him two or three action picture choices and repeat the instruction while he is looking at the pictures. Repeat with at least six common action pictures. Use pictures depicting actions that the parent thinks the child may know.

Credit: (see also Credit Notes in this strand's preface)
+   correctly picks at least three actions on two occasions with different action pictures.

Listens to stories   27-30

Definition: The child attends and understands the basic content of simple short stories told with or without a book. He especially likes stories he has heard before.

Parent Questions: Can you think of any stories that your child especially likes to hear? How does your child respond when you are telling him a story? Are there things he does that let you know he seems to be listening or understanding the story?

Example Observation Opportunities: Observe the child's apparent understanding and interest in a simple story book when you or his parent is reading to him. Use a story the child is familiar with, if available. The story should be short, have key repetitive phrases, and portray a simple plot and sequence of events which are relevant to the child, e.g., a short story about going to daycare or about having a new baby in the house, if child has a new sibling. If a book is used, it should have a few words on each page and large, colorful simple pictures that match the story line.

Credit: (see also Credit Notes in this strand's preface)

+ can attend for the duration of a short story with apparent understanding; this may be demonstrated in one or more of the following ways: interest in hearing the story over and over again; repeating words or phrases from the story, or displaying appropriate facial expressions and gestures indicating his interest and understanding; e.g., child smiles or laughs when something silly or funny happens, show signs of concern or curiosity if someone gets hurt or something is lost.

Understands many action verbs   27-30

Definition: The child understands many action verbs which include verbs he does not hear every day, e.g., "blow," "throw," "cut," "sneeze," "mix." Specific verb understanding will be dependent upon the child's experiences.

Example Observation Opportunities: Observe the child's responses anytime during to requests which occur naturally during play and daily activities; e.g., "*Blow* the bubbles," "*Throw* the ball," "*Give* the cup," "*Jump*," "Put baby doll to *sleep*," "It's time to *eat*," "*Stir* the pudding." The request may be in context but without gesture cues; e.g., if you suggest "*Kick* the ball," it is okay to point to the ball but the kicking action should not be gestured or pantomimed. The child's understanding of action words may also be observed when looking at pictures which depict actions as in #1.132 earlier in this strand, especially if child is motorically impaired.

Credit: (see also Credit Notes in this strand's preface)

+ understands at least ten action words; may credit if child demonstrates named action with himself or a doll, spontaneously says correct action, or points to or names action in picture. *[Note: Since it may be difficult to elicit understanding of this many actions, credit from combination of parent report and observation; you may also assume that if the child understands less common verbs such as "cut" or "mix," he also understands more common verbs which he hears every day]*

Understands more adjectives   30-33

Definition: The child understands many commonly used adjectives or descriptive words, e.g., "hot," "dirty," "cold," "big," "happy," "sad, " "wet," "dry." He may also understand some quantity words, such as "one," "many," "full," and "empty."

Example Observation Opportunities: Observe child's responses to adjectives used in phrases and his ability to follow directions during play and daily activities; e.g., "Your hands are *dirty*," after playing in paints or playdough; "Get the *big* block," if one block is at least twice the size of another, "Use the *wet* sponge to wipe," if there is a dry and a wet sponge available; "Give the baby doll the *little* cup," when two cups are available, one much smaller than the other.

Credit: (see also Credit Notes in this strand's preface)

+ demonstrates understanding of at least eight to ten adjectives as they apply to at least two different objects, e.g., correctly identifies the big ball and big spoon when it is compared to a smaller ball or spoon. The child may demonstrate understanding by spontaneously saying the adjective in correct context or by gesture, e.g., points to or gets *big* ball on request when two are available; wipes doll's face when an adult comments that it is *dirty*.

2.75 | **Formulates negative reasoning**   24-36

Definition: The child understands "no" or "not" as meaning non-existence or disappearance (e.g., no more, not there), and denial (e.g., "That's not yours," or "That's not a spoon; that's a fork"). The child also understands statements, such as "The car won't go," "You don't want juice?" and "You're not going out."

Example Observation Opportunities: <u>Incidental</u> - may observe when child whines or cries when told, e.g., "no more" cookies during snack time; or when child moves on to another toy when told that the wind-up toy he is approaching does not work; or if the child gets upset when he goes to the door and is told he cannot go out. <u>Structured</u> - ask the child to find a toy hidden in one of three boxes, keeping the empty box closest to him. When he starts to reach for the empty box, say, "It's not in there," being careful not to give gesture cues, such as shaking your head.

Credit: (see also Credit Notes in this strand's preface)
+ demonstrates understanding of negative reasoning as defined at least two times.

1.159 | **Understands all common verbs, most common adjectives, some prepositions**
33-36

Definition: The child understands common verbs, adjectives and prepositions and their relationship to other words in a sentence; e.g., that verbs describe what someone is doing and that adjectives describe objects. The types of relational words a child understands will be dependent upon his experiences; e.g., a child may not understand the verb "digging" if he has never dug in sand or watched others dig in a garden. In comparison to #1.141 and #1.155 earlier in this strand, he also understands (but may not always say correctly), various verb tenses, e.g., eat, eating, ate; more subtle adjective differences, e.g., warm versus hot, and bigger versus biggest; more abstract descriptive terms, e.g., scary; and a few prepositions, e.g., in, on, under.

Example Observation Opportunities: Same as #1.141 and #1.155 earlier in this strand. Additional example eliciting questions or comments directed to the child may include: "The baby is sleeping, can you *whisper* "night, night?"; "What are you *chewing*?" "*Lick* your spoon off," "Make it *stick* to the paper"; while playing with playdough, "Roll," "poke," "pinch"; "Put your blocks *on* the table," push the car *under* the table."

Credit: (see also Credit Notes in this strand's preface)
+ demonstrates understanding of at least 20 verbs, 10-15 adjectives and three prepositions as they apply to different objects.

[Note: since it may be difficult to elicit or keep track of this many actions and adjectives, may credit from combination of parent report and observation; may also assume that if the child understands less common verbs or adjectives, such as "lick," "mix," "biggest" that he understands for more common verbs which he hears every day]

B. BODY PARTS

 | **Identifies one body part**   15-19

Definition: The child understands the name of at least one major body part, such as eyes, head, nose, belly, or foot on himself, a doll, or on others.

Parent Questions: Does your child seem to know the names for any body parts such as his "nose" or "eyes" when you name them? How does he let you know that he understands?

Example Observation Opportunities: May observe when playing with child in front of a mirror, with a doll, or with a puppet. Ask him to touch or point to one body part at a time.

Credit: (see also Credit Notes in this strand's preface)
+ spontaneously names or touches, points to, or moves at least one body part named on self, doll, or another person. Note which part(s) and how the child indicated. If more than one part is identified, may also credit the next two items in this strand as appropriate.

Identifies three body parts   19-22

Definition: The child understands the names of at least three major body parts, such as eyes, head, nose, belly or foot on himself, a doll, or on others.
Example Observation Opportunities: Same as #1.91 above.
Credit: (see also Credit Notes in this strand's preface)
+   spontaneously names or touches, points to, or moves at least three body parts named on self, doll, or another person. Note which parts and how the child indicated. If six body parts are identified, may also credit the next item in this strand as appropriate.

 ### Identifies six body parts   22-24

Definition: The child understands the names of at least six body parts. At this stage, he should be able to identify some facial parts as well, such as leg, hand, arm, back, and belly on himself and others. He may begin to identify some smaller parts, such as tongue, knee and elbow if others have named them fairly often for him.
Example Observation Opportunities: Same as #1.91 earlier in this strand.
Credit: (see also Credit Notes in this strand's preface)
+   spontaneously names or touches, points to, or moves at least six body parts named on self and a doll, or another person. Note which parts and how the child indicated. If more than six body parts are identified, may also credit the next items in this strand.

 ### Knows more body parts   24-28

Definition: The child is able to identify most major body parts and some smaller parts, such as knee, elbow, neck, lips, tongue, eyebrow, fingernail.
Example Observation Opportunities: Same as #1.91 earlier in this strand.
Credit: (see also Credit Notes in this strand's preface)
+   identifies at least six major body parts <u>and</u> two smaller body parts on himself, others or on a doll.

 ### Points to six body parts on picture of a doll   30-36

Definition: Same as #1.119 "Identifies six body parts," but for this item he recognizes them on a picture.
Example Observation Opportunities: Show the child a clear simple full length picture of a person or doll that is at least 3 by 5 inches. This can be a separate picture or a picture in a magazine (clothing ads are frequently good for this). Ask him to point to various body parts. Let the child put stickers on named body parts to make the task more interesting.
Credit: (see also Credit Notes in this strand's preface)
+   spontaneously names, points to, or puts stickers on any six body parts on a picture when named; he may also miss one or two, but he should not miss major body parts, such as eyes, mouth, hair.

2-2 UNDERSTANDING AND FOLLOWING DIRECTIONS

1.43	7-12	Responds to simple requests with gestures
1.56	9-14	Responds to simple verbal requests
1.87	15-18	Indicates two objects from group of familiar objects
1.133		Obeys two part commands
	18-24	a. two related commands
	24-29	b. two separate commands

Family Friendly Interpretation of Strand Concepts, Assessment, & Purpose

We will be observing how your child is learning to understand and follow simple directions such as, "Give me your ball" or "Pick up your shoes." At first children need gestures and other cues to help them understand the meaning of a request. When you ask, "Give me the ball," your child needs to see you hold out your hand while you are making the request and needs to be holding the ball. Later, children are able to recognize different words within a request and can relate them together to help figure out the request. For example, if we say, "Put your doll in the bed," he focuses in on the words "doll" and "bed" and figures out the request without needing a lot of gestures to help him.

In addition to understanding the meaning of words in requests and directions, your child must also be able to remember what you've asked him to do and, be able to plan his movements in the correct sequence. For example, in the direction, "Put your doll in the bed," your child has to remember the words "doll" and "bed," as well as be able to plan a series of movements; e.g., pick up the doll, go over to the bed, and then place the doll in the bed.

Parent Questions   (Examples)

To help identify the child's unique strengths and needs related to this developmental area:

- Can you think of some simple directions or requests that your child seems to understand and be able to follow?
- Can you think of some requests or simple directions you might ask your child during mealtime?...during dressing? clean-up? bedtime?
- Have you noticed if you need to give your child extra hints to help him understand what you want, such as pointing to the object you are asking for?

To help identify family resources, priorities and concerns related to the child's development in this area:

What simple directions would you like your child to be able to understand better during the next few months?

Sample *Functional* Outcome Statements which may be generated by the Family

[Will be dependent upon identified individual child and family needs, and should incorporate objectives and activities from other domains]

My child will:
- Help pick up his toys when asked;
- Follow simple directions during mealtime, such as "Wipe your face" and "Give me your cup."

Transactional Assessment

May assess through observation and interview.

Assessment of Caregiver Interactions with the Child

1. Supportive
[Example interactions which support/facilitate child's development in this area]
The child's caregivers usually:
- Make requests which are clear; e.g., "Get your shoes," rather than "Get it";
- Use gestures when needed to help the child understand requests;
- Praise their child when he follows or attempts to follow a direction;
- Keep requests short and developmentally appropriate;
- Emphasize key words in requests.

2. Compromising
[Example interactions which may restrict, compromise, inhibit or be unsupportive of the child's development in this area]
The child's caregivers frequently:
- Give unclear directions, e.g., "Get it," "Do it";
- Give directions which are too complex for the child to understand.

Identifying and Interpreting Needs for Intervention

If a child is significantly delayed in this area, more so than in Strand 2-1, "Understanding the meaning of words," he may be having difficulty in <u>processing language and, or planning appropriate movements to carry out a direction</u>.

As noted in the Introduction to Language, page 87, this may be due to a hearing impairment, cognitive or social-emotional delay, or other sensory organization problems. <u>However,</u> before targeting one of these issues as the primary area of need for intervention, also consider and rule out, or adapt for other causes that may interfere with a true assessment of the child's <u>ability to process language and/or plan appropriate movements to</u> <u>carry out a direction</u>. These may include:

- <u>Lack of interest, attention or motivation</u> to complete the task; competing environment or activity;
- <u>Purposeful non-compliance</u>, especially during the "No" stage;
- <u>Requests contained too many words</u> which are not in child's receptive vocabulary;
- <u>Motor impairment</u> which interferes with child's ability to follow direction;
- <u>Visual impairment</u> which interferes with child's ability to observe visual contextual cues to help figure out requests and commands.

Assessment Adaptations   (Examples)

[Note any adaptations needed to credit and help plan interventions; also refer to General Adaptations on page 89 in the Introduction to the Language Domain]
- <u>Visually impaired</u>
  - Be sure the child has had plenty of time to explore each object and its relational location to himself and other objects before giving simple requests.
  - Do not expect the child to point to named objects on request. Instead, ask him to "Find," "Play with," or for example, "Give Mommy the..."
  - For item #1.88 "Brings objects from another room on request," assess only if you are observing in the child's familiar environment, requesting objects which are always kept in consistent places.
- <u>Hearing impaired</u> *[Refer to General Adaptations on page 89, in the Introduction to Language]*
- <u>Motor Impaired</u>:
  - Adapt all items as appropriate with an occu-

pational or physical therapist to make these items functional for the child; e.g., if you are working on teaching the child how to use switch toys or a communication board, it may be more appropriate to assess and plan for directions related to using these items.
  - Make requests which require movements within the child's motor abilities. Accept eye pointing when possible and watch for gestures which are consistent but may be more subtle or distorted, e.g., "Look at me," "Give Mommy a smile."
  - Physically help the child experience following simple functional commands when he physically cannot do so. For example, if an object from across the room is requested, carry him to the place he looks toward when you ask, e.g., "Let's get your radio."

General Assessment Procedures & Processes   (apply to all items in this Strand)

[Also refer to "Assessment Consideration Applicable to all strands in Language" page 88]
1. Assess **using the concrete words and actions verbs that you are sure the child understands**, as identified by the parent and/or in the preceding Strand 2-1 "Understanding the meaning of words.
2. **Most requests can be observed during the natural course of play or daily activities.** Contrived requests out of context will not be meaningful and are more likely to be less motivating to the child.

+ - A Credit Notes:

+ child usually follows direction as defined during play and daily activities by observation and/or caregiver report.

- not observed or reported.

+/- appears to be an emerging skill, e.g.,

needed extra repetition or cues.

N/A not appropriate to assess due to motor impairment.

A always appears confused at new directions even though they are simple, contain familiar words in his receptive vocabulary, and the child has the motor ability to carry it out; can follow simple directions only after demonstration and then may need step-by-step direction; e.g., in response to the request, "Feed the baby," the child needs step-by-step direction to: (1) pick up the baby, (2) pick up the bottle, (3) put the bottle in the baby's mouth.

O circle any credit if interactions compromise or restrict child's optimal skills in this area.

Note any adaptations used to credit.

1.43   Responds to simple requests with gestures   *7-12*

Definition: The child follows simple requests which are given <u>with</u> gesture hints, such as pointing, holding object out. The request must be meaningful and in context; e.g., adult smiling and saying, "Come here," while holding out arms to baby, or pointing to a toy and saying, "Look at the dog!" The child may follow the request or may shake his head "no."

Parent Questions: What simple requests or phrases does your child seem to understand? How can you tell? (Provide parent with examples of simple phrases if needed to clarify.)

Example Observation Opportunities: Observe the child's responses to simple requests which occur naturally during play and daily activities. The simple requests should be short two- or three-word phrases which are familiar to the child and are provided in context with gestural cues. These may include for example: "Get down?" "Come here!" "Play Peek-a-boo," "Pat-a-cake," "Give me," "You want up?" "Look at the dog!"

Credit: (see also Credit Notes in this strand's preface)
+   responds appropriately to a simple request provided with gesture cues; this should be observed on several occasions in different but meaningful contexts.

1.56   Responds to simple verbal requests   *9-14*

Definition: The child understands and follows simple requests or directions given <u>without</u> gesture hints (in contrast to #1.43 above). The request must be meaningful and given in a familiar context; e.g., parent saying without gestures, "Give me a kiss," when child is sitting on parent's lap enjoying a pleasant interaction, or "Give me the ball," when the child is holding the ball but the parent does not hold arms out.

Example Observation Opportunities: Observe the child's responses to simple requests that occur naturally during play and daily activities. Avoid giving excessive gestural cues, such as pointing to the object. Example contextual situations which may arise include: parent asking child to "Bring me the book," when child is holding or looking at a book; "Pick up the block," when parent or child drops it during play but does not point to it; "Give me a kiss," as in the definition; "Take out a diaper," when parent is getting ready to change diaper, has taken the child's pants off and the diaper box is within reach; "Drink your juice," when child is sitting in highchair and juice is available; "Get the ball," when a ball is within reach but the parent does not point toward it.

Credit: (see also Credit Notes in this strand's preface)
+   responds correctly to simple verbal requests without direct gestural cues; this should be observed on several different occasions in different but meaningful contexts.

1.87   Indicates two objects from group of familiar objects   *15-18*

Definition: The child can follow a simple direction that includes two related objects when other objects are also available; e.g., "Give the baby a bottle," when a doll and three other doll items are available.

Example Observation Opportunities: <u>Incidental</u> - may be observed, e.g., during dressing when parent asks child, "Get your shoes and socks," when his shirt and pants are also available; during mealtime when asking child, "Give me your cup and spoon," when a plate and napkin are also available; during playtime when asking, "Give the baby a bottle," when a cup, brush and spoon are also available. <u>Structured</u> - present four to six common objects to the child after confirming with the parent that each object is familiar to the child. Objects can be related, e.g., shoe and sock, cup and spoon, block and cup, baby doll and bottle. Allow the child to examine and play with the objects while you name and describe their function. Ask the child to give, pick up or otherwise indicate two named objects; e.g., "Put the spoon in the cup" or "Give the baby bottle."

Credit: (see also Credit Notes in this strand's preface)
+   follows a simple direction that involves two related objects when other objects are also available; this should be observed on several occasions with different objects.

1.133 Obeys two part commands

a. two related commands   18-24

Definition: The child can follow a direction that includes two simple but related commands involving one object; e.g., "Take your napkin, and wipe your face."

Example Observation Opportunities: During snack time ask the child to, e.g., "Pick up your cup and take a drink," "Take your napkin and wipe your face"; during play with toys, ask the child, e.g., "Get your blocks and put them in the box," "Take the bottle and feed the baby," "Get the baby doll and put it to sleep," "Let's put on these hats and look in the mirror." Repeat the command twice if needed, but avoid giving any gesture cues, such as pointing or looking. Use related commands that are novel to the child, i.e., not ones which he follows routinely by rote.

Credit: (see also Credit Notes in this strand's preface)

+   follows two simple but related commands in a meaningful context but without gesture; this should be observed on several occasions using different commands.

b. two separate commands   24-29

Definition: The child can follow a direction that includes two separate and distinct commands, e.g., "Take off your bib and then wipe your mouth," or "Give me your spoon and give Mommy your cup."

Example Observation Opportunities: During snack time and clean up ask the child, e.g., "Put your napkin in your lap and then eat your cracker," "Throw your cup in the trash and wipe the table," "Take off your bib and wipe your face," "Give me your spoon, and throw your napkin in the trash"; during play ask the child, e.g., "Get the doll from the bed and the brush on the table"; "Put your blocks down and let's go get the ball." The two-part command should be novel, i.e., not one that the child follows routinely by rote. Repeat the command twice if needed but avoid giving any gesture cues such as pointing or looking at the object. Use two-part directions that you are sure the child can follow each part if given separately. If the child does not follow the two-part command, repeat it giving only one part at a time to confirm that he understood each part.

Credit: (see also Credit Notes in this strand's preface)

+   follows a direction that involves two separate and distinct commands in a meaningful context but without gestures; this should be observed on several occasions using different directions.

2-3 VOCABULARY

2.29	11-14	Says "dada" or "mama" specifically
2.37	12-15	Uses expressive vocabulary one-three words
2.40	12.5-14.5	Uses exclamatory expressions - "oh-oh," "no-no"
2.41	13-15	Says "no" meaningfully
2.42	13-18	Names one or two familiar objects
2.45	15-17.5	Uses 10-15 words spontaneously
2.50	17.5- 20.5	Uses expressive vocabulary of 15-20 words
2.52	18-24	Uses own name to refer to self
2.56	19-21.5	Names two pictures
2.58	20.5-24	Uses nouns, verbs, modifiers
2.61	21.5-24	Names three pictures
2.71	24-27	Imitates spontaneously or requests new words
2.70	24-29	Names five pictures
2.66	24-30	Uses "self-centered" pronouns
2.69	24-30.5	Uses expressive vocabulary of 50+ words
2.76	25-30	Uses size words
2.78	27-40	Refers to self using pronoun
2.80	28-33	Verbalizes one preposition
2.83	29-36	Names eight or more pictures
2.89	30-33	Gives full name on request
2.92	30.5-35	Uses expressive vocabulary of 200 + words
2.93	33-35.5	Verbalizes two prepositions
2.99	35 +	Uses expressive vocabulary of 300-1,000 words
2.100	35.5 +	Verbalizes three prepositions

Family Friendly Interpretation of Strand Concepts, Assessment, & Purpose

We are interested in knowing the types and number of words your child is learning to say. This is sometimes termed "expressive vocabulary," in contrast to "receptive vocabulary," which refers to the words your child can understand but not necessarily be able to say yet. Children usually need to understand the meaning of words before they can learn to say them in a meaningful way. Since we know that young children do not always say the words they know in front of new people or in new situations, we will also be asking you questions about the words your child typically says at home.

There is a wide age range in terms of when children typically learn to say their first words. Some children are more quiet or interested in movement than in learning to say words. Others are more interested in playing with the sounds they make than in learning to say words. Some children may understand words but have diffi-culty figuring out how to combine their sounds to say a word.

The first words children usually learn to say are the ones they hear often and the ones that are most meaningful and important to them. "Mama" or "Dada" are often first words, because these words contain sounds that are often the first sounds a child makes during vocal play. Since parents usually respond quickly with delight when they hear their child make the "mama" or "dada" sounds, the child learns that these sounds can be used specifically to mean mother or father. Other first words are also usually related to the objects and events that are most meaningful to the child. For example, if your child has had many experiences with a ball, because he has touched it, played with it and heard the word "ball" said many times while he was playing with it, "ball" may be one of the first words he says.

Professional FYI

This strand focuses upon words the child can say rather than how well he says them or whether he uses them to initiate or maintain a "conversation" or interaction. Some children may have a large vocabulary but may not use these words in a dialogue with others (Strand 2-4B), or may not be able to say them in a relational way with other words (Strand 2-5), or not be able to say them clearly (Strand 2-6). Conversely, a child may have a more limited vocabulary but be able to say his words clearly or engage in a meaningful commu-nicative exchange with gestures and babbling. Communicative intent and intelligibility addressed in these other strands, however, can be assessed concurrently.

Be sure to refer to the Introduction to Language, page 87, regarding the relationship of speech and language with other domains, assessing this strand concurrently with other strands, notes regarding hearing impairments, and general assessment adaptations.

Parent Questions   (General Examples - see Skills for specific questions)

To help identify the child's unique strengths and needs related to this developmental area:

[If English is not the family's native language] What languages does your child hear at home?...at daycare?...What language(s) are you teaching your child?]

- About how many words have you heard your child say? Less than 10? 20? 30?
- Can you tell me some of the words you've heard your child say? *[It may be helpful to probe through various categories and daily activities; e.g., "Are there any names of foods your child says during mealtime?"]* Which of these do you hear him say every day? Once a week?
- Are there some words you've heard your child say once or twice but then have never heard him say again?
- When do you hear your child "talking" the most?
- Have you noticed some words your child really tries to say but can't seem to get the word out? Can you tell me a little more about that; for example, does he get upset?
- What do you think is the best way for us to assess which words your child is learning to say?
- Which toys would you say are the most familiar to your child, i.e., toys he has seen, played with and heard you name for him? *[Repeat for foods, utensils, clothing, furniture, people, pets, body parts.]*
- Has your child seen, played with and heard the names of the pictures and toys I've brought today?
- Are there any other important aspects about your child's speech that you think are important for us to know?

To help identify family resources, priorities and concerns related to the child's development in this area:

- Are there any words that you'd especially like your child to learn to say during the next six months? *[It may also be helpful to probe through various daily activities, e.g., What words would you especially like your child to say during mealtime?]*
- Have you noticed some things that have seemed to help your child learn some of the words he can say?

[If the child is significantly delayed in speech]

- What advice or information have you been given by other professionals, relatives or friends about why your child isn't talking? How does this fit with what you think might be going on?

Sample *Functional* Outcome Statements which may be generated by the Family

[Will be dependent upon identified individual child and family needs, and should incorporate objectives and activities from other domains]

My child will be able to say (or communicate):
- What he wants;
- The names of family members;
- The names of his favorite toys and foods.

We will know more ways to help our child learn to talk (or communicate).

Transactional Assessment

May assess through observation and interview.

Assessment of the Child's Environment

1. Supportive:
[Example environments which support/facilitate development in this area]

The child's caregiving environments have adults who are good speech models and sometimes other young children who are good speech models.

2. Compromising:
[Example environments which may restrict, compromise, inhibit or be unsupportive toward development in this area]

The child's caregiving environments are frequently over- or under-stimulating for the child's needs, e.g., loud television or stereo usually playing; child is typically isolated from daily activities, sounds and language models.

Assessment of Caregiver Interactions with the Child

1. Supportive:
[Example interactions which support/facilitate child's development in this area]
The child's caregivers often:
- Reinforce their child's vocalizations by renaming, expanding, or otherwise acknowledging his apparent intent; i.e., giving him what he requested, repeating his word in an expanded sentence, interpreting what the child may be saying into a true word;
- Name or describe the things their child is doing, looking at, playing with, listening to;
- Respond to and interpret their child's communicative attempts.

2. Compromising:
[Example interactions which may restrict, compromise, inhibit or be unsupportive of the child's development in this area]
The child's caregivers:
- Usually expect the child to say more than he is developmentally ready for;
- Expect the child to always speak clearly;
- Usually ignore the child's communicative attempts;
- Do not talk to their child;
- Overuse "baby-talk";
- Continually ask "What's this?" rather than providing verbal description and word labels.

Identifying and Interpreting Needs for Intervention

If a child is significantly delayed or displays atypical development in his expressive vocabulary, significantly more so than in other areas of language, motor (including oral motor and neuro-motor), cognitive and social-emotional development, <u>he may have a hearing impairment or expressive speech/communication disorder</u>. *Refer to an audiologist and/or speech-language therapist for further evaluation and consultations regarding intervention.*

<u>However</u>, before targeting any of these issues as the primary area of need for intervention, consider, rule out, or adapt for other causes that may interfere with a true assessment of the child's <u>expressive vocabulary abilities</u>. These may include:
- <u>Developmental</u>, e.g., the child is temporarily at a "plateau," as he is concentrating his efforts in other areas of development, such as learning to walk.
- <u>Situational</u>, e.g., the child talks at home or with familiar people but not in front of others or in new situations; is more irritable or ill.
- <u>Environmental</u>, e.g., the child does not have speech models to learn from, or others always talk for him.
- <u>Physical/medical issues</u>, e.g., the child has a tracheotomy, severe sore throat, cold.
- <u>Visually impaired:</u> the child may have a more limited vocabulary than peers who have vision. Speech is often spurred by vision, and children frequently learn words by constantly asking, "What's that?" either verbally or gesturally. Visual limitations can also affect the child's abilities to symbolize or to learn verbal concepts, because many objects and events do not lend themselves to concrete experiences, e.g., learning colors, learning names for objects which can not be touched or heard (e.g., the sun, a fly). Children who are blind may thus have a more limited vocabulary for referring to objects and events which rely upon vision. Children who are blind may also have delays in learning personal pronouns, which is thought to be related to establishing social identity.

Assessment Adaptations   (Examples)

[Note any adaptations needed to credit and help plan interventions]
- <u>Visually impaired</u> *[refer to General Adaptations on page 89 in the Introduction to Language]*
  - Assess using objects and events which are very familiar to the child. Let him thoroughly explore objects before encouraging him to name them.
  - Substitute tangible objects for items requiring pictures. Use only familiar, tangible objects which represent the real object; e.g., do not use imitation foods or objects which the child has not had frequent experience with; use the child's own clothing rather than doll clothes or adult clothing.
  - Although delays may be normal in learning some vocabulary words, such as personal pronouns and words related to objects and events which are not concrete, these words are still appropriate to assess and target for intervention.
- <u>Hearing impaired</u> *[also refer to General Adaptations on page 89 in the Introduction to Language]*
  - Credit signs and gestures the child is learning for communication.
- <u>Motor impaired</u> *[also refer to General Adaptations on page 89 in the Introduction to Language]*
  - Give the child plenty of time to use his vocalizations or words; do not interrupt to say words for him unless he is clearly frustrated.

Assessment Adaptations   (continued)

Confirm his apparent communicative attempt when you are sure he is finished with the appropriate word or sentence.

– Credit consistent vocalizations used as words which may be distorted due to motor impairment.

General Assessment Procedures & Processes   (apply to all items in this Strand)

[Also refer to "Assessment Consideration applicable to all strands in Language" page 88]

1. A child may have many words in his expressive vocabulary, but may only say them rotely with limited meaning, or to simply name things without using them to communicate to others. **A more comprehensive pragmatic assessment or analysis of the child's language behavior and understanding of concepts may be appropriate for children who present with or appear to have gaps in their vocabulary, or who do not appear to use their words communicatively.** In addition to observing and recording the number and specific words for these children, it will be important to further:

a. observe and note the child's apparent communicative intent of the word, i.e., observe if he use his words to:

   – seek attention to himself, an event, or an object;

   – request objects, information, or assistance;

   – protest, answer, or otherwise acknowledge what another person has said or asked;

   – name or make a comment about a person, event, or object;

   – greet or otherwise acknowledge or say good by to others;

   – engage another to share joy, give a warning, flirt, exclaim, etc.

b. observe and note the child's extent of understanding and ability to generalize the meaning of words, i.e., observe if he uses words:

   – to specifically represent only a particular object, e.g., "ball" is used to label only his small red ball (approximately 9-15 months);

   – to represent various similar objects and events, e.g., "ball" is used to label any ball, not just his small red ball (approximately 15-18 months);

   – in an over-generalized manner, e.g., "ball" is used to name all round objects, even if they are not truly balls (e.g., orange, necklace beads);

   – to indicate a relationship between objects and events; e.g., child says "gone" when he finishes eating his cookie, or "down" when his toys falls off his highchair (approximately 18 months and older);

   – to represent categories of objects which share common aspects, e.g., child says "animals" instead of naming each animal in a picture; or, "clothes" instead of naming each thing he is wearing (approximately 2 years and older).

2. **Note the environmental circumstances, events, materials and interactions which elicit and stimulate the child's vocalizations as well as those which are inhibiting.** This can be very useful when planning interventions.

3. **Describe the skill and example eliciting situations and procedures to family members and invite them to help observe and/or assess.** Be sure to ask them what situations they feel may help elicit their child's speech.

+ - A Credit Notes:

+ by observation or report, child has said word spontaneously or in response to "What's this?" more than once and within the past few weeks; he does not have to say the word clearly to credit (intelligibility is assessed in strand 2-6; note which words the child says frequently (every day) and less often (once a week dependent on certain occasions or stimulus).

- not observed or reported.

+/- has said word once, or says word in imitation of hearing another person.

A atypical: words are almost always used inappropriately without any contextual or communicative relevance; frequently repeats words perseveratively beyond its functionality or appropriateness (but not because he is practicing a new word).

O circle any credit if environment or interactions compromise or restrict child's optimal language skills.

Note any adaptations used to credit

Assessment Materials

- Video or audio tape, if possible, to record and analyze speech production and communication.
- Culturally meaningful materials that are motivating to the child and promote interactions and play. These will be dependent upon the child's individual interests and developmental skills in other areas of development. Examples of materials which often stimulate speech include: snack items (juice, cup, crackers, fruit); doll-play materials (doll, bed, spoon, bottle, brush); puppet; doctor kit; crayons and paper; a few small blocks and container; bubbles; picture books; grooming items (mirror, brush, tissue, pretend shaving or make-up kit), toy telephone.
- If over 18 months developmentally in speech:
  1. Culturally meaningful pictures of common objects, such as animals, actions and verbs. Use pictures which you are certain are in the child's receptive vocabulary.
  2. Two sets of similar objects that are very similar in every way except size, one at least twice the size of the other, e.g., big and little balls, big and little block, big and little spoon (e.g., soup spoon versus a baby spoon).

2.29   Says "dada" or "mama" specifically   11-14

Definition: The child says "dada," "mama," "papa," or other consistent label specifically to mean mother, father or primary caregiver.

Example Observation Opportunities: May observe child calling parent or other primary caregiver anytime he is trying to get their attention; e.g., when the parent leaves the room or moves out of sight; when the child wants something out of reach, wants to be picked up, or to get out of his crib, highchair or playpen; when the child wants parent to look at him or something he is holding; when the child needs help; or, to make sure parent is still there when the child moves away or is involved in an activity.

Credit: (see also Credit Notes in this strand's preface)
- \+   says "da da," "ma ma" or other consistent word to label appropriate parent or other primary caregiver
- \-   says "da da" or "ma ma" but <u>not</u> discriminately to mean mother or father; labels all women "mama" or all men "dada," but may credit #2.20 in Strand 2-6.

2.37   Uses expressive vocabulary one-three words   12-15

Definition: The child says one to three single words meaningfully in context. These words are in addition to "mama," "dada" or other names of family members and pets. A child's first words are typically approximations of adult words and refer to a particular object or situation. The child can say these words spontaneously; i.e., not in imitation, but not necessarily in response to "What's this?" First words are usually those which are most directly meaningful to the child and are in his receptive vocabulary, e.g., things he eats, drinks, plays with, or does.

Parent Questions: Can your child say any word besides "mama" or "dada"? When do you usually hear him say them?

Example Observation Opportunities: Observe child's use of words during play and daily activities. Avoid talking too much, especially avoid overuse of questions which may inhibit the child's spontaneous speech. Sometimes make comments about a particular toy he is engaged in, but if the child is slow to warm up, stay more in the background. Pause before automatically responding to the child when he is gesturing for something he wants. If the child is not generalizing his words, be sure to use the specific objects he his familiar with, e.g., use similar crackers or toys he has at home.

Credit: (see also Credit Notes in this strand's preface)
- \+   spontaneously says at least one word meaningfully, other than "mama" or "dada." The word can be a consistent approximation used specifically to label a particular object, e.g., "ba ba" for bottle.
- \-   uses a word approximation for many different things, e.g., says "ba ba," for mother, ball, bottle, toy.

2.40 Uses exclamatory expressions - "oh-oh," "no-no"   12.5-14.5

Definition: The child says any exclamation such as "oh-oh!" "uh-oh!" "oh!" "yea!" "no-no!" "Oops," "Aw," "Ow!" with matching facial and vocal expressions. He uses these expressions to express surprise, joy, or displeasure. The actual exclamations he uses will be dependent on those he has seen others use.

Parent Questions: Have you ever heard your child say "uh-oh!" "Oops!" or other similar expressions? Can you think of an example when you heard him say this?

Example Observation Opportunities: Exclamatory expressions may be elicited when something special or unexpected happens, e.g., juice spilling; tower of blocks toppling over; cheering after completion of a task; something dropping; child falling, slipping or bumping into something without hurting himself; toy suddenly appearing in pop-up or "Jack-in-the-box." The child may be observed to say "no no" to himself when he is approaching a situation in which his parent has previously said "no no," e.g., getting in to parent's purse.

Credit
+ any exclamation-type vocalization used meaningfully with matching vocal and facial expressions.

2.41 Says "no" meaningfully   13-15

Definition: The child says "no" to protest when he wants someone to stop an undesired action. He may accompany his "no" with a head shake, pushing another's hand away, turning away or some other gesture of resistance. At this beginning stage the child may sometimes say no when he really means yes because he understands "no" as a response word.

Parent Questions: Does your child sometimes say "no" instead of only shaking his head?

Example Observation Opportunities: May observe in any "protest" situations or in response to a question, e.g., parent telling the child to give or put back a toy; parent or another child taking a toy away that he's interested in; child saying "no" when parent tries to give him more food; or in response to an unfamiliar person putting arms out to pick child up.

Credit: (see also Credit Notes in this strand's preface)
+ says "no" spontaneously in an appropriate "no" situation.
(may also credit #5.39, Strand 5-2, if child's "no" is said frequently and is reflective of his emerging strive for independence in the "no" stage)

2.42 Names one or two familiar objects   13-18

Definition: The child names one or two familiar objects in response to "What's that?" FYI: Being able to respond to a question is a different language process than spontaneously naming, as the child must purposefully retrieve the correct word to say.

Example Observation Opportunities: Although you do not want to overuse "What's this?" during daily activities and play, sometimes ask the child to name objects that you are sure are in his spontaneous expressive vocabulary; e.g., ask, "What's this?" when pointing to an object the child is holding or looking at; before giving the child his cookie or juice at snack time; when you point to a familiar picture in a book; before giving child his bottle. Give the child plenty of time to respond as you maintain a questioning facial expression and continue to point to or hold the object (but not to the point of frustration). If the child does not respond after several seconds, be sure to answer the question for him and let him have the object.

Credit: (see also Credit Notes in this strand's preface)
+ correctly says the word or word approximation to label at least one object in response to "What's this?"

2.45 Uses 10 to 15 words spontaneously 15-17.5

Definition: The child says about 10-15 words appropriately and spontaneously during daily activities. These words are in addition to "mama" or "dada" and exclamatory words. The words he says are dependent upon his experiences. The words include names or labels for familiar objects and people, and may include some action or verb-like words, e.g., "go," "up," and sometimes a descriptor, such as "hot."

Parent Questions: Explore with parent the words child says. Probe frequency of use (has parent heard more than once, on a daily basis) and if words are said in imitation or spontaneously. It can be helpful to probe through categories of words; e.g., Does your child say the name of any toys? Foods? Feeding utensils such as spoon, cup or bottle? Body parts such as nose if you point to them? Names of characters he sees on TV, such as "Big Bird?" Does he say any action words, such as "up?"

Example Observation Opportunities: Elicit through parent report and observation during natural daily activities and play. If possible, observe with a playmate. Examples of materials that often stimulate speech include: snack items (juice, cup, crackers, fruit); doll-play materials (doll, bed, spoon, bottle, brush); puppet; doctor kit; crayons and paper; a few small blocks and container; bubbles; picture books; grooming items (mirror, brush, tissue, pretend shaving or make-up kit), toy telephone. Example eliciting situations may include:

1.) Offering choices to elicit child's naming, e.g., when the child is holding a doll, hold out a spoon and toy bottle and ask the child what the doll wants; at snack time hold out juice and milk and ask what he wants to drink;

2) Any situation where the child needs help, e.g., to get a desired object that is out of reach or in a container that he can't open;

3.) Playing next to the child with similar materials, letting him take the lead, sometimes mimicking his interactions.

4.) Pointing to or making a comment about a particular item or event and pausing to invite a response; e.g., saying, "Ring ring, oh, the telephone is for you!"; looking into a can of blocks and exclaiming, "Wow, what's in there?"

5.) Looking confused when the child only gestures to indicate what he wants; e.g., if he puts his arms out to be picked up or points to an out of reach object, look confused and ask, "What do you want?"

Credit: (see also Credit Notes in this strand's preface)

+ spontaneously says, not in imitation, at least 10 words other than "mama," "dada" or exclamations; these may be said singly or interspersed with jargon. Some words can be a consistent approximation used specifically to label a particular object, e.g., "ba" for ball.

- do not credit a word approximation that is used for many different things, e.g., "ba" for mother, ball, bottle, or toy.

2.50 Uses expressive vocabulary of 15-20 words 17.5- 20.5

Definition: Same as #2.45 above, but vocabulary is expanding to include several more words.
Example Observation Opportunities: Same as #2.45 above.
Credit: (see also Credit Notes in this strand's preface)

+ spontaneously says, not in imitation, at least 10 words other than "mama," "dada" or exclamations; these may be said singly or interspersed with jargon. These may include words credited in prior items in this strand. Some words can be a consistent approximation used specifically to label a particular object, e.g., "ba" for ball.

- do not credit a word approximation that is used for many different things, e.g., says "ba," for mother, by, ball, bottle, toy.

2.52 Uses own name to refer to self 18-24

Definition: The child knows and can say his first name. The name he calls himself may be an approximation or "nickname" that is used frequently by others. Some children say their name spontaneously to confirm possession e.g., "Johnny ball," but others may only do so when specifically asked, "What is your name?"
Parent Questions: Have you heard your child say his own name yet?
Example Observation Opportunities: Ask "who's there?" when talking on play telephones and/or when child is hiding during a game; ask "who's that?" when looking in a mirror or at a picture of the child. Introduce yourself and others in the room, then ask child his name. This can also be done in a game-like fashion, naming a few dolls or stuffed animals or pictures of family members.
Credit: (see also Credit Notes in this strand's preface)

+ sometimes uses his own name to refer to himself.

2.56 **Names two pictures   19-21.5**

Definition: The child recognizes pictures as symbols for real objects and can say the names of at least two pictures of familiar objects. He may name pictures on request in response to "What's that?" or spontaneously when looking at the picture.

Parent Questions: Have you ever heard your child name any pictures? These can be pictures in his favorite book, hanging on the wall, or pictures on food packages. Is your child familiar with the objects in the pictures I have here today?

Example Observation Opportunities: Call child's attention to pictures as they occur naturally during the observation period by pointing and making inviting remarks, such as "Look" or "Oh!" Be sure to use pictures that you are fairly certain are in child's receptive vocabulary. These may include pictures on the wall when he is exploring the assessment setting, in a book during story time with parent, on the carton of juice during snack time, on a box which contains the toy (e.g., box of blocks with a picture of colored blocks on the outside). If the child does not name pictures spontaneously while he is looking at them, encourage him with an inviting question, such as "what's that?" or "what's in there?" Allow the child several seconds of response time before providing him the answer.

Credit: (see also Credit Notes in this strand's preface)
+   spontaneously names at least two pictures of familiar objects.
-    names picture in imitation, immediately after hearing the picture named by another.
(if child names three pictures, may also credit #2.61, later in this strand)

2.58 **Uses nouns, verbs, modifiers   20.5-24**

Definition: The child's expressive vocabulary includes familiar nouns, verbs, and modifiers. They may be said meaningfully in a short phrase, interspersed with jargon, or said in isolation. Nouns are used to label people objects, events, and locations; verbs are used to describe movements and actions of objects and people (e.g., go, open, up); and modifiers are used to comment on or describe physical attributes, movements, existence of objects, events, people (e.g., more, gone, dirty, this).

Example Observation Opportunities: Same as #2.45 (earlier in this strand.) May also expand situations to include, periodically asking the child, "What are you doing?" or "What is Mommy (Daddy, sibling, baby doll) doing?" when the child or parent is engaged in an interesting activity; "What happened?" after something drops, spills, or breaks; "Where is the___(object in sight)?" or "Where did it go?" when a ball rolls *under* the table.

Credit: (see also Credit Notes in this strand's preface)
+   spontaneously says at least 20 meaningful words, some of which are verbs and modifiers.
(may also credit appropriate items in Strand 2-5, "Learning grammar and sentence structures" if the child combines verbs or modifiers with nouns or pronouns in a phrase)

2.61 **Names three pictures   21.5-24**

Definition: The child can say the names of at least three pictures of familiar objects. He may name pictures on request in response to, "What's that?" or spontaneously when looking at the picture.

Example Observation Opportunities: Same as #2.56 earlier in this strand.

Credit: (see also Credit Notes in this strand's preface)
+   spontaneously names at least three pictures of familiar objects.
-    names picture in imitation, immediately after hearing the picture named by another.
(if five or more pictures are named, credit, as appropriate, #2.70 and #2.83 which follow later in this strand)

2.71

Imitates spontaneously or requests new words 24-27

Definition: The child is interested in learning how to say new words. He spontaneously imitates words he hears others saying and often asks "What's that?" or "What's this" (or some other form of request), as a way to help himself practice and learn to say new words.

Example Observation Opportunities: May be observed when the child sees or plays with something novel. For example, try giving the child a few novel and interesting objects for the parent and child to explore. These can be anything that may spark interest for the child, e.g., "Slinky" toy, lotion, hair clip, magnet, stuffed bunny, small empty jewelry box. Include objects which the child does not already say.

Credit: (see also Credit Notes in this strand's preface)
+ sometimes imitates or requests words as defined. He may repeat the word, e.g., "cow," expand it, e.g., "cow moo," or simply acknowledge your answer, e.g., "Oh."
- repeatedly requests "what's this" without appearing to process, listen, or respond to the answer.

2.70

Names five pictures 24-29

Definition: The child can say the names of at least five pictures of familiar objects. He may name pictures on request in response to "What's that?" or spontaneously when looking at the picture.

Example Observation Opportunities: Same as #2.56 earlier in this strand.

Credit: (see also Credit Notes in this strand's preface)
+ spontaneously names at least five pictures of familiar objects.
- names picture in imitation, immediately after hearing the picture named by another.

(if eight or more pictures are named, credit #2.83 which follows later in this strand)

2.66

Uses "self-centered" pronouns 24-30

Definition: The child is able to substitute pronouns for names but not always correctly. First pronouns are typically those that are child-centered, i.e., "I," "me," "mine" and those used to give directives to others, e.g., "you."

Parent Questions: Have you ever heard your child use any pronouns such as "me," "my," or "you"? Can you think of an example?

Example Observation Opportunities: May observe anytime child is giving someone a directive, e.g., "You get it"; or in response to questions, such as, "Who wants a cookie?" "Whose car is this?" or to confirm his possession, e.g., child saying "mine" if another starts to take one of his toys.

Credit: (see also Credit Notes in this strand's preface)
+ spontaneously says at least two pronouns to substitute for a name singly or in a multi-word phrase. His use may be reversed, e.g., says "me" when meaning "you" and not be grammatically correct, e.g., "me go" instead of "I go."

(also in Strand 5-2 "Development of Self")

2.69

Uses expressive vocabulary of 50+ words 24-30.5

Definition: The child uses at least 50 words spontaneously, i.e., not in imitation of hearing the word immediately beforehand. He uses these words meaningfully either singly or in multi-word phrases to name something, request, comment, greet, or in some way to control or act on his environment. At this stage, words should include nouns, pronouns, adjectives, verbs, directives (e.g., "more," "help"), and social words (e.g., "hi," "please"). The child may say about eight to ten of these words several times a day, some on about a daily basis, and others only occasionally; e.g., "bird" if he happens to see a bird while taking a walk, in a pet store, or in a book. The child should be able to generalize most of these words to a variety of objects and situations; e.g., He says "dog" to comment or label any dog (black, brown, big, small, toy, real, his own, one he sees in the park). He may, however, over-generalize some words, especially if he does not have experience with a new word e.g., he may say "dog" the first time he sees a cow, bear, or other animal if it has some similar characteristics.

Parent Questions: Interview caregivers as in #2.45 and #2.66 earlier in this strand, including specific questions related to child's ability to generalize a word. If expressive vocabulary has been an area targeted for in-depth assessment or intervention, the parent may be interested in completing a written sampling of the words she hears her child say during daily activities. Dependent upon the parent's time and priority in this area, the parent could keep a one- or two-day record of: what words the child says in imitation and spontaneously during: (1) play outside; (2) mealtime; (3) solitary play

Uses expressive vocabulary of 50+ words   (continued)

with toys; (4) play with a sibling or playmate; (5) bath time; (6) dressing; and (7) looking in a book. It may be more practical for the parent to unobtrusively tape record the child during one or two of these activities.

Example Observation Opportunities: Identify the types and frequency of words the child uses meaningfully through parent interview and observation in familiar settings. If this has be an area targeted for intervention, at least two observation periods of 30-45 minutes are recommended. Video sampling can be especially helpful to analyze what types of words the child is using and how he is using them. Refer to previous items in this strand for example, eliciting situations that may encourage the child's language: #2.45, #2.55, #2.66.

Credit: (see also Credit Notes in this strand's preface)

+ This item is looking at overall growth of the child's vocabulary. Each word does not need to be recorded. Credit through observations and parent report if child has a great variety of words which are said spontaneously in meaningful situations.

A Frequently uses an excessive amount of gestures and facial expressions in place of words he can say, even though the child's expressive vocabulary is building.

2.76 Uses size words   25-30

Definition: The child understands and can say one or two adjectives to describe the size of something. "Big," "little," "tiny," "long" are typical first size words.

Parent Questions: Does your child seem to know the difference between big and little? Can you think of an example? Have you ever heard him refer to something as "big"? *[Observe other size words that the parent uses with the child during interactions, e.g., parent may typically say "teeny" instead of "little." Use these words as the basis for assessment]*

Example Observation Opportunities: Incidental - show the child either one unusually large object (e.g., large therapy ball; giant stuffed animal) or two objects which are similar but different in size, one at least twice the size of the other (e.g., 1/4 graham cracker and a whole cracker, ping pong ball and a large rubber ball, baby spoon and soup spoon, doll shoe and an adult shoe). Let the child explore the different-sized objects (two at a time), and note if he spontaneously says a size word to comment or request. If the child does not say a size word spontaneously during play, try saying, "I have two *[name of object],* which one do you want?" If the child only points or says "this one," further request with an inviting expression, "Do you want the big or little one? Tell me."

Credit: (see also Credit Notes in this strand's preface)

+ spontaneously or on request says at least one adjective correctly to comment on the size of the object.

(may also credit in Strand 1-7B "Size Discrimination and Classification")

2.78 Refers to self using pronoun   27-40

Definition: The child refers to himself with "I" or "me," rather than saying his name. Pronoun usage may be grammatically incorrect, e.g., "Me do it," but in contrast to #2.66 earlier in this strand, the child can switch perspectives of the speaker and substitute "I" and "me" for "you"; e.g., if asked, "Do you want juice?" the child responds, "I (or me) want juice" rather than sometimes saying "you" when he really means "me."

Parent Questions: Have you ever heard your child say "me" or "I" to refer to himself? Can you think of an example? Does he sometimes mix these words up and say for example, "me" when he really means "you" or say "you" when he really means "me?"

Example Observation Opportunities: May observe incidentally whenever the child is giving someone a directive or making a comment; e.g., "me do it" or "I get ball"; or when he responds to questions, such as "Who wants a cookie?" "Who does mommy love?" etc.

Credit: (see also Credit Notes in this strand's preface)

+ says "me" or "I" rather than his proper name when referring to himself; the pronoun does not need to be grammatically correct, but must be used in correct perspective as defined.

2.80 **Verbalizes one preposition**   28-33

Definition: The child says one preposition appropriately to describe the position, location or relationship of one object to another, e.g., "cookie <u>in</u> box." He should understand the meaning of a preposition before he can say it appropriately and may understand the meaning of more prepositions than he can say. First meaningful prepositions are usually: "in," "out," "on," "off," "under," or "next to."

Example Observation Opportunities: <u>Incidental</u> - may observe when the child is telling someone to do something; e.g., to help take *off* his bib; to help take his new toy *out* of the box; or when he is responding to a request which involves a location, e.g., saying "<u>in</u> there" or "<u>under</u> there," when adult asks, "where is your car?" <u>Structured</u> - show the child a block and a small box with a lid. Put the block in the box and say, "I put the block *in* the box." If he is still interested, repeat for *on, off, under,* and *next to* the box. Give the block and box to the child, requesting that he put the block *in* the box, assisting if necessary. When the block is in, ask, "Where is the block?" Give the child plenty of time to respond before giving him the answer. Repeat for "on," "off," "under," and "next to," as long as the child remains interested.

Credit: (see also Credit Notes in this strand's preface)
+   spontaneously or on request says at least one preposition appropriately either singly or within a phrase.
-    NOTE: If child is not observed to use any prepositions in his spontaneous speech, assess and note if he has them in his receptive vocabulary.

(may also credit #2.93 and #2.100 (which follow in this strand), if the child says two or three prepositions, and/or may credit appropriate items in Strand 2-5, "Learning Grammar and Sentence Structures" if the child combines prepositions meaningfully with nouns or pronouns in a phrase)

2.83 **Names eight or more pictures**   29-36

Definition: The child can say the names of at least eight pictures of familiar objects. He may name pictures on request in response to "What's that?" or spontaneously when looking at the picture.

Example Observation Opportunities: Same as #2.56 earlier in this strand.

Credit: (see also Credit Notes in this strand's preface)
+   spontaneously names at least eight pictures of familiar objects.

2.89 **Gives full name on request**   30-33

Definition: The child can say his first and last name (sometimes middle) when asked "What's your name?"

Parent Questions: Has your child learned to say his first and last names? [*If yes*] Can you give me an example of when you've heard him say this?

Example Observation Opportunities: This is often an especially difficult item to elicit in unfamiliar situations. When the child has "warmed up" and is enjoying play, try any of the following activities, or credit by parent report:
1) During doll or puppet play, introduce the full names of the dolls and yourself and others in the room to each other. After two or three introductions of first and last names, ask the child his name. If he does not respond, ask him if his name is "Sam Jones"(or another incorrect name) to see if he'll correct you. If the child responds only with his first name, repeat it and probe for his last name, e.g., "Johnny what?"
2). During telephone play introduce yourself (or a puppet) with first and last name. Then ask "Who's this?" or "What's your name?" again probing for last name if needed.

Credit: (see also Credit Notes in this strand's preface)
+   spontaneously says first and last name, with or without prompts, to elicit last name.

2.92 **Uses expressive vocabulary of 200 + words**   30.5-35

Definition: The child's vocabulary continues to grow with expanding experiences. By this age he can usually spontaneously say more than 200 words meaningfully but at this stage the number of words he can say is typically too high for parents to count. Words include nouns (which predominate), then verbs, adjectives, adverbs, prepositions, negatives and demonstrative pronouns, such as "this" and "that." Words include his understanding and use of "category words," e.g., "toys," "animals," "food," "clothes." Depending upon the child's daily encounters, some words are used many times each day (e.g., "Mommy," "dog," "potty," "mine," "toys," "get it"); many more are used less often but generally at least once a day (e.g., "bath," "dinner, "hamburger," "toothbrush"); and others are

Uses expressive vocabulary of 200 + words (continued)

used on a weekly or seasonal basis as the situation occurs (e.g., "church," "raining," "doctor," "Santa," "birthday").

Example Observation Opportunities: Same as #2.69 earlier in this strand.

Credit: (see also Credit Notes in this strand's preface)

+ This item is assessing the child's continuing and expanding growth of vocabulary. Each word does not need to be counted or recorded. Credit through observations and parent report if child has a great variety of words which are said spontaneously in meaningful situations.

A frequently uses an excessive amount of gestures and facial expressions in place of words he can say, even though the child's expressive vocabulary is building.

2.93 Verbalizes two prepositions   33-35.5

Definition: Same as #2.80 "Verbalizes one preposition" earlier in this strand, but the child can now verbalize two prepositions correctly.

Example Observation Opportunities: Refer to #2.80 earlier in this strand.

Credit: (see also Credit Notes in this strand's preface)

+ spontaneously or on request says at least two prepositions appropriately either singly or within a phrase.

(may also credit #2.100 which follows, if the child says more than two prepositions; may credit appropriate items in Strand 2-5, "Learning Grammar and Sentence Structures" if the child combines prepositions meaningfully with nouns or pronouns in a phrase)

2.99 Uses expressive vocabulary of 300-1,000 words   35 +

Definition: The child's expressive vocabulary continues to grow every day with expanding experiences. By now he should be incorporating relatively increasing percentages of adjectives, adverbs, and other words that indicate linguistic growth rather than predominantly nouns.

Example Observation Opportunities: Same as #2.69 earlier in this strand.

Credit: (see also Credit Notes in this strand's preface)

+ This item is assessing the child's continuing and expanding growth of vocabulary. Each word does not need to be counted or recorded. Credit through observations and parent report if child has a great variety of words which are said spontaneously in meaningful situations.

A frequently uses an excessive amount of gestures in place of words, even though the child's expressive vocabulary is building.

(may also credit appropriate items in Strand 2-5, "Learning Grammar and Sentence Structures" because at this stage the child should be combining many words using some grammatical "rules")

2.100 Verbalizes three prepositions   35.5+

Definition: Same as #2.80 "Verbalizes one preposition" earlier in this strand, but the child can now verbalize at least three prepositions correctly.

Example Observation Opportunities: Same as #2.80. Also observe or adapt some requests and note if child is beginning to understand and/or say more difficult prepositions, such as "beside," "behind," "through," "around," and "over," e.g., "Place block *behind* the box."

Credit: (see also Credit Notes in this strand's preface)

+ spontaneously or on request says at least three prepositions appropriately, either singly or within a phrase.

2-4 COMMUNICATING WITH OTHERS...
OVERVIEW (A. GESTURALLY; B. VERBALLY)

 ### *Family Friendly* Interpretation of Strand Concepts, Assessment, & Purpose

We will be observing how your child is learning to use gestures and vocalizations to purposefully participate in a "conversation" with a partner. Since we know that young children often do not communicate as well in new situations or with people who are new to them, we will also be asking you questions about the way your child typically communicates at home.

Participating in a conversation is a turn-taking process which involves being able to start a conversation and being able respond to the partner. "Conversations" usually revolve around a common topic, such as a toy or a feeling. Your child may start the conversation by looking at you, smiling, vocalizing or pushing a toy toward you. He may respond or take a turn in a conversation by vocalizing or smiling back, or by making a new gesture such as banging the toy and looking back at the partner for another response.

Children thus can usually learn to participate in a conversation in a variety of ways besides talking. They express thoughts, feelings and needs to others through gestures and facial expressions as well as with words or vocalizations. At first, it may be very difficult to figure out what a child is trying to say with his gestures or vocalizations. We need to guess by looking at different possibilities based on what is currently happening and what we know about the child. Later, children's gestures and vocalizations become more like adult gestures and vocal inflections, so it is much easier to figure out what they are saying. At this stage, they use gestures, such as pointing, pushing things away, or pulling on. Their vocalizations are also more like conversations even if no true words are used because they use a variety of inflections to help get their meaning across.

 ### Professional FYI

This strand focuses upon the child's use of gestures and vocalizations to participate purposefully in communicative exchanges or "conversations" with a partner. Although interrelated with other language strands, this strand is not totally dependent upon specific vocabulary words or articulation. It is, however, considered dependent on and strongly interconnected with each of the strands in the Social-Emotional domain.

This Strand 2-4, "Communicating with Others," has been separated into two parts, Gestural and Verbal, since children may exhibit strengths in one area more than in the other. Both strands, however, are assessed concurrently, as with other language strands during natural interactions, daily activities and play.

Communicative exchanges generally develop in a fairly sequential order; from simple to more complex, as well as from more of a one-way communication to more elaborate two-way communicative interchanges. Early forms of verbal and nonverbal communication also appear to revolve around expressing emotions, whereas later gestures and vocalizations become more focused on objects and people. This hierarchical progression can be briefly summarized as follows:

- The infant's initial vocal and nonverbal communicative signals or gestures include behaviors such as eye contact, crying, cooing and smiling. These signals are not thought to be purposeful forms of communication and may often be ambiguous, but caregivers perceive

them as such, and thus these signals help lay the groundwork for later more intentional communicative exchanges. After about 3 months, the infant's signals become more clear and purposeful, although they are still not thought to be for the purpose of true communicative intent with another person; e.g., the child may look toward an object and smile, and the parent interprets his looking and smiling as meaning that he wants the toy.

- By around 8 or 9 months, the child's communication becomes more purposeful. He use gestures and vocalizations in an intentional, reciprocal, cause and effect manner. His gestures and vocalizations may be used to express a variety of emotions, to get attention, to get information, to acknowledge or respond to someone, or to end an interaction. In contrast to earlier stages, at this stage the child purposefully draws another person into a communicative exchange with an object and expects or anticipates that the person will respond to him. If he does not get the desired response he often persists. The child can also now understand many of the communicative intentions of other's vocal and gestural expressions, and, can take two or three "turns" in a "conversation" using gestures and/or vocalizations with a sensitive partner.

Professional FYI   (continued)

- Beginning at about 12 to 15 months, the child's communicative efforts become more varied, complex, and conventional. He begins to communicate with conventional gestures and vocalizations which have adult-like inflections. He can communicate about objects or events that are out of immediate touch rather than only vocalizing about or gesturing with an object he is holding or touching. At this stage, he is able to maintain a communicative exchange, taking five to ten "turns" with a sensitive partner, whereby each turn builds upon the last; e.g., the child points to a dog and the parent says, "Wow, a big dog," and the child then nods his head or vocalizes and waits for the parent to make another comment. He also begins to sequence gestures together in a chain to communicate more complex needs. For example, the child may hand his parent his empty dish and look toward the refrigerator for more food, or later, get his coat and take his parent's hand to communicate he wants to go outside.

 Parent Questions   (General Examples - see Skills for specific questions)

To help identify the child's unique strengths and needs related to this developmental area:

- How does your child let you know what he wants? What he does <u>not</u> want?
- Is it fairly easy to figure out what your child is trying to say with his gestures, vocalizations and facial expressions?
- How does your child let you know when:
  – He wants to be picked up or get close to you?
  – Wants you to help him with something?
  – He is angry? afraid?
- Can you think of some other gestures and facial expressions your child uses to communicate with you?
- Can you think of an example when it seemed like you and your child had a conversation about something even though he may not have used any true words?

To help identify family resources, priorities and concerns related to the child's development in this area:

Are there some gestures or expressions your child uses that you wish you could figure out what he is trying to say?

 Sample *Functional* Outcome Statements which may be generated by the Family

[Will be dependent upon identified individual child and family needs, and should incorporate objectives and activities from other domains]

My child will be able to:
- Let me know what he wants instead of always whining;
- Participate in a conversation.

We will:
- Be able to figure out what our child is trying to tell us;
- Know ways to help our child communicate with us.

 Transactional Assessment

May assess through observation and interview.

Assessment of Caregiver Interactions with the Child

1. Supportive:

[Example interactions which support/facilitate child's development in this area]

The child's caregivers usually:
- Accurately interpret and respond to the child's apparent communicative intent;
- Give the child time to communicate what he wants before responding;
- Reflect the child's apparent intent into words, e.g., if child lifts arms, parent may say, "You want me to pick you up!"
- Encourage the child to keep the communication going; e.g., if the baby gestures or vocalizes, parent responds and then waits for the baby to gesture or vocalize again.

2. Compromising:

[Example interactions which may restrict, compromise, inhibit or be unsupportive of the child's development in this area]

The child's caregivers frequently:
- Ignore or do not respond contingently to the child's communicative gestures and vocalizations;
- Misinterpret or misread the child's gestures and vocalizations.

General Assessment Procedures & Processes   (apply to all items in this Strand)

[Also refer to "Assessment Considerations Applicable to All Strands in Language," page 88]

1. **Observe and note:**
   - the clarity of the child's communicative vocal and nonverbal signals and gestures,
   - the number of "turns" the child takes in the conversation;
   - the natural contexts (settings, objects, events, partners) that help elicit them.

2. If a more in-depth assessment of specific communication strategies is needed, it may be helpful to **develop a list of the child's vocalizations and gestures according to intent**; i.e., what gestures or other nonverbal signals does child use to:

   - get attention or achieve closeness;
   - request an object;
   - request help with a task;
   - protest or display fear;
   - acknowledge he is listening when someone talks to him;
   - terminate an interaction (e.g., turn head, close eyes, cover ears).

3. **Describe to family members the communicative interactions you are assessing and ask them for additional examples of situations which may encourage them.** Invite family members to help observe and/or assess.

4. Credit notes are included in each sub-strand.

2-4 COMMUNICATING WITH OTHERS

A. GESTURALLY

1.06	1-6	Shows active interest in person or object for at least 1 minute
1.21	4-5	Continues a familiar activity by initiating movements involved
5.21	5-9	Lifts arms to parent
2.19	6-9	Waves or responds to bye-bye
5.32	9-12	Extends toy to show others, not for release
1.73	12-14	Understands pointing
2.39	12-15	Greets with verbal cues
5.38	12-15	Gives toy to familiar adult spontaneously and upon request
2.38	12-19	Gestures spontaneously to indicate needs
1.97	17.5-18.5	Points to distant object outdoors
5.58	18-24	Interacts with peers using gestures

NOTE: [Refer to pages 117 to 119 for this strand's Overview on Family Friendly Definitions, Parent Questions, Sample Outcome Statements, Professional FYI, Transactional Assessment, and General Assessment Procedures]

Identifying and Interpreting Needs for Intervention

If a child is significantly delayed in this area, more so than in other areas of language, he may be having difficulty in the social-emotional and cognitive foundations for understanding and using gestures as an effective means to communicate to others.

However, before targeting this as the primary need for intervention, consider and, rule out, or adapt for other causes which may interfere with assessing the child's ability to understand and use gestures or vocalizations communicatively. These may include:

- Environmental, e.g., the child has not had an interactive or responsive partner for communication;

- Visual impairment: communicative gestures are learned through watching others conventional gestures. Children who are blind cannot learn conventional communicative gestures in the same way as their sighted peers;

- Motor impairment: atypical muscle tone and other motor delays or impairments can affect the child's ability to send clear communicative vocalizations and gestures; conventional gestures may be distorted or not possible to achieve.

Assessment Adaptations   (Examples)

[Note any adaptations needed to credit and help plan interventions]

- Motor impaired: consult with a therapist for optimal positioning to help facilitate freedom of movement and minimize the effects of abnormal muscle tone. Give special attention to more subtle or unconventional methods child uses to attempt communication, e.g., facial expression, eye gazing, arm raising. Mark N/A for items which are inappropriate to assess or plan for due to the child's motor limitations. If the child has severe motor limitations, plan alternative communication strategies for intervention with a pediatric speech-language therapist and occupational or physical therapist.

- Visually impaired: Expect delays in gestural communication unless the child has had specific hand-over-hand training in this area. Omit items related to pointing to objects out of reach, i.e., #1.73 and #1.97. Provide extra anticipatory guidance with families as needed to help read the child's more subtle and unconventional communicative gestures.

General Assessment Procedures & Processes   (apply to all items in this Strand)

+ - A   Credit Notes:

+   child displays communicative gestures or vocalizations as defined with a partner.

-   not observed or reported.

+/-   appears to be an emerging skill.

A   atypical: in the older child, uses only stereotypical or idiosyncratic, unconventional, concrete gestures to communicate wants without true interpersonal engagement, e.g., physically manipulating another person's hand to get something out of reach without looking at the adult.

O   circle any credit if caregiver interactions compromise or restrict the child's communicative efforts, or if the caregivers have difficulty interpreting their child's more unique or subtle cues.

(Note any adaptations used to credit)

1.06   Shows active interest in person or object for at least 1 minute   1-6

Definition: The child displays "communicative readiness" with his gaze and body position to initiate, maintain, terminate or avoid an interaction with a person or object. For example, he looks, leans, and may smile to initiate or maintain an interaction, and shuts his eyes, turns away or averts his gaze when he wants to end or avoid interaction. An infant typically has "cycles" of attention, looking away briefly four to five times during a minute.

Parent Questions: Are there some things your child does that tell you he wants you to play or talk to him? How does your child let you know when he's had enough play?

Example Observation Opportunities: May assess anytime throughout observation period, especially during parent-child interactions. Observe if the parent interprets and responds to the child's eye gaze, facial expressions and body position as having communicative intent; e.g., baby looks at parent and parent responds, "Oh, you want more," "Hi," or "You want to get up?" or the child looks at toy and parent says, "You like your bear" or "You want to play with your bear." If the caregiver does not do this spontaneously, sometimes make a comment such as, "Look how he's looking at you! What do you think he's trying to say?"

Credit: (see also Credit Notes in this strand's preface)

+   uses eye gaze, facial expressions and body movements to communicate interest and disinterest in people and objects.

O   if caregivers rarely assign communicative intent to the child's signals, or have difficulty interpreting child's weaker or distorted signals

1.21   Continues a familiar activity by initiating movements involved   4-5

Definition: The child makes a specific body movement or gesture to say that he wants "more" when an interesting or enjoyable activity stops. For example, if the parent is talking, rocking or bouncing the child on her lap and then suddenly stops, the child waves his arms, rocks, or bounces his body in an attempt to get his parent to talk or start rocking or bouncing again. The child also indicates when he wants to end an activity or interaction by looking or turning away for more than a few seconds.

Example Observation Opportunities: Incidental - may observe during any playful game or verbal interaction between parent and child. Observe if the parent pauses for the child to respond, and if the child responds with a particular gesture during pauses. If so, continue to observe if the parent recog-

Continues a familiar activity by initiating movements involved   (continued)

nizes the child's signals and continues the interaction. <u>Structured</u>: - identify with the parent interactive "games" the child is familiar with, e.g., "Peek-a-boo," blowing on tummy, tickling tummy, "So Big," bouncing on knees, raising him in the air. After a couple repetitions, stop the game and observe to see if the child makes a specific body movement, gesture or vocalization to restart the game. If so, restart the game immediately. Again, after a few repetitions, stop to see if he will repeat the *same* body movement or gesture. Continue this one or two more times.

Credit: (see also Credit Notes in this strand's preface)
+   makes the same specific body movement or gesture to indicate when he wants more of an activity, and to indicate when he has had enough and wants to terminate the interaction.
-     child was already making the body movement, gesture, or vocalization before the activity or interaction stopped.

(also in Strand 1-4C, "Cause and Effect")

Lifts arms to parent   5-9

Definition: The child puts his arms out to his parents and other trusted caregivers to achieve closeness and later to communicate that he wants to be "rescued" from an unfamiliar or strange situation, e.g., if a stranger approaches child.

Parent Questions: How does your child let you know when he wants you to hold him?...to pick him up out of his crib, playpen or highchair?

Example Observation Opportunities: May observe whenever child wants to achieve closeness or get out of an undesirable situation; e.g., if he wants another parent to hold him, if he wants parent to "save him" when another approaches or tries to pick him up, when he wants to get out of his highchair or crib, when parent starts to leave or enters room.

Credit: (see also Credit Notes in this strand's preface)
+   at 5-7 months if child lifts arms or pulls on parent to achieve close contact.
+   at 8-9 months if child lifts arms to communicate that he wants to be picked up or rescued.

(also in Strand 5-1, "Attachment/Separation")

Waves or responds to bye-bye   6-9

Definition: The child makes a wave-like gesture in imitation of an adult wave good-bye. His wave may be an approximation of a true wave with his arm, or a more subtle opening and closing of his hands when held by his side. He may wait to wave until the person is out of sight. At this stage, he probably does not have the full meaning of the wave gesture.

Example Observation Opportunities: <u>Incidental</u> - may observe when the examiner or child is leaving the assessment setting if others wave as a model. <u>Structured</u> - encourage the child to imitate waving "bye-bye" to the cars driving by when looking out a window; to pop-up toys when pushing the toy back into the box.

Credit: (see also Credit Notes in this strand's preface)
+   sometimes imitates waves gesture in the appropriate context. He may have a little physical prompting by his parent; e.g., parent gently taps or lifts child's hand or arm but does not actually complete the wave.

Extends toy to show others, not for release   9-12

Definition: The child holds out his toy or other interesting object to another person as a gesture to communicate that he wants them to look at, acknowledge, approve, share, or explain it (but not take it away!). He further communicates his message by alternating his gaze between the person and the object. Vocalizations may or may not accompany his gesture.

Example Observation Opportunities: <u>Incidental</u> - may observe when child is given any novel or interesting object to play with during the observation period. If the child shows you a toy, make a comment such as, "Yes, you have a ball." <u>Structured</u> - invite the child to take an unfamiliar or interesting toy out of a box while his parent is seated nearby. Observe to see if the child spontaneously "shows" his parent or other person the toy. Examples of objects include: plastic Slinky, Koosh™ ball, colorful squeak toy, crumpled tissue paper, doll, comb, book, cookie.

Credit: (see also Credit Notes in this strand's preface)
+   holds toy or other object out to show another person as a gesture to communicate; alternates glance between object and person.

(also in Strand 5-5" Social Interactions and Play")

1.73   Understands pointing   12-14

Definition: The child understands and uses the pointing gesture as a method to communicate "What's that?" "Look at that" or "I want that." He further communicates this message by alternating his gaze between the person and the object he is pointing toward.

Parent Questions: How can you tell if your child wants something? Does he ever point to things? (Explain it does not have to be an exact pointing gesture.) Can you give me an example? What does he seem to mean when he points?

Example Observation Opportunities: May be observed when child sees something he wants which is out of reach but nearby in clear sight; e.g., during snack time hold out two items and ask the child which one he wants; during play give the child one part of a two-part toy (e.g., the base of a ring-stack toy) placing the second part just out of reach but in view; during mirror play ask, "Where's (child's name)?" when looking in a large mirror a foot or two away.

Credit: (see also Credit Notes in this strand's preface)
+ looks when someone is pointing to an immediate object, and points to an immediate object as a gesture to attract another's attention to an object; the gesture does not have to be an exact finger point.

2.39   Greets with verbal cues   12-15

Definition: The child uses a waving gesture to communicate "Bye" or (less frequently) "Hi" when someone says "Hi" or "Bye." In contrast to #2.19, "Waves or responds to bye-bye," he does not need to see the waving gesture as a model to imitate. The child's waving gesture is also more mature than in #2.19.

Example Observation Opportunities: Same as #2.19 earlier in this strand.

Credit: (see also Credit Notes in this strand's preface)
+ spontaneously waves to greet or gesture good-bye meaningfully, not always in imitation; he may wait until the person has already left.

5.38   Gives toy to familiar adult spontaneously and upon request   12-15

Definition: The child spontaneously gives a trusted adult a toy or other interesting object as a gesture to communicate that he wants the person to look at, acknowledge, share, help him with it, or explain what it is. After "giving" the object, the child can take several "turns" to maintain the communicative exchange; e.g., gives toy to adult, adult makes a comment, child vocalizes or gestures back, adult hands toy back, and child proceeds to play with it with the adult.

Example Observation Opportunities: Same as #5.32 earlier in this strand.

Credit: (see also Credit Notes in this strand's preface)
+ gives an object to another for the purpose of initiating or responding to a communicative interaction as defined.
- gives an object because he is no longer interested in it; moves on to another activity.

(also in Strand 5-5 "Social Interactions and Play")

2.38   Gestures spontaneously to indicate needs   12-19

Definition: The child effectively uses a range of conventional gestures to communicate needs such as "help," "pick me up," "tell me what this is," "I don't want it," "I want that." Conventional gestures include: pointing, showing, putting arms out, shaking head, holding hands out, taking adult hand to help, pulling adult's hand to show, twisting palms to say "All gone." At this stage, he also combines gestures into a sequence to communicate more complex intentions and requests; e.g., he may nod head "no" and push food away; take adult's hand to go across the room to an out-of-reach toy and then point to request the object; hand an adult an empty cup, and point to the refrigerator for more drink.

Parent Questions: How can you tell when your child wants something or needs your help? Can you give me an example? Is it fairly easy to figure out what he wants?

Example Observation Opportunities: <u>During snack or mealtime</u>, observe if and how the child communicates that he wants some food or drink which is out of reach, that he wants more of something, that he does not want something, and that he's finished. <u>During play, observe</u> if and how child communicates that he wants a toy out of reach, wants to know what a new object is or what it can do, wants help with a toy to make it work (e.g., getting a lid off a bottle of bubbles, restarting a wind-up toy), wants to continue an activity or game (e.g., blowing bubbles), wants to stop an activity or

Gestures spontaneously to indicate needs   (continued)

game, and wants to attract someone's attention to play with him.

Credit: (see also Credit Notes in this strand's preface)
+   uses a variety and combination of sequenced gestures to communicate a message or need.
-    gestural requests are limited to looking or extending arm.

(may also credit in Strand 2-4B if child also *vocalizes* to communicate needs)

1.97 ### Points to distant object outdoors   17.5-18.5

Definition: The child spontaneously looks and points toward an inaccessible distant object such as an airplane, moon, bird, or truck. He points to attract attention to the object and to communicate, "See that!" "What's that?" or "There it is!"

Parent Questions: Have you ever noticed your child pointing toward something that is too far away to actually get, for example, an airplane, light, or fire truck? What does he seem to be saying to you when he points?

Example Observation Opportunities: May observe when the child notices any interesting distant object or event, e.g., looking out of a window, hearing an airplane or fire engine while playing outside, noticing a light fixture or ceiling fan.

Credit: (see also Credit Notes in this strand's preface)
+   points to distant objects to attract attention, request information, or to exclaim about something special.

5.58 ### Interacts with peers using gestures   18-24

Definition: The child uses gestures to communicate with other children. Many of these gestures are aggressive, such as pushing, pulling or grabbing. He may use these gestures to communicate; e.g., "That's my toy," "I want that," "Play with me," "Come here." He also uses friendly gestures to interact and communicate, e.g., patting, hugging, waving, showing sympathy, shrugging shoulders, and pointing. Depending upon the child's verbal abilities, vocalizations may accompany gestures.

Parent Questions: Does your child have opportunities to be around other children about his age? How would you describe how he gets along with other children during play?

Example Observation Opportunities: If a playmate is available, observe instances of communicative interactions. Have toys available which invite interactions, e.g., ball, cars, dolls, sand or water play, rocking boat.

Credit: (see also Credit Notes in this strand's preface)
+   sometimes interacts with other peers using a variety of gestures, some of which may be aggressive.

(also in Strand 5-5, Social Interactions and Play)

2-4 COMMUNICATING WITH OTHERS

B. VERBALLY

2.05	1-5	Cry varies in pitch, length and volume to indicate needs such as hunger, pain
2.11	3-6	Responds to sound stimulation or speech by vocalizing
2.14	5-6	Vocalizes attitudes other than crying - joy, anger
2.18	5.5-6.5	Babbles to people
2.21	6.5-8	Shouts for attention
2.27	11-15	Babbles in response to human voice
2.35	12-17.5	Experiments with communication - not frustrated when not understood
2.38	12-19	Vocalizes spontaneously to indicate needs
2.44	14-20	Uses voice in conjunction with pointing or gesturing
2.46	15-17.5	Vocalizes wishes and needs at the table; names desired items
2.49	17-19	Echoes prominent or last word spoken
2.59	21-24	Tells experience using jargon and words
2.72	24-28.5	Experiments with communication - frustrated when not understood
2.73	24-34	Relates experiences using short sentences
2.74	24-36	Answers questions
2.81	28.5-36	Frustrated if not understood - utterances have communicative intent
2.88	30-31.5	Vocalizes for all needs
2.90	30-36	Participates in storytelling
2.96	34 +	Relates experiences more frequently using short sentences
2.97	34.5+	Asks questions beginning with "what," "where," "when"

NOTE: [Refer to pages 117 to 119 for this strand's Overview on Family Friendly Definitions, Parent Questions, Sample Outcome Statements, Professional FYI, Transactional Assessment, and General Assessment Procedures]

Identifying and Interpreting Needs for Intervention

If a child is significantly delayed or displays atypical development in verbal communicative exchanges, significantly more so than in receptive language (Strand 2-1) and gestural communicative exchanges, (Strand 2-4A), and not due to delays or disabilities in other areas of development, <u>he may have a hearing impairment or expressive speech disorder</u>. *Refer to an audiologist and/or speech-language therapist for further evaluation and consultations regarding intervention.*

Assessment Adaptations (Examples)

[Refer to General Adaptations provided in the Introduction to Language, page 89]

General Assessment Procedures & Processes (apply to all items in this Strand)

+ - A **Credit Notes:**

+   child participates in communicative exchanges using vocalizations and words as defined.

-    not observed or reported.

+/- appears to be an emerging skill.

A   atypical:
- words and vocalizations are almost always used inappropriately without any contextual or communicative relevance; and/or;
- frequently repeats words perseveratively beyond their functionality or appropriateness (but not because he is practicing a new word);
- uses an excessive amount of gestures to communicate in place of words even though the child's expressive vocabulary is building.

O   circle any credit if caregiver interactions compromise or restrict child's optimal communication skills

Note any adaptations used to credit

2.05 Cry varies in pitch, length and volume to indicate needs such as hunger, pain
1-5

Definition: With maturation the child's cry becomes more differentiated and rhythmical and is easier to interpret. In contrast to the newborn's monotonous, nasal cry which is one breath long, the child's cry begins to vary in pitch, length and volume, sometimes dependent upon the type of discomfort he is experiencing. The parent begins to interpret the child's cries based on the "type" of cry, e.g., a hunger cry versus a cry from pain.

Parent Questions: When your child is crying, how do you figure out what the problem may be? Does he have one cry when he's hungry and another one when he's bored?

Example Observation Opportunities: Observe caregiver's responses to child's cries as they occur. When the child cries, ask parents why they think the child is crying. Note if there are variations in the child's cry and how easy it is to interpret them.

Credit: (see also Credit Notes in this strand's preface)

+   cries vary in pitch, length and volume to signal different needs.
O   if caregivers have difficulty differentiating cries, and/or interpret them as being "bad" or "spoiled."

2.11 Responds to sound stimulation or speech by vocalizing **3-6**

Definition: The child sometimes vocalizes with non-specific sounds when someone talks to him or when he hears an interesting sound, such as his rattle or squeak toy.

Parent Questions: Does your child ever seem to "talk" to you with his sounds?

Example Observation Opportunities: A familiar caregiver may be more likely to elicit the child's vocalizations than an unfamiliar person. Observe at any quiet time when parent and child are engaged in face-to-face interaction and the child is in an alert state. Imitating the child's sounds or saying a short high-pitched inflectional phrase may help elicit the child's sounds.

Credit: (see also Credit Notes in this strand's preface)

+   makes any sound as a way to "take a turn" and interact in response to someone talking to him or to hearing an interesting sound.
O   caregivers rarely talk to child or do not respond to child's vocalizations.

2.14 Vocalizes attitudes other than crying - joy, anger **5-6**

Definition: The child is no longer limited to crying or laughing to express his feelings. He can now express a variety of feelings, such as joy, interest, pleasure, excitement, frustration and anger through changes in his vocalizations and facial and bodily expressions; e.g., he may chortle, squeal, grunt, whimper, coo, babble, smack his lips, frown, look surprised, and cuddle.

Parent Questions: How does your child let you know he's happy?... upset?... mad?... frustrated?

Example Observation Opportunities: Observe incidentally throughout observation period. If child vocalizes an emotion, note parent's responses. If the parent does not make a remark related to the child's emotions incidentally e.g., "Oh you're mad!" or "I see you like that," ask a question, such as "What's your baby trying to tell us?" or "I wonder how he feels about that?"

Credit: (see also Credit Notes in this strand's preface)

+   frequently expresses a variety of emotions and feelings beyond laughing or crying.
O   caregivers have difficulty interpreting or responding to child's varied emotional expressions.

2.18 Babbles to people **5.5-6.5**

Definition: The child sometimes makes babble sounds (e.g., "bababa") to someone to start or respond to a verbal interchange or to attract attention.

Parent Questions: Does your child sometimes seem to talk to you with his sounds? Can you give me an example? When you talk to him does he ever seem to "talk" back with his babble sounds?

Example Observation Opportunities: May be observed anytime the child and a sensitive partner are engaged in a joint activity, e.g., looking at a toy, during a diaper change, during face-to-face play.

Credit: (see also Credit Notes in this strand's preface)

+   purposefully babbles to initiate or respond to an interaction with another person.
O   if caregivers rarely respond or attempt to interpret child's babbles as if they have communicative intent.

(may also credit #2.13 "Babbles consonant chains" and #2.17 "Babbles double consonants" in Strand 2-6, depending upon child's type of babbling)

2.21 Shouts for attention   6.5-8

Definition: The child makes a loud abrupt or prolonged vocalization to communicate that he wants someone's attention.

Parent Questions: Can you give me an example of how your child tries to get your attention when he wakes up from a nap or when you are busy doing something?

Example Observation Opportunities: May observe when parent is out of direct sight or not paying attention to the child; e.g., parent is talking to another person; parent is on the telephone or reading a paper; child is in highchair, crib, or playpen and wants to get out.

Credit: (see also Credit Notes in this strand's preface)
+   may sometimes shout to communicate that he wants attention.
-   primary method for attracting attention is whining, screaming or crying.

N/A child is not observed or reported to shout for attention but uses other methods such as babbling, smiling.

2.27 Babbles in response to human voice   11-15

Definition: The child babbles back in response to someone talking to him to "take a turn" in a conversation. At this stage, the child deliberately uses his vocalizations to communicate and expects to take a turn. The child's babbling at this stage is more communicative and developed than #2.18 earlier in this strand, because it contains more consonants and vowels, partial or true word attempts, and varied intonation patterns to help get his meaning across, and he is able to anticipate and take several turns in a communicative exchange.

Example Observation Opportunities: May be observed whenever the child is engaged in a joint activity with another person, e.g., during snack time, looking at books, playing with toy telephones, figuring out how to make a wind-up or pop-up toy work. Also observe caregiver interactions which help initiate or maintain "conversations." The following techniques may help encourage the child's vocalizations during play:
a. Play next to the child with a similar toy and imitate his actions. Occasionally comment on the object or action it makes.
b. Let the child choose which toys and objects to play with when two or three are available.
c. Limit your own talking, pause often to let the child take a turn.
d. Sometimes interpret what the child seems to be saying into simple comments or phrases, and pause for child to take another turn; e.g., if child vocalizes, looks at you and then at his toy, make a comment such as, "That's your Busy Box. Push the button."

Credit: (see also Credit Notes in this strand's preface)
+   babbles to communicate a range of intentions using a variety of inflections to help get his meaning across; can often take at least three consecutive "turns" in a communicative exchange.

2.35 Experiments with communication - not frustrated when not understood   12-17.5

Definition: Although the child may persist, he usually does not get upset or frustrated if others do not always understand or respond back to his sounds, words or word attempts. He is interested in experimenting with the types of sounds and inflections he can produce and may thus spend time "talking" to people, animals and objects to practice and play.

Parent Questions: How does your child react if you can't figure out what he saying? Do you ever hear him "talking" to himself or his toys, for example, when he is playing alone or is in his crib?

Example Observation Opportunities: May observe anytime child is trying to communicate with someone or is playing alone, "talking" to himself or his toys.

Credit: (see also Credit Notes in this strand's preface)
+   does not get overly upset if communicative intent is misinterpreted or not understood.
A   frequently tantrums or "falls apart" from frustration.

N/A not observed or reported.

2.38 **Vocalizes spontaneously to indicate needs**   **12-19**

Definition: The child effectively uses a variety of words, word approximations and inflectional babble or jargon to communicate needs, such as "help me open this," "pick me up," "tell me what this is," "I don't want it," "more juice." Vocalizations are usually coupled with matching facial expressions and conventional gestures, such as pointing and shaking his head to help get his meaning across. At this stage, he also combines vocalizations and gestures into a sequence to communicate more complex intentions and requests; e.g., he may nod head "no" while saying "no" with inflection and pushing his food away; take an adult's hand to go across the room to an out-of-reach toy and then point and vocalize to request the object; hand an adult an empty cup, and point to the refrigerator while saying "more" or "juice."

Parent Questions: How does your child let you know when he wants something or needs help? Is it fairly easy to figure out what he wants?"

Example Observation Opportunities: During snack or mealtime observe if and how the child communicates that he wants some food or drink which is out of reach, that he wants more of something, that he does not want something, and that he's finished. During play observe if and how child communicates that he wants a toy out of reach, wants to know what a new object is or what it can do, wants help with a toy to make it work (e.g., getting a lid off a bottle of bubbles, restarting a wind-up toy), wants to continue an activity or game (e.g., blowing bubbles), wants to stop an activity or game, and wants to attract someone's attention to play with him.

Credit: (see also Credit Notes in this strand's preface)
+ uses a variety and combination of inflections and vocalizations to communicate needs; includes words and word approximations in his expressive vocabulary (Strand 2-3).
- needs are expressed primarily through whining or grunting.
(may also credit in Strand 2-4A if child also uses a variety of *gestures* to communicate needs.)

2.44 **Uses voice in conjunction with pointing or gesturing**   **14-20**

Definition: The child uses words or word approximations with gestures to express thoughts and needs. Although this item overlaps with the previous item in this strand, #2.38 "Vocalizes or gestures spontaneously to indicate needs," it also includes communicating about other things in addition to needs. For example, he may comment and gesture about an action (e.g., child vocalizes and points down to comment that an object fell), about an object (e.g., child holds up a doll he's holding and says "doll") or to answer (e.g., parent asks "Do you want more milk?" and child shakes head and says "no.")

Example Observation Opportunities: May observe throughout observation period when child is involved in play, feeding, gross and fine motor activities. Eliciting situations and suggested observations for #2.27, "Babbles in response to human voice" earlier in this strand, are very applicable to this item.

Credit: (see also Credit Notes in this strand's preface)
+ uses a variety of words or other intonated vocalizations with gestures to initiate, respond, make a comment, request, answer and acknowledge in a communicative exchange; these communicative exchanges sound more like true conversations and the child continues to expand the number of turns he takes in the interaction, building upon previous responses.

2.46 **Vocalizes wishes and needs at the table; names desired items**   **15-17.5**

Definition: The child verbalizes at mealtime using the words and word approximations and gestures he has in his expressive vocabulary. He can express wishes and needs, such as "more," "all gone," "down," and "no." He also names one or two food, drink or utensil items that he wants, usually those that are visible but out of reach, e.g., "juice," "cookie."

Parent Questions: What is a typical mealtime like at home with your child? How can you tell when your child wants something at mealtime but can't reach it himself? Have you heard your child say any names of foods, drinks, or utensils such as spoon or cup, without hearing you name them first?

Example Observation Opportunities: During snack time give the child a small amount of his favorite snack and drink to encourage him to ask for more. Use items parent reports are in child's expressive vocabulary, if possible. You may also leave another item within sight but out of reach. Name the drink and food as you give it to him. When he is finished, if he points for more or to food which is out of reach, ask "What do you want?" If his response is "that" or "more" or some other whining type sound, inquire further with an inviting expression, "This? What is this?" or "More what?" If he is still unable to answer (but not to a frustration "breaking point"), pick up and name two items

Vocalizes wishes and needs at the table; names desired items   (continued)

for him to make a choice, e.g., "Do you want the cracker or juice?" Let him have the item regardless of his response, naming it as you give it to him. Observe how he indicates when he is finished.

Credit

+   often vocalizes different needs or requests during mealtimes.
-     primarily grunts, whines, points to make needs known.
- O   caregivers over-anticipate needs or have difficulty interpreting child's request.

2.49   Echoes prominent or last word spoken   17-19

Definition: The child may sometimes repeat aloud the last word or most prominent word heard in a sentence or phrase; e.g., if the parent says, "That's your shoe," the child may respond, "shoe"; or if parent says, "Daddy's home," the child may respond "Daddy." Children sometimes repeat or echo the last or most prominent word heard as a method to help remember and process the information and to take part in conversations.

Example Observation Opportunities: May observe any time. This is not a behavior to elicit.

Credit: (see also Credit Notes in this strand's preface)

+   sometimes echoes prominent or last word spoken.

N/A not reported or observed.

A   if older and does this to an extreme.

2.59   Tells experience using jargon and words   21-24

Definition: The child tells a listener about an activity or event that he was involved in or has observed. He uses the words he knows how to say filling in with jargon to communicate his thoughts. The listener may need to help his dialogue continue beyond one or two turns; e.g., when the child tries to tell about a dog that just ran by and knocked down his toy, the listener makes a remark such as, "The dog did what?" to encourage him to continue or expand his thoughts. At this stage, the activity or event is one that is typically occurring or occurred in the immediate past, that same day.

Example Observation Opportunities: During or immediately following a play activity ask the child to tell you or his parent what he just did, e.g., after playdough, "Tell Mommy what we played with"; after riding a Tyke bike, "What were you doing on the bike?"; if a crayon or broken toy is discovered, "What happened to the crayon?"; after sand play, "You still have sand on your hands! Tell daddy what you were doing!" Build on the child's "conversation" during his pauses to encourage him to continue, e.g., "Yes! I saw you make a cake with playdough. What else did you do?"

Credit: (see also Credit Notes in this strand's preface)

+   sometime tries to relate immediate experiences using some true words, jargon, gestures and word attempts.

O   caregiver rarely builds on child's attempts to communicate about an experience, e.g., does not respond or continue on the topic.

2.72   Experiments with communication - frustrated when not understood   24-28.5

Definition: The child may sometimes cry, whine, shout or give up when he cannot find the words (or say them clearly enough to be understood) to express his wants and needs. At this stage, he understands much more than he can say which helps "fuel" his frustration.

Parent Questions: How does your child react if you can't figure out what he saying? Does he ever seem to get upset or frustrated when he can't say want he wants? Can you tell me a little more about that? About how often does this happen? Are there some things you've tried that seem to help?

Example Observation Opportunities: Observe how parent and child handle situations when the child is trying to communicate a message. Does the parent try to help interpret and repeat back what the child may be trying to say rather than telling him to "talk better"? If the child is not understood, does he appear frustrated? How far does his frustration escalate and can he fairly quickly "recover" from his frustration?

Credit: (see also Credit Notes in this strand's preface)

+   is sometimes frustrated when wants and needs are not understood.

N/A not observed or reported.

A   displays extreme frustration during most communicative efforts, even with a sensitive partner; frequently has tantrums, "falls apart."

O   caregivers are interested in guidance to help minimize child's frustration.

2.73 Relates experiences using short sentences   24-34

Definition: The child tells a listener about an activity or event that he was involved in or observed. In contrast to #2.59 "Tells experience using jargon and words," earlier in this strand, words and one to three word sentences replace much of the jargon. He can now also relate some feelings and experiences that happened in the past rather than only talking about a physically present topics. He can initiate the conversation and take many turns in a dialogue with a responsive listener who questions and encourages the child to continue.

Parent Questions: Have you noticed if your child sometimes tries to tell you about something that happened to him earlier in the day or week, for example, what he did at daycare? Can you give me an example of one of his conversations with you or another friend or family member? Can you think of some interesting things that have happened today or in the past couple of days that he might want to tell us about?

Example Observation Opportunities: Try prompting the child to tell you about a meaningful recent event that the parent has suggested, e.g., going to a birthday party, a visit to the dentist, a trip to the zoo or park, lunch at McDonald's. Use leading questions such, as, e.g., "What did you do at Susie's birthday party? Then what happened?...Did Susie have presents?" If the child is shy, toy telephones or puppets may help. The parent or child's teacher may have some photos of recent events which may also stimulate the child to talk about his experiences.

Credit: (see also Credit Notes in this strand's preface)
   + effectively communicates about experiences in the recent past using one- to three-word sentences; can stay on the topic for many turns; sentence structure, articulation, or grammar does not need to be correct.

2.74 Answers questions   24-36

Definition: The child responds with relevant answers to simple questions using more than a "yes" or "no" response. At this stage, he can answer "What," "Where," and "Who" type questions, but generally *not* "Why" questions. He usually understands questions related to his experiences, but he may repeat part of the question as a strategy to answer, especially if he is unsure of the meaning; e.g., if asked, "Did you go to the circus?" he may respond, "I go to circus" even if he is unsure of the meaning of circus. This demonstrates his awareness and understanding of the role of questions and answers in conversation.

Example Observation Opportunities: Incidental - may observe questions parent asks incidentally during observation period, e.g., "Where did you put your coat?" "What are you doing?" "What did you draw?" Structured - ask the child about something he is involved in during activities or something you've noticed about him, e.g., "How did you hurt your knee?" "What did you eat for snack?" "Where should we put the doll?" or while looking at a book, "What is the boy doing?" "What happened to the dog?"

Credit: (see also Credit Notes in this strand's preface)
   + answers "What," "Where," and "Who" questions with a relevant answer; more than a "yes" or "no" response; sentence structure, articulation, or grammar does not need to be correct.

2.81 Frustrated if not understood - utterances have communicative intent   28.5-36

Definition: Although the child usually communicates his needs and wants fairly well, he may have more difficulty expressing his ideas, thoughts and feelings. For example, if the child is feeling lonely, anxious or bored and is asked, "What's the matter?" he may respond with something more concrete, such as "my toy bad," or whine and stomp his feet, which really does not express his emotions and feelings. His utterances have strong communicative intent, but he becomes frustrated by his inability to fully express his ideas and feelings so that others can be empathetic.

Example Observation Opportunities: Same as #2.72 earlier in this strand.

Credit: (see also Credit Notes in this strand's preface)
   + is sometimes frustrated when ideas, thoughts and feelings are not understood.
   N/A not observed or reported.
   A displays extreme frustration during most communicative efforts, even with a sensitive partner; frequently has tantrums or "falls apart."
   O caregivers are interested in guidance to help minimize child's frustration.

2.88   Vocalizes for all needs   30-31.5

Definition: The child is able to effectively express most of his needs verbally without relying only upon gestures or whining. He can spontaneously express his needs aloud or in response to a question; e.g., "What do you want?" if given enough time to respond.

Parent Questions: Can you give me some examples of how your child lets you know when he wants something or needs help?

Example Observation Opportunities: May observe child verbally expressing his needs incidentally throughout observation session, e.g., during snack time, telling what he wants to eat and when he is finished; during playtime, telling what toys he wants to play with; or asking for a second object out of reach or sight to use with an object he has (e.g., a doll for the doll bed, crayons for his paper, spoon for his pudding); or, requesting help with a difficult wind-up toy or to help open a jar of bubbles.

Credit: (see also Credit Notes in this strand's preface)

   +   typically is able to express his needs verbally without whining or only pointing.

2.90   Participates in storytelling   30-36

Definition: The child helps tell a favorite story he's heard several times by adding words, making comments and anticipating events in the story. He may correct the adult if the adult omits details or changes the story line. Stories can be from a short children's book or "homemade." *[This item also demonstrates the child's memory and ability to sequence events]*

Parent Questions: Does your child have any favorite stories he likes to hear, with or without books? Does he ever try to help you tell the story; for example, if you say something like, "and then what happened?" or if you omit or change a phrase he corrects you? Can you give me some other examples of how he participates in storytelling? Have you ever heard him trying to "read" the story when he's looking at a book or "reading" to one of his dolls?

Example Observation Opportunities: If available, use a book the parent says is a favorite of the child's. Pause frequently during the story to invite the child to tell you what's going to happen. Try saying something out of sync with the story; e.g., call a character by its wrong name or omit a story line.

Credit: (see also Credit Notes in this strand's preface)

   +   enjoys participating in storytelling as defined with familiar stories he has heard repeatedly; sentence structure, articulation, or grammar does not need to be correct.

2.96   Relates experiences more frequently using short sentences   34 +

Definition: The child regularly engages in conversations using short sentences to relay experiences about the past, present and near future. For example, if the family has been talking about going to the park tomorrow, the child may talk about going to the park and what he plans on doing. At this stage, his sentences are generally two and three words.

Parent Questions: Can you give me examples of conversations you hear your child get involved in? If he knows he is going to go somewhere soon, for example, later today or this weekend, have you heard him talk about that?

Example Observation Opportunities: If the child does not spontaneously initiate a conversation, ask a probing question about a favorite topic or pending event suggested by his parent. Use open-ended questions to elicit sentences, taking a turn during his pauses to encourage him to continue e.g., "Mommy said you are going to the park today. What will you do at the park. Wow! What else? Who else goes to the park?"

Credit: (see also Credit Notes in this strand's preface)

   +   regularly (i.e., throughout the day with familiar people) talks about his experiences in a conversation using two and three word sentences; sentence structure, articulation, or grammar does not need to be correct.

2.97   Asks questions beginning with "what," "where," "when"   34.5+

Definition: The child asks "what," "when," and "where" questions to seek information, and/or to initiate or maintain a conversation; e.g., "What's that?" "When see daddy?" "Where is baby?"

Example Observation Opportunities: May observe child asking "where" questions anytime he is looking for something during daily activities; e.g., during dressing, "Where my shoe?"; during play, "Where doll's bed?" Where my mommy?" May observe "what" questions anytime child sees a novel item, e.g., looking at a new toy, looking at new animals in a book. May observe "when" questions as child becomes tired or bored, e.g., "When go home," When eat dinner?"

Credit: (see also Credit Notes in this strand's preface)

   +   asks at least two types of "Wh___" questions to request information or initiate a conversation.

2-5 LEARNING GRAMMAR AND SENTENCE STRUCTURES

SEMANTIC-SYNTACTIC RELATIONSHIPS

2.36	12-14	Uses single-word sentences
2.54	18-21	Imitates two-word phrases
2.57	20.5-24	Uses two-word sentences
2.63	22-24	Imitates four-word phrases
2.67	24-30	Uses three-word sentences
2.68	24-30	Uses past tense
2.77	27-36	Uses plurals
2.87	30-36	Over regulates and systematizes plurals and verbs [foots, doed]
2.86	30-36	Uses most basic grammatical structures
2.95	33.5-36	Repeats five-word sentences

Family Friendly Interpretation of Strand Concepts, Assessment, & Purpose

After children can say about 20 or more single words meaningfully, they often begin to combine words into phrases or sentences. Combining words helps your child get his meaning across more accurately than by just saying single words. For example, if your child said, "Mommy" he could mean a number of things, such as, "Where's Mommy" or "Mommy, I want to get out of my highchair," or simply, "Hi Mommy." But if he says, "Mommy down," we have a better idea of what he really means.

As children begin to combine words into short phrases or sentences, they start to apply certain "rules" that they learn from listening to other people. For example, they begin to combine words in a certain order to help get their meaning across and they begin to learn things, such as when to add an "s" to a word to make it plural. At first children make many mistakes when they are learning about the "rules" of speech and language. For example, they may say "foots" instead of "feet," and they often do not combine words in the right order or use complete sentences, e.g., they may say "Out me," instead of "I want to get out." Children learn how to use and combine words correctly through lots of "trial-and-error," practice, and listening to how others respond to them. For example, if your child says, "I dided it!" and you respond, "Yes! You did it," this helps him learn that he does not need to add "ed" to the word "did."

Parent Questions (General Examples - see Skills for specific questions)

To help identify the child's unique strengths and needs related to this developmental area:
• Have you heard your child putting any words together in a phrase or sentence? Can you think of some examples?
• Do you have any questions or concerns about the way your child is learning to talk?

Sample *Functional* Outcome Statements which may be generated by the Family

[Will be dependent upon identified individual child and family needs, and should incorporate objectives and activities from other domains]
My child will:

• Be able to talk in short sentences;
• Start using some simple rules of grammar, such as when to add an "s" to a word.

Transactional Assessment

May assess through observation and interview.

Assessment of Caregiver Interactions with the Child

1. Supportive
[Example interactions which support/facilitate child's development in this area]
The child's caregivers sometimes:
• Expand their child's one-, two- and three-word phrases into a more complete sentence or phrase, depending upon the context; e.g., if the child says "Out," the caregiver may say, "You want to go out."
• Confirm the child's communicative intent and model the correct sentence or phrase structure when the child makes an error or omission; e.g., if the child says, "Put on foots," the caregiver may say, "Yes, you put them on your feet!"

Identifying and Interpreting Needs for Intervention

If a child is significantly delayed in this area, more so than in other areas of communication and language, he may be having difficulty in <u>processing language or, learning or expressing the early "rules" of semantic-syntactic relationships</u>.

As noted in the Introduction to Language, page 87, this may be due to a <u>cognitive delay, motor or medical impairments, or other sensory organization problems</u>.

Assessment Adaptations   (Examples)

[Refer to General Adaptations provided in the "Introduction to Language, page 89]

General Assessment Procedures & Processes   (apply to all items in this Strand)

[Also refer to "Assessment Considerations applicable to all strands in Language" page 88]

1. These items should be assessed concurrently with other language strands in the context of play and daily activities.
2. Language sampling and recording of utterances via video or audio tape during two sessions can be important for a thorough assessment and analysis of language structure and form.

`+ - A` Credit Notes:

+ child usually displays skill as defined during play and daily activities by observation and/or caregiver report; do not worry about articulation in this strand; the child may use inconsistent or inappropriate word orders in his early

sentences which is a normal variation in a child's language.

- not observed or reported.

+/- appears to be an emerging skill.

A atypical: always uses excessive facial expressions and gestures, and seems to have great difficulty, confusion or frustration putting words together although single-word expressive vocabulary is more than 20 words and is continuing to expand.

O circle any credit if caregiver's interactions compromise or restrict child's optimal skills in this area, or if caregivers have difficulty interpreting their child's communicative intent.

Note any adaptations used to credit.

Assessment Materials

Toys and objects used during daily activities and play.

2.36 Uses single-word sentences   12-14

Definition: The child says single words to communicate a more complete thought or sentence; e.g., "Mommy" may mean "Mommy come here," "Mommy pick me up," or "Mommy look at that." His intonations, facial expressions, gestures and context help him convey his full intent.

Parent Questions: When the child spontaneously verbalizes single words, ask the caregiver, "What do you think he is saying to you with just his single word?"

Example Observation Opportunities: Observe during the context of play and daily activities. Pay special attention to the gestures and vocal expressions the child is using to extend the meaning of his single words during a communicative exchange.

Credit: (see also Credit Notes in this strand's preface)

+ uses single words to communicate a sentence via varied facial expressions, gestures and intonational patterns.

- names or labels objects or events without an apparent intent to convey a more complete thought or sentence.

2.54 **Imitates two-word phrases   18-21**

Definition: The child can repeat a simple two-word phrase such as, "Daddy bye bye," in imitation of a model. His two-word phrase may be imitated from a short phrase which has more than two words but contains two key words, e.g., the child says, "Daddy bye-bye" when his parent says, "Daddy went bye-bye." *[Note: Imitation of two-word phrases generally is not expected until the child has at least 20 single words in his expressive vocabulary]*

Parent Questions: Have you noticed if your child has imitated a two-word phrase that he has heard you say; e.g., during mealtime if you ask him if he wants "more milk," does he repeat back "more milk"? Can you think of some examples?

Example Observation Opportunities: Pause after simple two- to three-word phrases during daily activities to give the child an opportunity to imitate, e.g., while looking at a book say a short phrase about the picture, "That's a big dog"; during snack time talking about what's happening, "You're eating cookie" or "Ready to get down?"

Credit: (see also Credit Notes in this strand's preface)
- + can imitate two-word phrases (or, credit if child already spontaneously says many two-word phrases or sentences.)
- - imitates only two words that are said as one word, e.g., "kittycat," "thank you," "bye-bye," "good girl."

2.57 **Uses two-word sentences   20.5-24**

Definition: The child spontaneously begins to combine two words to convey two concepts or thoughts, e.g., "go bye-bye," "baby bed," "push car," "doggie eat." This does *not* include two word combinations that the child often hears as one, e.g., "bye-bye," "good girl," "all gone."

Example Observation Opportunities: Comment about what you are doing, what the child is doing or what is happening, using short phrases. Pause often to encourage the child to make a comment. Refer to #2.59 "Tells experience using jargon and words" and #2.73 "Relates experiences using short sentences" in Strand 2-4B for example, eliciting situations.

Credit: (see also Credit Notes in this strand's preface)
- + says two or more spontaneous two-word sentences; words may be combined in any order to express a semantic relationship; e.g., action-noun–"push car"; or noun-action–"doggie eat."
- - combines two words used as one without a semantic relationship, e.g., "bye-bye," "all-gone" or says two words sequentially without apparent relational meaning, e.g., "Dog cat."

2.63 **Imitates four-word phrases   22-24**

Definition: The child can repeat a simple four-word sentence immediately after hearing someone say the same sentence. He may do this to practice as he experiments with learning to say longer phrases, and as a way to take a turn and maintain a conversation; e.g., if his parent says, "Mommy is brushing her hair," the child may respond, "Mommy is brushing hair?"

Example Observation Opportunities: (1) During doll play, model meaningful four-word sentences such as, "Time to eat baby," "Time to go sleep," "Sit down here, baby." Pause between phrases to give the child an opportunity to imitate your phrase. If he does not imitate, sometimes give a probe such as, "You say it" or "Tell the baby time for bed." If the child does not imitate after a few moments, repeat it for him and move on. (2) While looking at a book with action pictures, make directive comments to the picture, such as, "Doggie eat your dinner," "Baby, go to sleep." Then sometimes ask the child, e.g., "Tell the baby to go to sleep." Repeat the phrase as needed.

Credit: (see also Credit Notes in this strand's preface)
- + imitates at least one four-word phrase. Each word should be attempted but does not have to be accurate in articulation. (Or, may credit if the child already spontaneously says three- or four-word sentences.)

2.67   Uses three-word sentences   24-30

Definition: The child begins to spontaneously say three-word sentences to make a comment, to request something or to make a command. Most of his utterances average two to three words in length. At this stage, he incorporates the grammatical structures: *ing* in the present form as in "Me drinking juice"; prepositions, *in, on*; and plurals, *s, es* but these may be applied incorrectly.

Example Observation Opportunities: Same as #2.57 "Uses two-word sentences" earlier in this strand.

Credit: (see also Credit Notes in this strand's preface)

+ frequently uses two- and three-word sentences spontaneously; words are combined in any order to express a variety of semantic relationships, e.g., objects and actions ("Me spill juice"), objects and locations ("The ball here"), person, action, object ("Mommy sit bed"), possession ("dis my cookie"), etc.; accept but note grammatical and articulation errors.

2.68   Uses past tense   24-30

Definition: The child incorporates past tense verbs in his two- to three-word sentences. At this stage, he may use *-ed* incorrectly, e.g., "runned," "goed," until he learns the irregular forms, e.g., "ran," "went."

Example Observation Opportunities: If not observed incidentally, try asking the child to tell you or his parent about an activity or recent event, e.g., after finishing snack, suggest or ask, "Tell Mommy what you ate."; after going down a playground slide, ask, "Wow, what did you do?"; when his tower of blocks falls down, ask, "Oops! What happened?"

Credit: (see also Credit Notes in this strand's preface)

+ adds an *-ed* to a verb to indicate past tense or any use of irregular verbs, e.g., ate, saw, drank, fell; he may use them incorrectly.

2.77   Uses plurals   27-36

Definition: The child adds *s* or *es* to the end of a noun to indicate that he means more than one, e.g., cats, kitties, dogs. He may add an *s* incorrectly to show plural intent before he learns the rules for irregular plural form, e.g., "foots" or "feets" for *feet*, "mens" or "mans" for *men*. [*Note cognitive prerequisite: #1.123 "Understands concept of one," in Strand 1-6B*]

Example Observation Opportunities: Incidental - may observe incidentally while child is engaged in interactive activities which have duplicate materials, e.g., cookies, rings for the ring-stack, blocks, cars. Structured 1) Hold up two objects (e.g., blocks, shoes, cars, crayons) and ask, "What are these?"; then after praising the child for his correct response, to ensure intent of plural usage, hold up just one and ask, "What's this?" 2) Look at pictures in a catalogue or book and ask the child to name single and multiple items.

Credit: (see also Credit Notes in this strand's preface)

+ adds "s" at the end of a word, or uses an irregular plural form to indicate more than one; e.g., says "feet," "feets" or "foots" to mean more than one foot; he should also use the singular form of the same word when he uses it to indicate one. The child may substitute another consonant sound, such as "th" if he cannot say the "s" sound.

2.87   Over-regulates and systematizes plurals and verbs [foots, doed]   30-36

Definition: The child may use plurals and verb tenses incorrectly as part of natural language development, e.g., "I doed it!," "I eated the cookie," "See doggie's feets."

Example Observation Opportunities: Same as #2.68 and #2.77 above.

Credit: (see also Credit Notes in this strand's preface)

+ uses plurals and verbs but they may be used incorrectly as defined.

- no attempt to use verbs or plurals, not due to articulation problems.

2.86 **Uses most basic grammatical structures   30-36**

Definition: The child is able to use most basic sentence forms by about age three, i.e., statements, commands, negatives, questions. He should also use the following basic rules for grammar or syntax:

1.) Plurals (e.g., dogs, feet)
2.) Possessives (e.g., my, mine, his, its, yours, Daddy's)
3.) Past tense verbs (e.g., did, had, was)
4.) Verb forms of *be* (e.g., am, are, is)
5.) Adjectives (e.g., big, blue, two)
6.) Pronouns (e.g., I, me, you, he, she, it)
7.) Verb forms (e.g., to eat, eats, eating, ate)
8.) Contractions (I'm, he's, can't)

These "rules" may have some errors as noted in #2.87 above.

Example Observation Opportunities: Record/observe child's language over several observation periods as needed in a variety of meaningful and motivating situations: play, gross motor activities, mealtime, playing with a peer. Assess for basic sentence and grammar structures as defined which are present and which may be missing.

Credit: (see also Credit Notes in this strand's preface)

+   uses all of the basic grammatical structures defined at least once spontaneously in statements, commands, negative statements, questions.

2.95 **Repeats five-word sentences   33.5-36**

Definition: The child may repeat some five-word sentences from a model which contains many of the same words, e.g., If parent says, "Did you go to the zoo today," the child may respond, "go to the zoo."

Example Observation Opportunities: Model five- to six-word sentences during play and daily activities, pausing to see if the child will imitate some of the words to make five-word sentences, e.g., "I am playing with the playdough," "That is a big ball under the table" or "We are eating some cookies and apples."

Credit: (see also Credit Notes in this strand's preface)

+   sometimes repeats four to five words in a sentence which is similar to a model.
A   frequently echoes another's speech with no apparent communicative intent.

2-6 DEVELOPMENT OF SOUNDS AND INTELLIGIBILITY (PHONOLOGY)

2.01	0-1.5	Cry is monotonous, nasal, one breath long
2.03	0-2.5	Makes comfort sounds - reflexive vocal
2.04	0.5-3	Makes sucking sounds
2.09	2.5-4.5	Cries more rhythmically with mouth opening and closing
2.07	2-7	Coos open vowels [aah], closed vowels [ee], diphthongs [oy as in boy]
2.08	*2-7*	Disassociates vocalizations from bodily movement
2.13	4-6.5	Babbles consonant chains "baba-baba"
2.17	5-8	Babbles double consonants "baba"
2.20	6.5-11.5	Says "dada" or "mama" nonspecifically
2.23	7.5-9	Vocalizes in interjectional manner
2.24	7.5-12	Babbles with inflection similar to adult speech
2.25	8-12	Babbles single consonant "ba"
2.22	7-15	Produces these sounds frequently in babbling: b, m, p, d, t, n, g, k, w, h, f, v, th, s, z, l, r
2.28	11-12	Babbles monologue when left alone
2.31	11.5-15	Speech may plateau as child learns to walk
2.32	11.5-15	Unable to talk while walking
2.33	12-17	Omits final and some initial consonants
2.34	12-18	Babbles intricate inflection
2.47	15.5-21	Makes sounds in babbling, but often substitutes those sounds in words
2.48	17-19	Jabbers tunefully at play
2.51	18-22	Uses jargon with good inflection and rate
2.53	18-21	Imitates environmental sounds
2.60	21.5-24	Uses intelligible words about 65 percent of the time
2.62	22-24	Uses elaborate jargon
2.65	24-27.5	Produces the following sounds clearly: p, b, m, k, g, w, h, n, t, d
2.79	27.5-32	Produces sounds correctly at beginning of words
2.82	29-31	Replaces jargon with sentences
2.84	29-36+	Repeats words and sounds
2.98	35+	Uses intelligible words about 80 percent of the time

Family Friendly Interpretation of Strand Concepts, Assessment, & Purpose

While we are observing how your child is learning to communicate with others, we will also be assessing which sounds he is learning to say and how clearly he is able to say these sounds. Learning to say various speech sounds requires being able to hear and discriminate the different sounds in words as well as being able to coordinate many different muscles used in speech. Each sound requires a different type of precise coordination of lips, tongue, and breathing. Some sounds have patterns in common. For example, the "p", "b", and "m" sounds require your child to use both lips. The "h" sound requires more breath with less lip movement.

Children learn to say speech sounds, first in vocal play, such as cooing or babbling, and then purposefully to match the speech sounds of the language they hear from others. Some sounds and sound combinations are usually easier to produce than others so these are the ones a child usually begins to use first. For example, sounds such as "ba" and "da" are much easier to say than "ch" or "tr" which may not be said clearly in words for several years.

Professional FYI

This strand is closely related to and dependent upon Strand 6-1 "Oral Motor Development," as well as overall motor development. The production of sounds is a highly precise and practiced motor skill. It involves maturation and coordination of the muscular, skeletal and nervous system with breathing. For the most part, speech is produced with the same musculo-skeletal structures used for eating and breathing. The physical act of speaking or making sounds begins with signals from the brain to control the muscles used in speech (e.g., tongue, abdominal muscles). These muscles then move the parts of the skeletal system that are involved in speech (e.g., jaw, rib cage, larynx).

In addition to the neuromotor and musculo-skeletal basis of vocalizations, the ability to hear, process, and discriminate sounds is also a prerequisite to later intelligibility and articulation. An audiological evaluation should be part of any comprehensive assessment when a child displays difficulties in articulation and intelligibility. If

Professional FYI (continued)

hearing impairment, structural, and neuromotor problems have been ruled out, sensory organization or processing problems should also be considered for further evaluation, especially if a child displays many overreactive or underreactive responses in Strand 0.0 "Regulatory/Sensory Organization."

Parent Questions (Examples)

To help identify the child's unique strengths and needs related to this developmental area:
- What words or babble sounds have you heard your child say fairly often?
- Are there some words or sounds he uses which are not very clear?
- About how much of your child's speech can you understand?
- Can other people usually understand what your child is saying?
- Are there some sounds your child used to make that you don't hear him saying anymore?
- When your child babbles does it sometimes sound like he's holding a conversation by the way he changes the tone and pitch of his voice?

- Does your child have a history of ear infections or middle ear fluid? About how many? How long do they usually last? Are you aware if he has an infection or fluid now?

To help identify family resources, priorities and concerns related to the child's development in this area:
- Have you ever had any concerns about your child's hearing?

[If so.]
- Has his hearing ever been tested?
- Are you aware of places you can go to have your child's ears or hearing check?
- Are you interested in getting information about resources which may be available to help pay for having your child's ears and hearing checked?

Sample *Functional* Outcome Statements which may be generated by the Family

[Will be dependent upon identified individual child and family needs, and should incorporate objectives and activities from other domains]

My child will be able to speak more clearly.

We will:
- Be able to understand more of the words our child is using;
- Know which sounds our child can be expected to say clearly at this stage and which sounds develop later.

Transactional Assessment

May assess through observation and interview.

Assessment of the Child's Environment

1. Supportive:
[Example environments which support/facilitate development in this area]
The child's caregiving environments usually have good speech models who speak clearly.

Assessment of Caregiver Interactions with the Child

1. Supportive
[Example interactions which support/facilitate child's development in this area]
The child's caregivers usually naturally repeat the child's vocalization or words into a confirming phrase, using the correct pronunciation; e.g., if child says, "dat mine," the caregiver may say, "Yes, that is yours!"

2. Compromising:
[Example interactions which may restrict, compromise, inhibit or be unsupportive of the child's development in this area]
The child's caregivers frequently:
- Try to make their child speak more clearly, beyond what is developmentally appropriate;
- Overuse "baby-talk" with their child.

Identifying and Interpreting Needs for Intervention

If a child is significantly delayed or displays significant atypical development in this area, more so than in other areas of language development, this may be due to:
- Poor oral motor skills secondary to neuromotor or structural abnormalities, e.g., atypical tone, cleft lip or palate;
- Difficulty in auditory processing or oral motor planning;

- Hearing impairment.

The child should be referred to an audiologist and speech-language therapist for further evaluation.

However, before targeting one of these issues as the primary area of need, also consider other causes of delays or difficulties related to vocalizations and intelligibility. These may include:
- Cultural/dialect differences;
- Lack of good speech models.

Assessment Adaptations   (Examples)

[Refer to General Assessment Adaptations in the Introduction to Language section, page 89]

General Assessment Procedures & Processes   (apply to all items in this Strand)

[Also refer to "Assessment Consideration applicable to all strands in Language" page 88]

1. Voice quality and inflectional patterns are also important aspects of speech intelligibility and production. **Observe and note any of the following quality issues which should be further evaluated by a physician and a speech-language therapist:**
   - unusual pitch, monotone, or loudness of voice;
   - excessive breathiness;
   - excessive nasal quality, i.e., air seems to come out of the nose or words seem very nasal;
   - lack of nasal resonance; i.e., child always sounds as if he has a cold;
   - poor endurance during speech; i.e., child's vocalizations are weak and he needs to exert an inordinate amount of effort;
   - harsh or excessively husky, hoarse voice;
   - very soft or weak voice.

2. This strand is assessed/**observed concurrently to other expressive language strands** via observation and, if possible, when indicated due to delays, via video or audio tapes. Therefore, in most items only a definition and credit statement are provided.

3. As the child begins to use speech meaningfully, **primary caregivers should be asked to interpret unintelligible words.** This, in addition to video tape analysis, can help further identify patterns of errors, e.g., deletions, assimilations or substitutions.

4. **Provide anticipatory guidance related to which sounds a child should and should not be expected to say clearly at his stage of development.**

5. In contrast to other language strands, **direct observation of vocalizations should occur whenever possible.** If parent report is used, model the specific vocalization pattern to help ensure accurate reporting.

+ - A Credit Notes:

+   child usually displays skill or behavior as defined during play and daily activities; most items in this strand should be by direct in-person or video-tape observation whenever possible, <u>not</u> usually by caregiver report unless indicated.

-    not observed or reported.

+/-   appears to be an emerging skill.

A   atypical: poor or unusual voice quality, see #1 above; additional item specific atypical behaviors are incorporated in item credits.

O   circle any credit if environment or interactions compromise or restrict child's optimal skills, in this area.

Note any adaptations used to credit.

2.01 Cry is monotonous, nasal, one breath long   0-1.5

Definition: Crying sounds are primarily vowel-like with a nasal quality which are produced on exhalation as a total body response. By 1 month the baby's cry grows louder and longer with some rising and falling pitch changes. If the child was premature, his cry may be higher pitched or weaker.

Credit: (see also Credit Notes in this strand's preface)

+   cry is primarily produced on exhalation, is vowel-like, exhibits changes in loudness and duration, and, by 1 month, has minor pitch variations.

A   **atypical**, one or more of the following may warrant further evaluation by a physician: extremely high-pitched with a tense quality; lack of fluctuation; duration of cry is in short burst of less than a second much of the time; absent or very weak cry; flat or bunched tongue, i.e., no cupping.

2.03 Makes comfort sounds - reflexive vocal   0-2.5

Definition: The child's first sounds are reflexive, i.e., occur automatically and are produced with slight muscle changes as the infant breathes or during feeding. They often sound like clicks, short friction noises, or quiet "mmm," "nnn," "ah" sounds, and are typically produced in connection with body movements.

Credit: (see also Credit Notes in this strand's preface)
+   displays any non-crying soft reflexive sounds as defined.

2.04 Makes sucking sounds   0.5-3

Definition: When the infant is comfortable and relaxed he may make sucking sounds that are usually reflexive, not purposeful.

Credit: (see also Credit Notes in this strand's preface)
+   by observation or report, may sometimes make sucking sounds not related to feeding or hunger.

2.09 Cries more rhythmically with mouth opening and closing   2.5-4.5

Definition: The infant's cry becomes more rhythmical as muscular-skeletal movements for breathing and vocalizing mature and become more coordinated. The infant's mouth opens and closes in a rhythmical manner as he cries with an up and down intonation pattern.

Credit: (see also Credit Notes in this strand's preface)
+   by observation or report, cry includes up and down pitch intonations, and rhythmical opening and closing of jaw.

2.07 Coos open vowels [aah], closed vowels [ee], diphthongs [oy as in boy]   2-7

Definition: Cooing sounds are vowel-like sounds typically produced in connection with movement. Initially they are open mouth vowels, "aah." As jaw movements begin, other vowel sounds appear, "oo," "i," "ah-ee." By 3 months, pitch and inflectional changes occur and consonants appear, "m," "ng" (as in ring), "g." Sounds continue to be typically influenced by the child's body movements and position.

Example Observation Opportunities: Observe the child's sounds in different positions, noting which positions appear to promote different sounds.

Credit: (see also Credit Notes in this strand's preface)
+   coos a variety of vowels and some consonant sounds as defined with variable pitch and rising-falling intonations.

2.08 Disassociates vocalizations from bodily movement   *2-7*

Definition: The child is able to make soft vowel sounds without excessive body movement. True dissociation from body movement with many sounds does not occur until about 7 months.

Example Observation Opportunities: May observe when child is quiet and content, lying on his back with a mobile overhead, or on his tummy in front of a mirror.

Credit: (see also Credit Notes in this strand's preface)
+   sometimes makes soft vocal sounds without excessive body movement.

2.13 Babbles consonant chains "baba-baba"   4-6.5

Definition: The child begins to vocalize strings of consonant-vowel sounds such as "bababa." These are usually combined with body movements and influenced by the child's position. The sounds typically occur with mouthing, feeding, and visual exploration, not social interaction.

Credit: (see also Credit Notes in this strand's preface)
+   by observation or report sometimes vocalizes beginning babble sounds which are characterized by strings of consonant-vocal combinations of three or more duplicated syllables.

2.17 **Babbles double consonants "baba"**   5-8

Definition: As the child gains more control over his articulators and breathing patterns he is able to shorten his earlier consonant-vowel strings of babbling (e.g., babababa) to two syllables such as "baba" or "dada."

Credit: (see also Credit Notes in this strand's preface)
+ babbling includes two-syllable repetitions of a consonant-vowel combination, e.g., "baba," "mama," "dada," "didi."

2.20 **Says "dada" or "mama" nonspecifically**   6.5-11.5

Definition: Same as #2.17 "Babbles double consonants 'baba'" above. The child at this stage does not vocalize "dada" or "mama" specifically to label or name mother or father, but his parents may interpret it as such which helps him learn to do so later in #2.29 "Says "dada" or "mama," specifically (Strand 2-3 "Expressive Vocabulary").

Credit: (see also Credit Notes in this strand's preface)
+ by observation or report vocalizes "mama" or "dada" with or without meaning.
(may credit #2.29 "Says "dada" or "mama," specifically" in Strand 2-3, "Expressive Vocabulary," if used specifically)

2.23 **Vocalizes in interjectional manner**   7.5-9

Definition: The child is able to produce short, loud sounds of varying pitch which sound like exclamations of glee or surprise. They appear first as shouts and later as true exclamations, "Oh!" or "uh-oh." *[Note: This demonstrates the child's maturing control over his breath and vocal cords]*

Credit: (see also Credit Notes in this strand's preface)
+ by observation or report makes exclamatory sounds with variation in pitch.

2.24 **Babbles with inflection similar to adult speech**   7.5-12

Definition: The child uses varied intonations and rhythm in his vocalizations that are similar to adult speech. He may sound like he is asking a question, making a command, or simply making a comment.

Credit: (see also Credit Notes in this strand's preface)
+ vocalizes a variety of consonants and vowels with changes in pitch and loudness resulting in inflections similar to adult speech.

2.25 **Babbles single consonant "ba"**   8-12

Definition: The child is able to break down his earlier babbling couplets, e.g., "baba" into a single syllable such as "ba". Other single syllables typically used at this stage include: "da," "ma," "na," "ga." These single syllables at times sound as though the child is trying to say words such as "ba" for "ball."

Credit: (see also Credit Notes in this strand's preface)
+ uses one or more single syllable utterances consisting of a consonant-vowel.

2.22 **Produces these sounds frequently in babbling: b, m, p, d, t, n, g, k, w, h, f, v, th, s, z, l, r**   7-15

Definition: These are the consonant sounds which typically appear in a child's babbling and vocal play. They are listed in sequential order of difficulty and in the order in which they are typically acquired. Production of the first three sounds, "b," "m," and "p" require the child to use both of his lips together; "d," "t," and "n" require the child to bring his tongue to his teeth. The "ng," "k," and "g" sounds occur more from the back of the mouth. First words will typically also begin with the easier first sounds listed, while the more difficult sounds toward the end of the list will appear later in words; e.g., he is likely to say "ball" before he can say "sock."

Example Observation Opportunities: Note: All of these sounds may not always be easy to detect as they are often produced incidentally and not purposefully. Listen carefully and note all sounds produced in vocal play, babbling and in words.

Credit: (see also Credit Notes in this strand's preface)
+ vocalizes at least each of the first seven consonant sounds during vocal play, babbling or in words.

2.28 ### Babbles monologue when left alone   11-12

Definition: The child plays and experiments with making vocal sounds when left alone. His practicing may sound like conversation as it includes inflections which sound like questions and commands. This is the start of the jargoning stage.
Credit: (see also Credit Notes in this strand's preface)
+   sometimes practices and experiments making a variety of vocalizations without any apparent intent.

2.31 ### Speech may plateau as child learns to walk   11.5-15

Definition: Some children babble less or do not learn to say any new words while learning to walk. Their energies are focused on the intricate coordination and balance skills needed for independent walking. The child should, however, resume expansion of speech after he feels more competent in walking.
Example Observation Opportunities: If the child's speech has apparently plateaued while he is learning to walk, provide assurance and anticipatory guidance to family, if needed.
Credit: (see also Credit Notes in this strand's preface)
+   by report speech has plateaued for a few months while the child is learning to walk.
N/A speech does not appear to have plateaued.

2.32 ### Unable to talk while walking   11.5-15

Definition: Similar to #2.31. Even if the child's speech does not generally plateau, he may, as a new walker, be unable to use his speech while in the act of walking.
Credit: (see also Credit Notes in this strand's preface)
+   child does not vocalize while walking.
N/A walking does not appear to inhibit the child's vocalizations.

2.33 ### Omits final and some initial consonants   12-17

Definition: The child may distort or not include ending and some beginning consonant sounds in words as he is learning to talk. Examples include saying, "ca" for "cat," "ba" for "ball," "poon" for "spoon."
Credit: (see also Credit Notes in this strand's preface)
+   omits or distorts some beginning and ending consonant sounds; note omissions and distortions.
A   by 18 months continues to omit or distort most early consonant sounds, i.e., "b," "m," "p," "d," "t" "n," "g," and "k."

2.34 ### Babbles intricate inflection   12-18

Definition: The child babbles a variety of syllables with inflectional patterns and sound combinations which sound like conversation. This is often termed "jargon." His jargon may sound like he is telling a story, scolding, asking questions and answering them. Occasionally a true word may be interspersed with his jargon.
Credit: (see also Credit Notes in this strand's preface)
+   by observation or report if child frequently jargons as defined.

2.47 ### Makes sounds in babbling, but often substitutes those sounds in words 15.5-21

Definition: The child may be able to make some sounds incidentally in his babbling or jargon, but may not be able to use these same sounds in true words. For example, although he may say the "sh" sound in babbling, he may not be able to combine it with the correct sound to say "shoe" and thus substitutes "t" for "sh."
Credit: (see also Credit Notes in this strand's preface)
+   Makes some sounds in babbling, such as "sh," "l," or "r," but omits or distorts them in words.
A   over 18 months usually omits or distorts most early consonant sound in the beginning of words, i.e., "b," "m," "p," and "d."

2.48 Jabbers tunefully at play   17-19

Definition: Same as #2.34 "Babbles intricate inflection" earlier in this strand, but is evident during play as well as when communicating to others.
Credit: (see also Credit Notes in this strand's preface)
+   by observation or report if child sometimes jabbers with intricate inflections when playing alone.

2.51 Uses jargon with good inflection and rate   18-22

Definition: Same as #2.34 "Babbles intricate inflection" earlier in this strand, but now more true words begin to appear within jargoned utterances. Note: Some children do not go into this prolonged jargon stage but begin to use words earlier and more often.
Credit: (see also Credit Notes in this strand's preface)
+   combines jargon and words with conversational inflection.
N/A communicates primarily with true words or signs.

2.53 Imitates environmental sounds   18-21

Definition: The child is able to imitate animal, nature, machine or other environmental sounds. This often begins at an earlier age but by this stage he is able to use consonants, vowels, pitch and voice changes to imitate a variety of sounds making them more differentiated and distinct. Examples include: car sounds, "rhumm," "beep, beep"; crashing sounds; animal sounds, "moo, moo," "quack quack," "woof"; high-pitched whiny sounds for a siren; "choochoo" for a train.
Example Observation Opportunities: May observe while child is looking at pictures of or playing with toy cars, ride-on toys or animals. If child does not say sounds spontaneously, model the sound in an appropriate context during play or while looking at picture books.
Credit: (see also Credit Notes in this strand's preface)
+   imitates several environmental sounds.
A   makes environmental sounds excessively instead of using the word labels, or uses them frequently out of context without any apparent communicative intent.

2.60 Uses intelligible words about 65 percent of the time   21.5-24

Definition: More than half the child's words can be understood by family members and strangers (with similar culture and dialectical background) even though pronunciation of words is not always exact.
Parent Questions: If your child says something to someone he does not know very well, for example, at the grocery store, do others understand what he is saying? Do you need to interpret part of what he is saying to the other person?
Suggested Procedure: Use a language sampling from audio tapes or play and daily living observations; compare the number of utterances which are intelligible with those which cannot be understood.
Credit: (see also Credit Notes in this strand's preface)
+   more than half the child's words are understood by an unfamiliar observer who is familiar with the cultural or dialectical background of the child.
-   Reminder: refer to a speech therapist if more than half the child's words are unintelligible.

2.62 Uses elaborate jargon   22-24

Definition: The child's jargon usually peaks at this stage, and then declines as the child is able to use more true words to convey his message.
Credit: (see also Credit Notes in this strand's preface)
+   uses elaborate jargon interspersed with true words.
N/A primary uses words to communicate.

2.65 Produces the following sounds clearly: p, b, m, k, g, w, h, n, t, d   24-27.5

Definition: The child is able to say each of these consonant sounds clearly in words which begin with the consonant, e.g., "Put," "Ball," "More." He should also be able to use "b," "p," "m," and "n" as the final sound in a word, e.g., "cup," "some," "down." The child may, however, not be able to say some of these sounds when they involve certain sound combinations that are more difficult, e.g., he may be able to say the "t" sound clearly in the word "take," but not in the word "truck." [*Note: The child should also be able to use most vowel sounds correctly in words. Children with hearing loss often*

Produces the following sounds clearly: p, b, m, k, g, w, h, n, t, d   (continued)

distort vowel sounds in words]
Credit: (see also Credit Notes in this strand's preface)
+   produces all listed sounds clearly in the beginning position of a word.
A   vowels appear to have many distortions or only one or two vowels are used.

2.79 ## Produces sounds correctly at beginning of words   27.5-32

Definition: Same as #2.65 "Produces the following sounds clearly: p, b, m, k, g, w, h, n, t, d" plus "f" and most vowel sounds, e.g., "apple," "eat," or "open." Other sounds, i.e., s, z, ch, sh, j, l, r, may take longer to learn to say correctly because they require more precise placement and movement of the tongue against the teeth and palate. The most difficult sounds for a child to say are two consonant sounds together, such as " spoon," "please," and "drink."
Credit: (see also Credit Notes in this strand's preface)
+   produces all defined consonant and vowel sounds clearly at the being of words.

2.82 ## Replaces jargon with sentences   29-31

Definition: As the child's expressive vocabulary and ability to combine words effectively and appropriately increases, his use of jargon decreases and finally disappears.
Credit: (see also Credit Notes in this strand's preface)
+   rarely jargons.

2.84 ## Repeats words and sounds   29-36+

Definition: The child may appear to be stuttering as he sometimes repeats his first word in a sentence or question, or the first sound in a word. This is a normal stage of language development that some children go through as they learn to use more complicated grammatical structures and vocabulary. It may happen more often during stress, or when the child is tired or not feeling well. This stage usually passes within a few weeks if attention is not focused on it and caregivers allow extra time for the child to express himself.
Credit: (see also Credit Notes in this strand's preface)
+   may or may not sometimes repeat words as defined.
N/A not observed or reported.
A   "Stuttering" becomes more severe, has lasted for more than several months, occurs in more than ten percent of child's speech, and/or, child usually show signs of struggling to get a word out rather than making easy repetitions of the first syllable.

2.98 ## Uses intelligible words about 80 percent of the time   35+

Definition: A 3-year-old can typically be understood most of the time by his family as well as strangers (with similar culture and dialectical background) even though pronunciation of words is not always exact.
Parent Questions: If your child says something to someone he does not know very well, for example, at the grocery store, do others understand what he is saying? Do you need to interpret part of what he is saying to the other person?
Credit: (see also Credit Notes in this strand's preface)
+   most of the child's words and short sentences are understood by an unfamiliar observer who has the same or is familiar with the cultural or dialectical background of the child. The child's speech should be intelligible most of the time without needing context or gesture cues to help interpret what the child is saying.
-    Reminder: refer to a speech therapist if more than half the child's words are unintelligible.

2-7 COMMUNICATING THROUGH RHYTHM

2.15	5-6	Reacts to music by cooing
1.65	11-12	Moves to rhythms
2.43	13-16	Attempts to sing sounds to music
2.55	18-23	Attempts to sing songs with words
1.106	18-30	Enjoys nursery rhymes, nonsense rhymes, finger plays, poetry
2.64	23-27	Sings phrases of songs
2.91	30-36	Recites a few nursery rhymes

Family Friendly Interpretation of Strand Concepts, Assessment, & Purpose

We will be observing how your child responds to music and nursery rhymes. Music and language are related because, just as there is rhythm to music and the melodic verses of nursery rhymes, there is a rhythm to the way we speak. The rhythm of language helps children learn the meaning and intent of words. For example, in the game "Peek-a-boo," your child knows what you are saying by the rhythmic sound and changing inflections you use when you say the words. When your child moves his body to music, he is learning to associate the rhythm of music with the rhythm of his body, similar to the way he is learning to associate the rhythm of speech with the meaning of language. Your child's experiences with music can thus be enjoyable as well as enriching for learning language.

Parent Questions (General Examples - see Skills for specific questions)

To help identify the child's unique strengths and needs related to this developmental area:
• How does your child usually react when he hears music?
• Can you tell me a little about the types of music your child hears most often and seems to like best?
• Are there some types of songs or music that seem to upset him?
• Have you heard him try to sing with music?
• Are there any special nursery rhymes or songs that your child hears frequently at home, school, or daycare?

To help identify family resources, priorities and concerns related to the child's development in this area:
• Does your child have any musical toys, such as a wind-up radio, tapes or records, that he especially enjoys?
• Is there anyone in your family who plays a musical instrument or has other musical talents?

Sample *Functional* Outcome Statements which may be generated by the Family

[Will be dependent upon identified individual child and family needs, and should incorporate objectives and activities from other domains]

My child will:

• Enjoy musical activities;
• Try to sing during "circle time";
• Relax or calm down when he hears soothing music.

Transactional Assessment

May assess through observation and interview.

Assessment of Caregiver Interactions with the Child

1. Supportive:
[Example interactions which support/facilitate child's development in this area]

The child's caregivers:
• Reinforce the child's singing and dancing efforts with smiles and verbal praise;
• Play interactive communication games with simple nursery rhymes;
• Adjust the volume and types of music on stereos and radios to match the child's preferences or sensitivities;
• Incorporate a variety of musical activities into daily routines, e.g., caregiver sometimes sings during playful interactions and games; sings to soothe child, etc.

2. Compromising:
[Example interactions which may restrict, compromise, inhibit or be unsupportive of the child's development in this area]

The child's caregivers frequently keep loud or harsh music playing throughout the day.

Identifying and Interpreting Needs for Intervention

If a child is significantly delayed in this area, more so than in other areas of development, he may be having difficulty in <u>auditory processing skills that</u> <u>affect interpretation of musical tones. This may</u> <u>be due to a hearing impairment or</u> <u>regulatory/sensory organization problems.</u>

Assessment Adaptations (Examples)

[Note any adaptations needed to credit and help plan interventions; also refer to additional adaptations noted in the "Introduction to Language" on page 87]

• <u>Hearing impairment:</u> if the child has a mild hearing loss, specific adaptations are not usually needed; explore various songs and music to identify which frequencies and rhythms are most attracting. If the child has a severe to profound hearing loss, try turning the music louder and let the child experience the rhythmic vibrations which may occur from the speaker or on the floor. Let the child use musical instruments such as maracas and drums. Consult with an audiologist or speech therapist to identify specific adapta-tions and interventions.

• <u>Regulatory/Sensory organization problems:</u> pay special attention to the types of music and musical sounds which may be aversive to children who are hypersensitive to sounds. High-pitched music may be especially irritat-ing. Start at a very low volume, stopping if child shows signs of distress. If the child appears confused or becomes easily over-loaded, try using musical rhythms that are repetitive, with one beat per second. If the child has motor planning difficulties, model simple rhythmic movements for the child to imitate. Consult with a therapist who is experienced in sensory organization for specific adaptations and interventions.

General Assessment Procedures & Processes (apply to all items in this Strand)

1. **Describe the skill and eliciting procedures to family members and invite them to help observe and/or assess.**

+ - A Credit Notes:

+ child displays behavior as defined by observation or parent report.

- not observed or reported.

+/- appears to be an emerging skill.

A atypical: becomes very distressed or upset to certain musical tones, rhythms, singing, or pitches.

O circle any credit if environment or inter-actions compromise or restrict child's optimal skills in this area.

Note any adaptations used to credit.

Assessment Materials

Children's songs on tape or record, music box, picture book of nursery rhymes. Use songs and rhymes child is reported to be familiar with if available.

2.15 Reacts to music by cooing 5-6

Definition: The child is aware of and appears to enjoy soft, melodic rhythmic music. Individual reac-tions to music may vary with each child and type of music, e.g., music box versus singing. He may quiet, become very still, coo, and/or look toward the source of sound.

Parent Questions: Does your baby seem to like to hear you sing?...to listen to his music box or any other type of music? How can you tell? Have you ever tried humming, singing or playing music to help your child calm down if he's fussy? Does it seem to help? Does he seem to prefer certain types of music?

Example Observation Opportunities: When the child is getting fussy or becoming bored with a current activity, sing, turn on his favorite music box, or play taped music to observe if his responses change.

Credit: (see also Credit Notes in this strand's preface)

+ reacts to music in any positive way which is different than before hearing the music. The child does not have to "coo."

1.65   Moves to rhythms   11-12

Definition: The child bounces or in some way moves his body rhythmically, but not typically in tune with music. He usually will do so spontaneously, especially when in a playful mood, but sometimes waits to see if others react (dancing, singing etc.) or ask him to "dance" before "performing."

Example Observation Opportunities: Observe the child's initial responses when he hears commercial jingles on the television, his favorite song, or someone singing a song. Show your enthusiasm for the music and invite him to "dance" if he does not spontaneously do so.

Credit: (see also Credit Notes in this strand's preface)

+   responds by moving in some way to indicate he is aware of the rhythm, e.g., bouncing, rocking, moving his arms about, twisting, or moving his head from side to side. (If the child is significantly motor impaired, movements may be more subtle or undifferentiated. Credit if the child makes any attempts and note accordingly.)

2.43   Attempts to sing sounds to music   13-16

Definition: The child's "singing" at this stage, may sound more like talking, very quiet vocal play, or yelling. "Singing" at this age is also typically off-key and not in rhythm with the music. The child's "singing" is brief and may include using one or two approximations for familiar words, e.g., "woo" woo" for "Row Row your boat," but is primarily comprised of repetitive babble sounds such as, "ahhh, ahhhh," "oo," or "ya buh ya di."

Example Observation Opportunities: If available, play or sing the child's favorite songs. Invite the child and all others in the room to sing along. "Happy Birthday," "Row, Row Your Boat," "Old Mac Donald" and "The Wheels on the Bus" are simple repetitive tunes which may help elicit singing.

Credit: (see also Credit Notes in this strand's preface)

+   any attempts to sing as defined.

2.55   Attempts to sing songs with words   18-23

Definition: The child uses a few true words or word approximations, interspersed with humming, or other nonsensical sound combinations to sing repetitive phrases or sound sequences in a song. His singing is more sustained and melodic in comparison to his earlier attempts, but he still cannot sing in tune with the melody.

Example Observation Opportunities: Same as #2.43 above.

Credit: (see also Credit Notes in this strand's preface)

+   attempts to sing part of a song with two to three words, sings the last word of a line, or imitates a repetitive section (e.g., eiei-o in Old MacDonald) of a song. Do not worry about pronunciation.

1.106   Enjoys nursery rhymes, nonsense rhymes, finger plays, poetry   18-30

Definition: The child enjoys and participates in rhymes, finger plays or other gesture songs which are familiar to him. He may participate by singing as in #2.55 above, and/or by imitating hand and body gestures. Examples include, "Where is Thumbkin," "The Wheel on the Bus."

Example Observation Opportunities: Initiate a favorite rhyme, finger play etc. and/or sing and gesture along with a nursery rhyme book.

Credit: (see also Credit Notes in this strand's preface)

+   participates in at least one nursery or gesture type song or rhyme. This could be displayed in a variety of ways dependent upon child's expressive speech and gesture abilities and facial expressions. A child without motor or speech delays can be expected to imitate approximate or similar gestures and words of rhymes or "sing" favorite phrases.

Sings phrases of songs   23-27

Definition: The child "sings along" by imitating two- to four-word phrases heard repetitively in familiar songs or nursery rhymes. He sings in a rhythmic or melodic pattern but is usually off key. Examples of familiar songs with repetitive phrases may include "Jingle Bells," "Twinkle Twinkle Little Star," "Old MacDonald," "Happy Birthday," "Row, Row the Boat."

Example Observation Opportunities: Same as #2.43 earlier in this strand. If the child does not sing phrases during the observation period, ask the parent to sing the phrases the child likes to imitate from songs, commercials, finger plays, etc. Give examples of phrases from songs parent has identified as the child's favorites.

Credit: (see also Credit Notes in this strand's preface)

+ any imitation of song phrases that contain at least two different words said together e.g., credit "Row row boat" but not "row row." There should be some melody but do not be concerned with articulation.

Recites a few nursery rhymes   30-36

Definition: If the child has had experience with nursery rhymes, he is able to recite a familiar short nursery rhyme of about three or four lines. He may need some verbal, gesture or picture prompts.

Parent Questions: Ask parent if the child has had any experience with nursery rhymes at home, through his books, TV, cassettes, or at daycare. If so, probe for favorites and if parent has heard child recite lines.

Example Observation Opportunities: Use rhymes which the parent reports are familiar to the child. Favorites at this age may include: "Twinkle Twinkle Little Star," "Hey Diddle Diddle," or "Humpty Dumpty." If available, present a nursery rhyme book depicting a familiar rhyme and enthusiastically invite the child to tell you the rhyme; or without a book, invite the child to tell you a rhyme, saying the title as his opening cue, e.g., "Do you know Humpty Dumpty!? Tell me what happened to Humpty Dumpty?" If the child gets stuck or loses his place in the rhyme, offer the next word.

Credit: (see also Credit Notes in this strand's preface)

+ can say at least three lines in a rhyme without hearing the rhyme immediately beforehand. He may miss a word or two, need some minimal gestural or verbal cues, and his articulation may not be exact.

- Note if the child has not had experience with rhymes.

3.0 - GROSS MOTOR DEVELOPMENT
Introduction

Overview

The Gross Motor domain is divided into two sections according to developmental age and motor maturity:

I. Birth to 15 months
- 3-1 Prone
- 3-2 Supine
- 3-3 Sitting
- 3-4 Weight-bearing in Standing
- 3-5 Mobility and Transitional Movements
- 3-6 Reflexes/Reactions/Responses
  - A. Reflexes/Reactions
  - B. Anti-Gravity Responses

II. 15-36 months
- 3-7 Advancing Postural Control
  - A. Standing
  - B. Walking/Running
  - C. Jumping
  - D. Climbing
  - E. Stairs
  - F. Catching/Throwing
  - G. Riding a Tricycle
  - H. Balance Beam

Generally, if a child is walking well, you can go directly to Section II. However, if the child is unable to accomplish skills or is using poor quality in his movement patterns in Section II, his reflexes and postural responses (Strand 3-6) and transitional movements (Strand 3-5) *should be assessed with a physical or occupational therapist*.

General Notes and Precautions

- In addition to assessing motor milestones, it is important to observe the child's endurance, strength, general appearance, symmetry, and activity level. Each of these can influence the child's rate of achieving motor skills and quality of motor patterns. For example, it is important to observe the child's:
  - General appearance: is the baby chubby, stocky, or small, thin, or frail looking? Is there discrepancy in the size and/or shape of his arms or legs? Are his head, arms, legs or trunk in expected proportion?
  - Symmetry: does the child use each side of his body equally as well? Do his body parts on his left side look and move like his right side? In rest, does he appear symmetrical?
  - Endurance: does the child fatigue easily with movement? Does his respiration increase significantly?
  - Strength: does the child demonstrate strong, brisk kicking movements, or are they slow and weak? Does he have a weak grasp when pulling to sit?
  - Activity level: is the baby very active or is he a more sedentary, quiet baby?

- If the child has a diagnosed physical disability, this domain should be assessed by, or in close consultation with, a physical or occupational therapist.

- If the temperature, child, and family permit, observe the child's motor skills with as little clothing as possible, e.g., with only a diaper or shorts and a T-shirt.

- Be sure to identify medical limitations, precautions and contraindications of assessment and interventions. *It is important to review the child's medical history and current medical status carefully.* This can influence the child's strength, endurance, quality and age of achieving motor milestones. Consult with the child's family, medical records, and physician regarding existing conditions or a history of:
  - Respiratory and/or cardiac difficulties;
  - Medications;
  - Surgeries;
  - Seizures;
  - Use of G-tubes; colostomy bag, or history of long-term IV.

- Discontinue or modify the assessment at the first sign of physiological distress:
  - changes in skin color, temperature, clamminess;
  - shortness of breath, rapid breathing, or arhythmical breathing.

• Note: *Crediting use of "A" (Atypical)*: Variation in gross motor development is common. Atypical variation does <u>not</u> definitively indicate that the child is abnormal in his development. In addition, atypical motor patterns can be transient, especially during the first year. This, for example, can be especially evident in the premature infant. It is important not to unduly alarm families. If a child displays significant delays or atypical motor patterns, it is important to refer to a physical or occupational therapist and reassess over a period of several months before assuming that this is a more lasting area for concern.

Key definitions used in this domain

Supine: lying on back.

Prone: lying on stomach.

Flexion: in general, bending of a body part (most often located on or around the front side of the body).

Extension: in general, straightening of a body part (most often located on or around the back side of the body.

Hyperextension: straightening a body part beyond the typical range.

Disassociation: ability to move one body segment while holding other still, or ability to move one segment of the body in an opposite direction of another.

Retraction: shoulder blades are squeezed together; hands may be held near shoulders with arms flexed; elbows generally positioned behind back. This is an atypical posture.

Section I. Birth to 15 months

Professional FYI Notes regarding the order of assessment

• The child's motor development can be observed initially during play in prone, and then in supine, then sitting, and then in standing. Parallel mobility and transitional movements (Strand 3-5) can be observed simultaneously as these movements occur naturally. For example, while observing the child in prone (Strand 3-1) he may roll to supine, or when observing him in sitting (Strand 3-3) he may move into prone. Specific transition and mobility skills which can be observed while in prone or supine are listed in each strand.

• Conversely, in many cases, skills in prone and supine can be assumed as being attained by children who display higher level mobility and transition skills incidentally during play. For example, it may be difficult to observe the child lying on his stomach if he is already at the stage of creeping on his hands and knees. One may assume, therefore, that if he is creeping, the highest prone skill listed in Strand 3-1 has been accomplished.

• The assessment of reflexes and postural responses have been placed in a separate strand (3-6A & B). This does not imply that they can be viewed separate from other areas of motor development. Reflexes and postural responses are strongly interrelated with the accomplishment and quality of functional motor skills. They have been placed in a separate strand because the structured assessment procedure may be intrusive and upsetting to the child, whereas other strands can be observed during play and other daily activities without handling the child. It is usually unnecessary to formally assess this strand if a child is displaying functional motor skills with good quality.

3-1 PRONE

3.05	0-2	Holds head to one side in prone
3.03	0-2	Lifts head in prone
3.04	0-2.5	Holds head up 45 degrees in prone
3.09	1.5-2.5	Extends both legs
3.16	2-3	Rotates and extends head
3.15	2-4	Holds chest up in prone - weight on forearms
3.07	*3-5*	Holds head up 90 degrees in prone
3.26	4-6	Bears weight on hands in prone
3.43	6-7.5	Holds weight on one hand in prone

Family Friendly Interpretation of Strand Concepts, Assessment, & Purpose

We will be observing your child's muscle control and development while he is lying on his tummy, or in what therapists frequently refer to as the "prone position." This is the position where your child first uses the muscles that help him straighten his body and move against gravity – often termed the "development of extension." Babies first lie on their stomachs in a "curled-up" position. As they develop the muscles that help them extend or straighten their bodies, they no longer always hold their arms and legs tucked closely to their body. Initially, a baby develops control of the muscles in his neck. This helps him lift up his head to look around. His muscle control continues to develop along his back so that he can lift up his head *and* chest from the surface, pushing up with his arms. The development of these muscles help in later movement skills, such as crawling, sitting, and walking.

Parent Questions   (Examples)

To help identify the child's unique strengths and needs related to this developmental area:
• What position does your child seem to like best when he is resting?...playing?
• Does your child seem to like being on his tummy?
• About how much time does he spend on his tummy?
• What are some places that you put him on his tummy, e.g., crib mattress, floor, across your lap?
• Have you noticed if he lifts his head or chest up when he is on his tummy? Can he usually hold it up for more than a few seconds?

About how high?
• Has your child ever had medical needs or long-term use of an IV or other medical equipment which has kept him from lying on his tummy?

To help identify family resources, priorities and concerns related to the child's development in this area:
• If you could think of one thing that you'd like to see your child be able to do better when he is lying on his stomach, what would that be? What have you tried so far that seems to help?

Sample *Functional* Outcome Statements which may be generated by the Family

[Will be dependent upon identified individual child and family needs and should incorporate objectives and activities from other domains]
My child will be able to:
• Hold up his head well enough to look around;

• Push up on his arms;
• Reach for and play with a toy when he's on his tummy;
• Develop the muscles he needs to use to move around.

Transactional Assessment

May assess through observation and interview.

Assessment of the Child's Environment

1. Supportive:
[Example environments which support/facilitate development in this area]

The child's caregiving environments have safe, firm surfaces for the child to lie on his stomach.

Assessment of Caregiver Interactions with the Child

1. Supportive:
[Example interactions which support/facilitate child's development in this area]

The child's caregivers usually place interesting things in front of their child to play with or look at when he is playing on his stomach.

2. Compromising:
[Example interactions which may restrict, compromise, inhibit or be unsupportive of the child's development in this area]

The child's caregivers usually do not vary the child's position; e.g., the child spends most of his time lying on his back or in an infant seat.

Identifying and Interpreting Needs for Intervention

If a child is significantly delayed or shows persistent atypical development in this area, he may <u>have a neuromotor or musculo-skeletal problem</u> which is interfering with his development of controlled extension, e.g., abnormal muscle tone, absence of righting reflexes, torticollis. It will be important to consult with the child's physician and have a further evaluation by a pediatric physical or occupational therapist.

<u>However</u>, before targeting this as the primary area of need for referral and intervention, consider, rule out, or adapt for other causes which are *not* directly related to his neuromotor or musculo-skeletal status. These may include:

- <u>Sensory organization problems</u>: the child may be extra sensitive to touch and/or have other sensory organization problems which cause him to resist prone positions;

- <u>Experiential</u>: the child may not have had experience in prone positions due to medical history or environmental reasons (never placed in prone positions or frequently left in an environment that is visually unstimulating);

- <u>Medical issues</u>: e.g., gastrointestinal tube, surgery, severe reflux can restrict or compromise positioning in prone;

- <u>Head size</u>: if the child's head is unusually large, e.g., hydrocephalus or macrocephaly, he may have more difficulty lifting his head due to the extra weight;

- <u>Visually impaired</u>: if the child is severely visually impaired, he will not have the visual motivation to lift his head.

Assessment Adaptations (Examples)

[Note any adaptations needed to credit and help plan interventions]

- <u>Visually impaired</u>: expect the child to be delayed a few months according to norms based on sighted children.

- <u>Sensory organization problems</u>: try different surfaces to see if some are more tolerable than others. Some prone skills may be observed while the child is lying on the parent's trunk when the parent is reclined.

- <u>Medical issues</u>:
  - If pressure cannot be applied to the child's gastrointestinal area, a firm foam mat with a circular cutout may enable the child to be in a prone position comfortably. Check with the child's parent, nurse or physician about this adaptation.
  - If prone position is restricted after feeding due to reflux, plan to observe prone play before feeding.

/!\Safety Check
Remind Caregivers of SIDS precautions, e.g., "Tummy time is important for development, however, be sure to:
1. Only place your child on tummy when awake and within your sight.
2. Always place your child on back to sleep.
3. Only let your child lie on flat, firm surfaces.
4. Never place your child on soft pillow, bedding, bean bag chairs or other soft cushions because it can be to difficult for him to lift his head."

General Assessment Procedures & Processes (apply to all items in this Strand)

1. **The child should be lying prone on a safe, flat surface <u>without</u> a pillow.**
2. **Early items from Strand 3-5, "Mobility and Transitional Movements," which originate in the prone position, may be observed and assessed concurrently, i.e.,**
   #3.17 "Rolls prone to supine"
   #3.31 "Circular pivoting in prone"
   #3.48 "Brings one knee forward beside trunk in prone"
   #3.49 "Crawls backward"
   #3.52 "Crawls forward"
3. **Generally prone skills do not need to be elicited.** A several-minute observation will enable you to quickly review which skills in prone the child has without administering each item. Example observation opportunities are provided if needed. Describe the skill and eliciting procedures and invite family members to help observe and or assess.
4. **Be sure to assess if there is a significant medical history which has restricted or currently restricts child's positioning in prone.**

+ - A Credit Notes:
   + child usually displays prone skills as defined.
   - not observed or reported.
   +/- appears to be an emerging skill.

A atypical at all stages:
   – arms are held flexed and appear "trapped" under chest;
   – great difficulty moving into and out of position; appears "stuck";
   – elevated and retracted shoulders; elbows positioned behind trunk;
   – legs appear stiff, "stuck" or tight;
   – excessive head bobbing after three months;
   – obligatory head tilt.
O circle any credit if environment or interactions compromise or restrict child's optimal prone skills, e.g., lack of safe places for child to play in prone, unstimulating environment.
Note any adaptations used to credit.

Example Atypical Prone position

Assessment Materials

Safe firm surface, such as a mat or sheet on the floor or a firm crib mattress. Attractive sound and visual stimulus, such as a rattle, squeak toy, mirror, smiling face to encourage child to lift his head.

3.05 Holds head to one side in prone   0-2

Definition: The child lies on his stomach in a flexed posture with his head turned to either side. His arms are flexed close to his body and knees held under his tummy. His weight is held on his chest or cheek.
Example Observation Opportunities: When the child is lying in prone, observe to see if he effectively clears his face by turning his head to the side. Present a sound stimulus (parent's voice, rattle toy) to his opposite side to observe head turning and resting toward his other side (if not observed spontaneously during the observation period).
Credit: (see also Credit Notes in this strand's preface)
   + is able to rest with head turned fully and comfortably to each side; displays a symmetrically flexed posture.

3.03 Lifts head in prone   0-2

Definition: The child sometimes raises his head briefly in midline so that with his whole face is lifted from the surface. His weight is held on his chest, forearms and fisted hands.
Example Observation Opportunities: If not observed incidentally, present a visual and auditory stimulus, such as a squeak toy, rattle, or face about a foot away from and directly in front of the child's head. The stimulus should be very close to the surface.
Credit: (see also Credit Notes in this strand's preface)
   + lifts head briefly in midline.

3.04   Holds head up 45 degrees in prone   0-2.5

Definition: The child is developing enough control to hold his head up (facing forward) to the point where his face is at a 45 degree angle to the surface he is resting. By 2 months he begins to put some weight on his flexed forearms with his hands still fisted. He uses his shoulders to help push him up during head raising.
Example Observation Opportunities: Same as #3.03 above.
Credit: (see also Credit Notes in this strand's preface)
+   holds head up facing forward, with face at least at a 45 degree angle to the surface (about 2-3 inches above surface) for a few seconds.

3.09   Extends both legs   1.5-2.5

Definition: The child moves out of a totally flexed position in prone (i.e., with his arms and knees drawn close to his body), into a more extended posture. His arms are still somewhat flexed, elbows behind shoulders but are moving away from the body rather than tucked close to his chest. His knees are no longer always held under his tummy.
Example Observation Opportunities: This item may be observed incidentally without handling when in prone while the child is resting, playing or interacting with an adult.
Credit: (see also Credit Notes in this strand's preface)
+   does **not** always assume a totally flexed position as defined in prone.
A   head appears "stuck" and pressed into surface to bear weight rather than bearing weight on chest and forearms; legs stiff.
(also in Strand 3-2 "Supine")

3.16   Rotates and extends head   2-3

Definition: When the child is lying in prone, he can lift and turn his head about 45 degrees to each side.
Example Observation Opportunities When the child is lying prone with his head up, talk to him at his eye level toward one side or show him a toy. After a break, try this again toward his other side.
Credit: (see also Credit Notes in this strand's preface)
+   can rotate head to each side at least 45 degrees.

3.15   Holds chest up in prone - weight on forearms   2-4

Definition: The child can raise his upper chest off the surface, bearing weight on his forearms and hands, with his elbows in front of his shoulders. His head is raised at least to a 45 degree angle from the surface.
Example Observation Opportunities May be observed incidentally as child is resting or playing, or when parent talks to or presents a toy to him. The stimulus should be presented a few inches above the surface, directly in front of the child's head, about a foot away.
Credit: (see also Credit Notes in this strand's preface)
+   holds head and upper chest up, propping on forearms for at least 3-5 seconds.

3.07   Holds head up 90 degrees in prone   3-5

Definition: The child is able to hold his head up facing forward or in midline so that his face is held at a 90 degree angle to the surface he is resting on.
Example Observation Opportunities: same as #3.15
Credit: (see also Credit Notes in this strand's preface)
+   holds head up 90 degrees as defined for at least 10 seconds.
+/- has displayed this skill once or twice but for only a few seconds.
A   can lift head up but only with great effort and can only support it through hyperextension, i.e., with head held back on upper back.

3.26 Bears weight on hands in prone   4-6

Definition: In contrast to #3.15 "Holds chest up in prone-weight on forearms", the child now has developed enough control to push up on his hands with straight arms so that most of his chest is raised from the surface. His weight is supported on his hands, legs, and abdomen.

Example Observation Opportunities: Observe when the parent or a toy is directly in front of the child (at his eye level when he is lying on his tummy). After attracting his interest, raise the stimulus slowly a few inches and observe changes in the child's arm support.

Credit: (see also Credit Notes in this strand's preface)
+   raises head and chest off surface and bears weight on his hands with extended arms for several seconds; arms are in front of shoulders, and head and neck can move freely.
+/-   has displayed this skill once or twice but for only a few seconds.
A   chest tends to hang down; bears weight on back of flexed hands rather than positioning palm side on supporting surface; has difficulty moving out of position; can lift head up but only with great effort and can only support it through hyperextension, i.e., with head held back on upper back.

3.43 Holds weight on one hand in prone   6-7.5

Definition: The child is able to shift and maintain his weight to one side on an extended arm when he reaches with his opposite arm.

Example Observation Opportunities: After #3.26 "Bears weight on hands in prone," suspend a toy toward one of the child's arms a few inches above the surface. Encourage him to bat at or manipulate the toy at this level. After a few minutes rest, repeat with his other arm using a new, suspended toy.

Credit: (see also Credit Notes in this strand's preface)
+   can maintain his weight on one hand, elbow extended and chest off surface for at least 3-5 seconds, <u>on each side</u>.
+/-   shifts weight to one side while propped on <u>forearm</u> and side of chest while reaching with opposite arm.
A   bears weight on back of flexed hand rather than positioning palm side on supporting surface; asymmetrical, i.e., can bear weight on one side but not the other.

(may also credit #3.30 "Demonstrates balance reactions in prone" in Strand 3-6A)

3-2 SUPINE (DEVELOPING CONTROL OF FLEXION)

3.02	0-2	Turns head to both sides in supine
3.09	1.5-2.5	Extends both legs
3.11	1.5-2.5	Kicks reciprocally
3.14	2-3.5	Assumes withdrawal position
4.07	1-3.5	Brings hands to midline in supine
4.23	4-5	Looks with head in midline
1.29	5-6	Brings feet to mouth
3.35	5-6.5	Raises hips pushing with feet in supine
3.42	6-8	Lifts head in supine
5.27	6-12	Struggles against supine position

Family Friendly Interpretation of Strand Concepts, Assessment, & Purpose

We will be observing your child's muscle control and development while he is lying on his back, or in what therapists frequently call the "supine position." This is the position where your child first uses the muscles that help him bend or flex his body and move his arms and legs against gravity. Waving arms and kicking are the first movements a child usually makes when he is lying on his back. He then begins to use more controlled arm movements and can move his arms against gravity to reach for things held over his chest. Later, babies gain more control over their chest, belly and leg muscles and are able to bend and bring their legs up to their hands and mouth to play. The development of these muscles help in later movement skills, such as rolling, getting into sitting, and getting into a hands and knee position to prepare for crawling.

Parent Questions   (Examples)

To help identify the child's unique strengths and needs related to this developmental area:
- About how much time does your child spend lying on his back?
- What is your child's favorite position for sleeping?...for playing?
- When your child is lying on his back, have you seen him:
  - try to play with his feet?
  - stiffen up or arch his back? *If so*, When do you see this?

- Has your child ever had long-term use of an IV, any surgeries or other medical needs or equipment which kept him from moving freely while lying on his back?

To help identify family resources, priorities and concerns related to the child's development in this area:
- Do you have any difficulty changing your child's diapers? *If so*, What have your tried so far?

Sample *Functional* Outcome Statements which may be generated by the Family

[Will be dependent upon identified individual child and family needs and should incorporate objectives and activities from other domains]

My child will:
- be able to play with his crib gym while lying on his back;
- develop stronger tummy muscle so he can get into sitting by himself;
- not arch his back or become stiff when we put him down to play or rest.

We will be able to dress and change our child's diapers without him arching, fussing, or becoming stiff.

Transactional Assessment

May assess through observation and interview.

Assessment of the Child's Environment

1. Supportive:
[Example environments which support/facilitate development in this area]

The child's caregiving environments usually have safe firm surfaces for the child to rest on.

Assessment of Caregiver Interactions with the Child

1. Supportive:
[Example interactions which support/facilitate child's development in this area]
The child's caregivers usually:

• Change the child's position throughout the day;
• Give the child something interesting to play with or look at when he is lying on his back to play.

Identifying and Interpreting Needs for Intervention

If a child is significantly delayed or shows atypical development in this area, he <u>may have a neuro-motor or musculo-skeletal problem</u> which interferes with his development of flexion in supine. It will be important to consult with the child's physician and have a further evaluation by a pediatric physical or occupational therapist.

<u>However</u>, before targeting neuromotor or musculo-skeletal problems as the primary area of need, consider, rule out, or adapt for other causes.

These may include:
• The child may be <u>extra sensitive to touch or have other sensory organization problems</u> which cause him to feel disorganized or insecure in this position;
• <u>Supine positions may be (or have been) contraindicated</u>, painful or uncomfortable due to certain medical conditions, such as reflux or surgery to correct a spinal lesion.

Assessment Adaptations   (Examples)

[Note any adaptations needed to credit and help plan interventions]
• If the child <u>has reflux and is restricted from supine</u> after feeding, plan your observation of this strand prior to feeding.
• If the child appears <u>insecure on a flat surface</u>, some of the items may be observed in an infant seat or in supine on an adult's lap. Be sure to give him much support and move him very slowly as you place him in supine.
• <u>Visually impaired</u>:
  – Infants who are blind tend to keep their heads centered with minimal movement in supine and prone. Therefore, item #3.02 "Turns head to both sides in supine," may not be spontaneously observed.

– Infants who are blind do not have the same motivation as infants with vision to play with their feet or bring their hands to midline. Thus items #4.07 "Brings hands to midline in supine" and #1.29 "Brings feet to mouth" may be normally delayed if compared to norms based on infants with vision.
– Infants who are blind often prefer supine positions as they feel more secure. Thus they may not display item #5.25 " Struggles against supine position."
– Adapt item #4.23 "Looks with head in midline". Credit if the child is able to hold his head in midline; i.e., the child does not have to "look."

General Assessment Procedures & Processes   (apply to all items in this Strand)

1. Observe when the child is lying supine on a safe, flat surface <u>without</u> a pillow.
2. **Generally these skills can be observed spontaneously while the child is resting or playing.** A few minutes observation will enable you to quickly review which skills in supine the child has without administering each item. Example eliciting situations are provided if needed.
3. **Be sure to advise parent that although you are watching how the child uses his muscles when he is lying on his back, he also needs lots of experiences in other positions.**
4. Early items from Strand 3-5, "Mobility and Transitional Movements" which originate in the supine position may be observed and assessed concurrently, i.e., #3.28 "Rolls supine to side"

#3.38 "Rolls supine to prone"
5. **Describe the skill or eliciting procedures and invite family members to help observe and or assess.**

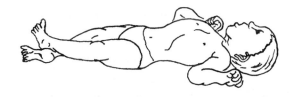

Example Atypical Supine position

+ - A **Credit Notes:**
+   child usually displays supine skills as defined.
-    not observed or reported.

General Assessment Procedures & Processes   (continued)

+/- appears to be an emerging skill.

A atypical at all ages:
- frequently stiffens, legs extended or crossed rigidly with toes pointed down, back pressed against surface;
- frequently arches back;
- asymmetrical posture or obligatory ATNR;
- shoulders elevated after 3 months near ears;
- legs widely spread, resting in a frog-like position on surface.

O circle any credit if environment or interactions compromise or restrict child's movements.

Note any adaptations used to credit.

 ## Assessment Materials

Safe firm surface, such as a mat or sheet on the floor or a firm crib mattress; attractive sound and visual stimuli, such as a rattle, squeak toy.

 ## Turns head to both sides in supine   0-2

Definition: The child can turn his head easily and completely to each side while lying on his back. He may have a preference for holding his head toward one side, but he should be able to turn his head freely.

Example Observation Opportunities: If head turning is not observed spontaneously, move to the opposite side the child is facing and try to attract his attention with a squeak toy, rattle or friendly voice. May also observe when the child is tracking a toy or face to each side. Give him plenty of time to respond.

Credit: (see also Credit Notes in this strand's preface)
+   turns head freely and completely to each side while lying on a flat surface at least once.

 ## Extends both legs   1.5-2.5

Definition: The child moves out of a totally flexed posture when lying on his back (i.e., with his arms and knees drawn close to his body), into a more extended posture where his arms and legs move out and straighten. His limbs are still somewhat flexed, but not tucked close to his chest and abdomen.

Example Observation Opportunities: May be observed spontaneously while the child is resting, playing or interacting with an adult when lying supine.

Credit: (see also Credit Notes in this strand's preface)
+   typically does NOT keep his arms and legs tucked close to his body; feet can rest on supporting surface or with soles somewhat facing each other; arms move freely.

(also in Strand 3-1 "Prone")

 ## Kicks reciprocally   1.5-2.5

Definition: The child kicks his legs alternately when excited.

Example Observation Opportunities: May observe when the parent approaches child, smiles or puts arms out to pick him up. May also observe when an interesting toy is held about 12 inches above his chest.

Credit: (see also Credit Notes in this strand's preface)
+   uses both legs equally and kicks them smoothly in an alternating pattern.
A   unable to move legs independent of one another, i.e., both legs are extended rigidly together with toes pointed down during kicking attempts; or only kicks one leg.

Assumes withdrawal position   2-3.5

Definition: When the child is lying on his back he sometimes spontaneously flexes his arms and legs and brings them close to his body.

Example Observation Opportunities: May observe when child is lying on his back and is practicing his movements.

Credit: (see also Credit Notes in this strand's preface)
+   spontaneously moves in and out of flexion (i.e., bends and straighten arms and legs) while lying on back.

4.07 **Brings hands to midline in supine** 1-3.5

Definition: The child can move both his arms against gravity to bring his hands together toward the middle of his body near his face or chest.

Example Observation Opportunities: Incidental - this can often be observed spontaneously while the child is in an active or quiet alert state in unrestricted clothing. It may be especially apparent when a bottle or toy is presented at midline, or if the child brings his hands to his mouth. Structured - position the child in supine with his head in midline. Play a game of "Pat-a-cake" or gently rub the child's hands together. Pause and see if he'll naturally bring his hands together.

Credit: (see also Credit Notes in this strand's preface)
+ brings both hands to midline in supine as defined. Both arms should move symmetrically, and head is generally in midline by 3 months.

(also in Strand 4-5 "Bilateral and Midline skills")

4.23 **Looks with head in midline** 4-5

Definition: The child can easily turn and maintain his head at midline when lying on his back.

Example Observation Opportunities: Observe child when he is lying on his back during play, while resting, or when looking at things held above his chest, e.g., watching his mobile; when parent presents his bottle.

Credit: (see also Credit Notes in this strand's preface)
+ spontaneously and easily brings and maintains head at midline; arms and legs appear symmetrical.

(also in Strand 4-5 "Bilateral and Midline skills")

1.29 **Brings feet to mouth** 5-6

Definition: The child can lift his pelvis against gravity to bring his feet to or near his mouth and hands. He brings his feet to his hands or mouth to play and explore his body and movements.

Example Observation Opportunities: May observe spontaneously when child is playing alone contentedly. If not observed spontaneously, try placing some brightly colored socks or a toy on his feet. Raise his feet gently, if needed, to initially attract his attention.

Credit: (see also Credit Notes in this strand's preface)
+ easily brings either or both feet simultaneously toward his face, with legs slightly flexed and buttocks raised slightly from the surface; hands are on or near his feet.
A brings feet to mouth without lifting his bottom off the surface and there is no rounding of his back.

3.35 **Raises hips pushing with feet in supine** 5-6.5

Definition: The child may sometimes raise his hips when he is supine by pushing with his feet flat on the surface. This is generally not a critical skill in development, but may occur while the child is experimenting with his body movements. NOTE: In contrast to other skills in this strand, his movement is demonstrating development of trunk and hip extension, rather than flexion.

Example Observation Opportunities: Not a behavior to elicit but may observe incidentally.

Credit: (see also Credit Notes in this strand's preface)
+ if present *[If present, it will be important that the child "Brings feet to mouth" (#1.29) to demonstrate that he has a balance of flexion and extension]*
A typically uses this as a means for locomotion; hyperextends neck or arches back.
N/A not observed; this item is for anticipatory guidance.

3.42 Lifts head in supine   6-8

Definition: The child sometimes lifts his head briefly from a flat surface when he is lying on his back, tucking his chin toward his chest.

Example Observation Opportunities: Hold an attractive toy over the child's chest when he is lying on a flat surface without a pillow. After attracting his attention, move the toy toward his feet. Observe if he attempts to watch the toy by lifting his head for a moment.

Credit: (see also Credit Notes in this strand's preface)

   +   momentarily lifts head slightly off the surface with chin tucked toward chest.

(may also credit #3.37 "Lifts head and assists when pulled to sitting" in Strand 3-6B)

5.27 Struggles against supine position   6-12

Definition: Now that the child has developed enough control in supine and can move easily against gravity, he may resist lying on his back by squirming, twisting, and trying to roll over. This is a typical stage as the child begins to prefer movement and upright positions.

Example Observation Opportunities: May observe incidentally or during a diaper change.

Credit: (see also Credit Notes in this strand's preface)

   +   if observed.

   N/A if not observed or reported; anticipatory guidance item.

3-3 SITTING

3.21	3-5	Holds head steady in supported sitting
3.22	3-5	Sits with slight support
3.32	*4-5*	Moves head actively in supported sitting
3.29	*5-6*	Sits momentarily leaning on hands
3.33	5-6	Holds head erect when leaning forward
3.34	5-8	Sits independently indefinitely but may use hands
3.51	8-9	Sits without hand support for ten minutes

Family Friendly Interpretation of Strand Concepts, Assessment, & Purpose

We will be observing how your child is learning to sit up by himself. Learning to sit requires your child to control the muscles of his neck and trunk to hold himself up against gravity. At first, children need to support all their weight on their hands propped in front of them. As balance and trunk control improve, children can sit more upright and free up their hands to play.

As children learn to sit, they may sit in a variety of positions. For example, a child may sit with his legs straight out in front of him (long sitting), with feet facing each other (circle sitting), or with both legs bent and feet to one side (side sitting). At other times, he may sit on the back of his heels or with his feet at each side of his hips in a "W" position. "W" sitting is not a good position for children who have high or low muscle tone.

Professional FYI

Sitting requires a balance between extensor and flexor muscles which began developing in supine and prone positions (Strands 3-1 and 3-2). Head righting, equilibrium and protective responses, which are located in Strand 3-6, help the child become an independent sitter. If the child can sit well independently, is able to free up his hands to play, can twist and turn to reach for toys, and does not topple over in sitting, you can usually assume that equilibrium and protective responses in sitting are maturing effectively.

Parent Questions   (Examples)

To help identify the child's unique strengths and needs related to this developmental area:
- What kind of seat or chair does your child usually sit in during mealtime?...During play?...When you are shopping? Does he slump down or need any help to stay upright?
- Can your child sit up by himself on the floor without leaning against you or against furniture?
- Can you describe the way or the different ways your child usually sits on the floor; for example, does he usually sit with his legs out in front of him?
- Do you feel you can let him sit safely by himself without falling?
- Have you seen your child use both hands to play with a toy while he's sitting on the floor?

- Are there any other important things about the way your child sits during feeding or play which we have not discussed, but you feel are important?

To help identify family resources, priorities and concerns related to the child's development in this area:
- Are you interested in getting information on community resources which can provide (if appropriate):
  – A free or low-cost highchair?
  – Special seating to help him sit upright?
- Does helping your child learn to sit better seem to be a priority now? *If so,* What kinds of things would you like to see your child be able to do when he is sitting up?

Sample *Functional* Outcome Statements which may be generated by the Family

[Will be dependent upon identified individual child and family needs and should incorporate objectives and activities from other domains]

My child will be able to:
- Sit and play without our worrying that he will fall;
- Sit in a highchair without slumping over to one side;
- Sit in the grocery cart when I go shopping.

Transactional Assessment

May assess through observation and interview.

Assessment of the Child's Environment

1. Supportive:
[Example environments which support/facilitate development in this area]
The child's caregiving environments have:
• Space which is safe and free of obstacles for the child to practice sitting independently;
• Seating which is appropriate to the child's developmental needs, e.g., a highchair which accommodates child's size; adaptive chair to help improve posture.

2. Compromising:
[Example environments which may restrict, compromise, inhibit or be unsupportive toward development in this area]
The child's caregiving environments usually:
• Have no safe places for the child to practice sitting independently, e.g., many obstacles for child to fall back on, floor too cold, many children and or pets running through;
• Do not have appropriate seating to accommodate the child's size or special postural needs.

Assessment of Caregiver Interactions with the Child

1. Supportive:
[Example interactions which support/facilitate child's development in this area]
The child's caregivers usually:
• Provide adequate supervision when the child is sitting independently;
• Make sure the surrounding area is safe (e.g., free of sharp objects or furnishings; carpet or pillows behind him) in case he topples over;
• Adjust seating to provide adequate support and freedom to accommodate the child's motor needs.

2 Compromising:
[Interactions which may restrict, compromise, inhibit or be unsupportive of the child's development in this area]
The child's caregivers frequently:
• Leave their child unattended in sitting when it may be dangerous to do so;
• Let the child stay in a slumped or awkward position when sitting;
• Do not place their child in independent sitting positions when developmentally he is ready to do so (e.g., leaves child lying in crib, playpen or floor most of the time.)

Identifying and Interpreting Needs for Intervention

If a child is significantly delayed or displays atypical development in this area, he <u>may be having difficulty in developing the control needed to balance flexion and extension against gravity due to neuromotor problems (e.g., atypical tone, lack of balance reactions).</u>

However, before targeting neuromotor prob-lems as the primary need for intervention, consider, rule out, or adapt for other causes of delays. These may include:
• <u>Lack of experience</u> in unsupported sitting;
• <u>Visual impairment</u>: child may tend not to hold his head erect in sitting;
• <u>Poor endurance</u> or weakness.

Assessment Adaptations (Examples)

[Note any adaptations needed to credit and help plan interventions]
• <u>Visually impaired</u>: assess in a familiar environment; suggest to the parent to use tactile and auditory cues to encourage more erect postures, e.g., gentle stroking down his back or engaging him in a toy.

General Assessment Procedures & Processes (apply to all items in this Strand)

1. **All items in this strand should be assessed on a safe, firm surface, free of obstruction in case the child topples over.** Pillows can be positioned nearby if the child has a tendency to fall, but they should not be supporting him to credit an item.
2. **All items may be observed incidentally during play or when assessing other developmental domains.**

3. **The following related sitting items from other gross motor strands may be observed spontaneously when the child is in sitting:**
   Strand 3-5 "Mobility and transitional movements"
      #3.44, "Gets to sitting without assistance"
      #3.57, "Goes from sitting to prone"
   Strand 3-6 "Reflexes/Reactions/Responses"

General Assessment Procedures & Processes (continued)

If the child is stable in sitting and can twist and turn, side-sit, and move in and out of sitting, it can usually be assumed that the following equilibrium and protective responses are maturing adequately and may not need formal testing:

#3.41 "Protective extension of arms to side and front"

#3.55 "Demonstrates balance reactions in sitting"

#3.56 "Protective extension of arms to back"

4. **Describe the skill or eliciting procedures and invite family members to help observe and or assess.**

+ - A Credit Notes:

+ child usually displays sitting skills as defined during play and daily activities; head is up and free to move in any direction.

- not observed or reported.

+/- appears to be an emerging skill.

A atypical at all stages:

– Poor head control, head is hyperextended or droops forward and is not free to move;

– Shoulders always retracted and elevated;

– Legs spread very far apart and child slumps forward, chest almost on surface;

– Bears weight on lower back rather than on his bottom- appears like he is struggling not to fall over, or looks "stuck" in position;

– Props on back of hands, wrists flexed, instead of propping on palms;

– Can only "W" sit;

– Asymmetrical posture: note which side.

O circle any credit if environment or interactions compromise or restrict child's optimal sitting skills, such as inappropriate positioning.

Note any adaptations used to credit.

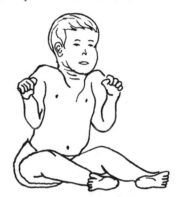

Example Atypical Sitting position

 ## Assessment Materials

Safe, flat firm surface, such as a carpeted floor; firm pillows.

 ### Holds head steady in supported sitting 3-5

Definition: The child is able to hold his head upright without it bobbing or drooping forward when he is in supported sitting.

Example Observation Opportunities: Observe when the child is sitting on his parent's lap or on the floor if held around his waist. There should be an interesting visual event (e.g., a toy, mirror, or another person) positioned at the child's eye level.

Credit: (see also Credit Notes in this strand's preface)

+ usually holds head upright and steady without bobbing for at least 1 minute, when supported around his waist in sitting.

 ### Sits with slight support 3-5

Definition: The child usually holds his trunk fairly upright when sitting with support provided through his hips and lower back.

Example Observation Opportunities: Observe when child is sitting on the floor in front of a mirror, an interesting person, or an object positioned at his eye level. Provide support at his waist with your hands or pillows.

Credit: (see also Credit Notes in this strand's preface)

+ usually keeps trunk fairly straight and upright in sitting when given support at his waist; shoulders are positioned in front of hips, and there may be some rounding of his back at this stage.

3.32 ## Moves head actively in supported sitting   *4-5*

Definition: When supported in sitting, the child has enough head and trunk control to move his head freely to look around.
Example Observation Opportunities: When the child is in supported sitting, observe if he can turn his head to each side when he is, for example, watching someone walk by or tracking a rolling toy. Support should be provided at his hips.
Credit: (see also Credit Notes in this strand's preface)
+   freely moves head to look around without bobbing or tipping his head from side to side or front to back; head is maintained in line with trunk.
A   can only turn his head to one side.

3.29 ## Sits momentarily leaning on hands   *5-6*

Definition: The child can sit alone for a few seconds if he props forward on his hands, arms straight. He may prop his hands on the floor or on his slightly flexed legs for support.
Example Observation Opportunities: Observe when child is sitting in front of a mirror, an interesting person, or an object positioned at his eye level. Provide support at his hips and lower back with your hands, and then gradually move your hands away. Also, observe if the child holds his head erect for the next sitting skill in this strand, i.e., #3.33.
Credit: (see also Credit Notes in this strand's preface)
+   sits independently, propped forward on hands, as defined, for at least 30 seconds; upper back should be fairly straight with some rounding of lower back; legs should be slightly flexed, feet in front of hips.
+/- sits propped forward on forearms rather than on palms of hands with arms straight.

3.33 ## Holds head erect when leaning forward   *5-6*

Definition: When the child is sitting propped forward on his hands as in #3.29, he is able to maintain his head upright and steady.
Example Observation Opportunities: Observe with skill #3.29 above.
Credit: (see also Credit Notes in this strand's preface)
+   holds head erect and steady, as defined, for the duration of propped sitting.

3.34 ## Sits independently indefinitely but may use hands   *5-8*

Definition: The child has developed enough head and trunk control and balance to be able to sit steady and erect independently for several minutes without falling. He may sometimes prop on one or both hands, but is able to use both hands to play. When he leans forward to reach for a toy, he can resume an erect position. He may still topple backwards unexpectedly.
Example Observation Opportunities: May observe whenever child is sitting on the floor, without leaning against a support, while playing with toys. Observe if he is able to free up both hands to play with a toy, and if he demonstrates trunk rotation, e.g., twists his trunk to reach for parent or toy positioned to one side.
Credit: (see also Credit Notes in this strand's preface)
+   sits steady and erect independently for several minutes at a time; is able to free up hands to play with a toy, but may intermittently use one or both hands for some minimal support. If child is 7-8 months, he should also be able to rotate his upper body while his hips remain stationary in sitting.
+/- briefly frees up both hands but usually uses one or both hands to prop; is not able to rotate his trunk in sitting.
A   sway back posture (lordosis)

3.51 **Sits without hand support for ten minutes** **8-9**

Definition: The child can sit independently with a straight back for at least 10 minutes. He rarely needs to prop on his hands for support, and he is able to rotate his upper body while his hips remain stationary. He may still topple backwards unexpectedly.

Example Observation Opportunities: Same as #3.34:

Credit: (see also Credit Notes in this strand's preface)

+ sits independently for 10 minutes; back should be straight with shoulders generally over hips and arms forward with both hands free to reach and play; head free to move in all directions. May sit in a variety of sitting positions, e.g., circle sit (feet in front facing each other), long-legged (both legs extended or one leg extended, other flexed); side-sitting, sometimes "W" sit (one or both legs), knees fairly close together.

A sway-back posture (lordosis)

3-4 WEIGHT-BEARING IN STANDING

3.23	3-5	Bears some weight on legs
3.36	5-6	Bears almost all weight on legs
3.45	6-7	Bears large fraction of weight on legs and bounces
3.46	6-10.5	Stands, holding on
3.60	9.5-11	Stands momentarily
3.68	11-13	Stands a few seconds
3.71	11.5-14	Stands alone well

Family Friendly Interpretation of Strand Concepts, Assessment, & Purpose

We will be observing how your child is learning to put weight on his legs and to balance as he is learning to stand. When a child is first learning to stand, the adult who is holding him has to do most of the work because the child can not put much of his weight on his feet. Then, as a child develops better head and trunk control and is able to put more weight on his feet, he needs less help in standing. At this stage, although you still need to hold your child under his arms, he is putting most of his weight on his feet and you only need to hold him to balance. He may begin to enjoy bouncing around this time. Finally, a child develops enough control and balance to stand first by just holding someone's hands, and then by not holding onto anything.

Parent Questions   (Examples)

To help identify the child's unique strengths and needs related to this developmental area:
- Have you ever held your baby up to stand? How do you typically hold him?
- Does he seem to put some of his weight on his legs and feet?

- Does he like to stand?
- Does your child use a walker? About how often? *[Families should be provided anticipatory guidance discouraging the excessive use of walkers and "jumpers"; explain that this will not help their child walk earlier. Also advise on the safety hazards of walkers]*

Sample *Functional* Outcome Statements which may be generated by the Family

[Will be dependent upon identified individual child and family needs and should incorporate objectives and activities from other domains]

My child will:
- Stand at our coffee table to play;
- Be able to stand up alone.

Transactional Assessment

May assess through observation and interview.

Assessment of the Child's Environment

1. Supportive:
[Example environments which support/facilitate development in this area]
The child's caregiving environments have safe furnishings for the child to pull up to stand, e.g., sturdy, no sharp corners, child-proofed.

2. Compromising:
[Example environments which may restrict, compromise, inhibit or be unsupportive toward development in this area]
The child spends excessive amounts of time in restrictive equipment, e.g., a walker, "jumper" seat, highchair.

Identifying and Interpreting Needs for Intervention

If a child is delayed in this area he may be having difficulty with <u>controlling the muscles needed for upright balance and weight-bearing.</u>

However, before targeting this as the primary need for intervention, consider, rule out, or adapt for other causes of delays which are <u>NOT</u> due to upright balance, control and weight-bearing abilities. These may include:
- <u>Hypersensitivity</u> in his feet, especially babies who were born prematurely or with other medical complications;
- Other <u>sensory organizational problems</u> (e.g.,

children who don't seem to enjoy standing or seem to stiffen when held in standing–as if frightened.)
- <u>Visually impaired</u>: many blind children do not hold their heads erect or may have a slumped posture;
- <u>Normal variance in child's development</u>; if no other atypical patterns or significant delays are evidenced, lack of early weight-bearing is not necessarily cause for alarm. Reassess in a month or two.

Assessment Adaptations   (Examples)

[Note any adaptations needed to credit and help plan interventions]
- If the child is <u>hypersensitive</u>, firm massage to his feet and heels prior to weight-bearing may be helpful (if he tolerates this). May also try different surfaces, e.g., linoleum, firm mat,

outdoor carpet, or assess with the child's shoes on.
- <u>Visually impaired</u>: suggest to the parent to use tactile and auditory cues to encourage more erect postures, e.g., gentle stroking down his back or engaging him in a toy.

General Assessment Procedures & Processes   (apply to all items in this Strand)

1. **If the child does not mind, ask the parent to remove his shoes and socks.**
2. In addition to weight-bearing, **observe the child's overall posture and symmetry.**
3. <u>Caution</u>: **If the child has cerebral palsy or hypertonicity, do not encourage bouncing while weight-bearing,** as this may increase tone further.
4. Observation of many movement-related skills in standing are in Strand 3-5 "Mobility and Transitional Movements". These can be **observed and credited simultaneously** (if displayed):
   #3.47 "Pulls to standing at furniture"
   #3.53 "Makes stepping movements"
   #3.58 "Lowers to sitting from furniture"
   #3.61 "Walks holding onto furniture"
   #3.65 "Walks with both hands held"
   #3.66 "Stoops and recovers"
   #3.67 "Stands by lifting one foot"
   #3.70 "Walks with one hand held"
   #3.72 "Walks along two to three steps"
   #3.74 "Falls by sitting"
   #3.75 "Stands from supine by turning on all fours"
   #3.79 "Walks without support."

5. **Describe the skill and eliciting situations and invite family members to help observe and or assess.**

+ - A **Credit Notes:**
+   child usually displays weight-bearing as defined.
-   not observed or reported.
+/- appears to be an emerging skill.
A   atypical at all stages:
   – Head hyperextended or flexed forward with chin tucked;
   – Definite asymmetric posture, e.g., one arm or leg held bent, other arm and or leg straightened;
   – Stiff crossed legs; standing with knees "locked" or pressed together;
   – Sway back (lordosis) or very rounded back.
O   circle any credit if environment compromises or restricts child's optimal weight-bearing skills.
Note any adaptations used to credit.

Assessment Materials

A sturdy piece of furniture, chest height to the child; lightweight toy which requires the child to

hold with two hands, e.g., ball, stuffed animal.

3.23 Bears some weight on legs   3-5

Definition: When held upright in standing, the child is able to briefly hold some of his weight on his legs. At this stage, the adult holding him is providing most of the support he needs for balance and trunk control.

Example Observation Opportunities: Observe when holding child upright, supporting him under his arms.

Credit: (see also Credit Notes in this strand's preface)

+ stands a few seconds, weight supported partially on feet and by adult; head upright at midline, hips generally behind shoulders and arms somewhat flexed.

3.36 Bears almost all weight on legs   5-6

Definition: When held upright in standing, the child is able to place most of his weight on his legs. At this stage, the adult holding him is providing less support than in #3.23 "Bears some weight on legs"; i.e., the child is doing more "work" than the adult.

Example Observation Opportunities: Observe when holding the child upright with your hands around his chest. Gradually reduce your support until your hands are only holding him for balance.

Credit: (see also Credit Notes in this strand's preface)

+ bears most of his weight on legs for at least 5 seconds; legs should be slightly bent and apart; hips generally in line with shoulders, maintaining good upright head control.

3.45 Bears large fraction of weight on legs and bounces   6-7

Definition: Same as 3.36 but now the child has enough control and balance to actively bounce when supported in standing.

Example Observation Opportunities: Same as #3.36. If not elicited spontaneously, sing a favorite song and ask the child to "dance," or *gently* help him bounce up and down a few times and pause to see if he continues.

Credit: (see also Credit Notes in this strand's preface)

+ actively moves up and down on legs a few times with good control and minimal adult support; hips are generally in line with shoulders; maintains good upright head control.

A locks knees or collapses through hips and knees and then straightens legs to stand.

3.46 Stands, holding on   6-10.5

Definition: The child can stand by holding onto a support at chest height. The support may be the child's crib or playpen rail, sturdy low table, or an adult holding his hands. Initially, the child holds on for support *and* balance, then for balance only.

Example Observation Opportunities: May observe spontaneously if child is standing at his playpen, crib rail, or chest-high furnishing such as a sturdy coffee table. If not observed spontaneously, place a toy on top of the low table and encourage him to pull up to stand. Place him in standing if he can not pull up, but *provide parent anticipatory guidance*; if the child is not pulling himself up to stand independently, he is *not* yet ready for prolonged standing.

Credit: (see also Credit Notes in this strand's preface)

+ stands for several seconds holding onto a chest-high support with hands; does not lean against support; bears weight on soles of feet.

+/- leans against support or props forearms on the furniture with weight supported on arms and chest; may initially stand up on toes.

A child has had practice in standing at a support for a month or two but continues to stand up on toes.

(may also credit in Strand 3-5: #3.47 "Pulls to standing at furniture" and #3.58 "Lowers self from furniture," if observed)

3.60 **Stands momentarily   9.5-11**

Definition: The child can stand alone for a few seconds. At this stage, his legs may be widely spread with arms held at "high guard," i.e., arms held high at his shoulder level, elbows bent.

Example Observation Opportunities: May be observed spontaneously if child lets go of the support he's standing at, e.g., crib, play pen, coffee table, adult hands. If he does not let go, try engaging him in a distraction (e.g., looking out a window or in a floor length mirror), and gradually remove your hands as he appears steady. *Be ready to provide him support as he begins to move off balance.*

Credit: (see also Credit Notes in this strand's preface)

+   stands alone momentarily with good head control; arms are held in high guard position for balance; toes may tend to curl a bit for balance; weight evenly distributed between legs.

3.68 **Stands a few seconds   11-13**

Definition: Same as #3.60 "Stands momentarily," but for more than about 3 seconds.

Example Observation Opportunities: Same as #3.60

Credit: (see also Credit Notes in this strand's preface)

+   stands alone at least 3 seconds; may still show wide base of support and a "high guard" arm posture.

3.71 **Stands alone well   11.5-14**

Definition: The child is able to stand alone with his arms free to play.

Example Observation Opportunities: May be observed spontaneously anytime during observation period, when child is standing and holding or watching a toy or other activity.

Credit: (see also Credit Notes in this strand's preface)

+   stands for at least 10 seconds; has complete head control and straight back; his arms appear relaxed and are free to use; feet are no longer widely spaced and are held generally under his hips; appears symmetrical.

A   always stands on toes; appears asymmetrical, weight always held toward one side.

3-5 MOBILITY AND TRANSITIONAL MOVEMENTS

3.10	1.5-2	Rolls side to supine
3.17	2-5	Rolls prone to supine
3.28	4-5.5	Rolls supine to side
3.38	5.5-7.5	Rolls supine to prone
3.31	5-6	Circular pivoting in prone
3.48	6-8	Brings one knee forward beside trunk in prone
3.49	7-8	Crawls backward
3.52	8-9.5	Crawls forward
3.57	*6-10*	Goes from sitting to prone
3.54	8-9	Assumes hand-knee position
3.44	6-10	Gets to sitting without assistance
3.53	8-10	Makes stepping movements
3.47	6-10	Pulls to standing at furniture
3.58	9-10	Lowers to sitting from furniture
3.59	9-11	Creeps on hands and knees
3.61	9.5-13	Walks holding onto furniture
3.63	10-11	Pivots in sitting - twists to pick up objects
3.64	10-12	Creeps on hands and feet
3.65	10-12	Walks with both hands held
3.67	11-12	Stands by lifting one foot
3.69	11-13	Assumes and maintains kneeling
3.70	11-13	Walks with one hand held
3.72	11.5-13.5	Walks along two to three steps
3.74	12-14	Falls by sitting
3.75	12.5-15	Stands from supine by turning on all fours
3.78	13.5-15	Creeps or hitches upstairs
3.79	13-15	Walks without support
3.66	*13-15*	Stoops and recovers

Family Friendly Interpretation of Strand Concepts, Assessment, & Purpose

We will be observing how your child moves from one position to another and how he moves from one place to another. Changing positions, such as moving from sitting to lying down, are called transitional movements. Moving from one place to another is frequently termed mobility. Rolling, crawling and walking are examples of mobility skills. These skills require that your child be able to balance and shift his weight from one part of his body to another.

Parent Questions   (Examples)

To help identify the child's unique strengths and needs related to this developmental area:
[General]

• What are some of the things you've noticed about how your child moves to change his position or to move from one place to another?

• Have you noticed if there are some positions or movements your child tries to make that he seems to be having some difficulty with?

[Specific: dependent upon child's apparent gross motor level]

• Has your child started rolling over? *If so,*
Can you tell me a little about how he rolls; for example, does he roll from his tummy to his back?...his back to his tummy? Does he seem to flop over quickly or roll more slowly, moving one body part at a time?

• If your child wants something (several feet away) on the floor, how does he try to get to it?

• What does your child do if he's sitting and wants to lie down?

• Has your child started pulling up to stand at a piece of furniture? *If so,*
  – Where does he do this?
  – Can he take any steps to move around?
  – What does he do when he wants to get down?

• About how long has your child been walking?

• Can he crawl up stairs yet?

To help identify family resources, priorities and concerns related to the child's development in this area:

• Do you have special concerns or questions about how your child is learning to move around?

• Imagine six months from now...what are the

Parent Questions   (continued)

kinds of things you would you like to see your child be able to do, or be better at, as he is learning to move around?
[Reminder: Some families may look forward to having their child move about and become independent. However, some families may not be as anxious because they worry that their child will be more difficult to manage or are not ready for their child to be less dependent]*
• What does it mean for you to see your child beginning to move around so much?

Sample *Functional* Outcome Statements which may be generated by the Family

[Will be dependent upon identified individual child and family needs and should incorporate objectives and activities from other domains]

My child will be able to:
• Move to get things he wants;
• Crawl;
• Walk.

Transactional Assessment

May assess through observation and interview.

Assessment of the Child's Environment

1. Supportive:
[Example environments which support/facilitate development in this area]
The child's caregiving environments usually:
• Have open areas for the child to move freely;
• Are child-proofed, e.g., padded corners on sharp edges; no sharp or dangerous objects.

2. Compromising:
[Example environments which may restrict, compromise, inhibit or be unsupportive toward development in this area]
The child's caregiving environments are frequently:
• Unsafe to freely move about;
• Have too many obstacles or not enough space to move freely.

Assessment of Caregiver Interactions with the Child

1. Supportive:
[Example interactions which support/facilitate child's development in this area]
The child's caregivers usually:
• Supervise their child's newly developing mobility skills;
• Encourage their child's newly developing mobility skills, e.g., attracting attention to a toy to motivate him to move.

2. Compromising:
[Example interactions which may restrict, compromise, inhibit or be unsupportive of the child's development in this area]
The child's caregivers frequently:
• Expect and try to make their child walk before he is developmentally ready;
• Place their child in walkers or restrictive equipment (playpen, highchair) for much of the child's waking hours.

Identifying and Interpreting Needs for Intervention

If a child is significantly delayed or displays atypical development in this area, he may be having <u>difficulty in developing the weight-shifting and balance skills needed for smooth transitional and mobility skills.</u>

<u>However</u>, before targeting balance and weight-shifting abilities as the primary area of need for intervention, consider, rule out, or adapt for other causes which may cause delays in this strand. These may include:
• <u>Limited experiences</u> to move due to environmental or medical conditions or restrictions;
• <u>Visual impairment</u>: a child who is significantly visually impaired may normally achieve milestones in this area in a difference sequence and at a slower pace than sighted peers. A child who is blind may not display hip or trunk rotation as readily as a child with sight because he does not have the visual stimulus which often motivates young children to turn and rotate their bodies to look at things. Many children who are blind also walk with an unusual gait, feet externally rotated, stiff-legged, and with the center of gravity lowered so that their walking appears to be almost waddling;

Identifying and Interpreting Needs for Intervention   (continued)

- Sensory processing problems: motor planning, postural or gravitational insecurity or other vestibular-related problems can make it difficult or frightening to the child when he moves his body in space;
- Social emotional concerns, such as depression and low motivation;

- Lack of energy, e.g., secondary to failure-to-thrive, heart problems, other medical conditions;
- General activity level of child: i.e., the child is quiet and sedentary, and is not as interested in movement.

Assessment Adaptations   (Examples)

[Note any adaptations needed to credit and help plan interventions]

- Medically involved: if movement is limited due to medical conditions, such as surgeries, medical devices, or cardiac status, consult with the child's physician before initiating any procedures to elicit skills in this strand.
- Visually impaired: assess only in comfortable familiar environments. If milestones are compared with sighted children, a considerable delay in self-initiated mobility can be normal for the child who is blind. Auditory cues may be used as a motivator, but remember that ear-hand coordination usually does not occur until late in the first year, and that

sound may not hold the same attracting qualities that vision does at this age.

- Sensory processing problems: refer to the Regulatory/Sensory Organization (Strand 0.0). If the child displays signs of sensory organization problems, involve a therapist who is experienced in sensory integration principles to help assess child's underlying needs and plan appropriate interventions.
- Limited experiences: if observing the child in an environment which does not have safe open spaces to observe, some of the items may be observed in a playpen, crib, or on a firm bed if *well supervised.*

General Assessment Procedures & Processes   (apply to all items in this Strand)

1. All items in this strand can be observed unobtrusively while observing the child play and while assessing of other areas of development.

    a. Helpful information can also be gleaned from observing how, and in what positions caregivers place the child because these are likely to be the child's most stable positions.

    b. Most of the items can also be assessed when observing the child's movements in the preceding gross motor strands; e.g., while observing the child in prone (Strand 3-1) he may be observed to roll over. Structured eliciting situations are provided as an option.

2. Each stage of mobility brings new safety concerns. This is an excellent opportunity to provide anticipatory guidance to caregivers regarding safety considerations related to the child's current and next level of mobility.

3. Many balance reactions in Strand 3-6 can be assumed as maturing normally if the child displays good quality transitional move- ments or mobility skills. These are noted accordingly to applicable skills in this strand.

4. Describe the skill and eliciting observation opportunities to family members and invite them to help observe and or assess.

+ - A   **Credit Notes:**

   +   child usually displays skill as defined during play and daily activities.

   -   not observed or reported.

   +/- appears to be an emerging skill.

   A   atypical (atypical patterns vary and are noted with each skill.)

   O   circle any credit if environment or interactions compromise or restrict child's optimal movement skills.

[It is also important to observe the child's frequency of movement and amount of effort he needs to use to move. This can help assess endurance and strength; e.g., if the child rolls, does he roll frequently with little outside motivation? Or, does he seem to need lots of coaxing with a favorite toy and then only rolls slowly with much effort]

Note any adaptations used to credit.

Assessment Materials

- Safe open area where child has room to move, e.g., flat surface, without throw rugs and sharp corners. A short-piled carpeted area is preferable.
- Interesting toys, objects and people which invite the child to move to explore (e.g., toys used when observing other developmental areas, such as a squeak toys, dolls, cars).
- Sturdy, safe supports for the child to pull up to at his chest height, e.g., sofa, coffee table, chair.
- 4 or 5 carpeted steps (#3.78 only).

Rolls side to supine   1.5-2

Definition: The child rolls from lying on his side to his back.

Example Observation Opportunities: Place the child in side-lying. Attract his attention to your face or a squeak toy positioned about a foot from his lower shoulder. Move it slowly in pace with his tracking, in an arc toward his opposite side. After a few minutes, repeat the procedure toward his opposite side.

Credit: (see also Credit Notes in this strand's preface)
- \+   rolls from each side to his back.
- A   rolls by strongly arching back; or can only roll to one side.

Rolls prone to supine   2-5

Definition: The child rolls from his stomach to his back, initiating the roll with his head, shoulder or hip. Initial rolls occur by "accident," and the child's body appears to roll as a total unit. As the child gains trunk control, rolling involves more twisting and rotating.

Example Observation Opportunities: When the child is lying prone on a firm surface, attract his attention to a toy or your face, and move it slowly across his line of vision around toward the back of his head. Give him the toy after he rolls over with or without help. Pause to see if he can reach for it (to observe reaching skills).

Credit: (see also Credit Notes in this strand's preface)
- \+   rolls from back to stomach in both directions.
- A   child usually "flips" over by arching his back; or can only roll to one side.

Rolls supine to side   4-5.5

Definition: The child can roll from his back to his side, initiating the roll with his head, shoulder or hip.

Example Observation Opportunities: When the child is lying on his back, attract his attention to a squeak toy positioned about a foot from his chest. Move the toy slowly in an arch, and leave the toy next to him, just out of reach. Repeat the procedure to observe rolling to his other side after a few minutes of play.

Credit: (see also Credit Notes in this strand's preface)
- \+   rolls from back to each side.
- A   child "flips" over by arching his back; or can only roll to one side.

Rolls supine to prone   5.5-7.5

Definition: The child rolls from his back to his stomach, initiating the roll with his head, shoulders or hips.

Example Observation Opportunities: Same as #3.28.

Credit: (see also Credit Notes in this strand's preface)
- \+   rolls from back to stomach in both directions; if the child has had some experience in rolling he should have some segmental or twisting movements during the roll; i.e., his shoulders are *not* in line with his hips during the roll.
- A   body appears stiff and roll is accomplished by arching back; or can only roll to one side.

3.31 Circular pivoting in prone   5-6

Definition: The child sometimes moves in a circular direction on his stomach without actually moving from one place to another. He "pivots" by pushing his arms and legs with somewhat random movements while shifting his weight from side to side. These movements help prepare him for later belly crawling.

Example Observation Opportunities: When the child is lying on his stomach, attract his attention to an interesting toy placed near his hands. While he is looking at it, move it slowly in an arc toward his hip to observe if he will pivot to obtain it. Repeat toward his opposite side.

Credit: (see also Credit Notes in this strand's preface)
+   pivots at least a quarter turn in each direction, displaying movement of his arms and legs; head is free to move with good control.
A   legs do not participate in the movement because they remain stiffly extended or crossed, or are floppy.

3.48 Brings one knee forward beside trunk in prone   6-8

Definition: The child's hip and knee flex up to one side when he shifts his weight to the opposite side. This usually occurs when the child tries to reach for a toy or as an attempt to move forward.

Example Observation Opportunities: May be observed incidentally when the child is playing on his stomach. If not, try dangling a toy in front of him, just out of reach and a few inches above the surface.

Credit: (see also Credit Notes in this strand's preface)
+   clearly shifts weight from one side to the other to bring one knee forward as defined; observed on each side; may also credit if child has accomplished skill #3.52, "Crawls forward," which follows.

3.49 Crawls backward   7-8

Definition: The child may be able to belly-crawl backwards before he learns to crawl forward. Crawling backwards is accomplished by the child using pushing movements of his arms to slide his body backwards. He may crawl backwards when he really wants to go forward, because he is using the arm movements which are most familiar to him, but which are not effective for propelling forward.

Example Observation Opportunities: Crawling backwards may be observed incidentally when child wants to move forward but moves backwards instead. When he is lying on his belly, place a favorite toy a few feet ahead to observe his attempts to get it. Be sure to give him the toy even if he does not obtain it independently. If child moves backwards, *provide parents anticipatory guidance* that this is a normal stage some children go through in preparation for crawling forward.

Credit: (see also Credit Notes in this strand's preface)
+   crawls backwards when attempting to move forward or to practice his movements.
N/A if not observed. This is *not* an item to teach or facilitate. Some children do not display this skill and move directly into forward crawling.

3.52 Crawls forward   8-9.5

Definition: The child is able to crawl forward on his belly by bending and straightening his arms and legs as his weight is shifted from side to side. This is often termed a "commando crawl." Some children use an "inch-worm" type movement, using tucking and pushing movements with their arms and legs.

Example Observation Opportunities: When the child is lying on his belly, place a favorite toy a few feet ahead to observe his attempts to get it. Do not move the toy further away as he gets closer.

Credit: (see also Credit Notes in this strand's preface)
+   crawls forward a few feet with trunk resting on floor. Both arms and legs contribute to the forward movement.
A   crawling is accomplished by only pulling with arms, with legs stiff or floppy and dragging along.

3.57 **Goes from sitting to prone** *6-10*

Definition: The child moves from sitting to lying on his tummy by moving briefly through a side-sitting position to lower himself to the surface.

Example Observation Opportunities: May be observed when the child tries to reach for a toy positioned just out of reach to one side, or when he just wants to change his position.

Credit: (see also Credit Notes in this strand's preface)
+ moves smoothly to stomach from sitting by shifting his weight to one side to move briefly through a side-sitting transitional movement.
A moves straight forward to prone through widely spread legs rather than shifting weight to one hip.

3.54 **Assumes hand-knee position** **8-9**

Definition: The child is able to move from his tummy or sitting into a hand-knee position. His chest and belly are raised off of the surface, supporting his weight on his hands and knees. First attempts usually occur when the child pushes back with his arms when prone. Initially, his legs may be widely spaced due to limited balance.

Example Observation Opportunities: <u>Incidental</u> - may be observed spontaneously when the child wants to get up from a prone position into sitting, or just to practice this new movement. <u>Structured</u> - when the child is lying on his tummy, attract his attention to a toy in front of him. Then place the toy behind an obstacle so that it is fully or partially hidden. The child may push up on hands and knees to see the toy.

Credit: (see also Credit Notes in this strand's preface)
+ moves into and maintains a hand-knee position for several seconds; he may rock forward or from side to side while in this position.
A neck hyperextended or flexed; back curved with weight on elbows.

3.44 **Gets to sitting without assistance** **6-10**

Definition: The child is able to get into sitting independently by using one of two methods. He may move from his back or tummy by: (1) moving into side-lying and then pushing up into sitting, or (2) moving into a hands and knees position and then pushing back so his hips drop to one side until sitting is assumed.

Example Observation Opportunities: May observe anytime child is lying down on his tummy or back and wants to get up (e.g., after a diaper change or dressing), or when he sees a toy that requires him to be in a sitting position. Observe the transitional movements he uses to move into sitting.

Credit: (see also Credit Notes in this strand's preface)
+ moves easily into sitting from either supine or prone using either of two transitional movements as defined.
+/- child usually needs a support to pull up with (e.g., an adult or crib rail).
A can only move into a "W" sit; or gets into sitting without a transitional movement, i.e., moves directly from prone to sitting by pushing up with arms while legs are spread widely.

3.53 **Makes stepping movements** **8-10**

Definition: The child has enough balance and control in supported standing to shift his weight from one foot to the other to make a few stepping movements. The support is used for balance only.

Example Observation Opportunities: <u>Incidental</u> - may be observed spontaneously when child is standing at a chest-high support (crib, playpen, coffee table). <u>Structured</u> - hold the child either lightly around his chest or by his hands at his shoulder height, arms fully extended. Gently tip his weight forward 1 or 2 inches to encourage stepping movements.

Credit: (see also Credit Notes in this strand's preface)
+ initiates a few reciprocal stepping movements in place, shifting weight easily from one foot to the other; movements appear symmetrical with complete head control.
A legs cross or knees press together.

3.47   Pulls to standing at furniture   6-10

Definition: The child is able to pull up to stand at a chest-high support. He may pull up to stand from sitting, prone or a hands-knee position. At this stage the child's arms do most of the work. His legs may straighten into standing together, or one at a time through a brief half-kneel transitional movement.

Example Observation Opportunities: <u>Incidental</u> - may observe spontaneously while child is in crib or playpen or is sitting next to a low table which has a toy on top. <u>Structured</u> - when the child is next to a low, sturdy furnishing, such as a couch, chair, or coffee table, attract his attention to an interesting toy or object resting on the support.

Credit: (see also Credit Notes in this strand's preface)
+   pulls easily up to stand at a support, using arms to do most of the work.
A   neck flexed with chin to chest; always stands on toes; moves slowly and struggles significantly while pulling to stand.

3.58   Lowers to sitting from furniture   9-10

Definition: When the child is standing at a chest-high support, he can safely lower himself into sitting without falling or plopping down quickly. He may lower himself by bending and reaching toward the floor with one hand, or continue to hold onto the support with both hands until his bottom is close to the floor.

Example Observation Opportunities: May observe when the child is standing at a support and becomes interested in changing positions or sees an object of interest on the floor.

Credit: (see also Credit Notes in this strand's preface)
+   usually lowers to sitting without falling as defined.
A   presses thighs tightly together as he drops to knees.

3.59   Creeps on hands and knees   9-11

Definition: The child moves forward on his hands and knees with his belly off the ground. Initially, creeping is accomplished by shifting his weight to one side while his arm and leg on the other side move forward, one at a time. With practice, creeping becomes reciprocal with the arm and leg on opposite sides moving together.

Example Observation Opportunities: May be observed when the child moves to go to something of interest, e.g., a toy, his parent, snack.

Credit: (see also Credit Notes in this strand's preface)
+   creeps on hands and knees as defined several feet before lowering belly to floor.
A   back sags downward toward floor and arms are widely spaced; or "bunny hops"; i.e., child makes a "hopping" movement by alternating his weight between hands and then shins of legs; head is hyperextended resting on upper back.

3.61   Walks holding onto furniture   9.5-13

Definition: The child is able to move sideways around furniture by holding on with one or both hands. He can do so without leaning his body against the support. This skill demonstrates his ability to shift his weight from one foot to another in standing.

Example Observation Opportunities: May be observed when the child is standing at a safe, sturdy support, such as his crib rail, playpen, or coffee table, and he then moves to get a toy out of reach.

Credit: (see also Credit Notes in this strand's preface)
+   moves sideways at least four steps while holding onto a support; does not lean body against the support.
+/- leans body against support while taking steps.

3.63   Pivots in sitting - twists to pick up objects   10-11

Definition: When sitting, the child can twist his trunk and pivot on his bottom in a circular fashion and turn his body to face the opposite direction. He uses his arms and legs to push and propel his body in a circle.

Example Observation Opportunities: May be observed when the child is sitting and is attracted to an activity or toy behind him.

Credit: (see also Credit Notes in this strand's preface)

    +   pivots 180 degrees, i.e., half circle, using trunk rotation and good head control.

(may also credit #3.55 "Demonstrates balance reactions in sitting" in Strand 3-6)

3.64   Creeps on hands and feet   10-12

Definition: The child may sometimes creep forward on his hands and feet with his trunk and knees off the floor. This may be observed when a child is between the stages of creeping on hands and knees, and walking. This is often referred to as "bear walking." Many children do not go through this transitional stage.

Example Observation Opportunities: May be observed spontaneously or reported by the parents.

Credit: (see also Credit Notes in this strand's preface)

    +   sometimes creeps on hands and feet as defined.

    A   knees always locked stiffly as legs swing forward.

    N/A if not observed or reported; this is not an item to teach.

3.65   Walks with both hands held   10-12

Definition: The child is able to walk a few steps forward when both hands are held at his shoulder level.

Example Observation Opportunities: Bend down or knee-walk backwards to hold the child's hands at his shoulder level.

Credit: (see also Credit Notes in this strand's preface)

    +   initiates at least four alternating steps forward, maintaining an upright posture; holds adult's hands only for balance and shifts weight easily from one foot to the other.

    -    "dragged" along by adult rather than child initiating the steps, or leans forward to bear weight against adult's hands.

    A   neck hyperextended with legs spread widely; slow awkward movements; lordosis (sway back); always walks on toes.

3.67   Stands by lifting one foot   11-12

Definition: The child pulls up to stand at a low support through a series of transitional movements: sitting to kneeling, then to half-kneeling to pull up to stand. This process is more mature than #3.47 "Pulls to standing at furniture," as it involves more weight-shifting and controlled use of his hip and legs rather than pulling up primarily with his arms.

Example Observation Opportunities (same as #3.47): <u>Incidental</u> - may observe spontaneously while child is in crib or playpen, or is next to a low table with a toy on top. <u>Structured</u> - when the child is sitting next to a low, sturdy furnishing, such as a couch, chair, or coffee table, attract his attention to an interesting toy or object resting on the support.

Credit: (see also Credit Notes in this strand's preface)

    +   pulls up to standing through controlled transitional movements as defined.

    A   struggles significantly and moves slowly while pulling to stand, using only arms; no controlled transitional movements; neck flexed with chin to chest; always stands on toes.

3.69 **Assumes and maintains kneeling   11-13**

Definition: The child is able to get into a kneeling position without holding onto a support. He does so by moving though a series of transitional movements, i.e., sitting to side-sitting, then to a hands-knees position, and finally to kneeling. He should bear his full weight on his knees rather than sitting back on his feet or the floor in a "W"-sit.

Example Observation Opportunities: When the child is sitting, present a toy about a foot away slightly out of reach above him. Let him play with the toy after getting into a kneeling position or after he attempts unsuccessfully.

Credit: (see also Credit Notes in this strand's preface)
+   assumes and maintains a kneeling position independently for several seconds; back is straight with good head control; hands are free to help balance or play with a toy.
+/- rests bottom on heels, needs a support to hold on to.
A neck usually hyperextended, arms held bent and "fixed" close to body.

3.70 **Walks with one hand held   11-13**

Definition: The child is able to walk a few steps forward when one hand is held by and adult.

Example Observation Opportunities: Hold one of the child's hands at his shoulder level to help him walk when he is transitioning to another nearby activity, e.g., after snack time when he is ready to go play with a toy.

Credit: (see also Credit Notes in this strand's preface)
+   takes at least four steps forward while maintaining an upright posture; holds adult's hand for balance only; smooth, slow reciprocal steps.
-   leans on adult's hand for support; does not initiate the steps but is "dragged" along.
A neck hyperextended with legs spread widely; asymmetrical or awkward movements; lordosis (sway back); or always walks on toes.

3.72 **Walks alone two to three steps   11.5-13.5**

Definition: The child is able to walk a few steps forward independently. At this beginning stage of walking, he holds his arms in "high guard" position, i.e., arms held out to side and flexed with hands facing outward near his shoulders. He walks with his feet spread apart to provide a wide base of support for balance. At this stage, creeping and cruising around furniture are more efficient and thus his primary means for mobility.

Example Observation Opportunities: If not observed spontaneously, may be elicited in one of three ways. *[Be sure you are doing this in a <u>safe area</u> as the child will probably fall into sitting, or fall into the support he is walking toward]:*
1. If the parent reports that the child is beginning to take a few steps alone, ask the parent to encourage him to do so the way she does at home.
2. After successfully observing #3.70, "Walks with one hand held," let go of the child's hand when he is a few steps from a support (person or furniture), and encourage him to finish the last few steps independently.
3. When the child is standing alone or holding onto a support with one hand, kneel a few steps away and encourage him to get a toy you are holding.

Credit: (see also Credit Notes in this strand's preface)
+   takes two to three small steps independently; generally with a "high guard" posture; weight may shift somewhat from side to side rather than completely forward.
A asymmetrical or awkward movements; knees pressed together; always walks on toes, one or both feet.

 Falls by sitting   12-14

Definition: The child moves out of his standing position when he tires or loses balance by "plopping" to the floor into sitting. His plopping gradually becomes less abrupt as he gains more control.

Example Observation Opportunities: May observe spontaneously during observation period, especially after #3.68 "Stands a few seconds," or #3.72 "Walks alone two to three steps."

Credit: (see also Credit Notes in this strand's preface)
+   moves out of standing by "plopping" down to a sitting position; is then able to maintain sitting position.

3.75 Stands from supine by turning on all fours 12.5-15

Definition: The child is able to move into a standing position from lying on his back without holding onto a support. At this stage, he may generally need to go through a series of transitional movements: rolling from back to side, then from side to a hands and knees position, then from hands-knee position to a hands and feet position, and then finally straightening up to stand.

Example Observation Opportunities: May observe after a diaper change if child is lying on the floor without a support nearby to pull up on.

Credit: (see also Credit Notes in this strand's preface)

+ stands up from supine without a support using smooth transitional movements as defined.

3.78 Creeps or hitches upstairs 13.5-15

Definition: The child is able to climb up a few stairs using a combination of hands and knees, and hands and feet creeping. Some children may instead "hitch up" by sitting on the steps and pushing up on their bottom to the next step.

Example Observation Opportunities: If carpeted or safe steps are not available, assess through parent interview. If low steps are available, place a toy on about the fifth step and encourage the child to get it. Remain at the bottom of the steps *for safety* and encouragement.

Credit: (see also Credit Notes in this strand's preface)

+ climbs up at least two steps in either of the defined methods.

3.79 Walks without support 13-15

Definition: The child walks independently. He can stop, start and turn while walking without losing his balance. Walking is becoming his primary method of mobility. He may, however, have more difficulty with uneven surfaces and rely on creeping for longer distances or speed. If the child is a new walker, he continues to walk with arms up in a "high guard" position using a wide-base, side to side rocking pattern.

Example Observation Opportunities: May observe anytime during observation period when child is walking indoors without obstacles.

Credit: (see also Credit Notes in this strand's preface)

+ walks across a small room independently; can stop, start and turn with control; arms are held at side, initially swinging forward with the leg which moves forward, or if more mature, swings arms reciprocally with legs; feet are becoming closer together, generally in line with shoulders.

+/- usually walks with a "high guard" position using a wide-base side to side rocking pattern.

A only walks on toes with one or both feet; asymmetrical movements; e.g., one foot moves forward, other foot drags; walks stiffly or with locked knees; lordosis (sway back).

3.66 Stoops and recovers *13-15*

Definition: The child is able to stoop down to pick up a toy and return to standing without falling or needing a support to hold onto for balance.

Example Observation Opportunities: May observe incidentally when child stoops to retrieve or look at a toy or other object; e.g., when parent asks him to pick up something that dropped or when child stoops to look in a low set mirror or at a something on the floor.

Credit: (see also Credit Notes in this strand's preface)

+ stoops with control about half of the time by bending knees and then returning to stand without a support.

+/- stoops holding onto a support or the floor with one hand.

3-6 REFLEXES/REACTIONS/RESPONSES

A. REFLEXES/REACTIONS

3.01	0-2	Neck righting reactions
3.13	1-2	Flexor withdrawal inhibited
3.12	2-4	Extensor thrust inhibited
3.19	4-6	Asymmetrical tonic neck reflex inhibited
3.39	4-6	Body righting on body reaction
3.24	5-6	Moro reflex inhibited
3.25	4-7	Protective extension of arms and legs downward
3.30	6-7	Demonstrates balance reactions in prone
3.41	6-8	Protective extension of arms to side and front
3.40	7-8	Demonstrates balance reactions in supine
3.55	7-8	Demonstrates balance reactions in sitting
3.56	9-11	Protective extension of arms to back
3.50	9-12	Demonstrates balance reactions on hands/knees
3.73	12-15	Demonstrates balance reactions in kneeling

Family Friendly Interpretation of Strand Concepts, Assessment, & Purpose

The term "reflex" refers to a specific movement or posture that occurs involuntarily when a particular stimulus occurs. For example, you may be familiar with your knee-jerk reflex. If a doctor taps a certain part of your knee, your leg automatically jerks outward. The reflexes we will be observing with your child are reflexes which are typically present at birth. These are called "primitive reflexes."

Postural responses also occur automatically or involuntarily. These responses help your child protect himself from falling or moving off balance. For example, when your child is on his tummy and lifts his arm up to reach for a toy, balance reactions help him keep his balance so he can reach without rolling over.

Your child may cry or be frightened by his sudden movement during a couple of the testing procedures. We can wait until the end of the observation period for these procedures, and I will describe them before we try them with your child. These procedures, however, do not hurt your child, and your words of reassurance well help comfort his fear.

Professional FYI

Reminder: The assessment of reflexes and postural responses has been placed in two separate sub-strands (3-6 A and 3-6 B). This does not imply that they can be viewed separately from other areas of motor development. Reflexes and postural responses are strongly interconnected with the accomplishment and quality of functional motor skills. They have been put in a separate strand because the assessment procedure may be intrusive and upsetting to the child, whereas other strands can be observed during play and other daily activities without handling the child.

If a child is displaying functional motor skills with good quality it is usually unnecessary to formally assess this strand.

Formal eliciting of individual reflexes and automatic responses is less important than observing their role in functional movement during daily activities. When possible, we have included responses that may be observed spontaneously under the "eliciting situation/Example Observation Opportunities" procedure for specific items. These responses indicate adequate reflex integration or presence of automatic reactions or responses.

Some responses may need to be elicited by handling the child. If it is necessary to formally assess these items, *they should be tested under the direction of a qualified therapist or physician.* It is usually better to wait toward the end of the assessment or schedule a separate session, as these procedures may frighten or upset the child.

Parent Questions (Examples)

To help identify the child's unique strengths and needs related to this developmental area:
- About how much time does your child spend playing on his tummy?... back?...sitting on your lap?...sitting on the floor?...sitting in his infant seat?
- Have you noticed if your child tries to protect himself when he starts to fall or lose his balance when he is sitting on the floor?
- Has your child spent long periods of time in the hospital? What position was he usually placed in? Did he have IVs? Where were they on his body?

To help identify family resources, priorities and concerns related to the child's development in this area:
- Does your child ever seem to get "stuck" in certain positions, for example, keeping his head turned to one side?
- Can you usually leave your child sitting on the floor without worrying that he will fall?

Sample *Functional* Outcome Statements which may be generated by the Family

[Will be dependent upon identified individual child and family needs and should incorporate objectives and activities from other domains]
My child will be able to:
- Sit in the grocery cart without falling over;
- Sit and play without toppling over;
- Have enough balance to crawl.

We will:
- Know positioning and handling techniques to help prevent our child from getting "stuck" in certain positions;
- Be able to put on our child's shoes and socks without his legs getting so stiff.

Transactional Assessment

May assess through observation and interview.

Assessment of Caregiver Interactions with the Child

1. Supportive:
[Example interactions which support or accommodate their child's current and continuing maturation of reflexes and responses]
The child's caregivers frequently provide safe opportunities for the child to practice balancing and moving his body, e.g.:
- Vary the child's position during the day;
- Let the child practice sitting by himself and provide the right amount of support he needs - not too much and not too little;
- Closely supervise the child in new, less stable positions;
- Make sure there are not dangerous obstacles for the child to fall into or on.

Identifying and Interpreting Needs for Intervention

If a child is significantly delayed or displays consistent atypical responses in this area, he <u>may have a central nervous system dysfunction</u>. The child should be referred for a further evaluation by a physician.

However, consider, rule out, or adapt for other causes which are *not* necessarily related to central nervous system dysfunction. These may include:
- <u>Hypersensitivity to handling and noxious stimuli</u> e.g., numerous heel sticks may prolong or exaggerate the flexor withdrawal reflex (#3.13);
- <u>Significant middle-ear infections</u> which may extend to affect the vestibular mechanism and have a subsequent affect on balance reactions;
- <u>Muscle weakness</u> not of central nervous system origin;
- <u>Peripheral nerve injury;</u>
- <u>Orthopedic involvement,</u> such as casting, surgery, congenital hip dislocation or torticollis that may limit movement and sensory experience;
- <u>Visual impairment:</u> balance reactions may be delayed due to lack of experience in unstable positions; protective reactions may be delayed because of the visual system's involvement in protection;
- <u>Hearing impairment:</u> may have difficulties in static balance as deafness can affect the vestibular mechanism of inner ear;
- <u>Postural insecurity related to sensory processing</u>: the child may become extremely frightened on unstable surfaces which tilt. This may be evident as the child displays an extreme facial expression and tries to grab onto the adult with even the slightest movement;

Identifying and Interpreting Needs for Intervention   (continued)

- Lack of experience in varied positions; e.g., if the child has had little or no experience lying on his stomach, balance reactions in prone may be delayed.

Assessment Adaptations   (Examples)

[Note any adaptations needed to credit and help plan interventions]

- If the child is overly sensitive to handling by strangers, the parent can be instructed in the eliciting techniques.
- Firm massage of child's feet may be helpful for the hypersensitive child prior to eliciting skills #3.12 and #3.13.
- Muscle weakness: the reflex or reaction should still be present, but do not expect the strength of the child's reaction to be the same or maintained. If weakness is associated with a heart condition, *be sure there are **no medical contraindications** before testing.*
- Visually impaired: may expect a delay of onset of postural and protective responses when using norms based on sighted peers.
- Postural insecurity: avoid testing on therapy balls and tilt boards.

General Assessment Procedures & Processes   (apply to all items in this Strand)

1. **The presence or absence of reflexes and automatic responses can often be observed during routine handling and volitional movement.** Example situations where these may be observed have been included when possible to avoid formal testing.

If the child displays this skill:	*You can assume this reflex or response is appropriately present or integrated:*
#3.38 "Rolls supine to prone" if child initiates roll with hip, rolling in a segmental fashion.	#3.39 "Body righting on body reaction"
#3.48 "Brings one leg forward beside trunk in prone" or #3.52 "Crawls forward"	#3.30 "Demonstrates balance reactions in prone"
#3.59 "Creeps on hands and knees"	#3.50 "Demonstrates balance reactions on hands and knees"
#3.63 "Pivots in sitting..."	#3.55 "Demonstrated balance reactions in sitting"

2. If formally assessed, **the child should be comfortable with the therapist and be able to tolerate some handling.** Children who are hypersensitive or have difficulty with state regulation may be difficult to test. If a child is upset, responses may appear exaggerated or atypical. It is best to test those items which are likely to produce crying **at the end of the observation period,** e.g., moro, flexor withdrawal, and protective extension

3. If balance and equilibrium responses are formally tested, **they can be introduced in a game-like fashion using playful interactions.**

4. **Describe the specific reflex or reaction being tested and the eliciting procedures to the family. Invite family members to help observe and or assess.**

`+ - A` Credit Notes:

- \+   child displays response as defined.
- \-   absence of expected response but not considered atypical.
- A   atypical: asymmetrical, note which side.
- O   circle any credit if environment or interactions frequently compromise or restrict child's movement.

Note any adaptations used to credit.

Assessment Materials

Firm, stable surface; surface that can be tilted (e.g., tilt board, cushion, mattress, therapy ball), blanket, toy for tracking.

3.01 Neck righting reactions   0-2

Definition: When the child's head is turned to one side while lying on his back, his body automatically rolls over in the same direction. This neonatal neck righting response is needed for the child to learn to independently roll from his back to his side.

Eliciting Situations: Smile and talk to the child (when he is lying on his back) until his head is in midline facing you. If his head does not move to midline, begin by gently moving his head to midline. Then, gently flex his chin toward his chest and rotate his head 90 degrees to one side. Move his head slowly and gently so his chin moves near the front of his shoulder. Have an interesting toy or his parent's face available to look at in this new position. After a few minutes, repeat the procedure going in the opposite direction.

Credit: (see also Credit Notes in this strand's preface)

+   turns whole body to the side as a unit in the same direction head is turned; present to each side.

A   if over 6 months, and neck righting reactions are still strongly present, preventing a segmental roll or asymmetrical response, i.e., automatically turns whole body when head is turned to one side but does not turn whole body when head is turned in the opposite direction.

3.13 Flexor withdrawal inhibited   *1-2*

Definition: Flexor withdrawal is a reflex in which the child automatically (and strongly) withdraws or pulls his leg away from a noxious stimuli applied to the sole of his foot. This reflex is typically present at birth, but by about 1 or 2 months the child moves his foot or body voluntarily to avoid the stimulus. A prolonged presence of this reflex or hypersensitivity of feet may impede progress in standing.

Eliciting Situations: <u>Incidental</u> - may be observed if the sole of child's foot accidentally touches something noxious during daily care or movement. <u>Structured</u> - smile and talk to the child when he is lying on his back and until his head is in midline to face you. When his legs are relaxed and semi-flexed, scratch or pinch the sole of one foot. Observe if he strongly and quickly draws his leg into flexion or if there is a more controlled, milder removal of his foot. Repeat with each foot if the child is not upset.

Credit: (see also Credit Notes in this strand's preface)

+   does *not* strongly and abruptly withdraw leg involuntarily when stimulus is applied to either foot.

A   if over 3 months, and reflex is still strongly present in one or both feet.

3.12 Extensor thrust inhibited   2-4

Definition: Extensor thrust, also referred to as "neonatal positive support," is a reflex normally present at birth. This reflex is present if the child suddenly extends his legs and appears to stand when pressure is applied to his feet. Around 2-4 months, this reflex should become integrated, so that pressure does not always result in automatic and sudden leg extension.

Eliciting Situations: <u>Incidental</u> - may be observed when parent holds child upright during play with his soles of his feet on parent's lap. May also be observed if soles of child's feet touch the end of his crib. <u>Structured</u> - (1) When the child is lying on his back with his legs loosely flexed toward his chest, press firmly on the sole on one foot. Observe if he strongly straightens that leg or if it remains flexed with minimal movement. Repeat with his other foot. (2) Hold the child upright under his arms and around his chest. Allow the child's feet to make firm contact with a flat surface. Observe if child's legs strongly extend, or if they remain somewhat bent and flexible. *Provide parent anticipatory guidance* that this procedure does not imply that the child is ready for standing.

Credit: (see also Credit Notes in this strand's preface)

+   does <u>not</u> strongly extend or straighten legs when pressure is applied to the soles of his feet.

A   if over 4 months, and still strongly extends one or both legs when pressure is applied to soles of one or both feet.

3.19   Asymmetrical tonic neck reflex inhibited   *4-6*

Definition: The asymmetrical tonic neck reflex (ATNR) is normally evident from birth to about 4 to 6 months. This reflex is displayed when the child is facing one side, and his arm and leg on that side are straight, while the arm and leg on his opposite side are bent or flexed. This is commonly referred to as the "fencer position." This reflex should never be obligatory; i.e., even though the child displays this reflex he can move out of it fairly easily.

After about 4-6 months, this reflex should become less evident as more functional and voluntary movements become more predominant.

Eliciting Situations: <u>Incidental</u> - you can generally assume this reflex is integrated if the child can easily bring his hand to his mouth while lying on his back, head turned to one side. <u>Structured</u> - when the child is lying on his back, encourage him to turn his head to one side by showing him a toy and letting him track it in an arc to one side until the toy rests on the surface. His head should turn until his chin is near his shoulder to see the toy. Observe his arms and legs as his head turns completely to one side. If the child does not track to the side, gently and slowly turn the child's head to the side. Repeat toward his other side.

Credit: (see also Credit Notes in this strand's preface)

+   does <u>not</u> automatically move arms and legs into a fencer position as defined when head turns completely to either side; can move easily out of this position.

A   if obligatory at any age; or if over 6 months, and child continues to move arms and legs into a fencer position when head turns completely to either side.

3.39   Body righting on body reaction   *4-6*

Definition: When lying supine, if the child's leg is flexed and drawn up and across to his opposite side, he rolls in that direction using a segmental rolling pattern. This is a "righting reaction," which is the body's attempt to straighten itself out so that the head, trunk, and extremities are in line, not twisted. This righting reaction supports the child's mature rolling patterns and later being able to transition into a sitting position.

Eliciting Situations: <u>Incidental</u> - may observe if the child spontaneously rolls from supine to prone, initiating the roll with his hip rather than head or shoulders. <u>Structure</u> - when the child is lying on his back, *gently* flex one leg, bringing it up and over toward his opposite side. Observe if he then turns his shoulder and then head to complete a roll into prone. Repeat with his other leg.

Credit: (see also Credit Notes in this strand's preface)

+   turns pelvis, shoulders, then head to segmentally roll into prone.

A   asymmetrical: rolls segmentally to one side but not the other; or child rolls or flips over as a unit.

3.24   Moro reflex inhibited   *5-6*

Definition: The moro reflex, normally present at birth, is evidenced when the child responds to a sudden loss of backward head control. When his head drops back suddenly, he quickly and automatically jerks his arms up and out with his hands open and then he quickly brings his arms back to cross his chest in an "embrace." There is often a cry. By 5-6 months, this reflex should become integrated as the child develops enough control to hold his neck from falling back.

Eliciting Situations: <u>Incidental</u> - may be observed if momentary support is accidentally lost behind the child's head when he is picked up or transferred from one person to another. <u>Structured</u> - slide your forearms and hands under the child to support his head, shoulders and upper back. Bring him to a semi-upright position with his head in midline and arms held close to his chest, cupping your hands behind his head. Quickly release your hands, *but only allow the child's head to drop back about 20-30 degrees relative to his trunk.* Let his parent console him if this is upsetting.

Credit: (see also Credit Notes in this strand's preface)

+   displays little movement of his arms which indicates presence of enough head control to inhibit this reflex.

A   asymmetrical response, i.e., one arm has little movement - other arm displays full response; and/or continues to display strong moro reflex if over 6 months.

3.25 Protective extension of arms and legs downward   *4-7*

Definition: This item includes two separate protective extension reactions which have different eliciting procedures:
1. "Protective extension of legs" or "protective extension downward" usually begins around 4-6 months. This protective response is observed in the child's legs as he straightens them when lowered suddenly to the ground (if suspended upright.)
2. "Protective extension of arms" or "protective extension forward" usually begins about 6-7 months. This protective response is observed in the child's arms as he brings them quickly forward when held suspended horizontally and suddenly moved face downward toward the floor.

Eliciting Situations:
1. Protective extension of legs: Hold the child upright in the air facing his parent. Suddenly lower him downward to the surface without letting his feet touch the surface. Observe if his legs straightened quickly.
2. Protective extension of arms: Hold the child securely around his chest in a horizontal plane, face down. Move him suddenly down toward the floor and observe if his arms move quickly forward, extended toward the floor.

Credit: (see also Credit Notes in this strand's preface)
+ at 4-6 months, if the child displays protective extension of his legs. Both legs should extend quickly, moving slightly apart as his toes are brought up in preparation for weight-bearing.
+ credit at 6-7 months if the child *also* displays protective extension of his arms by quickly extending both arms toward the floor.
+/- delayed response: extends legs or arms after the sudden movement has occurred rather than immediately as it occurs.
A asymmetrical; i.e., only one leg or one arm extends to protect a fall; or if over 7 months, and responses are not present or are significantly delayed in terms of time and speed.

3.30 Demonstrates balance reactions in prone   *6-7*

Definition: When the child is tilted slowly off balance while lying on his stomach, he automatically moves his head, trunk and limbs in the opposite direction of the tilt to maintain his balance.

Eliciting Situations: Incidental - may be observed if child tilts his body in prone to one side while lifting his opposite arm to reach for a toy. Structured - place the child on his tummy on a firm surface which can be tilted, e.g., tilt board, therapy ball, cushion, bed, blanket. *Slowly* tilt the surface until the child is moved *slightly* off balance. Repeat on his opposite side.

Credit: (see also Credit Notes in this strand's preface)
+ curves trunk in the opposite direction of the tilt and maintains balance; to each side.
- rolls over to supine; or not present.
A asymmetrical, i.e., balance reaction is only present when tilted to one side but not the other.

3.41 Protective extension of arms to side and front   *6-8*

Definition: If the child suddenly moves off balance when sitting, he extends his arms out in front or to the side to protect him from a fall.

Eliciting Situations: Incidental - watch for a brisk action that causes the child to lose his balance when sitting, e.g., reaching for a toy out of reach, turning his head or body quickly to find a visual or auditory event.
Structured -
1. Protective extension to the front: When the child is sitting stable without propping on his hands, gently push him forward at his shoulder.
2. Protective extension to the side: When the child is sitting stable without propping on his hands, gently push him toward one side at his shoulder. Repeat toward his other side.

Credit: (see also Credit Notes in this strand's preface)
+ Protective extension to the front: quickly extends both arms forward to floor with open hands.
+ Protective extension to the side: quickly extends the arm on the side to which he is pushed to the floor; with open hand, each side.
A asymmetrical response, i.e., holds one arm back while other goes to floor when pushed forward; or displays protective extension to one side but not to the other.

3.40 **Demonstrates balance reactions in supine**   *7-8*

Definition: As the child is tilted slowly off balance when he is lying on his back, he automatically moves his head, trunk and limbs in the opposite direction of the tilt to maintain his balance.

Example Observation Opportunities: <u>Incidental</u> - may be observed if child tips his body to one side when he is supine and reaches across midline to reach for a toy. <u>Structured</u> - place the child on his back on a firm surface which can be tilted, e.g., tilt board, therapy ball, cushion, bed, blanket. *Slowly* tilt the surface until the child is moved *slightly* off balance. Repeat on the other side.

Credit: (see also Credit Notes in this strand's preface)

+ moves body in the opposite direction of the tilt to maintain balance; to each side.
- rolls over into prone; or not present.
A asymmetrical, i.e., displays balance reactions toward one side but not to the opposite side.

3.55 **Demonstrates balance reactions in sitting**   *7-8*

Definition: The child automatically moves his head, trunk and limbs in the opposite direction of a tilt to maintain his sitting position and prevent a fall. Balance reactions enable the child to use a variety of sitting positions and help him to move into and out of sitting.

Example Observation Opportunities: <u>Incidental</u> - observe if the child pivots, twists, turns, side sits, and or moves easily into and out of sitting during play.

<u>Structured</u> -

1. Place the child on a safe surface which can be tilted, such as a tilt board or adult lap. The child's hands should be free. If observed on an adult lap, hold him lightly around his hips to protect him (but not for support). Tilt the support surface slowly to one side, then forward, backwards and to the other side.

2. When the child is sitting without support on the floor, gently move him off balance by slowly tipping his shoulders forward, back, and then to each side.

Credit: (see also Credit Notes in this strand's preface)

+ if child is stable in sitting and is observed to pivot, twist, turn, side sit, and/or move easily into and out of sitting, you may assume that he has adequate balance reactions in sitting, move into and out of sitting.
+ if formally tested, curves his trunk in the opposite direction of the tilt to maintain his balance.
A asymmetrical responses, i.e., curves in opposition direct of the tilt in one direction but not in others.

3.56 **Protective extension of arms to back**   *9-11*

Definition: If moved suddenly off balance when sitting, the child protects himself from falling backwards by automatically extending one or both arms out to the floor slightly behind him.

Example Observation Opportunities: <u>Incidental</u> - may observe if child happens to start to fall back in sitting during an activity, such as looking overhead or raising his legs off the surface, e.g., when extending his legs for his parent to put on his shoes. <u>Structured</u> - when the child is sitting without support on the floor, quickly tip him backwards at his shoulders. *There should be a person or pillow behind him to buffer a fall.* Note: If the push is not quick enough or the child's body does not move back enough, he may respond by pulling his arms, head and trunk forward in a balance reaction rather than putting his arms out to protect himself.

Credit: (see also Credit Notes in this strand's preface)

+ prevents falling backwards in sitting by extending one or both arms to the floor slightly behind him.

3.50 Demonstrates balance reactions on hands/knees   *9-12*

Definition: If the child is tilted slowly off balance when he is on his hands and knees, he automatically moves his head, trunk and limbs in the opposite direction of the tilt to maintain his balance.

Example Observation Opportunities: Incidental - may be observed if the child effectively reaches up for a toy while he is on his hands and knees and is able to maintain his balance. Structured - place the child in a hands-knee position on a firm surface which can be tilted, e.g., tilt board, cushion, bed, blanket. *Slowly* tilt one side of the cushion or bed until the child is moved *slightly* off balance. Repeat with his other side.

Credit: (see also Credit Notes in this strand's preface)

  + curves trunk in the opposite direction of the tilt to maintain balance on hands and knees.

  A asymmetrical, i.e., displays balance reactions when tilted to one side but not to the other side.

3.73 Demonstrates balance reactions in kneeling   *12-15*

Definition: If the child is moved off balance when he is kneeling, he automatically moves his head, trunk and limbs in the opposite direction of the tilt to maintain his balance.

Example Observation Opportunities: Note: It is often difficult to have a child maintain a kneeling position with hips extended (keeping his bottom off the floor not resting on ankles) without holding onto a support. At this stage, the child typically prefers to be in hands-knees or standing position. It is generally not necessary to test this item. However, if the evaluator wishes to assess this item, the following procedures may be used if the child is cooperative in kneeling:

Incidental - may observe when child is in extended kneeling if he moves off balance when trying to, e.g., reach for bubbles or a toy held slightly out of reach to one side.

Structured - the child should be kneeling hands free, with his hips extended on a surface which can be tilted. You may initially hold him lightly at his hips to encourage him to keep his bottom off his ankles. Slowly tilt the surface until the child is slightly off balance. Repeat toward his other side.

Credit: (see also Credit Notes in this strand's preface)

  + curves trunk in the opposite direction of the tilt to maintain his balance in kneeling; each side.

  N/A not tested.

3-6 REFLEXES/REACTIONS/RESPONSES

B. ANTI-GRAVITY RESPONSES

3.06	0-1	Lifts head when held at shoulder
3.08	1.5-2.5	Holds head in same plane as body when held in ventral suspension
3.18	2.5-3.5	Holds head beyond plane of body when held in ventral suspension
3.27	4-6	Extends head, back and hips when held in ventral suspension
3.20	3-6.5	Holds head in line with body when pulled to sitting
3.37	5.5-7.5	Lifts head and assists when pulled to sitting
3.62	10-11	Extends head, back, hips and legs in ventral suspension

Family Friendly Interpretation of Strand Concepts, Assessment, & Purpose

We will be observing how your child holds his body against gravity when he is held in the air like an airplane (by an adult), and when he is pulled up into sitting from lying on his back.

Parent Questions   (Examples)

To help identify the child's unique strengths and needs related to this developmental area:
• Do you have to hold your child's head when you hold him or move him around?

• When you are putting your child down on his tummy, have you noticed if he keeps his head up as you are placing him down?

Sample *Functional* Outcome Statements which may be generated by the Family

[Will be dependent upon identified individual child and family needs and should incorporate objectives and activities from other domains]

Our child will be able to hold his head up when:
• We lift him out of his crib and infant seat;
• We carry him in his baby carrier pack.

Transactional Assessment

May assess through observation and interview.

Assessment of Caregiver Interactions with the Child

1. Supportive:
[Example interactions which support/facilitate child's development in this area]
The child's caregivers usually:

• Place the child in a variety of positions during the day;
• Provide appropriate head support during handling to match the child's maturity of head control.

Identifying and Interpreting Needs for Intervention

If a child is significantly delayed or displays atypical development in this area he may be having difficulty in developing adequate muscle control against gravity. This often associated with atypical muscle tone.

However, before targeting atypical muscle tone or his ability to develop muscle control against gravity as the primary area of need for intervention, consider, rule out, or adapt for other causes of delays in this strand. These may include:
• Minimal or no experience in prone position;
• Intolerance or fear of ventral suspension positions from prolonged positioning in supine and or sensory organization problems;
• Visually impaired: may dislike and be fearful of suspended prone positions.

Assessment Adaptations   (Examples)

[Note any adaptations needed to credit and help plan interventions]
If the child is intolerant or fearful of handling and prone suspension activities, many of the items can be observed as the child is moved on and off the floor or in and out of his crib. *With proper anticipatory guidance,* the parent can also complete suspension items lying on the floor with the child prone against the adult to lift into suspension.

General Assessment Procedures & Processes   (apply to all items in this Strand)

1. Describe the anti-gravity response and eliciting procedures to the family and invite them to help observe and/or assess.

+ - A Credit Notes:

+   child displays response.

-   not observed or reported.

+/- appears to be emerging, earlier response present.

A   atypical:

Ventral suspension items: hands fisted; legs crossed;

Pull to sit items: strongly resists pull to sit; neck stiff with shoulders pulled back; legs pressed together.

O   circle any credit if caregivers are having difficulty providing the appropriate amount of support during handling and positioning

Note any adaptations used to credit.

Assessment Materials

Firm, flat surface.

3.06 Lifts head when held at shoulder   0-1

Definition: The child can lift his head momentarily from an adult's shoulder when held with support at his upper back. This is the child's earliest attempt to use the extensor (straightening) muscles of his neck to hold his head upright. This is easier than lifting his head when on his belly because he is not lifting against as much gravity.

Eliciting Situations: Incidental - may observe anytime caregiver is holding child up at her shoulder without holding back of child's head and neck. Structured - hold the child upright at your shoulder with one hand at his bottom and the other near his upper back, with fingers *supporting his neck*. When the child becomes active, gently withdraw your finger support. *Be prepared to provide immediate support back to his neck.* If he does not lift his head, try shaking a rattle, talking to him or gently rocking or bouncing.

Credit: (see also Credit Notes in this strand's preface)

+   lifts head for 1 or 2 seconds from an adult's shoulder without support to his head or neck.

A   hyperextends neck.

3.08 Holds head in same plane as body when held in ventral suspension   1.5-2.5

Definition: When the child is held horizontally face down in the air, he is able to hold his head in line with his trunk rather than hanging his head down. His back is still slightly rounded and hips are flexed down with legs bent.

Eliciting Situations: Incidental - may be observed when caregiver lowers child to crib or floor if child is held in a horizontal plane around chest. Structured - hold the child in ventral suspension as defined, holding him around his trunk.

Credit: (see also Credit Notes in this strand's preface)

+   holds head at or above the plane of his trunk for at least 3 seconds.

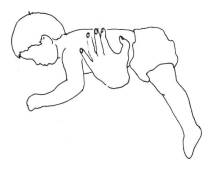

3.18 Holds head beyond plane of body when held in ventral suspension   2.5-3.5

Definition: When the child is held horizontally face down in the air, he is able to hold his head above his trunk. His back is fairly straight and hips are flexed down, legs bent.

Eliciting Situations: (same as #3.08)

Credit: (see also Credit Notes in this strand's preface)

+   holds head above trunk for a few seconds; back should be fairly straight and his head should be facing forward. May also credit #3.27 if his hips are less flexed and legs begin to move toward same plane as his trunk.

3.27

Extends head, back and hips when held in ventral suspension   4-6

Definition: When the child is held horizontally face down in the air, he is able to hold his head above his trunk with back straight and hips extended at the same level of his back as illustrated. His legs still hang down somewhat, but are held in a higher plane than #3.18 "Holds head beyond plane of body when held in ventral suspension."

Example Observation Opportunities: Same as #3.08.

Credit: (see also Credit Notes in this strand's preface)
+ holds head above his trunk, at least 45 degrees, for at least 3 seconds, with hips extended as illustrated; back should be straight and he should face forward.

3.20

Holds head in line with body when pulled to sitting   3-6.5

Definition: When the child is pulled up by his hands into sitting, he can hold his head in line with his body. This demonstrates that he has developed enough muscle control (neck flexors on the front of his neck) to keep his head from sagging backwards.

Eliciting Situations: <u>Incidental</u> - may assume child has developed the muscle control needed for this skill if he is observed to spontaneously lift his head in supine to look at something positioned near his feet, as in skill #3.42 "Lifts head in supine." <u>Structured</u> - when the child is lying on his back, hold his hands and gently pull him up to sitting. Make sure he is not looking up at something behind him. *Provide caregivers anticipatory guidance that this procedure is for evaluation purposes **only and not the recommended method for getting the child into a sitting.***

Credit: (see also Credit Notes in this strand's preface)
+ holds head in line with trunk during the entire pull-to-sit procedure; should initially tuck his chin to his chest. Some children may lift their shoulders up toward their ears at this stage to give added support.

3.37

Lifts head and assists when pulled to sitting   5.5-7.5

Definition: The child actively "helps" to get into sitting when pulled by his hands from supine. He "helps" by flexing his arms and lifting his head as soon as the pull begins to actively pull against the adult's grip.

Eliciting Situations: When the child is lying on his back, hold his hands and gently begin to pull him toward a sitting position; wait to see if he completes the movement by pulling with his arms and head.

Credit: (see also Credit Notes in this strand's preface)
+ flexes and actively pulls with arms; lifts head as soon as procedure begins.

3.62

Extends head, back, hips and legs in ventral suspension   10-11

Definition: When the child is held horizontally face down in the air, he is able to hold his head up at about a 90 degrees angle to his trunk, holding his back straight and hips extended with his legs held at the same level of his back as illustrated.

Example Observation Opportunities: Same as #3.08.

Credit: (see also Credit Notes in this strand's preface)
+ holds head above trunk, at about 90 degrees, for at least 3 seconds, with his hips extended and legs held slightly apart in line with his trunk, as illustrated. His back should be straight and he should face forward.

Section II. 15 to 36 months

3-7: Advancing Postural Control and Motor Planning

All of the skills in this strand require an "interplay" of advancing postural control and motor planning skills. This strand is divided into the following sub-strands based upon the position or motor activity being assessed:

A. Standing
B. Walking/Running
C. Jumping
D. Climbing
E. Stairs
F. Catching and throwing
G. Riding on a Tricycle
H. Balance Beam

The following introductory assessment issues apply to *each* of these sub-strands. Additional introductory information, which is exclusive to a sub-strand, is included within that respective sub-strand.

Family Friendly Interpretation of Strand Concepts, Assessment, & Purpose

[Applicable to all sub-strands for Gross Motor - Section II]

Now that your child is walking well, he is ready for more challenging gross motor activities. We will be observing how your child is learning to run, jump, climb, throw and catch balls, and use a kiddie bike. These motor skills are more challenging because they are dependent upon more difficult balance skills and require your child to think about and plan how he will move his body to accomplish a task. For example, when your child is learning to kick a ball, he needs to have good balance so he doesn't fall when he lifts and moves his foot to kick. However, he also needs to plan how he will move his foot so that it kicks the ball in just the right place with just the right amount of force to make the ball go.

Professional FYI

[Applicable to all sub-strands for Gross Motor - Section II]

The development of good quality gross motor skills in this strand stems from the foundations of motor development in the preceding Gross Motor Strands 3-1 through 3-6 for Birth to 15 months. Generally, if a child is walking well, you may begin your assessment with this strand (3-7). However, if the child is unable to accomplish the skills in this strand or is using poor quality in his movement patterns, *earlier strands should be assessed with a physical or occupational therapist.*

If a child has severe motor impairments, this strand is not likely to be appropriate for assessment or planning. *Consult with a pediatric therapist to design more appropriate functional methods for mobility.*

If the child's physical disability affects only his walking, skills related to catching, throwing, climbing, and moving on ride-on toys may be appropriate to assess and plan for individualized adaptations by a therapist.

Parent Questions   (Examples)

[Examples applicable to all sub-strands for Gross Motor - Section II]

To help identify the child's unique strengths and needs related to this developmental area:

• Does your child have any restrictions on his activities due to any medical needs?
• What kind of gross motor activities does your child seem to do well?
• Has your child started to run yet? Can you describe how he runs?
• Have you ever seen him do any jumping? How does he do this?
• Does he seem to stumble or bump into things a lot when he's moving around? Can you give me some examples? About how often does this happen each day?
• Has he had experiences throwing balls? How is he doing with this? What kind of balls does he seem to play with best?
• Has he had experiences playing on any playground equipment such as a tot-sized sliding board, jungle gym, or tricycle?
• Are there some types of play equipment that your child seems to avoid?

To help identify family resources, priorities and concerns related to the child's development in this area:

• Do you have any concerns about how your child is balancing or moving his body when he moves about during play or daily activities?
• If you could think of one motor activity that you would like your child to be able to do, what would that be?

Sample *Functional* Outcome Statements which may be generated by the Family

[Applicable to all sub-strands in this strand - will be dependent upon identified individual child and family needs and should incorporate objectives and activities from other domains]

My child will:
• Walk and run without bumping into objects;

• Be able to keep up with his friends on the playground;
• Need less help from adults when he is playing on playground equipment;
• Walk up and down stairs safely;
• Be able to ride his tricycle.

Transactional Assessment

May assess through observation and interview.

Assessment of the Child's Environment

[Applicable to all sub-areas in this strand]

1. Supportive:

[Example environments which support/facilitate development in this area]

The child's caregiving environments:
• Have ample safe places for the child to practice gross motor skills, e.g., large play room, fenced yard, or access to a playground;
• Have safe play equipment which challenges developing motor skills, e.g., sturdy ride-on toy, child-sized slide, balls.

2. Compromising:

[Example environments which may restrict, compromise, inhibit or be unsupportive toward development in this area]

The child's caregiving environments are frequently:
• Unsafe to run in/around, climb on, or practice other developing motor skills, e.g., many dangerous obstacles, broken or unsafe equipment.

Assessment of Caregiver Interactions with the Child

1. Supportive:

[Example interactions which support/facilitate child's development in this area]

The child's caregivers:
• Supervise the child as he is learning new but potentially dangerous motor skills, e.g., walking up steps, jumping on a mini-trampoline, riding a tricycle;
• Help the child try new motor skills that he is ready for, with verbal encouragement, praise, modeling and physical guidance, as needed;
• Let the child choose the types of playground

equipment he is most comfortable with.

2. Compromising:

[Example interactions which may restrict, compromise, inhibit or be unsupportive of the child's development in this area]

The child's caregivers frequently:
• Leave the child unattended around potentially dangerous playground equipment or stairs;
• Insist that the child play on playground equipment that frightens the child.

Identifying and Interpreting Needs for Intervention

[Applicable to all sub-strands in this strand]

All of the skills in this strand require an interplay of good postural control and motor planning abilities. <u>If a child demonstrates significant and persistent delays or atypical development in this strand, without evidence of overt neuromotor or musculo-skeletal impairments, he may be having difficulty with postural control and/or motor planning.</u>

Differentiating between postural control problems and motor planning problems can be difficult. Most often these advancing gross motor skills are dependent on both postural control and motor planning. For example, kicking a ball requires postural control for the child to remain balanced and upright when his foot is lifted to kick the ball. Kicking also requires motor plan-

ning in order to accurately lift and then aim his foot to kick the ball in just the right place with the right amount of force. When planning strategies for intervention, there are some important general guidelines to help differentiate these two areas:

• <u>Postural control</u>: Children with postural control problems often have difficulty integrating sensory messages from the muscles, joints, and the vestibular system, which provide the child feedback in order to move in a balanced and coordinated way. These children may lose their balance or stumble easily, even when there are no apparent obstacles, when they are walking, running, climbing or engaged in ball play. They may also appear more rigid and display extreme fearfulness when moving in space, especially when their feet are off the ground.

Identifying and Interpreting Needs for Intervention   (continued)

- Motor Planning: In contrast, children with motor planning problems may have good postural control and balance but have difficulty planning and sequencing their movements in space. These children may be able to complete a motor task such as climbing on a "Tyke bike," but only with extra practice and demonstration. Even with demonstration and practice, the child may move more slowly because he spends excessive amounts of time visually monitoring his movements and the environment. These children may also be more accident prone because they may move quickly and have difficulty changing the direction of their movements or may not sequence and plan their movements in advance to prevent falling or bumping into things.

If you suspect postural control or motor planning difficulties, *the child should be referred to a pediatric therapist for further evaluation and collaboration in planning.*

However, before targeting postural control or motor planning as the primary area of need for referral or intervention, consider, rule out, or adapt for other factors which may cause delays or atypical development in this strand. These may include:

- Neuromotor or skeletal deformities or diseases, e.g., atypical muscle tone; spina bifida, persistence of primitive reflexes, neuromuscular disease, arthrogryposis;
- Poor strength and endurance, or limited movement due to medical conditions;
- High or low physical activity level;
- Visual impairment: children who are blind appear to have a pattern of development which differs from their sighted peers. There is usually a considerable delay in self-initiated mobility and the quality of movement may differ. Many children who are blind walk with an unusual gait. Their feet are turned more outward; they may appear more stiff-legged; and their center of gravity is lowered. There may also be some head drooping and rounding of the child's back. The child's walking may appear more like waddling. The child will also not have the visual cues needed to help plan new movements.
- Tactile defensiveness: the child may resist standing barefoot on different textures, or be more anxious around certain textured surfaces, such as grass, even if they have shoes on, because they are concerned they may be forced to touch the texture if they fall or sit down.
- Current ear infection or middle ear fluid may have a transient effect on the child's balance.

Assessment Adaptations   (Examples)

[Note any adaptations needed to credit and help plan interventions]

- Neuromotor, orthopedic or skeletal deformities/problems: *consult with the child's therapist and physician to determine individualized adaptations.* Some gross motor activities are *not appropriate* to assess or plan for as they are not viable or functional skills to work on. Mark N/A for skills which are not appropriate to assess or plan for. Alternative mobility goals can be designed with the child's therapist and family.
- If the child has poor strength and endurance, limit the number of activities assessed at any one time. *Watch carefully for any signs of fatigue,* e.g., shortness of breath, rapid breathing, changes in the child's skin or his behavior. If the child has restricted movement due to surgeries, heart problems, or medical devices, consult with the child's physician to adapt the assessment as appropriate.
- Visual impairment:
  - Assess only in familiar environments where the child is thoroughly oriented to the placement of various furnishings. The floor should be even without any rugs or obstacles.
  - If milestones are compared with sighted children, a considerable delay in self-initiated mobility can be normal for the child who is blind.
  - If the child has not had specific teaching and experiences in many of these movement skills, he *will need hands-on physical guidance to understand what is expected of him in a formal assessment situation.* Do not consider initial assessment as a true indicator of the child's motor abilities.
  - Skills related to jumping and running may be quite frightening for a child who is blind. *If he has not had specific training or experiences in these skills, proceed slowly and cautiously, at the child's pace.* Children may feel more secure while holding onto an adult's hand, railing or rope.
  - Auditory cues may be used as a motivator, but remember that sound may not hold the same attracting qualities that vision does at this age. Use toys which produce a constant sound cue, such as a music box or radio.

Assessment Adaptations   (continued)

– Although the child's gait may appear awkward and wide-based, skills which require him to walk with a narrower base of support should be assessed and targeted for intervention, so that this does not become a more lasting posture.

– For items related to Strand 3-7D "Jumping," the child may not sense the distance of his jump. In addition to hands-on physical guidance to orient him to the motor task, be sure to let him explore the materials he may be jumping from or over, e.g., steps, strings.

– Balance beam activities: let the child try these activities barefoot. Add a stable landmark and sound cue at the end of the beam, e.g., another adult talking to him - *proceed slowly and cautiously, at the child's pace.*

– Mark N/A and omit assessment of the following skills:
Strand 3-7A: #3.82
Strand 3-7B: #3.119, #3.120, #3.138, #3.144, #3.146.

• Tactile defensiveness: avoid assessing the child standing on surfaces which are offensive. Explore which surfaces the child is able to tolerate well, e.g., carpet versus linoleum. The child may prefer to leave his socks and shoes on.

• Ear infection or middle ear fluid: delay full assessment until the child's ears are clear.

General Assessment Procedures & Processes   (apply to all items in this Strand)

1. **Provide much verbal encouragement and praise, but *do not force* a child to complete a task.** Fear or resistance is often a symptom that the child is having difficulty processing all of the sensory information required to complete the task.

2. It can be helpful to **have another child or sibling who has good motor skills to demonstrate the suggested activities.** A young child's smaller size and movement patterns will be a better model for the child to follow.

3. When temperature and conditions allow, it is **best to observe these skills with the child barefoot and wearing as few clothes on as possible.** Outdoor items may be observed with shorts, T-shirts and sneakers on.

4. **Most items can be observed spontaneously throughout the child's play and daily activities.**

5. **Describe the skill and eliciting procedures to family members and invite them to help observe and/or assess.**

+ - A   Credit Notes:

+   child usually displays motor skill as defined.

-   not observed or reported.

+/- appears to be an emerging skill.

A   atypical for any skill:
– asymmetrical movements or postures - the child completes a movement using one side of his body more than the other;
– legs appear rigid, pressed together at knees;
– is virtually always up on toes when standing or walking;
– legs are spread widely;
– slumped postures;
– excessive falling or bumping into things;
– displays excessive fear to changes in body position or when his feet lift from the ground, as in jumping, or climbing on equipment which is out of proportion to the real threat;
– explosive movement quality with poor judgment of force, speed and aim.

N/A not applicable due to disability.

O   circle any credit if environment or interactions compromise or restrict child's optimal skills.

Note any adaptations used to credit.

Assessment Materials

• Three different-sized soft balls, approximately 3, 8 and 12 inches across, e.g., tennis ball, rubber playground ball, small beach ball.

• Toy on a string, and toys to pick up and carry.

• Ride-on toys- sturdy "Tyke bike" and tricycle that accommodate child's size.

• Large box, trash can or laundry basket for the child to push and pull.

• Walking board- approximately 8 inches wide, 6 feet long, and 2 inches high.

• Balance beam- 2 by 2-inch board about 6-8 feet long.

• Playground chalk or masking tape to make a line.

• Portable or household stairs, with a support rail if available.

• Small trampoline.

• 4-foot length of string.

• Small child-sized chair and adult chair.

• Small child's slide and jungle gym with a ladder.

3-7 ADVANCING POSTURAL CONTROL AND MOTOR PLANNING

A. STANDING

3.82	14.5-15.5	Bends over and looks through legs
3.83	15-18	Demonstrates balance reactions in standing
3.84	15-18	Walks into large ball while trying to kick it
3.89	16-17	Stands on one foot with help
3.102	*16-23*	Picks up toy from floor without falling
3.96	18-24.5	Kicks ball forward
3.103	20-21	Squats in play
3.104	20-22	Stands from supine by rolling to side
3.109	23-25.5	Stands on tiptoes
3.122	24-30	Imitates one foot standing
3.113	24-36	Imitates simple bilateral movements -limbs, head and trunk
3.135	30-33	Stands from supine using a sit-up
3.136	30-36	Stands on one foot one-five seconds

NOTE: [Refer to the preface for Strand 3-7 on pages 191 to 194 for Family Friendly Definitions, Parent Questions, Sample Outcome Statements, Professional FYI, Transactional Assessment, and General Assessment Procedures]

3.82 Bends over and looks through legs 14.5-15.5

Definition: The child has enough balance and control in standing to bend over and look backwards through his legs and then move back to an upright position.

Example Observation Opportunities: May be observed incidentally as the child experiments with movement during free play or bends over to pick up a toy (e.g., car, ball) which rolls through his legs to slightly behind him.

Credit: (see also Credit Notes in this strand's preface)
+ child can bend over with slightly flexed legs. His head may or may not rest on the floor.
N/A if not observed or reported; it is unnecessary to actually test this item as it may be difficult to elicit. If the child displays higher skills in this strand, he probably has the balance and control required by this item.

3.83 Demonstrates balance reactions in standing 15-18

Definition: If tilted off balance when standing, the child's head, trunk, and extremities automatically move in the opposite direction of the tilt to maintain his balance and help prevent a fall.

Example Observation Opportunities: <u>Incidental</u> - during music time, sing a song and pretend to dance as you hold the child with your hands around his trunk. Gently tilt his weight over onto one foot until his opposite foot is off the floor. Repeat toward his other side. Balance reactions may also be observed spontaneously when the child is reaching for something overhead, or is standing on a moveable surface such as a mattress. <u>Structured</u> - if a tilt board is available, help the child stand on the board until he is balanced (without any support) while you hold the board steady. Gently tilt the board slowly an inch or two down on one side. Repeat in the opposite direction.

Credit: (see also Credit Notes in this strand's preface)
+ displays balance reactions as defined, equally on each side when moved off balance in standing.

3.84 Walks into large ball while trying to kick it 15-18

Definition: The child walks into a large ball as his method to kick it forward. He does not have enough balance to actually lift and propel his foot for a true kick.

Example Observation Opportunities: <u>Incidental</u> - may be observed during ball play, especially if another person demonstrates kicking. <u>Structured</u> - demonstrate kicking a large lightweight ball gently forward, so that it stops in the middle of an area that does not have a support for the child to hold on to. When the ball stops, invite the child to kick it back. Remind him as needed, "Use your foot to kick!"

Credit: (see also Credit Notes in this strand's preface)
+ tries to kick a ball by walking into it, using either foot, without holding onto a support; the ball should move forward.

3.89   Stands on one foot with help   16-17

Definition: The child can stand briefly on one foot when one hand is held.

Example Observation Opportunities: <u>Incidental</u> - may be observed if child lifts his foot briefly when holding an adult hand, to show you his shoe or to "help" when his parent is putting his pants or shoes on; to step into a sandbox or other large box with a low edge; or to try to kick a ball. <u>Structured</u> - demonstrate standing on one foot as the child watches. Then kneel or bend down in front of the child while he is standing and hold one of his hands at chest level. Ask him to pick up or lift his foot.

Credit: (see also Credit Notes in this strand's preface)
+ stands on one foot flat on the floor for 2-3 seconds by shifting his weight to that side; your hand is used for balance only. This should be observed with each foot.
- leans excessively into adult's hand to prevent falling.

3.102   Picks up toy from floor without falling   *16-23*

Definition: The child has enough balance and control to stoop or squat from standing to pick up a small object and then return to standing without holding onto a support.

Example Observation Opportunities: May observe anytime during assessment period when child retrieves something from the floor, e.g., parent asking child to bring something that is on the floor; child picking up a tennis ball when asked to play ball.

Credit: (see also Credit Notes in this strand's preface)
+ moves easily from standing to stoop or squat and then moves back easily to an upright position without holding onto a support. There should be some bending of legs evident and his heels should stay on the floor.

3.96   Kicks ball forward   18-24.5

Definition: The child can kick a ball in standing without holding onto a support. This skill demonstrates the child's maturing balance reactions as he is able to shift his weight onto one leg in order to swing his kicking leg.

Example Observation Opportunities: <u>Incidental</u> - may observe during ball play in a free open space. Use a lightweight ball about 8 inches in diameter. <u>Structured</u> - when the child is standing steady, without a support nearby to hold onto, place the ball in front of him, suggesting that he kick it to you. Demonstrate kicking if needed. Repeat with his opposite foot, placing the ball in front of that foot and making a comment and gesture such as, "Now try kicking with this foot!"

Credit: (see also Credit Notes in this strand's preface)
+ kicks ball by shifting his weight and swinging his foot without holding onto a support or losing his balance. He should be able to kick a ball with either foot but may be developing a preference for one. Note which foot he first chooses to kick with.

3.103   Squats in play   20-21

Definition: The child is able to move from standing into a squat position to play with a toy without needing to put his hands on the floor for balance.

Example Observation Opportunities: May observe when the child squats to play with a toy which is in the middle of an open area, e.g., xylophone, busy box.

Credit: (see also Credit Notes in this strand's preface)
+ can independently assume and maintain a squat position for at least 10-15 seconds. His feet should be flat on the floor, and he should not use his hands for balance or propping. He should be able to resume a standing position without difficulty.

3.104 ## Stands from supine by rolling to side   20-22

Definition: The child gets into standing independently from lying on his back by turning to one side and then pushing to a standing position with his hands and feet. He no longer needs to turn completely to a hands and knees position before standing up.

Example Observation Opportunities: May observe incidentally whenever the child stands up after lying on his back, e.g., after a diaper change; after resting to get up and play ball; during pretend play; during a "Simon Says" -type game.

Credit: (see also Credit Notes in this strand's preface)

+ typical method for moving from supine to standing is through rolling to one side as defined rather than turning fully to hands and knees. If the child stands by using a "sit-up," may also credit #3.135.

3.109 ## Stands on tiptoes   23-25.5

Definition: The child can *voluntarily* stand on his tiptoes a few seconds and maintain his balance without holding onto a support. *[Note: in addition to assessing maturing standing balance and postural control, this skill demonstrates development of foot muscles]*

Example Observation Opportunities: <u>Incidental</u> - may be observed when the child tries to obtain or see something out of immediate reach or vision, e.g., to look out a window, or in imitation during a "Simon Says" -type game. <u>Structured</u> - when the child is standing without a support nearby, offer him a toy just out of reach above him.

Credit: (see also Credit Notes in this strand's preface)

+ voluntarily stands on his tiptoes for 2-3 seconds without holding onto a support. *[This should not be a typical posture that he assumes – may be related to increased muscle tone, tight heel cords, or tactile defensiveness]*

3.122 ## Imitates one foot standing   24-30

Definition: The child can stand on one foot momentarily without holding onto a support.

Example Observation Opportunities: <u>Incidental</u> - may be observed if child lifts his foot briefly to show you his shoe or to "help" when his parent is putting his pants or shoes on. <u>Structured</u> - demonstrate standing on one foot and holding your arms out to the side as the child watches. Invite him to copy you. Repeat with the opposite foot.

Credit: (see also Credit Notes in this strand's preface)

+ can lift each leg momentarily without holding onto a support. His standing foot should remain flat on the ground. May also credit #3.136 (which follows later in this strand) if position is held more than momentarily.

3.113 ## Imitates simple bilateral movements - limbs, head and trunk   24-36

Definition: The child can imitate the large movements he watches another person make, including moving both arms up and down, to the front and back, held out to the side, and crossed in front of the body.

Example Observation Opportunities: Play "Simon Says" game while the child is standing. *[If the child is physically disabled, but has good arm and trunk control, this may be done in a supportive chair]* Model moving your head down and up; being a "windmill" and circling arms; lifting your arms high above head and bending over to touch toes; being a "tree" by lifting arms and bending trunk to each side; "hugging" yourself by crossing arms in front of body.

Credit: (see also Credit Notes in this strand's preface)

+ imitates simple bilateral gross motor movements as defined, immediately following the demonstration.

A imitation is always delayed for several seconds; imitations are awkward and inaccurate; child becomes upset by this game.

3.135 ## Stands from supine using a sit-up   30-33

Definition: The child gets into a standing position (from lying on his back) by sitting up rather than rolling to his side (as in #3.104).

Example Observation Opportunities: Same as #3.104.

Credit: (see also Credit Notes in this strand's preface)

+   typically moves independently from supine to standing by using a sit-up with little or no sideways movement. His hands may rest on the floor for support.

3.136 ## Stands on one foot one-five seconds   30-36

Definition: The child can stand on one foot for a few seconds without holding onto a support.

Example Observation Opportunities: Demonstrate standing on one foot holding your arms out to the side as the child watches. Invite him to copy you. Repeat with the opposite foot.

Credit: (see also Credit Notes in this strand's preface)

+   stands on each foot for at least 2-3 seconds without holding onto a support with an erect posture. His standing foot should remain flat on the ground, and his arms may be held out to the side.

A   can only stand on one foot with shoulders retracted and arms in "high guard" position; appears to be struggling to hold this position.

3-7 ADVANCING POSTURAL CONTROL AND MOTOR PLANNING

B. WALKING/RUNNING

3.80	14-15	Walks sideways
3.76	12.5-21	Walks backwards
3.81	14-18	Runs - hurried walk
3.87	15-18	Pulls toy behind while walking
3.91	17-18.5	Carries large toy while walking
3.92	17-18.5	Pushes and pulls large toys or boxes
3.99	18-24	Runs fairly well
3.110	23-25	Walks with legs closer together
3.118	24-30	Runs - stops without holding and avoids obstacles
3.124	25.5-30	Walks on tiptoes a few steps
3.127	28-29.5	Walks backward ten feet
3.137	30-36	Walks on tiptoes ten feet
3.144	34.5-36	Avoids obstacles in path
3.145	34.5-36	Runs on toes
3.146	34.5-36+	Makes sharp turns around corners when running

NOTE: [Refer to the preface for Strand 3-7 on pages 191 to 194 for Family Friendly Definitions, Parent Questions, Sample Outcome Statements, Professional FYI, Transactional Assessment, and General Assessment Procedures]

Family Friendly Interpretation of Strand Concepts, Assessment, & Purpose

Now that your child can walk, he is ready to learn more difficult motor skills which provide him with more options for moving about. We will be observing how he is learning to walk in different directions and at different speeds, if he can walk while carrying or pushing things, and if he can avoid obstacles in his way. We will also be observing how he is learning to run. Initially, running looks like a fast walk, but then becomes more like running as he is able to take both feet off of the ground. All of these advancing motor skills require good balance, coordination, and planning of movements.

Walks sideways   14-15

Definition: The child can take several steps sideways independently. This skill demonstrates the child's increasing motor planning skills and postural control as he is able to purposefully move his body in space in different directions without losing his balance or becoming confused.

Example Observation Opportunities: Incidental - may be observed if child needs to walks sideways to move through narrow areas, e.g., walking sideways between a sofa and coffee table; between the back of a sofa and wall. Structured - demonstrate walking in several directions in an open area with a pull toy on a string which makes special actions or sounds as it moves along a smooth surface. Walk sideways, backwards, and forward, pulling the toy behind. Offer the child the same or similar toy to copy or imitate. If the child has difficulty with grasp, adapt the string with a large bead or make a loop handle to go over his wrist.

Credit: (see also Credit Notes in this strand's preface)

+ takes at least three to five steps sideways independently with or without a pull toy. May also credit #3.76 and/or # 3.87 if child is observed to walk backwards or pull the toy behind him.

Walks backwards   12.5-21

Definition: The child can walk several steps backwards independently. This skill demonstrates the child's increasing motor planning skills and postural control as he is able to purposefully move his body in space in different directions without losing his balance or becoming confused.

Example Observation Opportunities: Incidental - may also be observed when the child is walking backwards when, for example, he is backing into a chair or backing up to play ball. Structured - same as #3.80 above.

Credit: (see also Credit Notes in this strand's preface)

+ takes at least five steps backwards while facing forward.

3.81 Runs - hurried walk   14-18

Definition: The child's run is considered a rapid walk at this stage as one foot is in contact with the ground at all times. His body is held stiffly upright and he may keep his eyes fixed towards the ground.

Example Observation Opportunities: May observe when child has opportunities and incentives to move quickly on flat, open surfaces, e.g., chasing a ball or toy car, running to parent for a hug, playing a chase game.

Credit:
+ "runs" using a rapid walk pattern, keeping one foot on the ground at all times. He may have difficulty stopping without a support and may hold his arms up flexed at shoulder height in a "high guard" position.

3.87 Pulls toy behind while walking   15-18

Definition: The child is able to walk well while pulling a toy on a string which trails behind.

Example Observation Opportunities: Same as #3.80 above.

Credit: (see also Credit Notes in this strand's preface)
+ walks several steps independently while pulling a toy on a string.

3.91 Carries large toy while walking   17-18.5

Definition: The child is able to walk well carrying large lightweight toys with one or both arms. His hands are free to carry things since he no longer needs to hold his hands out to his sides to help stabilize himself when walking.

Example Observation Opportunities: May be observed when child carries a large lightweight toy or object which requires two hands, during play or daily activities, e.g., stuffed animal, large doll, pillow, ball, small plastic trash can, large cereal box, box of diapers. *The object should not obstruct his view when walking.*

Credit: (see also Credit Notes in this strand's preface)
+ walks across a room at least 8-10 feet, carrying a lightweight object with both hands.

3.92 Pushes and pulls large toys or boxes   17-18.5

Definition: The child can push and pull large lightweight toys and boxes while walking. This skill demonstrates increased balance, control, and planning, as the child needs to exert more strength and force while his body has to work harder to control the force of his movements and to keep from falling.

Example Observation Opportunities: May observe during play in open areas when child pushes baby carriage, stroller, wagon, stools or child-sized chairs. Examples: during play, ask the child to help move several blocks from one area of the room to another, using a wagon with a stable handle, or suggest that he push a step stool into position to reach a toy; during snack time, ask the child to push his small chair to the table.

Credit: (see also Credit Notes in this strand's preface)
+ can push *and* pull large objects along the ground while walking. The child does not need to negotiate corners or obstacles.

3.99 Runs fairly well   18-24

Definition: The child can run about 10 feet without falling. He may still use a fairly flat-footed pattern.

Example Observation Opportunities: May observe when child has opportunities and incentives to move quickly on open, flat surfaces, e.g., chasing a ball or toy car, running to parent for a hug, playing a chase game.

Credit: (see also Credit Notes in this strand's preface)
+ can usually run on an open, flat area at least 10 feet with an upright posture without falling. In contrast to skill #3.81 above, his movements do not appear awkward or stiff and there is some movement of his arms as he no longer holds them in a high guard position for balance.

Walks with legs closer together   23-25

Definition: The child generally walks well with a mature gait pattern and erect posture. His legs are no longer wide-based.

Example Observation Opportunities: Observe the child's typical postures and position of arms and legs as he walks spontaneously throughout the observation period.

Credit: (see also Credit Notes in this strand's preface)
+ typically walks with a mature gait on smooth, flat surfaces; feet facing forward, aligned approximately under his shoulders with his arms relaxed at his sides free to play.

 ### Runs - stops without holding and avoids obstacles   24-30

Definition: The child can voluntarily avoid large obstacles, such as furniture, pets or other children when he is running, by moving around the obstacle or stopping before he reaches it. This skill demonstrates advancing motor planning abilities and control, as he is able to grade the speed of his run to stop and figure out how to move his body in space to avoid an obstacle.

Example Observation Opportunities: Incidental - may be observed during outdoor play when the child runs and stops voluntarily and runs around large obstacles such as a tree, person, or playground equipment. Structured - demonstrate a game of running toward a wall, but stopping before the wall without touching it. Place a taped line or stop sign about a foot or two before the wall. Or place a large obstacle, such as a chair, between you and the parent, and ask the child to run to his parent. His parent may be holding something special to encourage this as you verbally prompt, "hurry!"

Credit: (see also Credit Notes in this strand's preface)
+ usually automatically avoids large obstacles while running with minimal reduction in speed; is able to stop voluntarily at any time without moving off balance; he does not need to hold onto the obstacle to help him stop, or to help him move around it. He should not run into or otherwise use the obstacle to help him stop.

 ### Walks on tiptoes a few steps   25.5-30

Definition: The child can voluntarily take a few steps on his tiptoes. This item demonstrates advancing balance and postural control as well as further development of his foot muscles.

Example Observation Opportunities: Incidental - may be observed if the child takes tiptoe steps while playing with something overhead such as trying to "catch" bubbles. Structured - the child should be barefoot. (1) Make a 10 foot chalk or tape line. Demonstrate walking on tiptoes when barefoot with your hands on your hips the entire length of the line. Invite the child the child to try. (2) During doll play, put the dolls to bed and tiptoe as you invite the child to imitate, "Shh! Baby's sleeping; let's tiptoe by!"

Credit: (see also Credit Notes in this strand's preface)
+ voluntarily takes at least five independent tiptoe steps forward with a smooth reciprocal motion; there may be walking steps in between and he does not need to walk on the line.
A often walks on toes, but not deliberately as a way to "tiptoe." This may be an indication of increased muscle tone, tactile defensiveness or tight heel cords.

(may also credit #3.137 - if at least 10 feet)

Walks backward ten feet   28-29.5

Definition: The child is able to walk backwards several feet. This skill demonstrates the child's increasing motor planning skills and postural control as he is able to purposefully move his body in space in different directions without losing his balance or becoming confused.

Example Observation Opportunities: Incidental: may observe when child is walking backwards pulling a toy on a string.
Structured: Make a 10 foot chalk or tape line. Demonstrate walking backwards the entire length of the line. Invite the child to try.

Credit: (see also Credit Notes in this strand's preface)
+ walks backwards about 10 steps with a smooth, reciprocal motion. He does not need to place his foot directly behind his other foot and does not need to walk on the line, just in the general direction; he may initially glance behind him to assure that there are no obstacles.

3.137 Walks on tiptoes ten feet   30-36

Definition: The child can voluntarily walk on tiptoes about 8-10 feet. This item demonstrates advancing balance and postural control as well as further development of his foot muscles.

Example Observation Opportunities: Same as #3.124.

Credit: (see also Credit Notes in this strand's preface)

+   voluntarily walks 8-10 feet on tiptoes; there may be one or two walking steps in between and he does not need to walk on a line.

A   often walks on toes, but not deliberately as a way to "tiptoe." This may be an indication of increased muscle tone, tactile defensiveness, or tight heel cords.

3.144 Avoids obstacles in path   34.5-36

Definition: The child usually avoids small and large obstacles in his path when running or walking. He may move around the obstacle or step over it. This skill demonstrates advancing motor planning abilities and control, as he is able to figure out how to move his body in space to avoid small as well as large obstacles in his path.

Example Observation Opportunities: This may be observed throughout the assessment period as obstacles appear naturally, e.g., child stepping around or over a toy car when he is going over to the snack table; running around a box out of doors.

Credit: (see also Credit Notes in this strand's preface)

+   rarely falls or bumps into obstacles when walking or running during natural daily activities; does not excessively visually monitor the obstacle to the exclusion of the general environment.

3.145 Runs on toes   34.5-36

Definition: The child runs in a smooth coordinated fashion; both feet repeatedly leave the ground for a fraction of a second during the run. At this stage, the child is less flat-footed than in earlier running skills but he is not literally running on his toes. The child pushes off on his toes at the end of each stride and begins each stride on his heel.

Example Observation Opportunities: May be observed when the child is running to parent, to get something he wants, when chasing a ball, when playing a tag game or running in a "race."

Credit: (see also Credit Notes in this strand's preface)

+   usually runs smoothly with both feet leaving the ground as defined; arms may be bent at waist level. There should be some reciprocal arm swing.

3.146 Makes sharp turns around corners when running   34.5-36 +

Definition: The child has enough balance, control, and motor planning abilities to turn corners, avoid obstacles, make changes in speed, and stop without losing his balance while running.

Example Observation Opportunities: May observe when the child is running through an obstacle course, playing "baseball" and running around bases; or running around a circle in circle games such as "London Bridge," or playing "Hide-n-seek," as he runs behind furniture or behind a wall.

Credit: (see also Credit Notes in this strand's preface)

+   can typically run well. He should be able to turn corners, avoid obstacles, make changes in speed and stop without falling or needing to hold onto a support.

3-7 ADVANCING POSTURAL CONTROL AND MOTOR PLANNING

C. JUMPING

3.107	22-30	Jumps in place both feet
3.116	24-30	Jumps a distance of 8 to 14 inches
3.117	24-26.5	Jumps from bottom step
3.125	27-29	Jumps backwards
3.128	29-32	Jumps sidewards
3.129	29-31	Jumps on trampoline w/ adult holding hands
3.132	30-36	Jumps over string 2-8 inches high
3.133	30-36	Hops on one foot
3.134	30-34.5	Jumps a distance of 14 to 24 inches
3.143	34.5-36	Jumps a distance of 24 to 34 inches

NOTE: *[Refer to the preface for Strand 3-7 on pages 191 to 194 for Family Friendly Definitions, Parent Questions, Sample Outcome Statements, Professional FYI, Transactional Assessment, and General Assessment Procedures]*

Family Friendly Interpretation of Strand Concepts, Assessment, & Purpose

We will be observing how your child is learning to jump. Like running, jumping requires that your child be able to balance with both feet off the ground, but jumping requires more strength, balance, and coordination, so your child can push himself off the floor and land without falling as he comes to a sudden stop. Hopping on one foot is a more difficult variation of jumping because he has to balance on one foot.

When children are first learning to jump, they frequently hold their hands up and out near their shoulders in a "high guard" position, much in the same way as when first learning to walk. With increasing balance, control, and practice, children begin to lower their arms to the side and use their arms to help jump up from a crouched position by swinging them strongly forward.

Professional FYI

Observe the child's position of his arms and body to help determine the maturity of his jumping. A mature jump involves crouching to prepare for the jump and use of the arms to assist in the balance, direction, and distance of the jump. The achievement of these skills relies upon good endurance and muscle tone as well as balance and motor planning.

3.107 Jumps in place both feet   22-30

Definition: The child can jump in place, bringing both feet simultaneously off the floor.

Example Observation Opportunities: Model jumping and invite the child to try. This can be in the context of pretending you are bunnies or kangaroos, or jumping over a line or jumping to pop bubbles which land on the floor. Exaggerate the bending motion of your body and then jump up as your arms are propelled upward.

Credit: (see also Credit Notes in this strand's preface)
+   on at least one of three attempts jumps up, any height, with both feet leaving the floor simultaneously.

Jumps a distance of 8 to 14 inches   24-30

Definition: The child can jump forward ("broad jump") several inches.
Example Observation Opportunities: Model jumping forward, from standing at one marked spot to another marked spot several inches away. Invite the child to copy you. This can be in the context of pretending you are bunnies or kangaroos. Mark the starting and target jumping points with tape or chalk. Let the child try this several times, measuring and praising each try. Mark and measure from the starting point to the spot where the child's nearest heel lands on the floor to credit.
Credit: (see also Credit Notes in this strand's preface)
+   if furthest jump of several trials is 8-12 inches from the starting point. He may jump and land with both feet simultaneously, or have a leading foot, but both feet must be in the air at some point simultaneously.
+/- jumps 4-8 inches.

 Jumps from bottom step   24-26.5

Definition: The child can jump down from a shallow step independently.
Example Observation Opportunities: Demonstrate jumping off the bottom stairstep, or *safe* shallow curb, about 6-7 inches in height. There should *not* be a rail or support to hold for assistance. Invite the child to try. *Stand nearby for safety and security.* If the parents report that the child has not had experience with this, encourage the child to practice (hold his hand, let him jump, with one foot leading the other, etc.), before assessing for credit.
Credit: (see also Credit Notes in this strand's preface)
+   can jump down from a step about 6-7 inches high by lifting and landing with both feet together without falling or holding a support. He should display some bending in his legs as he takes off and lands and should be able to resume an upright posture.

3.125 Jumps backwards   27-29

Definition: The child can independently jump backwards without losing his balance.
Example Observation Opportunities: Demonstrate, standing with your heels next to a taped line on the floor and then jumping backwards over the line. Invite the child to try several times.
Credit: (see also Credit Notes in this strand's preface)
+   independently jumps backwards at least once, about an inch; i.e., the front of his feet clear the line; both feet taking off together.

3.128 Jumps sidewards   29-32

Definition: The child can independently jump sideways to each side without losing his balance.
Example Observation Opportunities: Stand with your feet parallel and just next to a taped line on the floor. Demonstrate jumping sideways over the line. Invite the child to copy you. Then jump back in the opposite direction, again encouraging him to follow. Let him practice a few times.
Credit: (see also Credit Notes in this strand's preface)
+   independently jumps sideways in each direction a few inches; the side of his feet should clear the line and both feet should take off together.

 Jumps on trampoline with adult holding hands   29-31

Definition: The child can jump a few times on a trampoline if an adult holds his hands.
Example Observation Opportunities: Use a child-sized trampoline, if available. If not available, you could use an old mattress or cushion on the floor. *Supervise carefully.* Hold the child's hands at his shoulder level as you encourage him to jump.
Credit: (see also Credit Notes in this strand's preface)
+   jumps with both feet off the trampoline or mattress for at least two consecutive jumps.

3.132

Jumps over string 2-8 inches high   30-36

Definition: The child can jump over a hurdle at least 2 inches from the ground.

Example Observation Opportunities: Tie a string, ribbon, or jump rope between two chairs so that it is raised about 2 inches from the ground. Demonstrate jumping over the string and invite the child to try. If he misses, invite him to try again as you praise his try. If successful, continue raise the string 2 inches for each successful try until it is raised 8 inches from the ground. *Supervise carefully to avoid tripping or a fall.*

Credit: (see also Credit Notes in this strand's preface)

+   jumps at least once over a barrier at least 2 inches high; he should use both feet to take off and land, and feet do not touch string at any point.

3.133

Hops on one foot   30-36

Definition: The child can independently hop a few times on one foot.

Example Observation Opportunities: Demonstrate hopping forward and invite the child to copy you. Pretend playing you each hurt your foot and need to hop to keep the game fun. Demonstrate and encourage him to try hopping on his other foot.

Credit: (see also Credit Notes in this strand's preface)

+   hops on one foot forward or in place at least two successive hops, foot clearing the floor, without losing his balance. Note if he can hop on each foot, or if not, which foot is successful. May credit if child is successful on only one foot.

3.134

Jumps a distance of 14 to 24 inches   30-34.5

Definition: The child can jump forward ("broad jump") at least 14 inches. To move this distance, the child will need more propulsive force, which is usually achieved by crouching down when preparing for the jump, and swinging his arms forward with a strong motion.

Example Observation Opportunities: Same as 3.116

Credit: (see also Credit Notes in this strand's preface)

+   furthest jump of several trials is at least 14 inches from the starting point. He may jump and land with both feet simultaneously or have a leading foot, but the heel of the following foot must be at least 14 inches from the starting point. He prepares for the jump by crouching and swinging his arms forward with a strong motion.

3.143

Jumps a distance of 24 to 34 inches   34.5-36

Definition: The child can jump forward ("broad jump") at least 24 inches.

Example Observation Opportunities: Same as #3.116.

Credit: (see also Credit Notes in this strand's preface)

+   furthest jump of several trials is at least 24 inches from the starting point. He may jump and land with both feet simultaneously or have a leading foot but the heel of the following foot must be at least 24 inches from the starting point. He prepares for the jump by crouching and swinging his arms forward with a strong motion.

3-7 ADVANCING POSTURAL CONTROL AND MOTOR PLANNING

D. CLIMBING

3.95	17.5-19	Backs into small chair or slides sideways
3.100	18-21	Climbs forward on adult chair, turns around and sits
3.108	23-26	Goes up and down slide
3.141	34.5-36	Climbs jungle gyms and ladders

NOTE: [Refer to the preface for Strand 3-7 on pages 191 to 194 for Family Friendly Definitions, Parent Questions, Sample Outcome Statements, Professional FYI, Transactional Assessment, and General Assessment Procedures]

Family Friendly Interpretation of Strand Concepts, Assessment, & Purpose

We will be observing how your child is learning to climb. Children use the same type of movement to climb as they do when they learn how to creep. But climbing requires more strength and planning, because the child needs to figure out how to move his body on and off objects, such as chairs or ladders. When your child practices climbing on outdoor play equipment, it is best if he wears sneakers, because the rubber helps give him more traction.

Professional FYI

If playground equipment is not available for assessment, items #3.108 and #3.141 can be accomplished through parent interview. Providing the child with experiences on *safe* playground equipment should be encouraged when the child is ready developmentally.

If the child displays excessive fear or extreme reactions when encouraged to move on equipment, do not force him to do so, as this may be a sign of sensory processing problems.

3.95 Backs into small chair or slides sideways   17.5-19

Definition: The child can seat himself independently in a small child-sized chair.
Parent Questions: Has your child ever had the opportunity to try sitting in small chairs which are his size?
Example Observation Opportunities: May observe when child independently sits in a sturdy child-sized chair at snack time, story time or circle time. If the child requests help, encourage him to try getting in the chair by himself.
Credit: (see also Credit Notes in this strand's preface)
+ directly seats himself in a small child's chair by backing into it or sliding sideways without any adult help. The child does not need more than a few seconds to seat himself, and does not seem confused or try to climb in forward.

3.100 Climbs forward on adult chair, turns around and sits   18-21

Definition: The child figures out how to seat himself in an adult chair by climbing forward into the chair and then turning around to sit. His success will be influenced by his height relative to the chair.
Parent Questions: Does your child climb into your chairs at home? What kind of chairs can he get into, e.g., straight-backed kitchen table chairs, cushioned recliners, etc.? *[If the child is relatively small for his age, let him try climbing on a sofa with the cushions removed]*
Example Observation Opportunities: If not observed incidentally or reported, place a chair next to you and invite the child to sit next to you to look at a book. The chair should be a sturdy straight-backed chair. If the child is relatively small for his age, let him try climbing on a sofa with the cushions removed.
Credit: (see also Credit Notes in this strand's preface)
+ climbs forward into an adult straight-backed chair independently and turns around to sit; he should do so fairly quickly and not appear overly confused.

Goes up and down slide   23-26

Definition: The child can climb up and slide down an small indoor slide.

Parent Questions: Has your child ever tried going on a small slide before? How is he doing with this?

Example Observation Opportunities: Use a small indoor-type ladder slide which has flat steps. If this is the child's first experience, provide him as much support as he wants and let him practice several times. *Supervise carefully.*

Credit: (see also Credit Notes in this strand's preface)

+ demonstrates good motor planning skills as he negotiates climbing up and going down the slide; e.g., after sliding down, he knows the best way to get back to the top is to walk around to climb the steps; after getting to the top, he can get into sitting. His actual sliding may not be smooth. He should not display extreme fearful reactions, such as screaming or grabbing onto an adult.

Climbs jungle gyms and ladders   34.5-36

Definition: The child climbs and plays on small jungle gym type equipment.

Example Observation Opportunities: May be observed if small jungle gym equipment is available. If this is the child's first experience, let him watch others and initially provide him as much support and encouragement as he needs to practice.

Credit: (see also Credit Notes in this strand's preface)

+ negotiates small jungle gyms with good motor planning skills; e.g., he can climb up a few rungs of the ladder and figure out how to get back down; can figure out how to swing from a low rung and let go to drop on his feet. He should not display extreme fearful reactions, such as screaming or grabbing onto an adult even when approaching easy equipment.

3-7 ADVANCING POSTURAL CONTROL AND MOTOR PLANNING

E. STAIRS

3.90	17-19	Walks upstairs with one hand held
3.106	15-18	Walks upstairs holding rail - both feet on step
3.115	15-18	Walks downstairs holding rail - both feet on step
3.101	19-21	Walks downstairs with one hand held
3.114	24-25.5	Walks upstairs alone - both feet on step
3.123	25.5-27	Walks downstairs alone - both feet on step
3.131	30-34	Walks upstairs alternating feet
3.140	34 +	Walks downstairs alternating feet

NOTE: [Refer to the preface for Strand 3-7 on pages 191 to 194 for Family Friendly Definitions, Parent Questions, Sample Outcome Statements, Professional FYI, Transactional Assessment, and General Assessment Procedures]

Family Friendly Interpretation of Strand Concepts, Assessment, & Purpose

We will be observing how your child is learning to walk up and down steps. At first, a child needs to hold onto something and place both feet on the step at the same time to help him balance and figure out how to coordinate his body to take the next step. Later, as his balance, coordination and planning skills mature, he learns to walk up and down steps without holding on and by alternating his feet on the steps.

Professional FYI

The following are specific issues related specifically to this sub-strand of climbing stairs.

An adult must remain next to the child at all times for safety.

Parent Questions   (Examples)

To help identify the child's unique strengths and needs related to this developmental area:
- Are there safe steps at home or daycare that your child has tried to use? *[Ask what types of steps, e.g., how steep, how many and if there is a rail]*
- How much help does he need to walk up steps? down steps?

To help identify family resources, priorities and concerns related to the child's development in this area:
- How do you feel about your child learning to use steps on his own?

General Assessment Procedures & Processes (apply to all items in this Sub-Strand)

1. **All items may be observed incidentally if portable steps or a short stairway is available.** *An adult must remain next to the child at all times for safety.* The child may also be observed negotiating steps outside as he enters or leaves the assessment session or during outdoor play; or inside if portable steps are available. A toy or other incentive may be placed on the top or bottom to encourage the child to climb.

+ - A Credit Notes:

+ to credit fully, the child should maintain an erect posture, with some bending of his hips and knees evident. There may be some visual monitoring of the steps.

A Atypical - the child is able to climb steps and is not generally delayed in gross motor development <u>but</u>, in spite of plenty of experience with stairs, displays <u>excessive visual monitoring and slow movements</u>, or is <u>extremely accident prone</u>, or is <u>extremely anxious or frightened</u> when approaching even short steps.

3.90 **Walks upstairs with one hand held**   *17-19*

Definition: The child can walk up a few steps when an adult holds his hand. He walks up by placing both feet on the same step before moving another foot up.

Example Observation Opportunities: Stand one or two steps behind the child and hold his hand at his side rather than overhead.

Credit: (see also Credit Notes in this strand's preface)
+ walks up at least three steps, two feet per step, while holding an adult's hand with one hand; he does not need to hold onto a rail or wall with his other hand, and should not need help or direction on how to move to the next step.

3.106 **Walks upstairs holding rail - both feet on step**   *15-18*

Definition: The child can walk up a few steps if one hand holds a rail or the wall for support. At this stage, his feet do not alternate.

Example Observation Opportunities: Remain one or two steps behind the child, but do not provide any assistance. The rail should be at the child's shoulder height.

Credit: (see also Credit Notes in this strand's preface)
+ walks up at least four steps facing forward while holding onto the wall or rail with one hand. He places both feet on each step before moving a foot to the next step but should not need any help in doing so.

3.115 **Walks downstairs holding rail - both feet on step**   *15-18*

Definition: The child can walk down a few steps if he holds a rail or the wall with one hand for support. At this stage, his feet do not alternate.

Example Observation Opportunities: Remain near the child, but do not provide any assistance. The rail should be at the child's shoulder height.

Credit: (see also Credit Notes in this strand's preface)
+ walks down at least three steps, two feet per step, while holding a rail or the wall for support with one hand; he does not need to hold onto a rail or wall with his other hand, and, should not need help or direction on how to move to the next step.

3.101 **Walks downstairs with one hand held**   *19-21*

Definition: The child can walk down a few steps when an adult holds his hand. He walks down by placing both feet on the same step before moving another foot down to the next step.

Example Observation Opportunities: Stand next to, or one step in front of, the child as you hold his hand at his shoulder height.

Credit: (see also Credit Notes in this strand's preface)
+ walks down at least three steps, two feet per step, while holding an adult's hand; he does not need to hold onto a rail or wall with his other hand and should not need help or direction on how to move to the next step.

3.114 **Walks upstairs alone - both feet on step**   *24-25.5*

Definition: The child can walk up a few steps independently without holding onto a support. He places both feet per step before moving onto the next.

Example Observation Opportunities: Remain nearby, but do not offer any assistance. If available, use free standing portable steps away from the wall.

Credit: (see also Credit Notes in this strand's preface)
+ walks up at least four steps, two feet per step, without holding onto a support.

3.123 **Walks downstairs alone - both feet on step**   25.5-27

Definition: The child can walk down a few steps independently without holding a rail or the wall for support. At this stage, his feet do not alternate.

Example Observation Opportunities: Remain nearby, but do not offer any assistance. If available, use free standing portable steps away from the wall.

Credit: (see also Credit Notes in this strand's preface)

+ walks down at least three steps without any support, two feet per step.

3.131 **Walks upstairs alternating feet**   30-34

Definition: The child can walk up a few steps independently without holding onto a support. At this stage, he has enough balance and coordination to alternate his feet on the steps.

Example Observation Opportunities: Remain nearby, but do not offer any assistance. If available, use free standing portable steps away from the wall.

Credit: (see also Credit Notes in this strand's preface)

+ independently walks up four steps, placing only one foot per step and alternating his forward foot.

3.140 **Walks downstairs alternating feet**   34 +

Definition: The child can walk down a few steps independently without holding onto a support. At this stage, he has enough balance and coordination to alternate his feet on the steps.

Example Observation Opportunities: Remain nearby, but do not offer any assistance. If available, use free standing portable steps away from the wall.

Credit: (see also Credit Notes in this strand's preface)

+ independently walks down four steps, placing only one foot per step and alternating his forward foot.

3-7 ADVANCING POSTURAL CONTROL AND MOTOR PLANNING

F. THROWING/CATCHING

3.77	13-16	**Throws underhand in sitting**
3.85	15-18	**Throws ball forward**
3.88	16-22	**Throws overhand within 3 feet of target**
3.97	18-20	**Throws ball into a box**
3.111	24-26	**Catches large ball**
3.142	35 +	**Catches eight inch ball**

NOTE: [Refer to the preface for Strand 3-7 on pages 191 to 194 for Family Friendly Definitions, Parent Questions, Sample Outcome Statements, Professional FYI, Transactional Assessment, and General Assessment Procedures]

Family Friendly Interpretation of Strand Concepts, Assessment, & Purpose

We will be playing some simple ball games with your child to see how he's doing with learning to throw and catch. Learning to throw a ball involves the interplay of several motor skills. A child needs to be able to have good release skills to let go of the ball at the right time, and good balance and control of his body so he doesn't fall down as he swings his arm quickly to throw the ball. Throwing also requires good planning of movements to help control the speed, strength and direction of the throw.

Learning to catch a ball usually happens much later than throwing. Catching involves being able to watch a ball and follow its movement while adjusting his body, arms, and hands to catch it. This requires a good perception of time and space. When children are learning to catch, they hold their arms out and trap the ball against their chest rather than catching it with their arms.

Assessment Adaptations   (Examples)

[Note any adaptations needed to credit and help plan interventions]

- <u>Physically disabled</u>: if the child has fairly good control of his upper body but cannot complete these skills in standing (e.g., spina bifida, spastic diplegic), the skills may be adapted with the child in sitting.
- <u>Visually impaired</u>: the child may be more reluctant to kick or throw because the ball is gone and he cannot be assured of its whereabouts. Use much verbal description and remain close by so you can return the ball more quickly. There are some specially made "beeper balls" which emit sounds that may be helpful and motivating for the child. The child will need physical guidance to teach him how to make the throwing and catching movements.

Throws underhand in sitting   13-16

Definition: The child throws a ball, with his arm positioned at his side and with his palm facing up. He may be standing or sitting and may not have control over the direction of his throw, but is able to propel it forward.

Example Observation Opportunities: Demonstrate throwing an easy-to-grasp ball, such as a tennis ball or soft rubber ball. Invite the child to join in this throwing game. The game can involve throwing the ball to each other or toward a target, but the child should not be expected to catch the ball or make it land in a specific place. If the child has good standing balance, this item may be observed in standing. Repeat several times alternating which hand you offer the ball to.

Credit: (see also Credit Notes in this strand's preface)

    +   throws the ball any distance with a definite forward fling with either hand; he may be standing or sitting.

3.85 Throws ball forward   15-18

Definition: The child can throw a small ball forward a few feet when standing (without falling).
Example Observation Opportunities: Same as #3.77, but the child should be standing.
Credit: (see also Credit Notes in this strand's preface)
+ intentionally throws ball in a forward direction a few feet, using either hand, and without falling. He may use an overhand or underhand throw.

3.88 Throws overhand within 3 feet of target   16-22

Definition: The child can control the direction of the ball so that it lands within 3 feet to the left or right of a target.
Example Eliciting Situations: After giving the child an easy-to-grasp ball, such as a clutch ball or tennis ball, stand about 3 to 4 feet in front of him and encourage him to throw it to you. Invite him to try several times, encouraging him to throw with each hand.
Credit: (see also Credit Notes in this strand's preface)
+ if on the child's best try out of three attempts, the ball travels at least 3 feet before touching the floor and lands within 3 feet to either side of the target; using either hand.

3.97 Throws ball into a box   18-20

Definition: The child can control the direction of his throw when throwing a ball into a large box which is about 3 feet away.
Example Eliciting Situations: Play a throwing game which involves throwing tennis balls, clutch balls or bean bags into a large container, such as a trash can, laundry basket or large box. Begin by placing it only a foot away from the child. Then move it 3 feet away. It may be helpful to have a barrier, such as a rope, on the floor as a guide so the child does not walk up to the box.
Credit: (see also Credit Notes in this strand's preface)
+ when standing, can throw a ball or bean bag into a target placed 3 feet away; at least one out of three tries.

3.111 Catches large ball   24-26

Definition: The child sometimes catches a ball which is thrown gently from 2-3 feet. He catches by "trapping" the ball against his chest.
Example Eliciting Situations: Play a "catch and throw" game with a large, soft ball, such as a partially deflated small beach ball or soft rubber ball about 12 inches in diameter. Stand about 3 feet from the child. Throw the ball gently underhand toward his chest. Remind him to "put his hands out" to catch the ball as needed.
Credit: (see also Credit Notes in this strand's preface)
+ catches a large ball which is thrown gently directly toward his chest from only 2-3 feet away; he may catch it by holding his arms out straight and then trapping it against his chest, one out of three trials.

3.142 Catches eight inch ball   35 +

Definition: The child can catch a ball about 8 inches in diameter. Around 3 to 4 years, he catches the ball with his arms bent in front of his body, rather than using straight arms with trapping.
Example Eliciting Situations: Play a "catch and throw" game with a soft rubber or foam ball about 8 inches in diameter. Stand about 5 feet from the child. Throw the ball gently underhand toward his chest. Remind him to "put his hands out" to catch the ball as needed.
Credit: (see also Credit Notes in this strand's preface)
+ at 3 to 4 years, if he catches a ball in standing with his elbows bent in front of his body, one out of two trials.

3-7 ADVANCING POSTURAL CONTROL AND MOTOR PLANNING

G. RIDING A TRICYCLE

3.98	18-24	Moves on "ride-on" toys without pedals
3.112	24-30	Rides tricycle
3.139	32-36	Uses pedals on tricycle alternately

NOTE: [Refer to the preface for Strand 3-7 on pages 191 to 194 for Family Friendly Definitions, Parent Questions, Sample Outcome Statements, Professional FYI, Transactional Assessment, and General Assessment Procedures]

Family Friendly Interpretation of Strand Concepts, Assessment, & Purpose

We will be observing how your child is learning to move on a ride-on toy or a tricycle (if he seems ready). Learning to ride a bike involves coordinating both sides of the body and planning movements to figure out how to get on the bike, how to propel forward, and how to steer. Sneakers are usually the best type of shoe to wear during this type of play, because they protect your child's foot, while offering flexibility and traction.

Assessment Adaptations   (Examples)

[Note any adaptations needed to credit and help plan interventions]
Some children with physical disabilities, such as diplegia, hemiplegia or spina bifida, may be able to use kiddie bikes with some adaptations, such as a wide seat with a seat back or seat belt; straps to help hold feet in place on the pedals. Consult with a therapist for possible adaptations.

General Assessment Procedures & Processes   (apply to all items in this sub-Strand)

1. Observe how the child approaches, climbs on and moves off the bike. If he seems confused or has much difficulty, this may be a sign of motor planning problems.
2. These skills should be observed on a *smooth, flat open* area.

Moves on "ride-on" toys without pedals   18-24

Definition: The child can propel a "Tyke bike" -wheeled vehicle forward by pushing with his feet against the floor.
Example Observation Opportunities: Invite the child to play on a "Tyke bike" -type toy which does not have pedals. Make sure the toy is sturdy and allows the child to put his feet firmly on the ground with his knees bent.
Credit: (see also Credit Notes in this strand's preface)
+   propels a ride-on toy forward a few feet; he may push with both feet simultaneously and may initially move the bike backwards. He should be able to get on and off the bike independently; however, an adult may hold the toy to keep it from rolling.

Rides tricycle   24-30

Definition: The child is learning to ride a tricycle a few feet. At this stage, he may sometimes push the bike with his feet and sometimes do some pedaling.

Example Observation Opportunities: Use a conventional tricycle on which the child can comfortably place his feet on the pedals, legs somewhat flexed. An adult may help the child get started and gently push him for part of the ride.

Credit: (see also Credit Notes in this strand's preface)

+ pedals a tricycle a few feet forward; he may have put his feet on the ground to push for part of the way and may have some adult assistance to help guide the bike. He should be able to get on and off the bike independently; however, an adult may hold the toy to keep it from rolling.

 Uses pedals on tricycle alternately   32-36

Definition: The child can move forward on a tricycle several feet by pushing the pedals with his feet in a reciprocal pattern.

Example Observation Opportunities: Use a conventional tricycle on which the child can comfortably place his feet on the pedals, legs somewhat flexed.

Credit: (see also Credit Notes in this strand's preface)

+ pedals a tricycle at least 4-6 feet forward. He may not be able to steer around obstacles but should be able to get on and off the bike independently.

3-7 ADVANCING POSTURAL CONTROL AND MOTOR PLANNING

H. WALKING ON A LINE OR BALANCE BEAM

3.86	15-17	Walks with assistance on 8-inch board
3.93	17.5-19.5	Walks independently on 8-inch board
3.94	17.5-18.5	Tries to stand on 2-inch balance beam
3.105	20.5-21.5	Walks a few steps with one foot on 2-inch balance beam
3.119	24-26	Walks on line in general direction
3.120	24-30	Walks between parallel lines 8 inches apart
3.121	24.5-26	Stands on 2-inch beam with both feet
3.126	27.5-28.5	Attempts step on 2-inch balance beam
3.130	30-32	Alternates steps part way on 2-inch beam
3.138	30-32	Keeps feet on line for 10 feet

NOTE: [Refer to the preface for Strand 3-7 on pages 191 to 194 for Family Friendly Definitions, Parent Questions, Sample Outcome Statements, Professional FYI, Transactional Assessment, and General Assessment Procedures]

Family Friendly Interpretation of Strand Concepts, Assessment, & Purpose

We will be encouraging your child to try to walk along a line and along a wooden beam. This is a difficult motor skill which requires that your child be able to balance while walking with his feet placed one in front of the other. It also requires him to plan his movements by paying attention to the boundaries on the floor. This is sometimes referred to as eye-foot coordination.

General Assessment Procedures & Processes   (apply to all items in this sub-Strand)

1. *If balance beams are not readily available, it is not absolutely necessary to evaluate skill requiring a balance beam in this strand.* This is especially true if the child's gross motor development is following an expected progression with good postural control.
2. **The procedure does not include using beams which are suspended, since this can be difficult to set up and may be more frightening for the child. Instead, boards can be** used which are 1 or 2 inches high to raise the beams from the surface.

+ - A Credit Notes:

A   Atypical - displays extreme anxiety, fear, or caution, even on a beam which is only 1 or 2 inches high; may grab parent, refuse to step up, crouch down to lower his base of support, or take very tiny steps.

N/A not assessed due to lack of equipment.

Walks with assistance on 8-inch board   15-17

Definition: The child can walk along an 8-inch wide board which is 1 or 2 inches high while holding an adult hand.

Example Observation Opportunities: Incidental - may observe outdoors as adult holds child's hand while he walks along a wide curb. Structured - use a sturdy walking board which is about 8 inches wide, 6 feet long and about 1 or 2 inches in height. Demonstrate walking along the raised board. Invite the child to try, as you or his parent holds one hand and walks at a slow pace next to him. His hand should be held at about his chest level rather than overhead.

Credit: (see also Credit Notes in this strand's preface)

+   walks at least 3 feet along an 8-inch board (or other similar raised surface) when holding an adult's hand.

3.93 Walks independently on 8-inch board   17.5-19.5

Definition: The child can walk the entire distance of a 6-foot long walking board which is about 8 inches wide and raised 1 or 2 inches from the surface.

Example Observation Opportunities: Incidental - may observe outdoors if child walks along a wide curb without holding an adult's hand. Structured - use a sturdy walking board which is about 8 inches wide, 6 feet long and about 1 or 2 inches in height. Place the board away from any supports for the child to hold. Demonstrate walking along the board and invite the child to try.

Credit: (see also Credit Notes in this strand's preface)

+ walks the entire distance of the board without stepping or falling off, or needing to hold onto an adult's hand.

3.94 Tries to stand on 2-inch balance beam   17.5-18.5

Definition: The child tries to stand on a 2-inch beam with his feet perpendicular to the board but then steps off quickly.

Example Observation Opportunities: Incidental - may observe if child steps up on the edge of a sandbox. Structured - use a sturdy walking board which is about 2 by 2 inches in height and width, and 6 to 8 feet long. Place it where the child does not have a support to hold onto. Demonstrate stepping up and standing on it with your arms straight out to the sides for balance. Invite the child to try.

Credit: (see also Credit Notes in this strand's preface)

+ tries to stand on a 2 inch beam by stepping up with one foot, and then attempting to place his second foot up, but steps off quickly.

(may also credit #3.121 if he places both feet on the board and balances for at least 2 seconds)

3.105 Walks a few steps with one foot on 2-inch balance beam   20.5-21.5

Definition: The child takes a few steps independently along a 2.5-inch wide balance beam.

Example Observation Opportunities: Structured - use a sturdy walking board which is about 2 by 2 inches in height and width, and 6 to 8 feet long. Place it where the child does not have a support to hold on to. Demonstrate stepping up and walking a few steps with one foot on the beam and one foot on the ground. Invite the child to try. You or his parent may initially hold his hand and demonstrate walking with one foot on and one foot off of the board to help him get the idea.

Credit: (see also Credit Notes in this strand's preface)

+ takes at least three steps with one foot on the beam and the other foot on the floor using either foot on the beam. He should not have to hold onto a support. If the child goes directly to walking with both feet on the beam, may credit this and higher level balance beam skills, i.e., #3.121; #3.126, #3.130.

3.119 Walks on line in general direction   24-26

Definition: The child can walk in the general direction of a marked line for about 10 feet.

Example Observation Opportunities: Incidental - may observe if child walks on lines which are available naturally in the environment, incidentally or in imitation during play, e.g., lines of parking spaces in an empty parking lot or lines on a sidewalk. Structured - make a line about 10 feet long on the floor in an open area. Use chalk or a high-contrast color tape. Demonstrate walking the entire length and invite the child to try. Also invite the parent to do so, as if this is a fun game. Comment on how you are following the line.

Credit: (see also Credit Notes in this strand's preface)

+ walks forward close to the line for its entire length. He may have one foot on the line with the other foot off, or have one foot on each side of the line.

3.120 Walks between parallel lines 8 inches apart   24-30

Definition: The child can walk between two parallel lines which are about 8 inches apart without stepping on the lines.

Example Observation Opportunities: <u>Structured</u> - make two parallel lines abut 10 feet long, 8 inches apart, on the floor in an open area. Use chalk or a high-contrast color tape. Demonstrate walking between the lines the entire length. Make a comment about not stepping on the lines. Invite the child to try. Also invite the parent to do so, as if this is a fun game.

Credit: (see also Credit Notes in this strand's preface)

+   walks about 10 feet between the parallel lines without ever fully stepping on the lines.

3.121 Stands on 2-inch beam with both feet   24.5-26

Definition: The child is able to independently step up and stand with both feet on a 2-inch wide balance beam, with feet perpendicular to the beam.

Example Observation Opportunities: Same as #3.94.

Credit: (see also Credit Notes in this strand's preface)

+   independently steps up and places both feet on the balance beam, for at least 2 seconds before placing one foot back on the ground.

3.126 Attempts step on 2-inch balance beam   27.5-28.5

Definition: The child attempts to walk forward on a 2-inch wide balance beam independently. He does not take a full alternating step.

Example Observation Opportunities: <u>Incidental</u> - may observe if child steps up and attempts to walk with both feet on the edge of a sandbox. <u>Structured</u> - use a sturdy walking board which is about 2 by 2 inches in height and width, and 6 to 8 feet long. Place it where the child does not have a support to hold onto. Demonstrate stepping up and walking a few steps. Invite the child to try.

Credit: (see also Credit Notes in this strand's preface)

+   independently steps up on beam and then places one foot in front of his other foot before stepping off the board. He may have one or two tries. He may hold his arms out to the side for balance but should maintain an upright posture.

3.130 Alternates steps part way on 2-inch beam   30-32

Definition: The child takes a few independent alternating steps on a 2-inch wide balance beam.

Example Observation Opportunities: <u>Incidental</u> - may observe if child steps up and takes a few alternating steps on the edge of a sandbox. <u>Structured</u> - same as #3.126. If he attempts and then places one foot on the floor, praise his try and encourage him to try again with both feet on the board.

Credit: (see also Credit Notes in this strand's preface)

+   independently steps up and then takes at least two alternating steps at any point along the balance beam before placing one of his feet back on the floor. He may hold his arms out to the side for balance but should maintain an upright posture.

3.138 Keeps feet on line for 10 feet   30-32

Definition: The child can walk, one foot in front of the other, along a line without stepping off for at least 3 feet.

Example Observation Opportunities: Same as #3.119.

Credit: (see also Credit Notes in this strand's preface)

+   walks at least 3 feet on a line; one foot in front of the other but not heel to toe; one part of the foot must be always touching the line.

4.0 - Fine Motor Development
Introduction

Overview

The Fine Motor domain is divided into two sections and their associated strands:

I. Foundations of Fine Motor Development (includes various sequences of basic fine motor skills):
>4-1 Visual Responses and Tracking
>4-2 Grasp and Prehension
>4-3 Reach and Approach
>4-4 Development of Voluntary Release
>4-5 Bilateral and Midline Skills

II. Perceptual-Motor: Integration of Fine Motor Foundations. (builds upon and are dependent upon the child's ability to integrate the skills in Section I):
>4-6 Spatial Perception and Planning
>>A. Pre-writing
>>B. Block Construction
>>C. Formboard
>>D. Paper Activities
>4-7 Manipulative Prehension
>>A. Pages
>>B. Pegboard
>>C. Stringing Beads.
>>D. Scissors

Relationship with other Domains

As in other domains, the Fine Motor domain is interdependent and strongly interconnected with other areas of development. The quality and development of skills in fine motor are affected by other areas of development, especially Gross Motor (3.0), Regulatory/Sensory Organization (0.0), and Cognition (1.0).

In addition, delayed or atypical fine motor development will affect the quality and development of skills in other areas of development, especially independent self help skills and cognitive skills which require visual tracking, perceptual and manipulative skills.

General Atypical Movements related to all Fine Motor Skills

When assessing any skills involving upper extremity movements, the following criteria can be used to note atypical (**A**) responses in all Fine Motor strands:

• Increased muscle tone; i.e., the child is more stiff or tight than other children you have handled at this age;

• Low muscle tone; i.e., the child is more loose and floppy than others at his age that you have handled;

• Hands fisted when reaching for objects (after about 7 months);

• Over about 15 months: poor release of objects or clumsy control; exaggerated finger opening or splaying during release.

Safety

Numerous fine motor activities involve manipulation or handling of small objects by the child. Be sure that all items are large enough to prevent the child from choking–blocks should be at least 1.25 inches in size–preferably even larger; beads not too small. Always use careful supervision, and provide guidance to the caregiver. "Inch cubes" refer to cubes that are at least 1.25 inches on each side.

4-1 VISUAL RESPONSES AND TRACKING

4.01	0-1	Regards colorful object momentarily
4.04	0.5-1.5	Follows with eyes moving person while in supine
4.03	0.5-2.5	Regards colorful object for few seconds
4.05	1-2	Stares and gazes
4.09	2-3	Blinks at sudden visual stimulus
4.06	1-3	Follows with eyes to midline
4.10	2-3	Follows with eyes past midline
4.17	2-3	Follows with eyes 180 degrees
4.11	2-3	Follows with eyes downward
4.19	2-3	Follows with eyes upward
4.18	3-4.5	Follows with eyes, moving object in supported sitting
4.24	4-6	Follows with eyes without head movement
4.31	4.5-5.5	Regards tiny object
4.32	5-6	Looks at distant objects

Family Friendly Interpretation of Strand Concepts, Assessment, & Purpose

We will be observing how your child uses his vision to look at things and if he can move his eyes together in various directions to follow moving objects. For example, we will watch to see if he keeps looking at his toy when we move it slowly from his left side to his right. This is sometimes referred to as "visual tracking."

Parent Questions   (Examples)

To help identify the child's unique strengths and needs related to this developmental area:
- Do you have any concerns about your child's vision?
- Does your child have any eye or vision problems that you are aware of?
- Have you noticed if your child watches you when you walk across the room?
- Are there certain colors, lights or things that he seems to prefer looking at?...that he seems to avoid?

[If child was premature]
- Has your child been diagnosed with any special eye problems related to being premature, such as ROP, retinopathy of prematurity?

[If yes,] Were you told what stage? Do you have a follow-up visit scheduled with an eye doctor?
- Are there any other things about your child's vision or the way he uses his eyes that you feel are important for us to know?

To help identify family resources, priorities and concerns related to the child's development in this area:
[If visual problems are known or suspected]
- Do you have an eye doctor or clinic you can go to for help in evaluating your child's vision ?
- Are you interested in receiving information about community resources which can help pay for or evaluate your child's eyes?

Sample *Functional* Outcome Statements which may be generated by the Family

My child will:
- Enjoy looking at his toys;
- Enjoy watching his mobile move;
- Be able to find his toy when it rolls out of immediate sight.

We will know:
- More about the kinds of things our child likes to look at;
- Local eye doctors to whom we can take our child.

Transactional Assessment

May assess through observation and interview.

Assessment of the Child's Environment

1. Supportive:
[Example environments which support/facilitate development in this area]
- The child's visual environment usually has a variety of interesting things to look at which are positioned so he can see them.

2. Compromising:
[Environments which may restrict, compromise, inhibit or be unsupportive toward development in this area]
- The child's visual environments are frequently over- or under-stimulating for the child's interests and needs.

Assessment of Caregiver Interactions with the Child

1. Supportive:
[Interactions which support/facilitate the child's visual development)]
The child's caregivers usually:
• Present toys and other visual stimuli to the child at a comfortable distance from his face;
• Make comments about what the child is looking at;
• Are able to read and respond sensitively to the child's unique signals and cues which show he is interested in or tired of looking at a toy;
• Place the child in a variety of comfortable, developmentally appropriate positions which help him see his environment.

B. Compromising:
[Interactions which may compromise, or be unsupportive of the child's optimal development)]
The child's caregivers frequently:
• Present toys too abruptly or too close to his face, causing him to wince;
• Ignore, misinterpret and or respond inappropriately to the child's signals that indicate he is overstimulated or does not want to look at a toy;
• Place the child in positions or places that do not allow him to see his environment.

Identifying and Interpreting Needs for Intervention

If a child displays significantly delayed or atypical development in this strand he may be having <u>difficulty seeing and, or coordinating his eyes together.</u> The child should be referred to a pediatric ophthalmologist and vision specialist.*

<u>However,</u> before targeting vision problems as the primary need for intervention or referral, consider, rule out, or adapt for other causes which can interfere with a true assessment of the child's ability to see or track objects. These may include:
• The child is <u>tired or overstimulated;</u>
• The <u>objects used are not visually attractive</u> to child;
• There is a <u>competing environment</u>; i.e., the child is busy looking, listening or playing with something else;

• The child has <u>attentional or other regulatory or sensory organization problems</u> (refer to Regulatory/Sensory Organization, Strand 0.0);
• The child has a <u>motor impairment</u> that prevents him from moving his head smoothly for tracking.
[*Additional warning signs of visual problems warranting referral to an eye specialist: eyeballs appear to bulge; eyes are not the same size; eyes make tremor-like movements; excessive blinking or tearing; one or both eyes turn out; unusually sensitive to light; rubs eyes excessively; keeps one eye shut; habitually tilts head, or thrusts head forward; and later, poor eye-hand coordination not related to fine motor development]

Assessment Adaptations   (Examples)

[Note any adaptations needed to credit and help plan interventions]
• <u>Visually impaired</u>: observe when the child is in a quiet environment. Use large, brightly colored and reflective toys and objects, e.g., small mirror, yellow and black toy, florescent colored ball, a flashlight shining on tinsel or small pie tin. Offer extra time for the child to look and follow; try presenting the object toward one side if he does not fixate on it presented at midline; try different lighting to determine best response.
• <u>Motor impaired</u>: be sure to consult with a therapist to ensure optimal positioning. The child

should be positioned so that his head and trunk are stable.
• <u>Regulatory/Sensory disorganization</u>: try one or more of the following techniques: observe in a quiet, dimly lit environment; try eliciting when the child is held upright at the parent's shoulder if the child is difficult to alert; let the child suck on a pacifier if he needs help achieving a calm alert state; present the objects slowly and give the child extra time to fixate before moving it for tracking. May also try swaddling or rocking prior to observing tracking skills.

General Assessment Procedures & Processes (apply to all items in this Strand)

1. **The child should be** well supported according to his gross motor abilities. He may be in supported sitting on his parent's lap facing outward to the facilitator, in his infant seat, held upright at parent's shoulder, lying supine, or supported in an adult's lap face-to-face.

2. **Shake the toy or use sound toys (if needed) to initially attract the child's attention**; the toy should not make a sound during the tracking process.

3. **Be sure to let the child explore the objects after he has looked at and tried to track them** (if he appears interested).

4. **If the child is more interested in looking at the adult instead of the toy, move out of the child's direct line of vision**.

5. The following items **can be assessed at one time** during the same eliciting procedure:
   #4.01 "Regards colorful object momentarily"
   #4.03 "Regards colorful object for few seconds"

#4.06 "Follows with eyes to midline"
#4.10 "Follows with eyes past midline"
#4.17 "Follows with eyes 180 degrees"
#4.11 "Follows with eyes downward"
#4.19 "Follows with eyes upward."

6. **Explain the assessment procedure to the parent and invite the parent to carry it out with the child.**

+ - A Credit Notes:

+ usually displays skill as defined.
- skill not present.
+/- emerging, e.g., can be elicited about half of the time and prior skill in sequence is present.
A atypical, skill present but of poor quality, e.g., after three months usually displays jerky eye movement, eyes do not move together; squints; voluntarily tilts head to see.

Assessment Materials

• Any small toys or objects that attract child's attention. Examples may include: small red yarn or rubber ball, squeak toy with a face.

Objects should be at least 3 inches in size.
• *Safe*, pellet-sized object, such as a cinnamon drop, raisin, or cereal bit.

4.01 Regards colorful object momentarily   0-1

Definition: The child looks at an object for at least 2 or 3 seconds when object is presented about 8-10 inches away from his chest.

Example Observation Opportunities: <u>Incidental</u> - may observe when child is lying quietly in his crib, sitting in his infant seat or on parent's lap if he looks at his mobile or other nearby toy or object. <u>Structured</u> - on at least three different occasions, present different toys of different colors and contrasts, about 8-10 inches from the child's chest toward the side on which he is looking. Use toys that the parent reports the child enjoys. Attract the child's attention (as needed) by gently shaking the toy and or squeaking it (once or twice if it is a rattle toy) until he focuses upon it. Move your face toward one side if he looks at you instead of the toy.

Credit: (see also Credit Notes in this strand's preface)
+ usually able to look at an interesting stationary object for at least 2 or 3 seconds. Note with the parent the child's visual preferences to color, contrast, and design.
(may also credit #4.03 if child looks at the toy for 4-5 seconds; then proceed directly to #4.06 "Follows with eyes to midline")

4.04 Follows with eyes moving person while in supine   0.5-1.5

Definition: The child, when lying supine, visually follows a person who is walking near him. At this age, the child can see contours and movement at a distance.

Example Observation Opportunities: May observe as natural situations arise when someone walks by, within a few feet, and in easy view of the child.

Credit: (see also Credit Notes in this strand's preface)
+ sometimes follows someone walking around a few feet away.

4.03 Regards colorful object for few seconds   0.5-2.5

Definition: The child looks at an interesting object for at least 4 or 5 seconds when it is presented about 8-10 inches away from his chest.

Example Observation Opportunities: Same as #4.01.

Credit: (see also Credit Notes in this strand's preface)

Regards colorful object for few seconds   (continued)

+   same as #4.01, but looks for at least 4 or 5 seconds. Proceed directly to #4.06 "Follows with eyes to midline."

4.05 **Stares and gazes   1-2**

Definition: The child may normally spend about half his waking hours displaying a vague, indirect expression. Sometimes he may appear as if he is not really looking at someone or something. He should, however, demonstrate alert and direct visual regard many times during the day.

Credit: (see also Credit Notes in this strand's preface)

+   sometimes stares or gazes.

A   if the child is over 2 months and rarely looks with a direct regard at people or objects, refer for further visual and or social-emotional evaluation.

N/A if not present; this item is for anticipatory guidance, *not an item to teach.*

4.09 **Blinks at sudden visual stimulus   2-3**

Definition: The child blinks his eyes as an automatic protective response when a visual stimulus is too bright or presented too close or abruptly to his face.

Example Observation Opportunities: It is usually not necessary to set up intrusive situations to assess. May observe naturally when lights are turned on, shades opened, or child goes outside.

Credit: (see also Credit Notes in this strand's preface)

+   blinks to sudden or bright visual stimuli which may occur during observation period.

A   blinks frequently without stimulus, or never blinks to sudden visual stimuli. Refer for further visual evaluation.

N/A if not observed because bright or abrupt stimuli did not incidentally occur.

[Note: This item is for evaluation purposes only. It is not an item to teach]

4.06 **Follows with eyes to midline   1-3**

Definition: The child visually follows an object that moves slowly from the side he is facing to his midline, but then he "loses" it as it passes his midline to the other side.

Example Observation Opportunities: Attract the child's attention to an object held about 10-12 inches from his chest. When the child is focused on the object, move it slowly in a horizontal or lateral arc toward one side. If the child is still watching, move the object in an arc in the opposite direction. The child may be in supported sitting or in supine.

Credit: (see also Credit Notes in this strand's preface)

+   follows object to midline at least twice, but then loses it when it passes midline. His tracking may be somewhat jerky.

(if the child tracks smoothly past his midline, may credit #4.10, and #4.17 accordingly).

4.10 **Follows with eyes past midline   2-3**

Definition: The child visually follows an object that moves slowly from the side he is facing, towards and a few inches past his midline, but then "loses" it before the object completes a full 180 degree arc.

Example Observation Opportunities: Same as #4.06.

Credit: (see also Credit Notes in this strand's preface)

+   coordinates eyes and follows object at least 2 inches past his midline, at least twice in each direction.

4.17 **Follows with eyes 180 degrees   *2-3***

Definition: The child visually follows an object which moves slowly from the side he is facing to his other side, in an 180 degree arc.

Example Observation Opportunities: Same as #4.06.

Credit: (see also Credit Notes in this strand's preface)

+   coordinates eyes and follows object smoothly 180 degrees from one side to the other at least twice in each direction.

4.11 Follows with eyes downward   2-3

Definition: The child can visually follow an object which moves slowly downward from eye level toward his chest.

Example Observation Opportunities: Attract the child's attention to an object held about 10-12 inches from his face. When the child is focused on the object, move it slowly toward his chest. If he visually follows it and is still attentive, proceed directly to #4.19 "Follows with eyes upward." Repeat 2-3 times.

Credit: (see also Credit Notes in this strand's preface)
+ coordinates eyes and follows object smoothly from eye level down toward his chest at least twice.

4.19 Follows with eyes upward   2-3

Definition: The child can visually follow an object which moves slowly upward from his chest to his brow.

Example Observation Opportunities: Attract the child's attention to an object held about 10-12 inches from his chest. When the child is focused on the object, move it slowly upward toward his brow about an inch above his eyes. Be sure that the object is not moved so far above his eye level that he must arch his back or hyperextend his neck to track it.

Credit: (see also Credit Notes in this strand's preface)
+ coordinates eyes and follows object smoothly upward from his chest to his eyebrow.

4.18 Follows with eyes, moving object in supported sitting   3-4.5

Definition: The child can visually follow moving objects and people from a few feet away. In contrast to #4.04 "Follows with eyes moving person while in supine," by this age a child can typically see things well which are a few feet away, not just contours.

Example Observation Opportunities: Observe to see if the child visually follows the movement of any of the following while he is in supported sitting: toy car or ball moving across a table, bubbles floating, person or pet walking by.

Credit: (see also Credit Notes in this strand's preface)
+ coordinates eyes and follows a moving object.

4.24 Follows with eyes without head movement   4-6

Definition: The child can move his eyes without moving his head (and without other body movements) to visually follow objects in his visual field.

Example Observation Opportunities: Incidental - same as 4.18. Structured - attract the child's attention to an object held about a foot away from his chest. When the child is focused on the object, move it slowly within his visual field a few inches to his left, right, and in a small circle.

Credit: (see also Credit Notes in this strand's preface)
+ coordinates eyes and follows a slowly moving object in all directions with little or no head or body movement.

4.31 Regards tiny object   4.5-5.5

Definition: The child can see an object as small as a raisin from about 1 to 2 feet away.

Example Observation Opportunities: Incidental - may observe child spontaneously looking at tiny objects of interest, e.g., an adult's earring or ring, button on a shirt, drop of food on his tray. Structured - place a cereal bit or other small piece of food on a tray in front of the child. Be sure the object is a different color than the surface it lies on. Tap on the tray as needed to attract the child's attention.

Credit: (see also Credit Notes in this strand's preface)
+ looks intently at the object, possibly reaching or swiping.

4.32 Looks at distant objects   5-6

Definition: The child can see as well as an adult at all distances.

Example Observation Opportunities: May observe at anytime during observation period, e.g., if child notices a picture on the wall, enjoys looking out the window, is observed looking over your shoulder at an object behind you.

Credit: (see also Credit Notes in this strand's preface)
+ shows interest in stationary objects which are several feet away.

4-2 GRASP/PREHENSION

4.12	2-3	Indwelling thumb no longer present
4.22	3.5-4.5	Uses ulnar palmar grasp
4.28	4-5	Uses palmar grasp
4.30	4.5-6	Uses radial palmar grasp
4.40	5.5-7	Attempts to secure tiny object
4.44	7-8	Rakes tiny object
4.43	7-9	Uses radial digital grasp
4.45	7.5-10	Uses inferior pincher grasp
4.51	9-12	Pokes with index finger
4.52	10-12	Uses neat pincer grasp
4.55	11-12	Grasps crayon adaptively
4.63	12-16	Points with index finger
4.78	23-25	Holds crayon with thumb and fingers
4.89	*36-48*	Holds pencil with thumb and fingers - adult-like grasp

Family Friendly Interpretation of Strand Concepts, Assessment, & Purpose

We will be observing how your child uses his hands, fingers and thumbs to pick up and handle small toys and objects. For example, at first children use their whole hand to pick up a block and hold it in the palm of their hand *[demonstrate].* Later, they learn to pick up a block with the tips of their fingers and thumb in opposition *[demon-* *strate].* We use our eyes and hands together to determine what type of grasp we will use. For example, when I hand you a coffee cup, you open your whole hand to grasp the cup, but when I give you a Cheerio, you are more likely to reach for it with only your thumb and fingertips.

Professional FYI

Poking and pointing skills were included in this strand since they are closely related to the refined fine motor and finger isolation skills associated with prehension.

Parent Questions   (Examples)

To help identify the child's unique strengths and needs related to this developmental area:
- Have you noticed how your child uses his hands and fingers to pick up his toys or food?
- What types of toys or objects does your child seem to pick up easily?
- Are there some things that you child seems to have more difficulty picking up?
- Have you ever seen your child try to pick up tiny objects like a Cheerio or a piece of fuzz from the floor? Show me how he does this.
- Has your child ever played with crayons before? *If not,* Would it be okay if we let him try

using a crayon today?
- Are there things your child can do with his hands and fingers to grasp objects which I did not ask, but you feel are important?

To help identify family resources, priorities and concerns related to the child's development in this area:
- If you could think of one thing that you'd like to see your child be able to pick up better with his hands what would that be? What have you tried so far that seems to help? Are there things you've tried that haven't seemed to help?

Sample *Functional* Outcome Statements which may be generated by the Family

[Will be dependent upon identified individual child and family needs and should incorporate objectives and activities from other domains]
My child will be able to:
- Pick up his smaller toys;

- Pick up his pacifier if he drops it;
- Hold his crayon to color;
- Push buttons;
- Operate a switch toy.

Transactional Assessment

May assess through observation and interview.

Assessment of the Child's Environment

1. Supportive:
[Environments which support/facilitate development in this area]
The child's caregiving environments usually have safe and developmentally appropriate smaller toys and objects which are accessible to the child.

2. Compromising:
[Environments which may restrict, compromise, inhibit or be unsupportive toward development in this area]
The child's caregiving environments frequently have dangerous materials within reach of the child; e.g., objects which are less than 1.25 inches in size, objects which have removable parts less than 1.25 inches in size, or safe toys or objects are not available for the child to manipulate.

Assessment of Caregiver Interactions with the Child

1. Supportive:
[Interactions which support/facilitate child's development in this area]
The child's caregivers usually:
• Place the child in positions which enable him to move his hands and arms freely during play and feeding;
• Encourage their child to pick up safe small toys and finger foods during feeding and play.

2. Compromising:
[Interactions which may restrict, compromise, inhibit or be unsupportive of the child's development in this area]
The child's caregivers frequently place the child in positions which prevent him from using his hands to play or eat most effectively.

Identifying and Interpreting Needs for Intervention

If a child is significantly delayed or displays atypical skills in this strand, he may have <u>neuromotor problems, a joint disorder, or peripheral nerve injury which interferes with the fine motor coordination and control</u> needed for effective grasping and prehension. *Refer for a complete evaluation by an occupational therapist.*

<u>However</u>, before targeting grasping skills as the primary need for intervention, consider and, rule out, or adapt for other causes which may interfere with a true assessment of the child's grasping abilities. These may include:
• <u>Lack of experience playing with small objects or finger feeding;</u>
• <u>Visual impairment;</u>
• <u>Tactually defensive;</u>
• <u>Lack of attention or interest</u> in assessment materials;
• <u>Unstable positioning</u> if child has not developed adequate postural control.

Assessment Adaptations   (Examples)

[Note any adaptations needed to qualify credit and help plan interventions]
• <u>Visually impaired:</u>
  – Blind: use the child's familiar toys and foods. Name and place objects in the child's hand to let him explore the size and shape of the object before assessing his grasp. Place the object in a consistent place on a firm surface, and guide his hand to it as needed.
  – Low vision: use high contrast materials, e.g., present a dark toy on a white highchair tray.
  – Specific item adaptations:
    Items #4.55, #4.78, and #4.89: provide initial hand-over-hand modeling if the child has not had much experience with using crayons or a pencil.
    Item #4.63: omit and mark N/A for totally blind child.

• <u>Motor impaired:</u>
  – The child should be positioned in a manner that provides adequate head and trunk support with his arms and shoulders positioned forward. *Consult with an occupational or physical therapist for specific individualized optimal positions.* A tilt board or other adaptive materials and seating may be helpful.
  – A child with severe motor impairments may not develop typical or mature grasping or prehension patterns. Mark N/A for skills which may be inappropriate to assess, and when appropriate, replace skills with more functional skills in collaboration with an occupational therapist, e.g., replace skills #4.40, #4.44, and #4.45 with "picks up small objects using an adapted wrist band for support."
• <u>Tactually defensive:</u> use materials which you know the child tolerates.

General Assessment Procedures & Processes (apply to all items in this Strand)

1. **Items in this strand can usually be observed when assessing other areas of development,** especially Independent Feeding (Strand 6-3), Play (Strand 1-1) and most other fine motor strands.

2. If assessing this area independently, **present or have available in a free play situation, at least two of the example eliciting materials listed for each item.** Present items one at a time and observe how the child approaches and picks up the object in his hand. Attract child's attention to the item, as needed, by tapping it on the surface.

3. **Note if and how the child adjusts his grasp according to the shape and size of various objects:** cube; rattle with a handle; Cheerio or other small piece of food; tissue out of a box; rotary dial play phone; thick versus thin crayons.

4. **Allow the child to play with the object until he is no longer interested or becomes repetitive in his play before introducing new objects.**

5. **Positioning: Items may be observed with the child in prone or in a well-supported sitting position according to his level of gross motor development.** If the child is not successful when he is in prone, repeat the procedure in sitting.

6. **Assess each item with the child's left and right hands.** This can be accomplished by placing the object closer to one hand. Be sure to note and refer for further evaluation as appropriate if there are <u>significant</u> and <u>persistent</u> differences in grasp and prehension skill abilities between left and right hands. *Note: Each hand is <u>not</u> exactly equal in maturity of grasp at all stages of early development.*

7. *Provide caregivers anticipatory guidance as* needed regarding safety issues associated with the development of grasp, e.g., child-proofing for tiny materials child is learning to pick up; using safety electrical plug caps as child learns to poke and probe.

8. **Describe the skill and eliciting procedures and invite the parent to help observe and/or assess.**

+ - A **Credit Notes:**

+ child usually displays grasp and prehension skills as defined during play and daily activities.

- not observed or reported.

+/- appears to be an emerging skill; child does not consistently use this grasp.

A atypical grasp: thumb held in palm (beyond 5 months.)

O circle any credit if environment or interactions compromise or restrict child's grasping patterns, such as inappropriate positioning, lack of small, easy-to-grasp, safe toys. (Refer to Assessment of Caregiver Interactions above.)

<u>Be sure to note</u> any adaptations used to credit performance.

Note: There is an artificial age gap between skill #4.63 which emerges between 12-16 months, and #4.78 which emerges between 23-25 months. During this period, the child continues to refine and practice prehension and grasping patterns. Thus, if a child is 20 months old, for example, and has achieved grasping patterns through #4.63, do not report that the child's development in this area is at the 12-16 month level, because that would imply a delay. It would be more appropriate to make a statement such as, "The child displays grasping and prehension patterns expected for his age."

 ## Assessment Materials

Small, safe, square blocks; rattles, other small toys or objects parent has, e.g., rattle, springless clothespin; teething ring or biscuit; preschool crayons; edible pellet-sized objects (e.g., Cheerios); toys to poke, e.g., doll's face, pegboard, telephone dial. *[Emphasize safety to caregivers]*

4.12   Indwelling thumb no longer present   2-3

Definition: The child's thumb is usually <u>not</u> held tightly in his palm. *[Note: during the first month or two, this may be observed, but through maturation and movement experiences, the child should move out of this "fixed" position]*

Example Observation Opportunities: Observe when child is relaxed in various positions and when child is actively engaged with a toy or person. *[Note: If indwelling thumb is observed, do <u>not</u> physically manipulate or pry open the child's hand. Refer child for a further evaluation]*

Credit: (see also Credit Notes in this strand's preface)
+   does <u>not typically</u> hold thumb tightly to palm; can freely move thumb away from his palm.

4.22   Uses ulnar palmar grasp   3.5-4.5

Definition: The child grasps small objects using his middle, ring and little finger to hold it against his palm with a flexed wrist. His thumb is not involved. The object may be offered directly to his hand, if needed.

Example Observation Opportunities: Offer the child two or three small objects, one at a time on different occasions, toward the little finger side of his palm. Suggested objects: rattles with thin handles, brightly colored small block, springless clothespin, small teething biscuit, teething ring.

Credit: (see also Credit Notes in this strand's preface)
+   usually holds object the size of a small block against palm using his middle, ring and little finger; wrist is flexed; thumb not involved.

4.28   Uses palmar grasp   4-5

Definition: The child uses all his fingers to grasp and hold a small object against the center of his palm. His thumb is not tucked into the palm, and it is <u>not</u> in opposition to his fingers and does not assist in the grasp. The object may be offered directly to his hand if needed.

Example Observation Opportunities: Observe how the child grasps small objects during play and feeding, e.g., small block, small squeak toy, teething biscuit, or spoon.

Credit: (see also Credit Notes in this strand's preface)
+   usually holds a small object against his palm using all fingers.

4.30   Uses radial palmar grasp   4.5-6

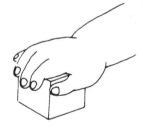

Definition: The child picks up and grasps a small object using his thumb and fingers to hold it against the radial side of his palm. His thumb is in opposition to his fingers.

Example Observation Opportunities: Observe how the child grasps small objects during play, e.g., small block, small squeak toy.

Credit: (see also Credit Notes in this strand's preface)
+   typically uses thumb in opposition to fingers to grasp and hold a small object about the size of a small block, against his palm.

4.40 | ## Attempts to secure tiny object   5.5-7

Definition: The child looks at and tries to pick up a tiny object by placing his palm or fingers on the object. He is usually unsuccessful in securing it unless it incidentally sticks to his hand.

Example Observation Opportunities: <u>Incidental</u> - may be observed when child tries to obtain a bit of food on his tray during feeding, a piece of fuzz on the rug, or other *small*, safe object during daily activities and play. <u>Structured</u> - confirm with the parent that it is okay to offer the child a Cheerio, cookie crumb or other bit of food. Present a tiny food bit on a firm surface with a contrasting color, e.g., tan-colored Cheerio on white or dark-colored highchair tray or table. Tap on the tray next to the food (as needed) to attract child's attention. If he does not attempt to grasp the food, try a different food bit. After a few attempts, help the child secure and taste the object (if approved by the parent), or distract him to a new, more interesting toy.

Credit: (see also Credit Notes in this strand's preface)
   +   looks at and tries to pick up a tiny object, making contact. He does not have to secure it.
   A   uses fist to contact object.

4.44 | ## Rakes tiny object   7-8

Definition: The child obtains a tiny object by moving it with his fingers in a raking or scooping motion into his palm. His thumb is not necessarily used and may be held close to his palm.

Example Observation Opportunities: Same as #4.40.

Credit: (see also Credit Notes in this strand's preface)
   +   can pick up tiny object by raking it into his palm with one or more fingers.
   -    obtains object because it stuck to his palm or fingers rather than using fingers to move it into the palm.

4.43 | ## Uses radial digital grasp   7-9

Definition: The child picks up small objects the size of a small block using his fingertips with thumb in opposition to his index and middle fingers. He no longer needs to hold the object against his palm.

Example Observation Opportunities: Observe how the child grasps small objects during play and feeding, e.g., grasping a small toy, such as a small block or empty thread spool, thick peg in a board, or a cube of food (e.g., cheese, apple).

Credit: (see also Credit Notes in this strand's preface)
   +   typically picks up and holds small objects the size of a block with his thumb and fingertips without using his palm; thumb is in opposition to his fingers.
   A   wrist is held flexed; fingers cross.

4.45 | ## Uses inferior pincer grasp   7.5-10

Definition: The child picks up a tiny object between his thumb and the side of his index finger. His thumb is only beginning to oppose his index finger. He will probably need to support his forearm on the surface.

Example Observation Opportunities: Same as #4.40.

Credit: (see also Credit Notes in this strand's preface)
   +   picks up a tiny object using only his thumb and the side of his index finger at least twice.

4.51 Pokes with index finger   9-12

Definition: The child can isolate his index finger from his other fingers. This is demonstrated by his ability to poke or probe holes with the tip of his index finger. At this stage, his other fingers remain nearby or on the same approximate plane as his index finger, rather than the more advanced skill of holding his fingers close to his palm, as in pointing. This skill helps prepare the child for using a "neat pincer" grasp.

Example Observation Opportunities: Provide the child one or two toys which have interesting holes or crevices, and observe if he pokes or probes while exploring or probing them. Demonstrate if not observed spontaneously. <u>Suggested eliciting toys:</u> Plastic narrow-necked bottle with a pellet inside; dial of a rotary telephone; holes of a thick pegboard; empty egg carton; facial features of doll or stuffed animal.

Credit: (see also Credit Notes in this strand's preface)
+   isolates index finger to poke or probe.

4.52 Uses neat pincer grasp   10-12

Definition: The child can pick up tiny or thin objects using the tips of his index finger and thumb. In contrast to #4.45, his thumb is flexed and in opposition to his index finger and he does not need to rest his forearm on a the surface.

Credit: (see also Credit Notes in this strand's preface)
+   typically picks up tiny or thin items using tip of index finger in opposition to thumb; he does not need to rest his forearm on the surface.

4.55 Grasps crayon adaptively   11-12

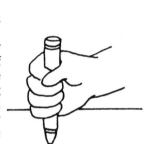

Definition: The child holds a thick crayon in a fist grasp, with his fifth finger usually oriented down towards the paper.

Example Observation Opportunities: <u>Suggested eliciting materials:</u> May use a thick, **non-toxic**, preschool crayon without a wrapper, a piece of chalk or a "Magna Doodle" wand and slate. <u>Incidental</u> - may observe when child is engaged in paper and crayon activities when assessing strand 4-6A, "Pre-writing skills." <u>Structured</u> - demonstrate making a few marks on a sturdy piece of paper in clear view and within easy reach of the child. Offer him the crayon and invite him to try. Place the crayon on the table in front of him with the point of the crayon facing away from him. Observe which hand he uses and how he picks up and grasps the crayon. The child may explore the crayon with some minimal mouthing, but call his attention to the paper or distract him to a new, more interesting toy if mouthing or biting becomes excessive. The "Magna Doodle" may be best to use if child is prone to mouthing.

Credit: (see also Credit Notes in this strand's preface)
+   holds crayon in fisted hand, wrist slightly flexed.
A   wrist is very extended.

4.63 **Points with index finger** **12-16**

Definition: The child can isolate his index finger from the rest of his hand more adeptly than in #4.51 "Pokes with index finger." He can now hold his fingers and thumb close to his hand to make a direct pointing gesture with his index finger.

Example Observation Opportunities: May observe during assessment in #4.51 "Pokes with index finger" and/or while engaged in activities, such as pointing to pictures in a book, pointing to an airplane, finger play songs, flipping a light switch.

Credit: (see also Credit Notes in this strand's preface)

+ can isolate index finger to point while holding remaining fingers and thumb close to palm.

4.78 **Holds crayon with thumb and fingers** **23-25**

Definition: The child can hold a crayon with his thumb and fingers, with fingers nearest to thumb oriented down towards the paper.

Example Observation Opportunities: Same as #4.55.

Credit: (see also Credit Notes in this strand's preface)

+ typically holds a crayon effectively with thumb and fingers when making marks on paper. (He may revert to using a fist grasp if he is trying to make heavy or intense marks.)

4.89 **Holds pencil with thumb and fingers - adult-like grasp** *36-48*

Definition: The child can hold a pencil with his thumb, index and middle fingers. He can use the pencil with fairly good control, but he moves his hand as a unit, rather than isolating his finger movements. The child may sometimes revert to a less mature grasp when purposefully making heavy or intense marks with a crayon.

Example Observation Opportunities: Incidental - may observe when child is engaged in paper and crayon activities when assessing Strand 4-6A, "Pre-writing skills." Structured - demonstrate making a few marks with a pencil on a piece of paper in clear view and within easy reach of the child. Place the pencil on the table within easy reach and invite him to try. Observe which hand he uses and how he picks up, adjusts, and grasps the pencil. May use a short pencil with blunt tip or water-based felt tip coloring pen.

Credit: (see also Credit Notes in this strand's preface)

+ usually holds a pencil with thumb, index and middle fingers to draw; some children who need greater stability may also use ring finger which is often considered an acceptable variation.

4-3 REACH/APPROACH

4.08	1-3	Activates arms on sight of toy
1.11	2-3	Inspects own hands
4.16	2.5-4.5	Reaches toward toy without grasping
4.27	4-5	Reaches for toy followed by momentary grasp
4.29	4.5-5.5	Reaches and grasps object
4.34	5-6	Recovers Object
4.42	7-8.5	Reaches and grasps object with extended elbow
4.49	9-10	Extends wrist
4.57	11-12	Supinates forearm

Family Friendly Interpretation of Strand Concepts, Assessment, & Purpose

We will be observing how your child is learning to use his arms and hands to reach for objects he wants. At first children "reach" only with their eyes, because they haven't quite figured out that they have arms and hands to help them do this. Then as they discover their hands, they begin to use them to reach. At first, the child may not be able to actually get the object because their hand and arm movements are not accurate. At this stage, the child reaches by first moving his arms out to the side and then toward the object, often swiping it instead of actually grasping it. With practice and maturity, the child learns to reach directly for the object and grasp it.

Parent Questions   (Examples)

To help identify the child's unique strengths and needs related to this developmental area:

• What are some of the things you've noticed about how your child uses his arms and hands when he tries to reach for something he wants to touch or play with?

• Has your child ever had long-term use of an IV or other medical needs or equipment that kept him from freely using one or both of his arms to reach for things?

• Does your child seem to use one arm more than the other?

• Have you noticed if your child ever seems to avoid or refuse to use one arm when he reaches for things? *[If so]* Has this been evaluated by a doctor?

• Are there any other important things about the way your child uses his arms and hands to reach for things that I did not mention but you feel are important?

Sample *Functional* Outcome Statements which may be generated by the Family

[Will be dependent upon identified individual child and family needs and should incorporate objectives and activities from other domains]
My child will be able to:
• Pick up his pacifier and bottle when he accidentally drops it;

• Bat at and make his mobile move;
• Reach for things I hand him;
• Reach for me when he wants me to pick him up.

We will know positions that help our child to use his arms and hands to play and eat.

Transactional Assessment

May assess through observation and interview.

Assessment of the Child's Environment

1. Supportive:
[Environments which support/facilitate development in this area]
The child's caregiving environments usually have a few safe and developmentally appropriate toys and other interesting objects placed within easy reach of the child.

2. Compromising:
[Environments which may restrict, compromise, inhibit or be unsupportive toward development in this area]
The child's caregiving environments frequently have:
• Dangerous materials within reach of the child;
• No developmentally appropriate interesting toys or objects for the child to reach and play with.

Assessment of Caregiver Interactions with the Child

1. Supportive:
[Interactions which support/facilitate child's development in this area]
The child's caregivers:
- Frequently place the child in positions which enable him to move his hands and arms freely to reach for toys and other interesting objects during play and feeding;
- Sometimes encourage the child to reach for an object before handing it to him;
- Usually let the child have the objects they hold out to him to play with (rather than taking it away or pulling it back further out of reach)

2. Compromising:
[Interactions which may restrict, compromise, inhibit or be unsupportive of the child's development in this area]
The child's caregivers frequently:
- Place the child in positions which prevent him from reaching;
- Tease or frustrate the child by removing or moving toys or foods further away when the child reaches for them.

Identifying and Interpreting Needs for Intervention

If a child is significantly delayed in this area he may need intervention related to developing <u>adequate motor or visual-motor control needed for reaching</u>.

However, before targeting fine motor control as the primary area for intervention, consider, rule out, or adapt for other causes which may interfere with a true assessment of the child's reaching abilities. These may include:
- <u>Visual impairment</u>: the child may not be motivated to reach or may reach inaccurately because he does not have the visual cues needed for accurate reach. If the child has monocular vision he will have difficulty with depth perception;
- <u>Cognitive delays</u> in the area of "means-ends" (see Strand 1-4B);

- <u>Sensory organization problems</u>, e.g., difficulty processing proprioceptive information, which helps a child direct and position his arms in space; and/or tactile defensiveness which causes the child to pull away from rather than reach for certain textures;
- <u>Lack of adequate opportunities</u> which motivate and help the child practice reaching;
- <u>Lack of interest</u> in the assessment materials or procedures;
- <u>Medical condition or history</u> which imposed significant restrictions on child's positioning and use of arms, such as having long-term use of an IV and/or long-term supine positioning;
- <u>Significant respiratory problems,</u> causing weakness or atypical posturing which prevent reaching.

Assessment Adaptations   (Examples)

[Note any positioning or material adaptations needed to credit and to help plan interventions]
- <u>Visually Impaired</u>
  - It is very important to assess using toys and objects that are familiar to the child. The child may be defensive with new textures or forms. Use a bright or reflective familiar toy that makes a continuous sound while the child is reaching for it, e.g., rattle, music box. Let the child hold and play with each toy <u>before</u> encouraging him to reach.
  - Children who are blind may typically develop reaching skills later than children who have vision, because reaching skills rely heavily on vision.
  - If child is blind, adapt individual items as follows:
    Mark N/A for #4.08 "Activates arms on sight of toy" and #1.11 "Inspects

own hands." However, it is appropriate to assess if the child "inspects" his hands tactually, but he may not do so for a few more months.
    Assess #4.34 "Recovers object" when an object drops on the child's body and or makes a sound; e.g., observe if the child picks up a squeak toy or rattle which drops on his bare leg.
- <u>Motor Impairment:</u> if the child has atypical muscle tone, assess when the child is positioned securely in a seat or the crux of an adult's arm, so that his shoulders and arms are positioned forward, and head is upright and stable. Item #1.11 "Inspects own hands" may be assessed in side-lying. *Consult with an occupational or physical therapist for specific individualized optimal positions.*

General Assessment Procedures & Processes   (apply to all items in this Strand)

1. **Many items in this strand can be observed while observing skills in other fine motor strands** and other developmental domains, e.g., during play in Strand 1-1, during independent feeding in Strand 6-3.
2. **Observe with the child in a well-supported position which enables him to move his hands and arms freely;** he may be supine or sitting. If ATNR is still present, *be sure* to have child positioned with his head in midline.
3. There are two credit columns on the strand checklist for this strand to **note the presence of each item with the child's left and right hands.**
4. If the child does not reach for a toy, **try a few different toys to ensure his lack of reaching is not due to lack of interest.**
5. Describe the skill and eliciting procedures and invite the parent to help observe and/or assess.

+ - A   Credit Notes:

(credit individually for left and right hands):
- **+** child usually displays reaching skills, as defined, during play and daily activities.
- **-** not observed or reported.
- **+ -** appears to be an emerging skill.
- **A** atypical use of hands/arms, to reach e.g., jerky stiff movements; or loose, limp movements.
- **O** circle any credit if environment or interactions compromise or restrict the child's optimal reaching skills, such as inappropriate positioning, lack of safe toys, keeping toy inaccessible. (Refer to Assessment of Caregiver Interactions above.)

Note any adaptations used to credit.

Assessment Materials

- Brightly colored rattles and squeak toys; plastic container (e.g., empty Cool Whip tub, or sour cream container); small blocks or large, empty thread spools.
- Ask parents to suggest or bring the toys or objects their child enjoys.

4.08   Activates arms on sight of toy   1-3

Definition: The child moves or waves his arms randomly in direct response to seeing an interesting object that is within potential reach. He may seem to be "reaching" for it with his eyes.

Example Eliciting Situations: <u>Incidental</u> - may be observed anytime child is lying quietly on his back and parent offers a toy to play. <u>Structured</u> - when the child is lying quietly on his back, hold an interesting toy about 8-12 inches above his chest within his line of vision. Attract his attention to the toy (as needed) by shaking or squeaking it. Avoid competing facial/vocal expressions to help ensure the child is activating his arms to "get" the toy rather than expressing excitement at seeing the person. To confirm that the child is doing this in response to seeing the object rather than excitement at seeing a person, remove the toy; the child's arm movements should stop. Repeat the procedure with a different object. Help him hold or touch the toy after showing it to him.

Credit: (see also Credit Notes in this strand's preface)
- **+** arms usually become active immediately upon seeing a toy and stop when the toy is removed.

1.11   Inspects own hands   2-3

Definition: The child sometimes brings one or both hands into view to watch and explore the movements he can make with his hands and fingers. This helps prepare him for purposeful reaching and develops an awareness of his hand in space. He may watch his hands for up to 1 minute several times a day, but should easily "break out of it" to look at a person or interesting object.

Parent Questions: Have you noticed your child watching his hands as he waves or wiggles them in front of his face? When do you see him doing this? About how often?

Example Eliciting Situations: Hand-watching usually occurs at this age when a child is alone and content lying on his back in a quiet environment. May observe anytime during observation period if setting is conducive.

Credit: (see also Credit Notes in this strand's preface)
- **+** under 5 months and the child sometimes watches movements of his own hands, even briefly.
- **A** over 5 months and the child spends a significant amount of time hand-watching or prefers hand-watching to interacting with people.

(may also credit #1.11 in Strands 1-4C "Cause and Effect" and 5-2 "Development of Self")

4.16 **Reaches toward toy without grasping** 2.5-4.5

Definition: The child reaches toward a desired object using a backhand approach. He may touch or swipe at the object with his hand but cannot grasp it. Around 3 months he can reach for an object held toward his side, keeping his elbow and wrist flexed or bent. Around 4 months he can reach toward his midline with his elbows less flexed and hands partially open, approaching with both arms as a unit.

Example Eliciting Situations: *Observe in supine.* Incidental - may be observed when child is in crib reaching for a mobile or parent's face, as parent leans over to talk; during play when parent holds out a favorite toy. Structured - dangle an attractive toy, such as a rattle or squeak toy, about 6-8 inches from the child's chest. If needed, tap the child's hand with the toy if his hands are out of his direct sight. Observe for several seconds. If the child does not reach for the object positioned at midline, repeat with the toy positioned toward one side near his hand, and then his other side.

Credit: (see also Credit Notes in this strand's preface)

+ at 2.5-3 months, if child can only reach toward a toy positioned toward his side as defined.
+ at 4-4.5 months, if child can reach toward a toy positioned at midline as defined.

(may also credit #4.26 in Strand 4-5 "Bilateral and Midline skills," if he reaches with both arms moving as a unit)

4.27 **Reaches for toy followed by momentary grasp** 4-5

Definition: The child reaches toward an object to make contact. Sometimes he is able to grasp it briefly. At this stage, the child still typically reaches with both arms, elbows somewhat flexed but becoming more extended. His hands are now open, one hand grasping and the other one joining. He may initially under-reach before adjusting his arms to more accurately reach and make contact.

Example Observation Opportunities: *Observe in supine or supported sitting.* Incidental - may observe when child is reaching for a toy dangling from a mobile or crib gym or during play when parent holds out favorite toy. Structured - present an attractive object within reaching distance of the child's chest, about 8-12 inches away. The object should be small enough to grasp with one hand. If needed, tap the child's hand with the toy if his hands are out of his direct sight. If the child does not reach, try a few different toys to ensure his lack of reaching is not due to lack of interest.

Credit: (see also Credit Notes in this strand's preface)

+ reaches and grasps toy momentarily as defined at least half the time.

4.29 **Reaches and grasps object** 4.5-5.5

Definition: The child is successful when he reaches for a small object, grasping and holding it for several seconds. At this stage, the child usually reaches with an angular approach in which both arms move out to the side and then to the object.. His hands are now open, one hand grasping and the other one joining. He may initially under-reach before adjusting to accurately reach and grasp.

Example Observation Opportunities: *Observe in supported sitting.* Place an attractive object within easy reach of the child, e.g., at a table or tray in front of child's chest. The object should be small enough to grasp with one hand, e.g., squeak toy, crumpled paper. If needed, tap the child's hand with the toy and let him hold it if he does not reach for the toy or if his hands are out of his direct sight. Then place the toy on the surface in front of him.

Credit:

+ reaches and grasps an object placed in front of him, holding it for at least 5 seconds. He may initially under-reach but then adjusts to obtain the object.

4.34 **Recovers object** 5-6

Definition: The child picks up and grasps a small object he has dropped. The object needs to be within his visual and reaching range, or to have dropped where he can easily feel and or hear it, e.g., dropping a squeak toy to his side in supine and when he squirms he may feel and hear it squeak.

Example Observation Opportunities: *Observe in supported sitting or supine.* May be observed whenever child drops a small toy or object incidentally, e.g., his pacifier, a block, spoon, squeak toy.

Credit: (see also Credit Notes in this strand's preface)

+ can sometimes recover easy-to-grasp objects which child drops accidentally within easy reach.

4.42   Reaches and grasps object with extended elbow   7-8.5

Definition: The child can reach directly for and grasp an object with a straight arm, i.e., his elbow fully extended at 180 degrees. At this stage, the child can reach with one arm, and he can adapt his trunk to lean forward during reaching.

Example Observation Opportunities: *Observe in supported sitting.* <u>Incidental</u> - may observe anytime during play or feeding when the child is sitting with adequate support and reaching for a toy, food or object which is placed an arm's length away. <u>Structured</u> - offer the child an easy-to-grasp toy at a distance that requires the child to fully extend his arm. If the child does not fully extend his arm, bring the object closer until he is successful to credit earlier reaching skills. When the child has finished playing with the first toy, offer another toy toward his opposite arm.

Credit: (see also Credit Notes in this strand's preface)

+ reaches and grasps an object with his elbow fully extended. His reach should be direct, accurate and smooth.

A continues to move both arms when reaching for a toy which can be held in one hand, and/or, cannot reach toward objects held at midline (refer to Strand 4-5); keeps hand fisted when reaching.

 4.49   Extends wrist   9-10

Definition: The child approaches and grasps small objects with his hands fully open and wrist extended, i.e., bending his hand at his wrist slightly upwards. This enables the child to move his hands independently of his arms for finer motor control when reaching for and manipulating objects.

Example Observation Opportunities: *Observe in a variety of positions* <u>Incidental</u> - may observe anytime during play or feeding when child is reaching for an object, handing an adult his toy, patting his image in the mirror, grasping a small block, reaching for and ringing a bell by its handle. <u>Structured</u> - (1) place the child in a well-supported sitting position in front of a large mirror within the child's reaching distance. Encourage him and demonstrate, as needed, to "pat the baby" in the mirror; and/or (2) Place or hold out an interesting toy with a handle, such as a bell, within the child's reach. Observe if child approaches the mirror or toy with wrist extension. Also observe if child manipulates the toy using wrist extension.

Credit: (see also Credit Notes in this strand's preface)

+ hands appear relaxed and bend freely at the wrist, as defined, when reaching for and grasping objects the size of a small block.

A strongly splays or overextends fingers.

 4.57   Supinates forearm   11-12

Definition: The child can turn his forearms so his palms face upward when he approaches objects. This skill also enables him to reach for objects in mid-supination, i.e., palm facing object with thumb facing upward.

Example Observation Opportunities: *Observe in a variety of stable positions* <u>Incidental</u> - may observe when child is reaching for an object, taking blocks out of a box; "showing" a toy to someone; turning a bell by its handle to look inside; or while playing gesture games, such as "All gone" or "Give me five." <u>Structured</u> - present a toy, such as a brightly colored tennis ball or squeak toy to the child using an overhand grasp to encourage him to reach for it with an underhand grasp.

Credit: (see also Credit Notes in this strand's preface)

+ can easily rotate forearms independently of his upper arms to turn his hands, palms facing upward, to obtain an object, when needed, or incidentally during play.

4-4 DEVELOPMENT OF VOLUNTARY RELEASE

4.13	2-4	Grasps toy actively
4.15	2.5-3.5	Keeps hands open 50 percent of the time
4.20	*4-6*	Grasp reflex inhibited
4.25	4-8	Keeps hands open most of the time
4.33	5-6	Drops object
4.38	5.5-7	Transfers object
4.41	6-8	Manipulates toy actively with wrist movements
1.52	*8-10*	Drops objects systematically
4.50	*9-10*	Releases object voluntarily
4.56	*10-11*	Puts objects in container
4.60	12-13	Puts three or more objects into container
4.67	14-15	Puts many objects in container without removing any
4.84	*15-23*	Puts tiny object into small container

Family Friendly Interpretation of Strand Concepts, Assessment, & Purpose

"Voluntary release" fine motor skills reflect how your child is learning to let go of or purposefully release objects he is holding. Voluntary release involves coordinating and controlling the arm, wrist and hand muscles.

The development of voluntary and purposeful release goes through several stages. During the first few months, children can not purposefully let go of something because they have a grasp reflex that causes them to automatically hold things placed in their hand. When they let go, they are unaware of how this happened. As this reflex begins to fade, release becomes more voluntary.

At first, children need something to place the object against before they can let go of it. For example, they cannot let go of a block in a controlled manner until the block is placed on the table or in someone's hand. Later on, children learn how to let go of things in a controlled manner, in mid-air. For example, a child can drop a block into a coffee can without needing to put his hand in the can. Finally, as grasping and releasing skills become more mature and refined, children learn to release little objects into little holes, such as putting a penny into a piggy bank slot or dropping a raisin into the hole of a plastic bottle.

Parent Questions (Examples)

To help identify the child's unique strengths and needs related to this developmental area:
- Have you noticed how your child lets go of something he's holding, such as a toy or a spoon? Flings it? Tosses it? Suddenly it's just gone? Hands it to you? Lays it down?

To help identify family resources, priorities and concerns related to the child's development in this area:
- Is there anything about the way your child is learning to let go of or release objects that you have concerns about or think is important for your child to learn?

Sample *Functional* Outcome Statements which may be generated by the Family

[Will be dependent upon identified individual child and family needs and should incorporate objectives and activities from other domains]

My child will be able to put things in containers, e.g., his blocks in a box, food in a bowl, toy in his toy box.

We will know ways to help our child let go of things he is holding.

Transactional Assessment

May assess through observation and interview.

Assessment of the Child's Environment

1. Supportive:
[Environments which support/facilitate development in this area]
The child's caregiving environments usually provide opportunities for the child to play with small safe (at least 1.25 inches in size, clean, etc.) objects, toys and containers

2. Compromising:
[Environments which may restrict, compromise, inhibit or be unsupportive toward development in this area]
The child's caregiving environments frequently have:
- Dangerous materials within reach of the child, e.g., objects that are removable, or have removable parts less than 1.25 inches;
- No safe materials or toys accessible.

Assessment of Caregiver Interactions with the Child

1. Supportive:
[Interactions which support/facilitate child's development in this area]
The child's caregivers usually place the child in positions that enable him to move his hands and arms freely during play and feeding.

2. Compromising:
[Interactions which may restrict, compromise, inhibit or be unsupportive of the child's development in this area]
The child's caregivers frequently place the child in positions that prevent him from using his hands to play or eat.

Identifying and Interpreting Needs for Intervention

If a child is significantly delayed or displays consistent atypical development in this strand, he may be having difficulty in <u>coordinating and controlling his arm, wrist and hand muscles needed for controlled release</u>.

   However, before targeting this as the primary area of need for intervention, consider, rule out, or adapt for other causes which interfere with a true assessment of the child's voluntary release skills. These may include:

- <u>Lack of interest in materials</u> or having difficulty attending;
- <u>Delayed or atypical development in other fine motor skills</u>: grasp (Strand 4-2), reach (4-3), bilateral and midline skills (Strand 4-5);
- <u>Visual impairment;</u>
- <u>Inappropriate positioning</u> of child and or materials;
- <u>Delayed cognitive skills</u>, i.e., container and contained relationships (see Strand 1-4);
- <u>Tactually defensive.</u>

Assessment Adaptations   (Examples)

[Note any adaptations needed to qualify credit and help plan interventions]
- If the child has <u>delayed or atypical grasp</u>, consult a pediatric occupational or physical therapist for optimal positioning. Use materials which accommodate the child's current grasping abilities, e.g., larger blocks. Mark N/A for items which require grasping patterns the child has not achieved and for those skills which are not functional items to teach because of severe motor impairments e.g., #4.84 "Puts tiny object into small container."
- If the child is delayed or has <u>difficulty with bilateral or midline skills</u>, may assist or adapt for his affected arm; e.g., for #4.38 "Transfers object," help position arms at midline; for items which involve dropping objects into containers, help hold the container steady.

- If a child is <u>delayed in reaching skills</u>, place objects directly in his hand or positioned within easier reach.
- <u>Visually impaired:</u>
  - Use objects which are high in color and texture contrast with containers and table surface; use objects which will make sounds when dropped.
  - Provide extra time for the child to explore the materials. Physically guide the child (as needed) to drop an object into a container, and let him remove it several times before expecting him to do so independently.
  - To help establish boundaries, the child may continue to release objects against a container's surface rather than releasing it in mid-air.
- <u>Tactually defensive</u>: use materials that you know the child tolerates.

General Assessment Procedures & Processes (apply to all items in this Strand)

1. Assess child's release skills with left and right hands.
2. Be sure the child is positioned with adequate support which enables child to move arms and hands freely. Skills can be assessed in sitting, supported sitting, corner chair, standing at a support or in a prone stander, or side-lying, depending on the child's level of gross motor development, needs, and preferences.
3. Most items in this strand can be assessed spontaneously, when observing the child's play and independent feeding skills.
4. Describe the skill or eliciting procedures and invite family members to help observe and/or assess.

+ - A Credit Notes:

(right and left hand credit columns)
+ child usually displays release skills, as defined, during play and daily activities.
- not observed or reported.
+/- appears to be an emerging skill.
A persistent atypical release pattern, e.g., after about 15 months, always releases with poor or clumsy control, exaggerated finger opening or splaying upon release.
O circle any credit if environment or interactions compromise or restrict child's grasp and release skills, such as inappropriate positioning, lack of safe toys.

[Note any adaptations used to credit. Refer to an occupational therapist if the child displays significantly delayed or atypical development]

Assessment Materials

- Eight to ten small, safe, blocks.
- A variety of other small, <u>safe</u>, objects, such as: large wooden stringing beads, thick pegs, squeak toys.
- Container with at least a 3-inch opening, such as a plastic Cool Whip tub, shoe box, or plastic bowl.
- Container with an opening about 2 inches wide, such as a small plastic cup or small box.

- Container with a narrow neck opening (approximately 1/2 inch in diameter), e.g., a small empty plastic "trial-size" shampoo bottle, small hole punched in the top of a box or other container.
- Tiny *safe*, edible object such as a sugar pellet, Cheerios or raisin, *depending on the child's oral motor abilities and parent preference.*

4.13 Grasps toy actively 2-4

Definition: The child curls his fingers actively around a small toy placed in his hand. At this stage, the child still has a grasp reflex, but his holding is becoming intentional and voluntary.

Example Observation Opportunities: <u>Incidental</u> - may observe anytime someone puts a small graspable toy or object in child's hand. <u>Structured</u> - place a small block, rattle, teether or other *safe* object with a slender handle in the child's hand. If the child quickly drops it, try another toy of different texture and shape.

Credit: (see also Credit Notes in this strand's preface)
+ usually voluntarily holds an object for several seconds before dropping.
- immediately drops or usually holds toy involuntarily due to a grasp reflex; i.e., he holds the rattle in a very tight or strong grasp and you have difficulty removing it.

(may also credit #1.13 "Begins play with rattles" in Strand 1-1, if child shakes, mouths, looks at it)

4.15 Keeps hands open 50 percent of the time 2.5-3.5

Definition: The child holds his hands in a relaxed, partially open position when resting. This is in contrast to earlier fisting.

Example Observation Opportunities: This may be observed best when child is not actively engaged with people or toys. Observe in supine, side-lying, or when held with good support. *[NOTE: If the child's hands are tightly fisted, do not try to pry them open. Refer to a therapist for further evaluation]*

Credit: (see also Credit Notes in this strand's preface)
+ hands appear relaxed when in quiet state at least half of the time.

4.20 Grasp reflex inhibited *4-6*

Definition: The child no longer automatically and strongly grasps with a tight fist every time a stimulus touches his palm.

Example Observation Opportunities: <u>Incidental</u> - may observe anytime during observation period when an object touches child's palm. <u>Structured</u> - place your finger or the handle of rattle against the child's thumb side of his palm to observe how he grasps it.

Credit: (see also Credit Notes in this strand's preface)

+ does <u>not</u> automatically close hand tightly around objects that touch palm.

4.25 Keeps hands open most of the time   *4-8*

Definition: The child typically holds his hands in an open position during rest and when exploring objects.

Example Observation Opportunities: Observe child's hands at rest and when he touches things to explore his environment, e.g., to touch large toys or to explore parent's face or clothes. Child should be well supported (e.g., in prone, supine, held, or in an infant seat), to ensure he does not "fist" as a method to "fix" or hold himself if he feels unstable.

Credit: (see also Credit Notes in this strand's preface)

+ empty hands usually remain open.

+/- hands remain loosely closed.

4.33 Drops object   *5-6*

Definition: As the child's grasp reflex becomes integrated, he is able to release an object either incidentally or more voluntarily when an adult removes it. This is not a true voluntary release but helps the child prepare for one.

Example Observation Opportunities: May observe incidentally when child is holding easy-to-grasp toys. If not observed incidentally, offer the child an interesting toy when he is already holding one to encourage him to drop one.

Credit: (see also Credit Notes in this strand's preface)

+ easily drops at least two different small objects, about the size of a small block, to free up his hand or when he is no longer interested in holding the object.

4.38 Transfers object   *5.5-7*

Definition: The child purposefully moves a small object he is holding in one hand to his empty hand. Initially, at about 5 or 6 months, he may use a two-stage transfer; i.e., his empty hand joins his first hand holding the object, and then his first hand releases it. Thus, there is a brief period when both hands are holding the object and the child's "taking" hand assists in the release by a subtle pull. At around 7 months, his transfer is more adept as he displays a one-stage transfer, i.e., simultaneously releasing with his first hand as he grasps the object with his second hand.

Example Observation Opportunities: <u>Incidental</u> - anytime during play or feeding if the child is observed to transfer an object purposefully from one hand to the other to explore it or to free up his hand to obtain another object, e.g., his cracker during feeding, a block during play. <u>Structured</u> - offer the child a small toy, such as a block or rattle. Objects should be chosen according to the child's grasping abilities. For example, a small object, such as a toy bead or inch cube, may be too small to easily move from hand to hand. Generally, a small toy with a handle or stem (e.g., rattle, toy keys, plastic rings), or one that is flexible (e.g., crumpled paper, squeak toy) is easier to transfer. If the child does not transfer the toy spontaneously after a few minutes, offer a second, equally attractive object to the hand which is already holding an object.

Credit: (see also Credit Notes in this strand's preface)

+ at 7 month level, if the child usually transfers an object directly from one hand to the other (and visa versa); both hands do not hold the object simultaneously during the transferring process.

+/- (or + at the 5-6 month level) if the child usually transfers using a two-stage method as defined.

- no purposeful transfer; may accidentally transfer an object after holding it with both hands for more than a few seconds or has to obviously pull the object out of one hand and cannot transfer back.

(also in Strand 4-5 "Bilateral and Midline Skills")

4.41 Manipulates toy actively with wrist movements   6-8

Definition: The child is able to grasp, explore and manipulate objects by twisting or rotating his forearm and flexing (bending) and straightening his wrist. These maturing wrist movements help the child release objects with more control.

Example Observation Opportunities: Observe when child is shown two or three novel toys which encourage him to manipulate and explore, e.g., a bell with a handle, spoon, or an extra soft animal squeak toy. Observe his wrist and forearm movements as he explores the object and then releases it to pick up another.

Credit: (see also Credit Notes in this strand's preface)

+   rotates forearm and bends wrist when exploring and releasing small objects.

1.52 Drops objects systematically   8-10

Definition: The child drops one or two objects at a time, repeatedly and purposefully, e.g., dropping one or two blocks or pegs on the table or bowl, then picking them back up to drop them again. He is practicing his emerging voluntary release skills.

Parent Questions: At mealtime, does your child ever seem to purposefully drop his spoon or cracker on the tray, pick it up and then do it again?

Example Observation Opportunities: May be observed during play on a hard surface (table or highchair tray), or with a plastic bowl or small tin cookie sheet and about six small objects which invite grasping and dropping, e.g., small blocks, large wooden beads, thread spools, rattles.

Credit: (see also Credit Notes in this strand's preface)

+   sometimes drops an object repeatedly to practice release. Release may be very crude; i.e., he grabs object with whole hand and drops by opening hand without regard for where he is releasing the object.

A   over 1 year and perserverates, i.e., is not interested in <u>doing anything else</u> with the objects.

4.50 Releases objects voluntarily   9-10

Definition: The child purposefully lets go of objects (with control) on a surface or into a large container. Release skills are not refined enough at this stage to release accurately into a small container.

Example Observation Opportunities: <u>Incidental</u> - may observe anytime during observation period, e.g., child handing parent a toy (cup, bottle, etc.) on request; child putting cracker or spoon on tray when finished; helping parent drop bath toys in tub; placing blocks into a shallow box or moving them to another area during play, such as moving them from one pan to another. <u>Structured</u> - give the child a few blocks to play with. If voluntary release is not observed incidentally while he plays, offer him another more interesting toy. If he shows interest but is already holding a block in each hand, suggest and gesture that he put his blocks on the table, pointing to a particular area.

Credit: (see also Credit Notes in this strand's preface)

+   usually releases objects intentionally (with control) on a surface and from mid-air into a large container.

+/- (or credit at 7-8 month level) if release is voluntary but is assisted by pressing the object down on the surface or against the container before releasing it, rather than dropping it in mid-air or placing it on a surface with control.

4.56 Puts objects in container   10-11

Definition: The child can release a small object about the size of a small block into a small container, such as a cup or small bowl. This skill demonstrates both his awareness of "container and contained" relationships and the continued development of controlled voluntary release.

Example Observation Opportunities: <u>Incidental</u> - may observe during mealtime if child puts some of his finger foods into a bowl or cup; during play if he puts toys in a container. <u>Structured</u> - when the child is seated at a support, show him a container and two or three interesting objects or toys. Invite him to play with these objects. Use containers such as a plastic butter or Cool Whip tub, small box, or plastic cup or bowl. The size of the objects should accommodate the child's grasping abilities, e.g., blocks, large wooden stringing beads, thick pegs, squeak toys. After a few minutes of play, invite him to place the objects back in the container if this is not observed spontaneously.

Credit: (see also Credit Notes in this strand's preface)

+   (with or without demonstration) releases one or two objects into a cup-sized container without putting his hand into or leaning it on the container.

Puts three or more objects into container   12-13

Definition: The child can drop at least three small objects consecutively, one at a time, into a small container with precise controlled release. This skill is similar to #4.56 but requires additional persistence and interest to place three or more objects.

Example Observation Opportunities: Same as #4.56.

Credit: (see also Credit Notes in this strand's preface)

+   (with or without demonstration) releases at least three objects consecutively into a cup-sized container without putting his hand into or leaning it on the container.

(also in Strand 1-5 "Spatial Relationships")

Puts many objects in container without removing any   14-15

Definition: The child can drop at least six pellet-sized objects into a container with controlled release and before taking any objects out. This skill also requires persistence, motivation and interest to complete the task. (Note: a pincer grasp is a prerequisite skill.)

Example Observation Opportunities: <u>Incidental</u> - may observe during snack time if child puts several bits of food into a cup. <u>Structured</u> - when the child is seated at a support, provide a small plastic cup and several tiny, edible objects such as Cheerios. Encourage him to drop them in the container before eating them. If he is more interested in eating the edible objects, let him eat a few before encouraging the task.

<u>Make a note of</u> how much structure and encouragement was needed. May target for intervention if child displays voluntary release but became distracted after releasing one or two; or needed more than usual structure and encouragement to continue.

Credit: (see also Credit Notes in this strand's preface)

+   releases four to five Cheerios or other tiny food items in a cup; he should not lean his hand against the edge.

Puts tiny object into small container   *15-23*

Definition: The child's grasp and release skills are controlled and precise enough to put an object the size of a pellet into a narrow-necked bottle or other tiny opening.

Example Observation Opportunities: Demonstrate putting a tiny edible object into a narrow-necked container. Empty it back out and invite the child to try. Let him eat the food bit first if he seems interested, and offer him another. If the child has delays or difficulty with bilateral skills, hold the container as needed. Tiny objects can be a sugar pellet, Cheerios, raisin, dependent upon parental and child preference. Containers can be a small empty plastic "trial-sized" shampoo bottle, or a closed box or other container with a small hole (approximately 1/2 inch in diameter), punched in the top.

Credit: (see also Credit Notes in this strand's preface)

+   releases tiny object into small hole without leaning hand against the container.

4-5 BILATERAL AND MIDLINE SKILLS

4.02	0-2	Moves arms symmetrically
4.07	1-3.5	Brings hands to midline in supine
4.21	3.5-5	Clasps hands
4.23	4-5	Looks with head in midline
4.26	4-5	Reaches for object bilaterally
6.16	4.5-5.5	Places both hands on bottle
4.35	5-6	Retains small object in each hand
4.37	5.5-7	Reaches for object unilaterally
4.38	5.5-7	Transfers object (also in 4-4)
4.46	8.5-12	Bangs two cubes held in hands
1.61	10.5-12	Unwraps a toy
4.54	11-13	Uses both hands freely; may show preference for one
4.68	16-18	Uses both hands in midline - one holds, other manipulates

Family Friendly Interpretation of Strand Concepts, Assessment, & Purpose

We will be observing how your child is learning to use his arms and hands together to play, to reach, or to accomplish a task. At first, children usually cannot use one arm independently of the other, so they move both arms at the same time to do something, even if they only need one arm. For example, when reaching for an object, they reach with both arms even though the object is small enough to grasp with one hand. Later, they learn to use each arm and hand independently of the other so that they can, for example, reach for a small object with just one arm instead of moving both arms at the same time. Finally, in addition to being able to use each hand separately, children learn that they can use each hand to do different things at the same time. For example, a child learns he can hold his cereal bowl with one hand while he uses his other hand to hold the spoon.

Also included in these skills are what professionals term "midline" skills, which are closely related to using both hands together in a cooperative way. These are skills that involve a child's ability to bring his hands together at midline or together at his chest or mouth. Being able to bring hands together at midline is important in order to allow one hand to interact well with the other. After a child is able to bring his hands to midline, he learns how to reach across midline to play with or get something which is on his other side.

During the first couple of years, children generally use each hand equally as well. Although a child may seem to prefer one hand more than another, he usually does not develop true "left-handedness" or "right-handedness" until later.

Parent Questions (Examples)

To help identify the child's unique strengths and needs related to this developmental area:
- What are some of the things you've noticed about the way your child uses his arms and hands to play, eat, or reach for things?
- What kinds of things have you noticed that your child can do especially well with his hands?
- Have you noticed some things your child tries to do with his hands that he seems to be having some difficulty with?

[More specific as appropriate]
- Have you ever seen your child bring his hands or toys to his mouth?
- Has your child ever had long-term use of an IV or other medical needs or equipment which kept him from freely using one or both of his arms?

- Does your child seem to use one hand more than the other?
- Does he ever seem to avoid or refuse to use one hand or arm more than the other? *(If so)* Has this been evaluated by a doctor?
- Are there any other important things about the way your child uses his arms and hands which I did not mention, but that you feel are important?

To help identify family resources, priorities and concerns related to the child's development in this area:
- If you could think of one thing that you'd like to see your child be able to do better using both hands, what would that be? What have you tried so far that seems to help? Are there things you've tried that haven't seemed to help?

Sample *Functional* Outcome Statements which may be generated by the Family

[Will be dependent upon identified individual child and family needs and should incorporate objectives and activities from other domains]
We will know ways to help our child use both hands to:
• Eat;

• Play;
• Dress.

My child will be able to:
• Feed himself;
• Hold his own bottle;
• Clap hands when we play "Pat-a cake."

Transactional Assessment

May assess through observation and interview.

Assessment of the Child's Environment

1. Supportive:
[Environments which support/facilitate development in this area]
The child's caregiving environments usually:
• Provide ample opportunities to hold and play with safe, developmentally appropriate toys;

2. Compromising:
[Environments which may restrict, compromise, inhibit or be unsupportive toward development in this area]
The child's caregiving environments frequently do not have any safe easy-to-grasp toys accessible to the child.

Assessment of Caregiver Interactions with the Child

1. Supportive:
[Interactions which support/facilitate child's development in this area]
The child's caregivers usually:
• Position the child in ways that help him use his hands and arms freely; e.g., feeding and play positions provide adequate support to trunk and head; child is positioned with arms forward;
• Help the child reach and hold safe toys and objects if he needs help.

2. Compromising:
[Interactions which may restrict, compromise, inhibit or be unsupportive of the child's development in this area]
The child's caregivers frequently:
• Do not vary the child's position;
• Position the child so it is difficulty for him to bring his arms forward;
• Try to make the child be "right-handed" or "left-handed."

Identifying and Interpreting Needs for Intervention

If a child is significantly delayed or demonstrates consistent atypical development in bilateral or midline skills, this may be due to <u>poor upper extremity coordination or difficulty processing information between cerebral hemispheres.</u>

However, before targeting bilateral and midline skills as the primary area of need for intervention, consider, rule out, or adapt for other causes which may be causing the delays and warrant intervention. These may include:
• <u>Medical condition or history</u> which imposed significant restrictions on child's positioning and use of arms, such as having long-term use of an IV and/or long-term supine positioning;

• <u>Delayed or atypical development in other fine motor skills:</u> Grasp (Strand 4-2), Reach (Strand 4-3);
• <u>Lack of interest</u> in the assessment materials or procedures;
• <u>Significant respiratory problems,</u> causing weakness or atypical posturing of the child's arms.
• <u>Visually impaired:</u> Skills #4.26 "Reaches for object bilaterally" and #4.37 "Reaches for object unilaterally" typically may be delayed because the child does not have the visual motivation or cues to reach;
• <u>Hypersensitive to touch:</u> the child may refuse or become upset when he touches or holds certain textures.

Assessment Adaptations   (Examples)

[Note any positioning or material adaptations needed to credit and to help plan interventions]
- Motor Impairment:
    - If child has diagnosed hemiplegia or nerve damage which affects the use of one arm, help position the child's affected arm at midline and place the object in his hand. Observe the child's functional ability to use and maintain his hands at midline, noting the adaptive strategies employed.
    - If the child has atypical muscle tone, assess bilateral and midline skills while the child is positioned in a seat or the crux of an adult's arm so that his shoulders and arms are positioned forward. Some items may be assessed in side-lying (skill #'s 4.07, 4.21, 4.26, 6.16, 4.35, 4.37, 4.38). *Consult with an occupational or physical therapist for specific individualized optimal positions.*
    - If the child has a severe motor disability, some items may cause frustration and are not likely to be functional for him in curriculum planning. *Consult with a therapist to determine which skills in this strand are not appropriate to assess and to help*

assess and plan for adapted or alternative activities that are more likely to lead to the development of functional skills.
- Visually Impaired:
    - It is very important to assess using toys and objects which are familiar to the child. The child may be defensive with new textures or forms. Familiar toys that make sounds may work best.
    - If the child is under a year and not reaching due to visual problems, do not consider items #4.26 and #4.37 when determining the child's estimated age range of bilateral and midline skills.
    - If hand-clasping or bringing hands to midline is not observed spontaneously, ask the parent to initially help him do this, for example, by playing "Pat-a-cake" or other game. Observe if the child is able to easily bring his hands to midline with assistance and if he can maintain that position independently after the parent reduces assistance.
- Tactile sensitivity: only use toys you know the child can tolerate.

General Assessment Procedures & Processes   (apply to all items in this Strand)

1. **Many items in this strand can be observed while observing skills in other fine motor strands and other developmental domains**, e.g., during play in Strand 1-1, during independent feeding in Strand 6-3.
2. **The child should be in a well-supported position which enables him to move his hands and arms freely; he may be supine or sitting. If ATNR is still present,** *be sure to have child positioned with his head in midline.*
3. **Describe the skill or eliciting procedures and invite the parent to help observe and/or assess.**

+ - A **Credit Notes:**

+   child usually displays bilateral and midline skills, as defined, during play and daily activities.

-     not observed or reported.

+/- appears to be an emerging skill.

A   atypical use of hands/arms, e.g., asymmetrical; avoids one arm; jerky, stiff or loose movements*.

O   circle any credit if environment or interactions compromise or restrict child's optimal bilateral or midline skills, such as inappropriate positioning, lack of safe toys. (Refer to Assessment of Caregiver Interactions above.)

Note any adaptations used to credit.
[* If a child displays atypical or significantly delayed bilateral or midline skills, he should be referred to a pediatric occupational or physical therapist]

Assessment Materials

Two or three easy-to-grasp toys (e.g., brightly colored rattles, rings, toy keys, squeak toy, Koosh™ ball); child's bottle, two or three small blocks; tissue or other paper (to wrap

up small toy); two or three toys which encourage use of two hands, e.g., blocks, spoon and cup; doll and comb or spoon; book, crayon and paper.

Moves arms symmetrically   0-2

Definition: The child moves both arms equally in a random but smooth manner. He does <u>not</u> use one arm significantly more than the other, or avoid or neglect using one arm. Other body parts may move simultaneously; e.g., legs may kick, head may turn.

Example Observation Opportunities: This may be observed incidentally when the child is in active alert state in unrestricted clothing lying on his back, especially when he initially sees a familiar face or interesting object.

Credit: (see also Credit Notes in this strand's preface)
+   typically moves each arm equally and as much as the other.
A   only moves one arm, or one arm moves significantly more than the other.

(may also credit #4.08 (Strand 4-3) if this occurs in direct response to seeing a desired object; and #1.08 (Strand 5-4) if arms are waved in apparent anticipatory excitement.)

Brings hands to midline in supine   1-3.5

Definition: The child can bring his hands together to the middle of his body near his face or chest.

Example Observation Opportunities: <u>Incidental</u> - this can typically be observed spontaneously while child is in active or quiet alert state in unrestricted clothing, lying supine. It may be especially apparent when a bottle or toy is presented at midline or if the child brings his hands to his mouth. <u>Structured</u> - position the child in supine with his head in midline. Play a game of "Pat-a-cake", or gently rub the child's hands together. Pause to see if he'll naturally assume this position. If the child does not easily bring his hands to midline in supine, position him in an infant seat or cradled in adult's arms with child's arms free to move.

Credit: (see also Credit Notes in this strand's preface)
+   brings <u>both</u> hands to midline as defined. The child may be supine or supported sitting in an infant seat or held cradled. Both arms should move symmetrically. He does not have to clasp hands and his hands may still be fisted.

(may also credit #4.21 if child "Clasps hands.")

(may also credit #4.07 in Strand 3-2, but <u>only if</u> child does this in supine.)

Clasps hands   3.5-5

Definition: The child sometimes holds his hands together in midline at rest and fingers one hand with the other as exploratory play. This skill helps the child prepare for later transferring.

Example Observation Opportunities: Observe incidentally when the child, empty-handed, is in active or quiet alert state. He should be in unrestricted clothing and may be positioned in prone, supine or supported sitting. Observations may be more successful when child is looking quietly at his mobile or a toy while others are not directly distracting or interacting with him.

Credit: (see also Credit Notes in this strand's preface)
+   easily brings hands together at midline to clasp at least once during observation period.
A   hands are tightly fisted.

Looks with head in midline   4-5

Definition: The child can easily turn and maintain his head at midline to look directly in front of him.

Example Observation Opportunities: Observe child when he is lying on his back and in supported sitting during play, while resting, or when looking at things held above his chest, e.g., watching his mobile, when parent presents his bottle.

Credit: (see also Credit Notes in this strand's preface)
+   spontaneously and easily brings and maintains head at midline.
A   arms and legs are not symmetrical.

(also in Strand 3-2 "Supine")

4.26 **Reaches for object bilaterally   4-5**

Definition: The child reaches for a desired object by moving both arms as a unit, even though the object can be held in one hand. At this stage, a child usually cannot move one arm independently from the other.

Example Observation Opportunities: Incidental - should observe many times during observation periods when child is supported sitting or in supine, e.g., child in crib reaching for a mobile or adult's face, as adult leans over to talk; during play or feeding, when parent holds out favorite toy or bottle. Structured - present a small toy about 8 inches away from the child's chest; squeak or rattle toys may work best. If needed, tap the child's hand with the toy if his hands are out of his direct sight, e.g., lying at his side.

Credit: (see also Credit Notes in this strand's preface)

+   moves both arms as a unit to reach for objects during play or feeding. He does not need to grasp object.

N/A if child is over 6 months, and can reach with either arm, but only uses one arm at a time to reach for small objects.

6.16 **Places both hands on bottle   4.5-5.5**

Definition: The child spontaneously or with initial prompting, periodically places both hands on a bottle held for him during feeding.

Parent Questions: Does your child sometimes put his hands on his bottle while you are feeding him? Does he use both hands at the same time? Does he keep his hands open or closed? About how long does he keep his hands there?

Example Observation Opportunities: May observe incidentally during feeding. If child is breast fed, may substitute item by observing if child holds a toy with both hands.

Credit: (see also Credit Notes in this strand's preface)

+   places both hands on bottle (or on top of parent's hands holding bottle) for a few seconds. This should be more than just a brief pat. He does not have to control /support the weight of the bottle.

(also in Strand 6-3 "Independent Feeding")

4.35 **Retains small object in each hand   5-6**

Definition: The child can hold a small object in each hand for several seconds. At this stage, the child may pick up the first object, but he may need to have the second object placed in his hand.

Example Observation Opportunities: Incidental - may observe when two or three interesting objects or toys are immediately available, e.g., during play - toy keys, small blocks, piece of crumpled paper; during dressing or diapering - if child holds one sock in each hand; during feeding - when child is holding a cracker and then picks up another. Structured - while the child is holding a toy in one hand, offer a second, equally attractive toy toward his empty hand. If he incidentally drops the first, help him (as needed) pick it back up. Objects should be lightweight and easy-to-grasp in one hand, e.g., rattle, squeak toy, crumpled paper, small block.

Credit: (see also Credit Notes in this strand's preface)

+   holds an object in each hand for a few seconds on at least two occasions.

(may also credit #4.38 if child transfers one toy to obtain the second and/or #4.46 if he purposefully bangs the two objects together at midline)

4.37 **Reaches for object unilaterally   5.5-7**

Definition: The child can reach for a small object with one arm rather than moving both arms as a unit (as in #4.26 "Reaches toward object bilaterally"). This demonstrates that he is able to disassociate his shoulder movements, which enables him to use each arm independently. Note: if the object is too large to be held in one hand, he may appropriately use both arms to reach and grasp.

Example Observation Opportunities: Incidental - may observe anytime during play or feeding when the child is reaching for a toy or food. Observe if he can reach with each arm unilaterally. Structured - when the child is sitting well-supported on parent's lap or infant seat, offer an easy-to-grasp toy toward one side of the child, shaking or squeaking the toy, as needed, to attract attention. After letting the child play a little with the first toy, offer another toy toward his opposite arm.

Credit: (see also Credit Notes in this strand's preface)

+   usually reaches for a small toy using only one arm. He should be able to reach unilaterally with each arm, equally as well by about 7 months.

A   non-reaching arm always makes associated or mirroring movements when other arm reaches.

4.38 Transfers object 5.5-7

Definition: The child purposefully moves a small object he is holding in one hand to his empty hand. Initially, at about 5 or 6 months, he may use a two-stage transfer; i.e., his empty hand joins his first hand holding the object and then his first hand releases it. Thus, there is a brief period when both hands are holding the object, and the child's "taking" hand assists in the release by a subtle pull. At around 7 months, his transfer is more adept as he displays a one-stage transfer, i.e., simultaneously releasing with his first hand as he grasps the object with his second hand.

Example Observation Opportunities: <u>Incidental</u> - anytime during play or feeding if the child is observed to transfer an object purposefully from one hand to the other to explore it or to free up his hand to obtain another object, e.g., his cracker during feeding, a block during play. <u>Structured</u> - offer child a small toy, such as a block or rattle. Objects should be chosen according to the child's grasping abilities. For example, a small object, such as a toy bead or inch cube may be too small to easily move from hand to hand. Generally, a small toy with a handle or stem (e.g., rattle, toy keys, plastic rings) or one that is flexible (e.g., crumpled paper, squeak toy) is easier to transfer. If the child does not transfer the toy spontaneously after a few minutes, offer a second, equally attractive object to the hand which is already holding an object.

Credit: (see also Credit Notes in this strand's preface)
+   at 7 month level, if the child usually transfers an object directly from one hand to the other (and visa versa); both hands do not hold the object simultaneously during the transferring process.
+/-   (or + at the 5-6 month level) if the child usually transfers using a two-stage method as defined.
-    no purposeful transfer; may accidentally transfer an object after holding it with both hands for more than a few seconds.

(also in Strand 4-4 "Voluntary Release")

4.46 Bangs two cubes held in hands 8.5-12

Definition: The child is able to bang two small objects together at midline, one held in each hand. His arm movements should be symmetrical, i.e., both arms move toward the center of his body in a fairly smooth fashion.

Example Observation Opportunities: Offer the child two small toys, such as two blocks, small plastic cups, or rings from a ring-stack toy. If he does not spontaneously bang them together during a brief exploration period, demonstrate playing "Pat-a-cake" with two similar toys, or the same toys, if he puts them down. Invite the child to copy your motions.

Credit: (see also Credit Notes in this strand's preface)
+   brings both objects together at midline, moving both arms.

1.61 Unwraps a toy 10.5-12

Definition: The child uses both hands to obtain a loosely wrapped object he has watched being wrapped. He may tear, shake or pull the paper off.

Example Observation Opportunities: When the child shows interest in a small toy, cookie, etc., let him watch you wrap it in wax paper or a napkin. Wrap it loosely by twisting or folding the paper. Invite him to open it. If the child is delayed in object permanence, use a transparent wrap or use a toy that makes sounds.

Credit: (see also Credit Notes in this strand's preface)
+   unwraps the toy, using both hands in any cooperative manner without help.

4.54 **Uses both hands freely; may show preference for one   11-13**

Definition: The child uses both hands easily during play and daily activities. Although he may begin to use one hand more than the other, or assign different tasks to each (e.g., using his right hand as the manipulator and left hand as the holder), he should <u>not</u> neglect or show a strong preference for one.

Example Observation Opportunities: May be observed throughout assessment period, e.g., during play - holding a ball or book with both hands, holding a box while dropping in blocks; during feeding - eating a cracker with one hand while resting his other hand on the tray, wiping tray with a cloth, alternating hands; during dressing - using both arms/hands cooperatively.

Credit: (see also Credit Notes in this strand's preface)
+ can use each hand during activities which require one or two hands; does NOT neglect or avoid using one hand.

4.68 **Uses both hands in midline - one holds, other manipulates   16-18**

Definition: The child uses both hands cooperatively at midline to complete a task. He uses one hand as the "place-holder" to hold the object and the other hand to manipulate or explore it. Hand dominance may become evident around this time, so the manipulative hand is usually the child's dominant hand.

Example Observation Opportunities: <u>Incidental</u> - may be observed: during play - child brushing a small doll's hair, putting blocks in a can held by the other hand, holding the stick or base of a ring-stack toy and putting rings on it, holding a toy telephone–one hand holds receiver/base while the other hand tries to dial; during feeding–child stirring a spoon inside a cup, dabbing jelly on a piece of toast; during bath–pouring water from one cup to another. <u>Structured</u> - demonstrate a two-part activity and then invite the child to try, e.g., putting blocks in a cup, brushing a doll's hair, pouring sand from one cup to another, turning the key of a simple wind-up toy, unscrewing a loose lid.

Credit: (see also Credit Notes in this strand's preface)
+ typically uses both hands at midline cooperatively, using one as a holder and one as a manipulator (when needed) to make a task easier. Note if the child happens to consistently choose one hand as the manipulator.

4.0 FINE MOTOR

Section II. Perceptual-Motor: "Integration of Fine Motor Foundations"

Overview

The remaining fine motor strands build upon and are dependent on the child's ability to integrate prerequisite foundation skills that were developed in Part I, i.e., visual responses and tracking, bilateral and midline skills, reach/approach, grasp/prehension and release skills. In addition to skilled hand movements, these skills require motor planning to implement goal-directed fine motor movements

   NOTE: If a child has severe motor impairments, many of these items will be frustrating and not appropriate to include in curriculum assessment or planning as they are not likely to be enjoyable or functional life skills. Items which are considered inappropriate for assessment and planning should be marked N/A (Not Applicable). *Consult with a physical and occupational therapist to identify alternative functional and enjoyable skills and appropriate adaptations.*

   For example, stringing beads or turning pages of a book singly, using a pincer grasp would be an inappropriate skill to assess or include in an intervention plan for a child who has severe cerebral palsy. However, since these skills can be important for later daily living (e.g., stringing shoelaces, reading books), it would be more meaningful and appropriate to assess and plan for the child to learn to use other fasteners, such as Velcro tabs, and to use adaptive equipment, such as special page turners.

   This section includes the following strands:
   4-6 Spatial Perception and Planning
       A. Pre-writing
       B. Block Construction
       C. Formboard
       D. Paper activities
   4-7 Manipulative Prehension
       A. Pages
       B. Pegboard
       C. Stringing Beads
       D. Scissors

   Strand 4-6 "Spatial Perception and Planning", includes fine motor skills which rely heavily upon visual discrimination, spatial relationships and accuracy of hand movements, as well as motor planning, such as the ability to interpret, plan and reconstruct drawings and block structures.

   Strand 4-7 "Manipulative Prehension", includes coordinated fine motor skills. They rely heavily on the ability to incorporate a variety of hand movements to complete a task, including the ability to separate and move fingers in different directions, as well as depth perception, bilateral skills and motor planning to carry out the activity.

4-6 SPATIAL PERCEPTION AND PLANNING

A. PRE-WRITING

4.36	5.5-7	Watches adult scribble
4.53	10.5-12	Tries to imitate scribble
4.59	12-13	Marks paper with crayon
4.65	13-18	Scribbles spontaneously
4.71	18-24	Imitates vertical stroke
4.73	20-24	Imitates circular scribble
4.75	24-30	Imitates horizontal stroke
4.82	24-36	Imitates a cross
4.83	24-35	Makes first designs or spontaneous forms
4.86	25-36	Copies a circle

Family Friendly Interpretation of Strand Concepts, Assessment, & Purpose

We will be observing how your child uses a crayon to mark on paper. Scribbling and drawing require good eye-hand coordination and help your child learn that he can cause something to happen on the paper by moving the crayon on it. *[Continue for children whose developmental skills are over 18 months]*

We will also be observing how your child is learning to imitate or copy simple lines as he watches an adult draw a line. This helps us understand how your child is learning to "take in" what he sees and then be able to reproduce it.

These skills help your child prepare for later writing skills and also help him feel proud that he can create things!

Parent Questions   (Examples)

To help identify the child's unique strengths and needs related to this developmental area:
• Has your child ever played with crayons before?
    If not, Would it be okay if we let him try using a crayon today?
• *If so,* What types of things have you seen your child do with a crayon and paper?

To help identify family resources, priorities and concerns related to the child's development in this area:
• Are you interested in your child's learning to use crayons and paper at this age?
[Some families may prefer not to have child play with crayons. If the parent is concerned about coloring on the walls, eating the crayon, etc., ask if it is okay to introduce alternatives such as a "Magna Doodle" (magic slate-type toy). If not, mark N/T for not tested, noting parent preference, if applicable]
• *If so,* Are there certain times during the day that would work best for your child to play with crayons?

Sample *Functional* Outcome Statements which may be generated by the Family

[Will be dependent upon identified individual child and family needs and should incorporate objectives and activities from other domains]

My child will:
• Enjoy coloring;
• Be able to imitate drawing simple lines.

Transactional Assessment

May assess through observation and interview.

Assessment of the Child's Environment

1. Supportive:
[Environments which support/facilitate development in this area]

The child's caregiving environments:
• Sometimes have appropriate crayons and paper for the child to play with.

Assessment of Caregiver Interactions with the Child

1. Supportive:
[Interactions which support/facilitate child's development in this area]
The child's caregivers:
• Praise the child for his "artwork";
• Position the child and materials so that the child can use them easily;
• Supervise the child's coloring activities and sometimes join in.

2. Compromising:
[Interactions which may restrict, compromise, inhibit or be unsupportive of the child's development in this area]
The child's caregivers frequently:
• Make negative remarks about the child's drawings;
• Leave the child unsupervised with crayons.

Identifying and Interpreting Needs for Intervention

If a child is significantly delayed in this area, he may be having difficulty in <u>coordinating accurate eye-hand movements and or spatial planning</u>. *Refer to an occupational therapist for further evaluation and intervention recommendations.*

<u>However</u>, before targeting eye-hand coordination and spatial planning problems as the primary need for intervention or referral, consider, rule out, or adapt for other causes which may interfere with a true assessment of the child's pre-writing

abilities. These may include:
• <u>Atypical or delayed grasp</u> (see Strand 4-2);
• <u>Gross motor impairment</u>;
• <u>Visual impairment</u>;
• <u>Cognitive delays in the area of play schemes and or cause and effect</u>;
• <u>Poor position of child or materials</u>;
• <u>Difficulty attending to the task</u>;
• <u>Lack of interest or experience</u>.

Assessment Adaptations (Examples)

[Note any adaptations needed to credit and help plan interventions]
• <u>Motor Impairments</u>: *Consult with a physical and/or occupational therapist for optimal positioning of the child and materials, as well as adapted equipment.* It may be inappropriate to assess this area of fine motor development (refer to the NOTE in the Fine Motor II Overview - page 250.) The following general strategies may be helpful for some children:
– If the child has compromised use of one hand/arm (e.g., hemiplegia), tape the paper down on the surface or let him mark on something stable, such as a washable tray or table top.
– Try using a tilted surface, e.g., tilt board or easel; vary the degree of the tilt to identify the best position for the child.
– Position the child in supported standing or sitting using adaptive equipment.
– Try using chubby crayons, beveled crayons, or a pencil grip.
– A variety of adaptive materials are available for children who can not grasp a crayon or pencil, e.g., writing orthosis, wrist supports, pencil holders, weighted or contoured pens. Consult with an occupational therapist for individualized suggestions.
– Help the child position his arm to the writing surface.

– Position the crayon in the child's hand, pointing toward the surface.
• <u>Visually impaired</u>:
– For children with low vision, use high-contrast markers on glare-free surfaces, e.g., use a black crayon on yellow construction paper. It may be helpful to let the child stand at an easel, or place the paper in a tray with low edges to provide boundaries.
– If the child has total or severe vision loss, place a screen or other heavy-textured material under the paper. When the child marks on the paper, he will create a tactile line. Allow the child to feel the line. For items which require the child to imitate or copy strokes, make a tactile line as you describe the motion, e.g., "down", across", "around and around", "circle", and let the child tactually explore it. The child should not be expected to accomplish these tasks in the same time a child with vision does. It would thus be inappropriate to assign a developmental age for this strand based on children who have vision.
• <u>Poor attention or lack of interest</u>: Try using novel and varied colored crayons and paper or a "Magna-Doodle" in a quiet environment.

General Assessment Procedures & Processes   (apply to all items in this Strand)

1. **Lay the crayon on the paper in front of the child, and allow him to choose which hand to use**; note which hand child prefers, if any.
2. The child should be in a position which **promotes good posture and enables him to move his arms and hands freely**; for later skills, this should generally be in a seated position, with his feet flat on the floor, and his trunk supported by the back of the chair. Some children who do not have delayed or atypical motor development may prefer to stand or sit on the floor.
3. **May assess child's prehension skills** (Strand 4-2) while assessing this strand.
4. **Describe the skill or eliciting procedures and invite family members to help observe and/or assess.**

+ - A   Credit Notes:

+   child usually displays pre-writing skills as defined.

-    not observed or reported.

+/-   appears to be an emerging skill, e.g., displayed once, or attempted imitation but did not meet criteria for crediting.

A   atypical: displays skill, but child exhibits poor or atypical quality, e.g., exerts such extreme pressure with crayon on paper that the crayon breaks; cannot judge where to make the line and usually goes off paper.

O   circle any credit if environment or inter-actions compromise or restrict child's optimal pre-writing skills, such as safe crayons are not available at home.

[Note any adaptations used to credit. If the child displays a significant delay or several atypical credits, refer to an occupational therapist]

Assessment Materials

• Several sheets of heavy white paper;
• Drawing utensil of child's choice and/or grasp-ing abilities: chubby or thin crayons, primary pencil, felt tip washable colored marking pen.

4.36   Watches adult scribble   5.5-7

Definition: Although the child typically cannot use a crayon at this age, he demonstrates his interest as he watches an adult scribble. This interest can be thought of as a prerequisite to his later scribbling.

Example Observation Opportunities: <u>Incidental</u> - may observe child looking at your paper as you take notes during the assessment; child watching when parent is filling out forms, coloring with an older sibling etc. <u>Structured</u> - attract the child's attention to a blank paper placed in front of him. Make bold marks with a dark crayon using inviting verbal description; e.g., "See the line go around and around and around!" Let him play with the paper if he is interested.

Credit: (see also Credit Notes in this strand's preface)
   +   watches someone making marks on the paper for at least a few seconds.
(may also credit #1.23 in Strand 1-1 "Play Schemes", if child "Plays with paper")

4.53   Tries to imitate scribble   10.5-12

Definition: After watching someone scribble, the child makes a definite attempt to scribble. His attempts are usually brief, light marks, although as the crayon makes contact with the paper, it may not leave any visible marks.

Example Observation Opportunities: <u>Incidental</u> - may observe in a free play situation. If child chooses to play with or shows interest in paper and crayons, make a scribble and offer him the materials to explore. <u>Structured</u> - attract the child's attention to blank paper placed in front of him. Make bold marks with a dark crayon using inviting verbal description, e.g., "See the line go around and around and around!" Invite the child to try. Help the child grasp crayon adaptively, and hold paper down as needed.

Credit: (see also Credit Notes in this strand's preface)
   +   makes any effort to imitate marking on paper as long as there is some contact with the crayon on paper. Marks do not need to be visible.
(may also credit #4.59 if several definite visible marks are produced)

4.59

Marks paper with crayon   12-13

Definition: The child makes visible marks on a paper with a crayon, using a back-and-forth motion. At this stage, the marks are typically short and wavy lines.

Example Observation Opportunities: Same as #4.53.

Credit:

+   makes at least three visible marks on the paper with or without demonstration.

4.65

Scribbles spontaneously   13-18

Definition: The child scribbles on his own accord without needing a demonstration. His scribble marks are more definable than #4.59, with repetitive line and circular patterns. [*These repetitive marks demonstrate that he is learning to imitate or copy his own marks, which help prepare him for later copying skills*]

Example Observation Opportunities: Attract the child's attention to the paper and crayon. Invite him to "draw a picture," but do not provide a demonstration.

Credit: (see also Credit Notes in this strand's preface)

+   scribbles spontaneously with definite marks.

4.71

Imitates vertical stroke   18-24

Definition: The child purposefully makes an upward or downward stroke in a general vertical direction after watching an adult draw a vertical stroke.

Example Observation Opportunities: After interest in paper/crayon activities has been established with the child, e.g., following #4.65 "Scribbles spontaneously," introduce a new blank paper with enthusiasm (to attract child's interest). Let the child use the crayon he already has, and you use your own crayon. While the child is watching, draw a vertical stroke, marking from the top of the paper down toward the child. Emphasize the direction of the stroke by exaggerating your downward movement and saying, "down" or "zip." Demonstrate this once or twice, and invite the child to try with his crayon, e.g., say, "It's your turn!" as you point to a blank space next to your line. Repeat two more times.

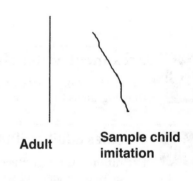

Adult   **Sample child imitation**

Credit: (see also Credit Notes in this strand's preface)

+   imitates a definite stroke, at least twice, in the general vertical direction of the demonstrated model. The line may overlap or be longer or shorter than the model, but it should have a beginning and an end, and be drawn within about a 30 degree angle of the demonstrated line.

 4.73

Imitates circular scribble   20-24

Definition: After watching someone scribble in continuous circles, the child imitates a similar circular scribble.

Example Observation Opportunities: If the child is still interested, this item can be administered directly after #4.71 "Imitates vertical stroke," or after he is engaged in spontaneous play with crayons and paper. Move to a blank part of the paper and demonstrate scribbling, using a definite repetitive circular line. May use a concurrent verbal prompt, such as "around and around and around." Invite the child to "go around and around" with his crayon as you point to a blank space on the paper next to your scribble, which remains in clear view.

Credit: (see also Credit Notes in this strand's preface)

+   imitates a circular scribble.

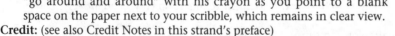

4.75 **Imitates horizontal stroke** *24-30*

Definition: After watching someone draw a horizontal line, the child can switch the direction of his marks to imitate a horizontal stroke.

Example Observation Opportunities: When the child is making marks on his paper; e.g., after #4.71 "Imitates vertical stroke" or #4.73 "Imitates circular scribble," move to a blank part of the paper and draw a horizontal stroke while he is watching. Use a concurrent verbal description, such as, "Now try this...across... (or, 'zoom')." If you are sitting facing the child, draw your line from right to left; if sitting next to or behind child, draw from left to right. Invite the child to try with his crayon, as you point to a blank space next to your mark.

Credit: (see also Credit Notes in this strand's preface)

+ imitates a stroke in any horizontal direction (left to right or right to left); stroke may be longer or shorter than the demonstration and may not be exactly horizontal, but it is clearly different than the marks he was making before you demonstrated a horizontal stroke.

4.82 **Imitates a cross** *24-36*

Definition: After watching an adult draw a + (cross/plus sign), the child imitates drawing a similar cross.

Example Observation Opportunities: While the child is looking and interested, present a clean piece of paper and draw a cross, starting with a vertical line and then the horizontal. Describe your marks as you make the cross, e.g., "Down and across to make a cross!." Invite the child to try, pointing to a blank space next to your cross. Repeat the demonstration one or two more times as needed.

Credit: (see also Credit Notes in this strand's preface)

+ imitates drawing a cross by intersecting two lines; may look more like an X than a cross, and the lines may be uneven.

+ credit at 36 months, if the rotation of the lines are closer to a + than an X, even if the lines are longer, shorter or uneven.

4.83 **Makes first designs or spontaneous forms** *24-35*

Definition: The child, without demonstration, makes definite and purposeful controlled markings that look as if he is trying to make pictures or letters.

Example Observation Opportunities: If parent reports that the child has done coloring, ask to see a recent sample, if available. May also be observed during free play situation.

Credit: (see also Credit Notes in this strand's preface)

+ any markings the child makes spontaneously which display controlled, purposeful and varied markings.

4.86 **Copies a circle** *25-36*

Definition: When the child is presented with a drawing of a circle as a model, he can draw a similar one. He does not see the circle being drawn. *[This is a more difficult task than imitating lines because curved lines are more difficult to recreate, and the child does not observe when the circle is made and must thus recreate it from the model. The child is learning that a circle is a curved line which must be closed to make a circle and that curved lines are different from straight lines]*

Adult

Example Observation Opportunities: Draw a bold circle on a blank piece of paper without the child seeing you draw it. Give the child the paper with the circle and make a comment such, as "See the circle; it looks like a ball!" Offer him a crayon or pencil, and invite him to make a circle or ball just like your model on a blank space next to the model or on a new piece of paper with the model in clear view. Praise the child for all attempts. If his first attempt is unsuccessful, praise his good try and invite him to make another one.

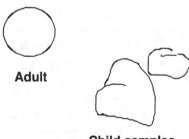

Child samples

Credit: (see also Credit Notes in this strand's preface)

+ copies circle using one circular motion; the circle may be a crude imitation of a model, i.e., end point may not touch beginning point, and may be larger or smaller than the model.

- continuous circular scribbles.

4-6 SPATIAL PERCEPTION AND PLANNING

B. BLOCK CONSTRUCTION

4.58	11-12	Places one block on top of another without balancing
4.61	12-16	Builds tower using two cubes
4.69	16-18	Builds tower using three cubes
4.72	18-22	Builds tower using four cubes
4.77	22-24	Builds tower using six cubes
4.79	23-26	Imitates three-block train using cubes
4.87	28-31	Builds tower using eight cubes
4.91	31 +	Imitates three-block bridge using cubes
4.92	32-36	Builds tower using nine cubes

Family Friendly Interpretation of Strand Concepts, Assessment, & Purpose

Building towers with blocks is a difficult fine motor skill which requires your child to use his eye-hand coordination skills cooperatively with his release skills. Your child needs to accurately align one block on top of another and use precise timing when he lets go of the block so that he lets go of it at just the right time. The actual number of blocks that a child can stack will depend upon a number of factors: age, level and control of fine motor development, degree of interest, attention span, experience with blocks, and the size of the blocks; e.g., a child may be able to stack four big blocks but only two tiny ones.

Professional FYI

Skills #4.79 "Imitates three-block train" and #4.91 "Imitates three-block bridge" assess the child's ability to reconstruct a block pattern. These skills also assess a more difficult visual-motor process-ing skill as the child must perceive the spatial arrangement accurately and then be able to have the motor-planning ability to reproduce the pattern.

Parent Questions   (Examples)

To help identify the child's unique strengths and needs related to this developmental area:

• Has your child ever played with blocks? *If yes, Can you describe how he plays with them? Also explore the size of blocks and child's interest and attention span.*

• Have you seen your child stack up other items at home, such as books, boxes, sponges, or his toy cars?

To help identify family resources, priorities and concerns related to the child's development in this area:

• Can you think of any materials or toys at home that your child might be able to play with which are "stackable," for example, sponges, books, boxes, or blocks?

[Be sure to check if parents support assessment and/or intervention in this area. Some families may prefer not to work on playing with blocks as their child is in a throwing or "acting out" stage, and playing with blocks is too hazardous at this time. Mark N/T for not tested, noting parent preference if appropriate, or if parent allows for assessment purposes only, may note accordingly]

Sample *Functional* Outcome Statements which may be generated by the Family

[Will be dependent upon identified individual child and family needs]

My child will:
• Stack his own picture books up when finished;

• Enjoy playing and learning to build with his blocks.

Transactional Assessment

May assess through observation and interview.

Assessment of the Child's Environment

1. Supportive
[Environments which support/facilitate development in this area]

The child's caregiving environments sometimes have toys or other safe materials for the child to stack or build towers.

Assessment of Caregiver Interactions with the Child

1. Supportive:
[Interactions which support/facilitate child's development in this area]

The child's caregivers sometimes play with their child when he is playing with blocks or other safe, stackable materials. While playing, caregivers:

- Show the child how to make a simple tower, but let the child choose if he wants to try;
- Praise the child's attempts, even if unsuccessful;
- Change activities when the child is no longer interested or begins to throw them.

2. Compromising:
[Interactions which may restrict, compromise, inhibit or be unsupportive of the child's development in this area]

The child's caregivers usually:

- Expect the child to play with blocks in only one way;
- Expect the child to build structures beyond his developmental abilities.

Identifying and Interpreting Needs for Intervention

If a child is delayed in this strand, he may be having difficulty in <u>fine motor planning and perceptual skills</u>.

However, before targeting this as the primary area of need for intervention, consider, rule out, or adapt for other causes of delay. These may include:

- <u>Delayed or atypical grasp and or release skills</u>;
- <u>Gross motor delays or impairments</u>;

- <u>Delayed or atypical cognitive skills</u> especially in the area of spatial relationships (e.g., understanding the concept of equilibrium) or play skills (e.g., if mouthing, banging are predominant play schemes);
- <u>Visual impairment</u>;
- <u>Lack of interest in task or difficulty attending to task</u> (Note: Since this is a common "test" item on most developmental assessments, some children are bored with the task.)

Assessment Adaptations   (Examples)

[Note any adaptations needed to qualify credit and help plan interventions]

- <u>Delayed or atypical grasp and or release skills</u>: try using larger and/or different weight blocks. *[Do not use slippery plastic blocks]* Consult with a therapist to ensure optimal positioning and appropriateness of activities. Note any adaptations needed to qualify credit and help plan interventions. If the child is frustrated, this may not be an appropriate area for curriculum assessment or planning.
- <u>Motor impaired</u>:
  – The child should be positioned in a manner which provides adequate head and trunk support with his arms and shoulders positioned forward. *Consult with an occupational or physical therapist for specific individualized optimal positions.* Adaptive materials and seating may be helpful.
  – A child with severe motor impairments may not develop typical or mature grasping or release patterns that are prerequisite for stacking. Mark N/A for items that may be inappropriate to assess and plan for functional skill development (Refer to the NOTE in the Fine Motor II Overview on page 250.).
- <u>Cognitive delays</u>: plan interventions in cognitive area prior to or concurrent with setting outcomes related to block stacking.

- <u>Visually impaired</u>: provide plenty of time for the child to explore and manipulate the blocks so he can become familiar with their sizes and weights. Use larger blocks rather than inch cubes if this is the child's first experience. Stack two or three blocks, and encourage the child to tactually explore and knock down the tower. Physically guide the child through the stacking process, showing him how to use one of his hands to hold onto the bottom block as a physical guide. It may be useful to let the child play on a sound-absorbing surface, or use foam blocks so that the topple of blocks is not startling. Describe the action when the blocks fall down, and let the child have ample time to explore what happened.
- If the child has <u>difficulty attending to table tasks</u>, be sure the room is relatively free of other competing toys and activities. Offer only one or two blocks at a time. Use extra praise and verbal encouragement to continue. Follow the child's lead; if for example, he prefers banging the blocks together, imitate him. Then, after he has experienced banging, try stacking a few. Vary the task by using alternatives to small blocks if they are not interesting to child, e.g., stacking thread spools, foam blocks. If the child is not interested, don't force the activity; let the child move on to something else of interest.

General Assessment Procedures & Processes (apply to all items in this Strand)

1. Present blocks in front of child to allow him to **choose which hand to use.** Note preferred hand. if any.

2. **The child should be in a position which promotes good posture and enables him to move his arms and hands freely;** for later skills, this should generally be in a seated position with his feet flat on the floor, back supported by back of chair, and at a child-sized table. Some children who do not have delayed or atypical motor development may prefer to stand at a small table or to sit on the floor.

3. The eliciting procedure identified for skill #4.61, "Builds tower using two cubes," is applicable to all remaining stacking items and thus not repeated.

4. **Describe the skill or eliciting procedures and invite family members to help observe and/or assess.**

+ - A Credit Notes:

+   child can complete task as defined.

-   not observed or reported.

+/- appears to be an emerging skill; e.g., stacks two cubes easily but the third block usually topples off, or the child does not release his hand from the third block.

A   tower always falls apart due to poor grading of movement (too much pressure <u>not</u> due to inexperience).

O   circle any credit if environment or interactions compromise or restrict child's optimal block play abilities.

Note any adaptations used to credit.

 ### Assessment Materials

• Five blocks at least 2 inches on one side. These do not need to be perfect cubes; e.g., they could be 2 inch by 3 inch by 1 inch cubes.

• 10 small, safe, square blocks. *Make sure the blocks are **not** small enough to be placed inside the child's mouth.*

4.58 Places one block on top of another without balancing 11-12

Definition: The child puts one block on top of another but does not release it. But if he does let go, the block is not placed in good alignment with the first, and thus it typically falls over. The child is demonstrating his perceptual awareness of how objects can relate in equilibrium to one another. At this stage, however, he does not have the precise release and eye-hand coordination skills needed to accurately line the blocks up for balancing.

Example Observation Opportunities: <u>Incidental</u> - may observe in play as child stacks items, e.g., his books, play saucers, blocks, small boxes or sponges. <u>Structured</u> - attract the child's attention to four blocks on the table. Enthusiastically stack two and invite him to try; e.g., point to the extra blocks and request, "Build a house like mine!" Let him use your blocks or the remaining ones. Use blocks sized according to his fine motor abilities. Sponges or flat blocks may be easier.

Credit: (see also Credit Notes in this strand's preface)

+   attempts to stack two blocks or other stackable items by placing one on top of the other. The "tower" may fall over, or the child may keep his hand on top of the second block.

(also in Strand 1-4 "Spatial Relationships")

4.61 Builds tower using two cubes 12-16

Definition: The child places a small block on top of another to make a two-block tower. *NOTE: This procedure is applicable to all stacking items.*

Example Observation Opportunities: <u>Incidental</u> - may observe incidentally when child is engaged in block play. <u>Structured</u> - give the child about three or four small blocks of the same size (1.25 inch cubes). After the child has had several minutes to play with and explore the blocks, build a tower of two or three cubes with another set of blocks. Invite the child to build a tower just like yours. Continue to offer additional cubes according to the child's ability until his interest wanes. If the child does not try, you build a tower, knock it down and invite the child to make a tower, so he can play this "knock-down" game. Distract to a new activity if the child starts to throw blocks.

Credit: (see also Credit Notes in this strand's preface)

+   builds a tower of at least two small blocks, releasing his hand from the second cube. May credit higher level stacking skills according to highest number stacked.

4.69　Builds tower using three cubes　16-18

Definition: The child balances three small blocks on top of each other.
Example Observation Opportunities: Same as #4.61 "Builds tower using two cubes."
Credit: (see also Credit Notes in this strand's preface)
+　builds a tower of at least three small blocks, releasing his hand from the third cube. May credit higher level stacking skills according to highest number stacked.

4.72　Builds tower using four cubes　18-22

Definition: The child balances four small blocks on top of each other.
Example Observation Opportunities: Same as #4.61 "Builds tower using two cubes."
Credit: (see also Credit Notes in this strand's preface)
+　builds a tower of at least four small blocks, releasing hand from the fourth cube. May credit higher level stacking skills according to highest number stacked.

4.77　Builds tower using six cubes　22-24

Definition: The child balances six small blocks on top of each other.
Example Observation Opportunities: Same as #4.61 "Builds tower using two cubes."
Credit: (see also Credit Notes in this strand's preface)
+　builds a tower of at least six small blocks, releasing hand from the sixth cube. May credit #4.87 "Builds tower using eight cubes" if child continues to stack at least eight.

4.79　Imitates three-block train using cubes　23-26

Definition: The child aligns three small blocks horizontally; pushes them like a train in imitation of an adult.
Example Observation Opportunities: During block play, demonstrate making a three- or four-block train. Attract the child's attention to the building process by announcing you will be making a train and then counting each block as you line it up; e.g., "Here's one car, two cars, three cars!" Then enthusiastically push it around, making "choo choo" sounds. Dismantle the train and invite the child to make one.
Credit: (see also Credit Notes in this strand's preface)
+　aligns three small blocks and pushes it a few inches. Alignment does not need to be exact, but close enough to allow effective pushing of the train.

4.87　Builds tower using eight cubes　28-31

Definition: The child balances eight small blocks on top of each other.
Example Observation Opportunities: Same as #4.61 "Builds tower using two cubes."
Credit: (see also Credit Notes in this strand's preface)
+　builds a tower of at least eight small blocks, releasing his hand from the eighth cube.
(may credit #4.92, which follows, if child continues to stack at least nine)

4.91　Imitates three-block bridge using cubes　31+

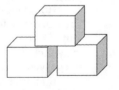

Definition: The child can reproduce an exact replica of a three-block bridge after watching an adult build one. This demonstrates his expanding visual motor and planning ability to reproduce a block pattern.
Example Observation Opportunities: Gather six small blocks of the same color. Announce enthusiastically that you are going to build a house, using blocks as the bricks. With three small blocks, construct the bridge while the child is watching. The two bottom blocks should be spaced about 1/2 inch apart. Attract his attention to each block in the process by saying something like, "One brick here, one brick here, and one on top!" Point out the space between the bottom blocks, pushing a pencil or crayon through the space to emphasize it. Give the child the remaining three blocks and invite him to make a house, leaving your model in sight. He may need some trial-and-error time.
Credit: (see also Credit Notes in this strand's preface)
+　reconstructs a bridge in imitation, leaving a small space between the two bottom blocks.
+/- builds bridge but does not leave space between the two bottom blocks.

4.92　Builds tower using nine cubes　32-36

Definition: The child balances nine cubes on top of each other.
Example Observation Opportunities: Same as #4.61 "Builds tower using two cubes."
Credit: (see also Credit Notes in this strand's preface)
+　builds a tower of at least nine small blocks, releasing his hand from the ninth cube. Should observe at least twice if tower was not built higher than nine. *Inside* HELP © 1992, 2006 VORT Corporation　**259**

4-6 SPATIAL PERCEPTION AND PLANNING

C. FORMBOARD

1.57	10-11	Removes round piece from formboard
1.63	11-12	Places cylinders in matching hole in container
1.71	12-15	Places round piece in formboard
1.86	15-21	Places square piece in formboard
1.114	21-24	Places triangular piece in formboard

Family Friendly Interpretation of Strand Concepts, Assessment, & Purpose

We will be observing how your child is learning to fit shapes, such as circles and squares, into the matching holes of a shape puzzle/box or formboard. Fitting shapes in the correct spaces helps your child practice using his eyes and hands together and helps him learn to about characteristics of objects that are the same and different.

Professional FYI

Items in this strand require perceptual skills which include cognitive and fine motor skills. Formboard skills can help us assess the child's classification/discrimination skills and spatial and motor planning skills. The child must be able to perceptually interpret and match the shapes, and then be able to rotate it to fit the corresponding hole.

Parent Questions   (Examples)

To help identify the child's unique strengths and needs related to this developmental area:
• Has your child ever played with a shape toy before? Can you describe the toy and how he played with it?

Sample *Functional* Outcome Statements which may be generated by the Family

[Will be dependent upon identified individual child and family needs and should incorporate objectives and activities from other domains]

My child will:
• Be able to fit small objects in small spaces;
• Enjoy playing with his shape sorter toy.

Identifying and Interpreting Needs for Intervention

If a child is delayed in this area he may be having difficulty in <u>visual perceptual and visual-motor skills.</u>

However, before targeting this as the primary area of need for intervention consider and rule out, or adapt for other causes of delays. These may include:
• <u>Delayed or atypical grasp and or release skills</u> that interfere with his ability to manipulate the shape pieces;
• <u>Gross motor delays or impairments;</u>
• <u>Delayed cognitive skills</u> especially in the area of spatial relationships (Strand 1-5) and classification skills (Strand 1-7A);
• <u>Visual impairment;</u>
• <u>Poor tactile discrimination;</u>
• <u>Lack of interest</u> in task or difficulty attending to task.

Assessment Adaptations   (Examples)

[Note any adaptations needed to qualify credit and help plan interventions]
• <u>Delayed or atypical grasp and or release skills:</u> try using larger shape blocks or shapes with knobs attached. Help stabilize or tilt the board or shape box if this is useful. If the child can match the shape to the correct hole but does not have the fine motor abilities to fit or rotate it, credit his matching skills under Strand 1-5C.

If the child is frustrated, this may not be an appropriate area for curriculum assessment or planning. *Consult with a therapist to ensure optimal positioning and appropriateness of activities.* Note any adaptations needed to qualify credit and help plan interventions.
• <u>Motor impaired:</u>
  – The child should be positioned in a manner which provides adequate head and trunk support with his arms and shoulders

Assessment Adaptations   (continued)

positioned forward. *Consult with an occupational or physical therapist for specific individualized optimal positions.* Adaptive materials and seating may be helpful.

- Help stabilize or tilt the board or shape box if this is useful.
- Mark N/A for items which may be inappropriate to assess and plan for functional skill development. (Refer to the NOTE in the Fine Motor II Overview on page 250.)

• <u>Cognitive delays</u>: plan interventions in the cognitive area prior to, or concurrent with, setting outcomes related to formboards; refer to Strands 1-5 and 1-7.

• <u>Visually impaired</u>: provide plenty of time for the child to explore and manipulate the shapes so he can become familiar with their size and tactile differences. Use shapes that have contrasting colors to the board. While the child is exploring, point out unique differences, such as points on the triangle and round edges on the circle. Orient the child to the holes of the formboard and shape box. Let him take the shapes out of the board. Guide him to the correct hole, using a hand-over-hand technique a few times until the child understands the game.

• <u>Poor tactile discrimination</u>: emphasize the visual differences in the shapes, e.g., rounded versus pointed corners.

• If child has <u>difficulty attending to table tasks</u>, be sure room is relatively free of other competing toys and activities. Follow the child's lead. For example, if he prefers banging the shape pieces together, imitate him. Then, after he has experienced banging, try placing one in the board and invite him to try one. Make the puzzle more interesting by putting a sticker on the formboard hole for the child to cover with the shape and then find it when he removes it. If the child is not interested, don't force the activity; let the child move on to something else of interest.

General Assessment Procedures & Processes   (apply to all items in this Strand)

1. The child should **be in a position that promotes good posture and enables him to move his arms and hands freely.** Generally, the child should be in a seated position with his feet flat on the floor, back supported by chair back, at a child-sized table. Some children who do not have delayed or atypical motor development may prefer to stand at the table or sit on the floor.

2. **Describe the skill or eliciting procedures and invite family members to help observe and/or assess.**

+ - A Credit Notes:

+   child completes activity as defined.
-   not observed.
+/- appears to be an emerging skill; e.g., places triangle in correct hole and rotates it partially, but it still does not fit.

Note any adaptations used to credit.

Assessment Materials

Use a commercial or "homemade" formboard and shape box, which has only primary shapes, e.g., circle, square, triangle. The shapes should <u>not</u> provide color cues, e.g., blue circle and red square that corresponds to a blue and a red hole.

Removes round piece from formboard   10-11

Definition: The child can take the round- or circle-shaped piece out of a three-shape formboard. He typically uses his thumb to get under the edge and lift it out. *[The round piece is the easiest to remove because there are no corners to negotiate]*

Example Observation Opportunities: If not observed spontaneously during play, attract the child's attention to the formboard. Demonstrate removing the circle piece, replace it and invite the child to try. Let the child play with the piece after he has removed it. If the child has difficulty, do not credit but help remove it, and let him play with the piece.

Credit: (see also Credit Notes in this strand's preface)
    +   removes the circle from a formboard using his fingers, with or without demonstration.
(may also credit #1.71 "Places round piece in formboard" if child places the piece back)

1.63 Places cylinders in matching hole in container   11-12

Definition: The child places a cylindrical block into the round hole of a container when the container has a round and a square hole to choose from.

Example Observation Opportunities: Give the child one or two cylindrical blocks and a container with a matching shaped round hole and a square hole. Invite him to put the block in the hole but do not demonstrate. If he is successful, give him another cylinder and rotate the shape box to help ensure he did not place it in the correct hole by chance. <u>Materials</u>: use a commercial shape sorter if only two holes can be exposed at a time. May alternatively use "homemade" materials, e.g., hair rollers or large thread spools as the cylinders; cut out the top of a box or plastic cover on a coffee can. Be sure that the cylinder shape cannot fit into the square shape.

Credit: (see also Credit Notes in this strand's preface)

   + places at least two cylinder shapes into the round hole. The child may initially try to place the cylinder in the square hole, but should then immediately look at the round hole and place the first and second cylinders correctly.

1.71 Places round piece in formboard   12-15

Definition: The child correctly places the round piece in a formboard which has a circle, a square, and a triangular hole available.

Example Observation Opportunities: Present an empty three-shaped formboard to the child. Let him explore the holes a few moments (if interested) as you name the shapes. Place the round piece on the table at the child's midline, and ask him to put it in the correct hole. Allow him to explore through trial and error. If he is successful, offer him the square piece.

Credit: (see also Credit Notes in this strand's preface)

   + places the round shape into the round hole of the formboard without demonstration, or verbal or gestural cues. He may initially try to place it in the wrong hole but should then look at the round hole and place it correctly without any suggestion to do so.

1.86 Places square piece in formboard   15-21

Definition: The child correctly places the square piece in a formboard which has a circle, a square, and a triangular hole available.

Example Observation Opportunities: Present an empty, three-shaped formboard to the child. Let him explore the holes a few moments (if interested) as you name the shapes. Place the round and square pieces on the table at the child's midline and ask him to put them in the correct holes. Let him explore through trial and error. If he is successful, offer him the triangle piece to assess #1.114 "Places triangular piece in formboard."

Credit: (see also Credit Notes in this strand's preface)

   + places and fits the round and square shapes into the corresponding holes of the formboard without demonstration, or verbal or gestural cues. He may initially try to place the square in the wrong hole, but should then correct himself after one trial without any suggestion to do so.

1.114 Places triangular piece in formboard   21-24

Definition: The child correctly places the triangle piece in a formboard which has a circle, a square, and a triangular hole available.

Example Observation Opportunities: Present an empty, three-shaped formboard to the child. Let him explore the holes a few moments (if interested) as you name the shapes. Place the three shapes on the table in front of him in random order, and invite him to place them all in. Allow him to explore through trial and error, especially when negotiating the corners of the square and triangle, to complete the proper rotation necessary.

Credit: (see also Credit Notes in this strand's preface)

   + places and fits the round, square and triangular shapes into the corresponding holes of the formboard without demonstration, or verbal or gestural cues.

4-6 SPATIAL PERCEPTION AND PLANNING

D. PAPER ACTIVITIES: PASTING, PAINTING, FOLDING

1.100	18-24	Pastes on one side
1.101	18-24	Paints within limits of paper
4.76	21-24	Folds paper imitatively, not precisely
4.85	24-30	Folds paper in half
1.121	24-30	Pastes on appropriate side

Family Friendly Interpretation of Strand Concepts, Assessment, & Purpose

Items in this part of the assessment include painting, pasting and folding activities. These activities help your child learn to sequence and plan his hand movements. For example, when he learns to paste, he needs to learn different steps in the pasting process, i.e., applying the paste, turning the pasted piece over and then applying it to something. These activities also help him develop an awareness of boundaries and space as he learns to paste, paint and fold within the limits of paper.

Parent Questions   (Examples)

To help identify the child's unique strengths and needs related to this developmental area:
- Has your child ever tried using paste? Would it be okay if we see how he plays with paste and paper today?
- Has your child ever used tape to stick things down or used stickers?
- Has your child ever painted on an easel? Does he usually keep the paint on the paper when he's painting? Would it be okay if we let him paint at an easel today? We have smocks and the paint is non-toxic and washable.

To help identify family resources, priorities and concerns related to the child's development in this area:
- Are you interested in your child learning to use paints and paste with paper at this age?
- *If so*, Are there certain places and times that would work best for your child to play with these materials? Sometimes it can become messy!

[The family may prefer that their child not get into "messy" activities. It is important to respect these preferences during assessment and planning]

Sample *Functional* Outcome Statements which may be generated by the Family

[Will be dependent upon identified individual child and family needs and should incorporate objectives and activities from other domains]
My child will:
- Enjoy craft activities that involve pasting;
- Keep his crayon and paint markings on the paper;
- Help with simple household tasks that involve folding, e.g., fold socks, napkins, papers;
- Be able to spread jelly on his crackers during mealtime.

Transactional Assessment

May assess through observation and interview.

Assessment of the Child's Environment

1. Supportive:
[Environments which support/facilitate development in this area]

The child's caregiving environments provide structured opportunities for the child to play safely with paints, paste and paper.

Assessment of Caregiver Interactions with the Child

1. Supportive:
[Interactions which support/facilitate child's development in this area]

The child's caregivers usually praise their child's "artwork" and ignore mistakes and spills.

Identifying and Interpreting Needs for Intervention

If a child is delayed in this area, he may be having difficulty in <u>visual-motor, spatial and planning skills</u>.

However, before targeting this as an area of need for intervention, consider and rule out or adapt for other causes which interfere with a true assessment of his visual-motor, spatial and planning skills related to pasting, painting and fold-ing. These may include:
- <u>Tactile defensiveness</u> (refer to Strand 0.0 Regulatory/Sensory Organization);
- <u>Gross motor delays</u> or impairments;
- <u>Fine motor delays</u> or impairments related to grasp and bilateral skills;
- <u>Lack of experience</u> or interest in the activity.

Assessment Adaptations   (Examples)

[Note any adaptations needed to credit and help plan interventions]
- <u>Tactile defensiveness</u>: If the child does not like to touch the paste, let him use a flat stick to apply it, or liquid paste from a small squeeze bottle or a glue stick instead.
- <u>Motor impaired</u>: *Consult with a therapist for optimal positions of child, placement of materials, and adaptive seating and materials.* Adaptations for fine motor delays (below) may also be suitable (refer to the NOTE in the Fine Motor II Overview on page 250.)
- <u>Fine motor delays or impairments related to grasp and bilateral skills</u>:
  Consult with a therapist to determine specific adaptations. Examples include:
  – If the child has compromised use of one hand/arm (e.g., hemiplegia), help stabilize paper or other marking surface, tape it down or let him mark on something stable such as a marking surface on a washable tray or table top. Help him stabilize on side of the paper during folding skills.
  – If the child has an immature or atypical grasp, let him paste three dimensional objects, such as a block or a small jewelry box to the paper, instead of paper scraps; try using a thick glue stick; try brushes with fat or built-up handles; tilt the table surface or use an easel. If the child can not carry out all the steps in the pasting or painting process, let him tell you what to do next.
- <u>Visually impaired</u>:
  – <u>Pasting and folding skills</u>: Delays should be expected, depending upon the child's experience. If the child is totally blind, he will need to have an understanding of the function of paste. Provide extra exploration and teaching time of this concept before assessing pasting skills. When assessing, if the child pastes on the appropriate side, use materials that have definite tactile differences on the front and back, e.g., show him how to paste the smooth side of sand paper or corrugated cardboard shapes.
  – <u>Painting</u>: Orient the child to the boundaries of the paper. Place the paper on a contrasting tactile and/or colored surface; e.g., let him paint on a carpet or tile square. Use high-contrast paints. Use paints that produce a textured product; e.g., mix sand in the paint.

General Assessment Procedures & Processes   (apply to all items in this Strand)

1. This strand may be **assessed while involved in or immediately following other fine motor strands,** which include paper activities. For example, after assessing a child's skills with a scissors, cut out some shapes for him to paste, or after scribbling on a paper, show him how to fold it to make a book or a card.
2. If parents prefer not to assess or provide intervention in messy materials, such as paint and paste, **mark NT** (Not Tested) **for appropriate items,** noting parent preference, or use alternative materials, such as crayons or stickers, noting adaptations.
3. **Describe the skill or eliciting procedures and invite family members to help observe and or assess.**

+ - A **Credit Notes:**

+   child displays skill as defined.
-    not observed or reported.
+/- appears to be an emerging skill.
NT not tested due to parent preference.
N/A not a functional skill to test do to child's disability.
Note any adaptations used to credit.

Assessment Materials

A small plastic tub with about 2 tablespoons of preschool, non-toxic washable paste (or may put large dab of paste on plastic top of butter or coffee container, etc.); easel, if available; smock or old T-shirt for painting; preschool paints in easy-to-use cups and brush; large sheets of paper, approximately 18 by 22 inches; two or three pieces of construction paper; paper shapes to paste that have a distinct front and back, e.g., corrugated cardboard, stripes on one side and blank on the other; piece of regular note paper to fold.

Pastes on one side   18-24

Definition: The child can apply paste to only one side of a small paper and turn it over to stick it on another paper or object. At this stage, he may not paste on the correct side and may need a verbal reminder to turn the paper over.

Example Observation Opportunities: May try any of the following activities to engage child in pasting activities, depending on his interest: pasting eyes on a large, outlined picture of a face with a nose and mouth; pasting a tail on a large outlined picture of a dog; pasting 2-inch shapes cut out of colored construction paper onto a contrasting piece of construction paper. Demonstrate pasting a piece in clear view of the child, as you comment about the steps involved in pasting; e.g., "Dip your fingers in the paste, spread it on the paper piece ("eye", "tail", etc.), turn it over, and press it on the (e.g., face, dog, etc.)." Lift the paper up to show him how it sticks. Offer the child another paper shape to paste. Provide verbal and gestural prompts, as needed.

Credit: (see also Credit Notes in this strand's preface)
+ applies paste to either side of at least two shapes and pastes it on another paper. May have verbal and gestural prompts.

Paints within limits of paper   18-24

Definition: The child can paint and color within the limits of a large sheet of paper (approximately 18 by 22 inches).

Example Observation Opportunities: May best be observed when child is painting at an easel. The paper should be smaller than the easel surface, and the easel surface should be a different color. When the child begins to paint or color, ask him to keep his color on the paper to try to keep the easel clean.

Credit: (see also Credit Notes in this strand's preface)
+ does not make any marks off the paper with a paintbrush or crayon.

Folds paper imitatively, not precisely   21-24

Definition: The child uses both hands cooperatively to fold a piece of paper after seeing an adult fold another piece. He may not be able to crease the fold, and the fold may not be exactly in half.

Example Observation Opportunities: Incidental - may be observed as child helps adult fold napkins for mealtime or during doll play for a tea party. Structured: - demonstrate folding a small piece of note paper in half explaining to the child how you "made a book." Exaggerate how you fold it, crease it and can then open and close the book. Put a colorful sticker inside, as needed, to keep it fun. Then give the child a similar piece of paper and tell him to "make a book." Demonstrate again, as needed.

Credit: (see also Credit Notes in this strand's preface)
+ uses both hands cooperatively to fold one side of the paper towards the opposite side. His folding may be clumsy, may not have a crease and not be folded exactly in half.

4.85 **Folds paper in half**   24-30

Definition: The child turns one edge of a small piece of paper over toward the opposite edge to fold a piece of paper in half.

Example Observation Opportunities: Same as #4.76 "Folds paper imitatively, not precisely."

Credit: (see also Credit Notes in this strand's preface)

+   folds a piece of paper in half. He does not have to make a definite crease, but the paper should be folded in half.

1.121 **Pastes on appropriate side**   24-30

Definition: The child independently applies paste to the appropriate side of a shape and turns it over to stick it on paper.

Example Observation Opportunities: Suggest that the child make a special picture to give to his parent or to hang up on the wall. Use shapes to paste that have a distinct front and back, e.g., corrugated cardboard, stripes on one side and blank on the other. Demonstrate the pasting process, emphasizing pasting on the correct side. Invite the child to try, but do not provide verbal or gestural cues to assess for credit.

Credit: (see also Credit Notes in this strand's preface)

+   pastes on the correct side at least two of three shapes onto another paper with or without a demonstration.

Strand 4-7 "Manipulative Prehension"

Includes fine motor skills which rely heavily on the child's ability to incorporate a variety of hand and finger movements to complete a task, including the ability to separate and move fingers in different directions. These items also involve depth perception, bilateral, and motor planning skills.

4-7 MANIPULATIVE PREHENSION

A. MANIPULATING PAGES

1.83	14-15	Helps turn pages
1.89	15-18	Turns two or three pages at a time
1.116	21-24	Turns pages one at a time

Family Friendly Interpretation of Strand Concepts, Assessment, & Purpose

We will be observing how your child uses his hands and fingers to turn the pages of his books when he is looking at them. At first, children need help turning them. As they are able to use their fingers more precisely, they learn to turn pages a few at a time, then one at a time.

Professional FYI

This strand isolates only the fine motor skills involved in looking at books. Other concepts related to picture books are in the cognitive and language domains.

Parent Questions   (Examples)

To help identify the child's unique strengths and needs related to this developmental area:
- Have you noticed how your child turns the pages of his books?
- Does your child have favorite books he likes to look at? Can you describe the books he likes, e.g., size, thickness of page and the pictures they contain?

To help identify family resources, priorities and concerns related to the child's development in this area:
Can you think of some books, catalogs or magazines at home that would be okay for your child to play with?

Sample *Functional* Outcome Statements which may be generated by the Family

[Will be dependent upon identified individual child and family needs and should incorporate objectives and activities from other domains]

My child will be able to look at his books independently.

Transactional Assessment

May assess through observation and interview.

Assessment of the Child's Environment

1. Supportive:
[Environments which support/facilitate development in this area]
The child's caregiving environments have books available which are:
- Interesting to the child;
- Okay for the child to tear accidentally;
- Accessible to the child.

Assessment of Caregiver Interactions with the Child

1. Supportive:
[Interactions which support/facilitate child's development in this area]
The child's caregivers:
- Have quiet playtimes built into the child's routines;
- Sometimes look at books with their child;
- Give the child an opportunity to explore books independently and let him try turning the pages before they help.

Identifying and Interpreting Needs for Intervention

If a child is delayed in this area he may be having difficulty in <u>the grasping, bilateral, and motor planning skills needed for turning pages</u>.

However, before targeting this as the primary need for intervention, consider, rule out or adapt for other causes which are <u>not related to his abil-</u><u>ity to turn pages</u>. These may include:
• <u>Lack of interest</u> in the book;
• <u>Poor positioning</u> of the child or book;
• <u>Pages of book are difficult to turn</u> for any child, e.g., tight bindings, new or slick pages.

Assessment Adaptations (Examples)

[Note any adaptations needed to credit and help plan interventions]
• <u>Visually impaired:</u> use familiar textured books and/or high-contrast color picture books. Let the child have plenty of time to explore the weight and size of the book and thickness of the pages.
• <u>Motor impaired:</u> *consult with a therapist for specific optimal positions of child, placement of the book, and adaptive seating and books.* Adaptations for fine motor delays below may

also be suitable. (Refer to the NOTE in the Fine Motor II Overview on page 250.)
– If the child has compromised use of one hand/arm (e.g., hemiplegia), help stabilize the book, using a book holder or placing his affected arm or your hand on the book.
– If the child has an immature or atypical grasp, use books that have thicker pages or add tabs to the pages. An adaptive page turner may be appropriate.

General Assessment Procedures & Processes (apply to all items in this Strand)

1. **Let the child choose which books to look at.**
2. **This strand may be assessed incidentally** when observing the child's interest and play with pictures and books.
3. **Describe the skill or eliciting procedures and invite family members to help observe and/or assess.**

+ - A Credit Notes:

+ child usually turns pages as defined.
- not observed or reported.
+/- appears to be an emerging skill; child still needs some assistance or sometimes uses less mature method.
O circle any credit if environment or interactions compromise or restrict child's skills in this area, e.g., no books available.

Note any adaptations used to credit.

Assessment Materials

Use the child's favorite books, if available. Have books available which have various qualities to see which types the child can manipulate best, e.g., different sizes, thin pages, cardboard pages.

1.83
Helps turn pages   14-15

Definition: The child helps flip the page of a book after an adult has separated and lifted the page.

Example Observation Opportunities: Offer the child a small picture book that has thick or thin pages. Observe to see if he tries to open the book, or help him if he shows interest. As you point to and label the pictures, invite him to help turn the page to find the next picture. Help him (as needed) by lifting and separating the pages. If the child does not appear interested in the book, this is not a valid observation situation and the skill can be reassessed later or with a different book.

Credit: (see also Credit Notes in this strand's preface)
+   helps turn a few pages in a book by placing his hand on the adult's hand as the adult turns the page, or by pushing the page after the adult has lifted it about halfway.

1.89
Turns two or three pages at a time   15-18

Definition: The child independently turns the pages of his picture book, two or three pages at a time. He turns the pages by pushing or flipping the pages over while his other hand holds or tries to stabilize the book. His page turning at times may be nonfunctional, e.g., he may turn pages backwards and or not bother to look at the pictures because he is more interested in the process of page turning.

Example Observation Opportunities: Same as #1.83 but adult does not always help. Books with worn pages and bindings are recommended.

Credit: (see also Credit Notes in this strand's preface)
+   can turn pages of a book a few at a time independently.

1.116
Turns pages one at a time   21-24

Definition: The child can independently turn the pages of a small book, one at a time. Both hands work cooperatively as one hand stabilizes the book and his other hand turns the pages.

Example Observation Opportunities: Observe when the child is looking at a picture book which has thin pages. He may be looking at a book during solitary play or with an adult. Verbally encourage him (as needed) to turn the page to see what picture is on the next page. If he is not interested in the book, try a different book or observe at a later time.

Credit: (see also Credit Notes in this strand's preface)
+   can turn pages of a book one at a time.

4-7 MANIPULATIVE PREHENSION

B. PEGBOARD

4.47	*8.5-12*	Removes pegs from pegboard
4.62	12-15	Places one round peg in pegboard
4.70	16-19	Places six round pegs in pegboard
4.90	29-31	Places six square pegs in pegboard

Family Friendly Interpretation of Strand Concepts, Assessment, & Purpose

We will be observing how your child plays with a pegboard and pegs. Working with a pegboard is a somewhat difficult fine motor task because it requires your child to attend to a task, to have an understanding that things can combine to fit together, and to use his eyes and hands together to precisely grasp, place and release the pegs in the right place. These skills help your child learn how to fit small things in small places, such as his toothbrush in its holder.

If your child has never played with pegs and a pegboard, he may first just want to explore the pegs and board by poking and probing at the holes, and tasting, banging and/or dropping the pegs.

Professional FYI

- Prerequisite skills include adequate grasp and release skills.
- Refer to NOTE in Fine Motor II Overview on page 250.

- Skill #4.90 "Places six square pegs in pegboard" may be omitted if materials are not available. *[This particular skill could not be located in current developmental scales or literature]*

Parent Questions   (Examples)

To help identify the child's unique strengths and needs related to this developmental area:
- Has your child ever played with a pegboard or peg-type toys, such as Fisher Price "Little People"?
- *If so*, How does he play with them?

To help identify family resources, priorities and

concerns related to the child's development in this area:
- Can you think of some activities at home that can help your child practice fitting things in holes, e.g., his crayons in a container, toothbrush in its holder, or certain toys that include this?

Sample *Functional* Outcome Statements which may be generated by the Family

[Will be dependent upon identified individual child and family needs and should incorporate objectives and activities from other domains]
- My child will be able to fit small things in small

places, e.g., his crayons back in their box, his toothbrush back in its container, utensils in their drawer holders.

Identifying and Interpreting Needs for Intervention

If a child is delayed in this area, he may be having difficulty in <u>visual-motor planning or visual perception</u>.

However, before targeting this as the primary area of need for intervention, consider, rule out or adapt for, other causes which may interfere with a true assessment of the child's visual motor plan-

ning or perceptual skills. These may include:
- <u>Cognitive delays</u> in spatial relationships (Strand 1-5) or combining objects in play (Strand 1-1);
- <u>Attention or distractibility problems;</u>
- <u>Lack of interest in playing with pegs and pegboards;</u>
- <u>Delayed or atypical grasp and release.</u>

Assessment Adaptations   (Examples)

[Note any adaptations needed to qualify credit and help plan interventions]
- <u>Visually impaired</u>: orient the child to the pegboard (with two or three pegs already inserted.) Provide ample time for him to poke and probe the holes and pull out a peg, as you describe it. Keep the remaining pegs in a container that he has already explored next to the pegboard, hand him one peg at a time, or let him use the original pegs he may pull out. Help him feel a hole with one hand while he places a peg with the other. If needed, initially help him place a peg in the hole, using hand-over-hand demonstration until he understands the task.
- <u>Motor impairment or fine motor delays in grasp and release</u>: use larger pegs or knobbed pegs to accommodate the child's grasp; tilt the pegboard; allow and expect the child to take more time to accomplish the task. *Consult a*

therapist for optimal positioning and preliminary relaxation activities as appropriate. Note all adaptations needed to credit.
- <u>If the child is highly distractible or has difficulty attending</u>:
  – Introduce the activity in a quiet, familiar room; keep the activity structured, e.g., give the child only one peg at a time, sit at a table, give frequent verbal cues and reinforcement;
  – At first signs of distractibility, change the activity or make it more interesting; e.g., make a silly sound each time the peg is inserted;
  – Follow the child's lead; e.g., if he wants to bang the peg on the table, imitate him. After he has experienced doing the things he wants to do with the peg, demonstrate putting pegs in the board.

General Assessment Procedures & Processes   (apply to all items in this Strand)

1. **Positioning:** Be sure child is positioned so that he has enough stability to use his arms and hands freely. Typically this can be at a table, supported on parent's lap at a table, in a highchair or prone stander.

2. ***Safety First!*** If the child is reported or observed to explore materials with his mouth, use *only* large pegs even if you are closely supervising him. If these are not available, do not worry about assessing this strand.

3. If the child repeatedly tries to grasp the peg with a fist grasp, forearm in mid-supination, **present him a peg held underhand** with only the top inch available to encourage him to grasp the peg from above with his fingers.

4. **Describe the skill or eliciting procedures and invite family members to help observe and/or assess.**

+ - A Credit Notes:

+   child places pegs as defined.
-   not observed or reported.
+/- appears to be an emerging skill.
A   atypical: always overshoots or undershoots the hole.

Note any adaptations used to credit.

Assessment Materials

Eight to ten pegs of varying diameters and heights, depending on the child's grasping abilities and safety precautions needed. *If the*

*child continues to mouth objects, the pegs should be **large**.* Accompanying pegboards.

Removes pegs from pegboard   8.5-12

Definition: The child can take a few 1/2-inch diameter pegs out of a pegboard. When the child is first learning, it may appear a bit awkward as he may not have learned the concept of "pulling up and out."

Example Observation Opportunities: Provide a pegboard that is holding four pegs spaced apart for easier grasping. Observe to see if the child spontaneously tries to remove any. If not, demonstrate taking one out and invite the child to try. Let him continue to play with the pegs if he shows interest, so that you can observe if he can replace any pegs to credit higher level peg skills.

Credit: (see also Credit Notes in this strand's preface)
+   removes one or two pegs by pulling the pegs up.
+/- if his pulling motion appears awkward, e.g., pulls peg toward himself rather than a smooth, pulling-up motion.

4.62   Places one round peg in pegboard   12-15

Definition: The child places one or two, 1-inch diameter pegs into a pegboard.

Example Observation Opportunities: Present the child with a pegboard which already has a few pegs in it. Encourage him to remove the pegs, taking turns with you (if he is interested). Then ask him to put the pegs back in the holes, gesturing your request as needed. (Note: The child may continue to place one peg in and out repetitively-this is normal. If repetitiveness continues for more than a few trials, distract him with another peg or move to a new activity.)

Credit: (see also Credit Notes in this strand's preface)

+   places at least one peg, 1-inch in diameter or less.

4.70   Places six round pegs in pegboard   16-19

Definition: The child can put six round, 1/2-inch diameter pegs into the pegboard before removing any.

Example Observation Opportunities: Present a pegboard and container which has about eight pegs in it to the child. Encourage him to place pegs in the board, taking turns if he is interested.

Credit: (see also Credit Notes in this strand's preface)

+   consecutively places at least six pegs, each 1/2-inch in diameter or less, in a pegboard.

4.90   Places six square pegs in pegboard   29-31

Definition: The child can put six square, 1/2-inch diameter pegs into the pegboard before removing any.

Example Observation Opportunities: Present to the child a pegboard and a container which has about eight square pegs in it. Encourage him to place pegs in the board, taking turns if he is interested.

Credit: (see also Credit Notes in this strand's preface)

+   consecutively places at least six pegs, each 1/2-inch in diameter or less, in a pegboard.

N/A if materials are not available.

4-7 MANIPULATIVE PREHENSION

C. STRINGING BEADS

4.74	20-23	Strings one one-inch bead
4.80	23-25	Strings three one-inch beads
4.93	33.5 +	Strings 1/2-inch beads

Family Friendly Interpretation of Strand Concepts, Assessment, & Purpose

We will be observing how your child is learning to use his hands cooperatively to string beads. Stringing beads is a difficult task which involves combining three important skills: (1) using a precise grasp to hold and manipulate the string and beads; (2) using each hand independently of the other to cooperate (one hand holds while the other hand threads); and (3) planning the two-step sequence of pushing the string through the hole and then pulling out the other side.

Parent Questions (Examples)

To help identify the child's unique strengths and needs related to this developmental area:
• Has your child ever played with stringing beads?
• *If so,* ask what size of beads, type of string and if he is able to string any.

To help identify family resources, priorities and concerns related to the child's development in this area:
• Can you think of some safe materials at home that your child could play with to practice stringing skills?

Sample *Functional* Outcome Statements which may be generated by the Family

[Will be dependent upon identified individual child and family needs and should incorporate objectives and activities from other domains]

My child will:
• Enjoy playing with his stringing beads toy;
• Be able thread beads and other similar objects in preparation for learning to lace his shoes.

Identifying and Interpreting Needs for Intervention

If a child is delayed in this area, he may be having difficulty integrating bilateral and motor planning skills.

However, before targeting this as the primary area of need for intervention, consider, rule out or adapt for other causes. These may include:

• Delayed or atypical grasp;
• Limited use of one arm, e.g., hemiplegia, nerve damage;
• General motor impairment;
• Visually impaired;
• Lack of interest in task.

Assessment Adaptations   (Examples)

[Note any adaptations needed to qualify credit and help plan interventions]

- <u>Motor impairment and or delayed or atypical grasp</u>:
  - Use larger beads with larger holes and thicker materials for laces; e.g., sturdy leather lace; help stabilize his forearms on the table surface if helpful.
  - The child should be positioned in a manner which provides adequate head and trunk support with his arms and shoulders positioned forward. *Consult with an occupational or physical therapist for specific individualized optimal positions.* Adaptive seating may be helpful.
  - A child with severe motor impairments may not develop typical or mature grasping or release patterns which are prerequisite for stringing beads. Mark N/A for items which may be inappropriate to assess and plan for functional skill development. (Refer to the NOTE in the Fine Motor II Overview on page 250.)

- <u>Limited use on one arm</u>: help position and stabilize the child's affected arm at midline on the table to hold the bead and/or hold the bead for him.
- <u>Visually impaired</u>: allow ample time for the child to explore the materials and a model that has beads strung. Demonstrate the stringing process through hand-over-hand method once or twice. Have him hold the sturdy end of the string in his fingertips with one hand, and the bead in the other with his index finger partially over the hole, helping him guide the string to his fingertip next to the hole.
- If the child is <u>not interested</u> in stringing commercial beads, try varying the materials to make them more novel, e.g., thread toothbrushes (brushes that have holes at opposite end of brush), spools, or Cheerios.

General Assessment Procedures & Processes   (apply to all items in this Strand)

1. **Positioning**: Be sure child is positioned so that he has enough stability to use his arms and hands freely. Typically this can be at a table, supported on parent's lap at a table, or with a prone stander. Some children, who do not have delayed or atypical motor development, may prefer to sit on the floor.
2. ***Safety First!*** If the child is reported or observed to explore materials with his mouth, *use only large beads* (at least 1.25 inches) or edible items, even if you are closely supervising him. Do not be concerned about assessing his skills with small beads.
3. If the child repeatedly tries to grasp the bead with a fist grasp, **try presenting the bead in your underhand grasp with only the top part of the bead available**. This can encourage him to grasp the bead from above with his fingertips.
4. **Describe the skill or eliciting procedures and invite family members to help observe and/or assess.**
5. **Note if child uses a consistent dominant hand as the manipulator of the string.**

`+ - A` Credit Notes:

- **+** child strings beads.
- **-** not observed or reported.
- **+/-** appears to be an emerging skill, e.g., puts string in hold but does not pull it out from the other side.
- **A** atypical: always overshoots or undershoots the hole.

Note any adaptations used to credit.

Assessment Materials

- Commercial stringing breads, three small (1/2-inch-*watch for safety*) beads (or Cheerios as edible alternative); six large beads (1.25 inches in diameter).

- Two sturdy strings or laces with stiff tips and a knot tie at the end.

4.74 ## Strings one one-inch bead   20-23

Definition: The child can string one large wooden bead (at least 1.25 inches in diameter) by holding the bead in one hand as he threads a heavy string with the other. He may not be able to pull the string out fully from the other side and may need an adult to demonstrate the task.

Example Observation Opportunities: <u>Incidental</u> - when the child is playing dress-up, show him a "jewelry" container which has large beads and two laces. Demonstrate making a necklace and invite him to make one to wear. <u>Structured</u> - demonstrate stringing two or three beads, using large commercial toy beads, which are at least 1.25 inches in size, with heavy corded, sturdy-tipped strings or laces. String the beads slowly as you describe the two-step threading process, i.e., push the string in, pull it out on the other side. Provide the child a similar set of three beads and a lace and invite him to try. Note what type of beads the child was successful with. The flattened, thinner wooden beads with larger holes will be easier than larger rounded beads with deeper holes. Initially, you may emphasize verbally and through demonstration the two-step process of pushing the string through the hole and pulling it out. When the child tries, do not give him help.

Credit: (see also Credit Notes in this strand's preface)

+ strings at least one bead using both hands cooperatively, one as the bead holder and one as the manipulator of the string.

4.80 ## Strings three one-inch beads   23-25

Definition: The child can string three large wooden beads (at least 1.25 inches in diameter) by holding the bead in one hand as he threads a heavy string with the other. He should be able to pull the string out fully from the other side, but he may need an adult to demonstrate the task.

Example Eliciting Situations: Same as #4.74 "Strings one 1-inch bead." May initially demonstrate, but do not provide verbal prompting through the two-stage process while the child is stringing.

Credit: (see also Credit Notes in this strand's preface)

+ strings at least three large beads independently after an adult demonstration.

+/- note if child needs verbal prompting through the two-stage stringing process or loses interest in the task.

4.93 ## Strings 1/2-inch beads   33.5+

Definition: The child is able to string at least one small wooden bead, using both hands cooperatively to manipulate the string and bead.

Example eliciting situations: <u>*Safety caution*</u>: *if the child is <u>developmentally</u> under three years or continues to place objects in his mouth, omit this item or try using an editable alternative, such as stringing Cheerios to make a necklace.* Same as #4.74 but uses half-inch beads or Cheerios. Do not provide verbal prompting through the two-stage process while the child is stringing.

Credit: (see also Credit Notes in this strand's preface)

+ can string at least one small bead or Cheerio, pulling the string out through the other side after threading it without verbal prompting.

4-7 MANIPULATIVE PREHENSION

D. SCISSORS

| 4.81 | 23-25 | Snips with scissors |
| 4.88 | 28-35 | Snips on line using scissors |

Family Friendly Interpretation of Strand Concepts, Assessment, & Purpose

Cutting with a scissors is a difficult skill which requires good fine motor coordination and involves a variety of arm, hand and finger movements. A child must be able to separate and figure out how to move his fingers in different directions to make the scissors cut. At this stage, we would not expect a child to be able to cut across a piece of paper. Instead, he needs to practice "snipping", which requires him to make only one small cut in the paper. "Snipping" helps your child prepare for later, more advanced cutting skills.

Parent Questions   (Examples)

To help identify the child's unique strengths and needs related to this developmental area:
• Has your child ever tried to use a scissors?
If so,
• What type of scissors has he used?
• Is he able to make any cuts or snips on the paper?

To help identify family resources, priorities and concerns related to the child's development in this area:
• Are you interested in having your child learn to use scissors at this age?
• *If so, are* there times during the week when someone could play with and supervise craft activities with your child?

Sample *Functional* Outcome Statements which may be generated by the Family

[Will be dependent upon identified individual child and family needs and should incorporate objectives and activities from other domains]

My child will be learning how to cut safely with a scissors.

Identifying and Interpreting Needs for Intervention

If a child is delayed in this area, he may be having difficulty with <u>coordinating and controlling a variety of arm, hand, thumb and finger movements</u> which are needed to manipulate a scissors.

However, before targeting this as the primary area of need for intervention, consider and rule out, or adapt for other causes which may interfere with a true assessment of the child's ability to coordinate and control a variety of thumb and finger movements. These may include:
• <u>Hand weakness or sore, swollen joints;</u>
• <u>Lack of interest.</u>

Assessment Adaptations   (Examples)

[Note any adaptations needed to credit and help plan interventions]
• <u>Visually impaired</u>: thoroughly orient the child to the scissors and the process of snipping by using hand-over-hand guidance (or a double-handle grip scissors) before assessing. Show him how you cut the paper and then assist him to make a snip, letting him feel the cut. Describe how the paper was once one piece and now there are two parts to it. Omit #4.88 for the totally blind child, and use darkened lines on high-contrast paper for the child with low vision.
• <u>Motor Impaired</u>:
  – The child should be positioned in a manner that provides adequate trunk support with his arms and shoulders positioned forward. *Consult with an occupational or physical therapist for specific individualized optimal positions.* Stabilize hand and forearm in mid-range on the tabletop; adaptive scissors and seating may be helpful.
  – If the child has difficulty using one arm and hand, hold the paper taut for him.
  – A child with severe motor impairments may not develop typical or mature grasping patterns, range of motion, arm and wrist stability, or finger disassociation, which are prerequisites for cutting. Mark N/A for these items which may be inappropriate to assess and plan for functional skill development. (Refer to the NOTE in the Fine Motor II Overview on page 250.)

General Assessment Procedures & Processes   (apply to all items in this Strand)

1. Note child's hand preference.
2. The child should be in a position that promotes safety, good posture and enables him to move his arms and hands freely; this should generally be in a seated position with his feet flat on the floor, back supported by chair back, and at a child-sized table.
3. **Demonstrate and make remarks about the** <u>safe use</u> **of a scissors**; e.g., "Only use scissors to cut paper; always hold it with the point facing away; only use a scissors when you are sitting at a table; put scissors away, point down in a container when you are finished."
4. **This strand may be assessed when the child is playing with paper and crayon activities** in previous fine motor strands.
5. Describe the skill or eliciting procedures and invite family members to help observe and/or assess.

+ - A Credit Notes:
+   child snips paper as defined.
-   not observed or reported.
+/- appears to be an emerging skill; child is interested and has the fine motor control, but can not actually snip paper.
A   atypical, e.g., arm pronated (palm down); wrist flexed.

Note any adaptations used to credit.

Assessment Materials

- Small, blunt preschool-type scissors;
- Eight 1/2 by 11 inch piece of blank, sturdy paper, cut in half;
- Black marker.

4.81 Snips with scissors   23-25

Definition: The child cuts a paper edge randomly one snip at a time, rather than using a continuous cutting motion.

Example Observation Opportunities: <u>Incidental</u> - may observe while child is preparing for a "tea party" with stuffed animals or dolls. Demonstrate making fringe on paper placemats and invite the child to help. <u>Structured</u> - using a half-piece of sturdy paper and blunt scissors, make three snips in separate places along the edge of the paper while the child is watching. Exaggerate the opening and closing motions of your hand. Offer the child the scissors and invite him to make a cut. Let him explore the scissors (if interested), helping him position the scissors in his hand, as needed.

Credit: (see also Credit Notes in this strand's preface)
+   snips paper in one place, holding the paper in one hand and scissors in the other.

4.88 Snips on line using scissors   28-35

Definition: The child can cut on a line using a snipping movement rather than a continuous cutting motion.

Example Observation Opportunities: <u>Incidental</u> - may observe as in #4.81 if you draw lines along the edge of the paper placemats to cut, or during a craft activity demonstrate snipping 1/2-inch strips of colored paper or ribbon to make squares for a pasting activity or collage. <u>Structured</u> - draw bold 1/2-inch lines across a 6-inch long, 1/2-inch wide strip of paper with a black marker. Demonstrate snipping with the scissors to cut off a piece of paper along the line. Exaggerate the opening and closing motions of your hand. Offer the child the scissors and invite him to make a cut on the line. Let him explore the scissors, if interested, helping him position the scissors in his hand, as needed. Point to the line the child should cut on.

Credit: (see also Credit Notes in this strand's preface)
+   makes at least one snip on two different lines.

5.0 - Social-Emotional Development
Introduction

Overview

This domain has been divided into five (5) interrelated strands:
- 5-1 Attachment/Separation/Autonomy
- 5-2 Development of Self
- 5-3 Expression of Emotions and Feelings
- 5-4 Learning Rules and Social Expectations
- 5-5 Social Interactions and Play

Key Points

- *Include an infant mental health therapist in assessment and planning:* If the child displays significant delays or atypical social and emotional behaviors, it will be *especially important* to involve a qualified child psychologist or other infant mental health specialist in assessment and planning.
- Structure of Assessment: The child's social-emotional behaviors cannot be assessed nor understood in isolation of other areas of development nor in one setting. Assessment should occur through sensitive parent interview and through several observations of the child, in multiple settings with his primary caregivers, siblings and peers, and during play, dressing, feeding, diapering and while assessing other areas of development.
- Dependence on transactional assessment: The child's social interactions, emotions, and behaviors develop and evolve within the context of family-child and peer relationships and the environments in which they occur. It is within this context that the child experiences the security of relationships, learns which emotional expressions are acceptable, and learns to interact socially with others. It is only within this transactional inter-play that the child's social-emotional development can be assessed and understood. Assessment of environments and interactions that support or compromise the child's social-emotional development is included in the preface of each strand and *should be carefully considered during assessment and intervention planning*.

5-1 ATTACHMENT/SEPARATION/AUTONOMY

5.01	0-3	Enjoys and needs a great deal of physical contact and tactile stimulation
5.04	0-2	Establishes eye contact
5.06	0-3	Draws attention to self when in distress
1.18	3-6	Awakens or quiets to parent's voice
5.11	3-5	Socializes with strangers/anyone
5.10	3-6	Discriminates strangers
5.17	4-8	Recognizes parent visually
5.21	*5-9*	Lifts arms to parent
5.22	5-7	Explores adult features
5.20	5-8	Displays stranger anxiety
5.25	*6-10*	Shows anxiety over separation from parent
5.31	8-12	Lets only parent meet his needs
5.36	9-12	Explores environment enthusiastically- safety precautions important
5.37	12-13	Likes to be in constant sight and hearing of adult
5.41	12-15	Attempts self-direction; resists adult control
5.69	24-30	Displays dependent behavior; clings/whines
5.68	24-36	Feels strongly possessive of loved ones
5.85	30-36	Separates easily from parent in familiar surroundings
5.86	30-36	Shows independence; runs ahead of parent outdoors, refuses to have hand held
6.75	30 +	Insists on doing things independently

Family Friendly Interpretation of Strand Concepts, Assessment, & Purpose

During the first 2 years of life, children develop special relationships and attachments to their parents. Your child learns to trust and feel secure in his world by this special relationship with you. Since this relationship is so important to him, he may do many things to get your attention or to be close to you. Before he can talk or move around, he may try to get close by crying, looking at you, or smiling. Since he knows he needs you to feel protected, he may go through a stage of getting upset when you leave because he worries you may not return. Developing a secure attachment is thought to be important for a child's later relationships with other people.

Developing a special attachment with you helps give your child the trust he needs to also be able to move away from you to explore and be independent. This is both frightening and exciting to a young child because he is eager to explore his world and be independent, but he also realizes he is dependent on his parents and relies on them to feel safe. That is why, as your child learns to move around, he may want to follow you or keep you in sight.

Professional FYI

This strand can be considered the core area and foundation of the other four strands in the Social-Emotional domain. The quality and development of a positive self-esteem, expression of emotions, social relationships with others, the development of social expectations, and the learning of limits and rules have their roots in the development of a healthy and secure infant-caregiver attachment.

Both partners, the parent and the child, play critical and interdependent roles in the attachment process. Attachment is a "two-way" process. Infants attach to caregivers and caregivers become attached to infants. Thus, this strand provides a framework for infant-caregiver attachment rather than just infant attachment.

• Caregiver risk factors that may compromise a secure attachment relationship include: premature delivery, disabilities, extended separations or hospitalizations, parent's own attachment history with their parents, and parent's mental health status and emotional availability.

• Infant risk factors that can compromise an infant's ability to contribute to the attachment relationship include: prematurity, delays and disabilities, atypical muscle tone, sensory and regulatory disorders, temperament, extended separations and/or hospitalizations and related trauma.

• System/social risk factors can include separation of parents from their child during hospitalizations and a series of foster care placements.

Parent Questions   (General Examples - see Skills for specific questions)

To help identify unique strengths and needs related to the development of a secure attachment relationship:
- How does your child let you know you he loves you and that you are special to him? When did you first notice this?
- Can you tell me a little about how your relationship seems to be going with your child?
- Does your child seem to act differently with you than with other people? *If so,* Can you give me some examples? Do you have any thoughts on why he does this?
- Who are the people to whom your child seems to feel closest?
- What adults does your child see most often? *[Continue to probe the roles of significant adults, e.g., who feeds, bathes, plays, as well as the frequency]*
- Have you been away from your child for more than one or two days? *[If so, inquire–how old the child was at the time of separation, the child's reactions, and circumstances of separation]*
- Are there any events that your child has been through that may have been painful, traumatic or scary for him (e.g., hospitalization, divorce, other trauma)?
- Is this a fairly typical day for your child? Does he usually act like this?
- Do you think your child is feeling pretty good today? Is he tired? When did he last eat? Has he been sick?

To help identify family concerns, priorities and resources related to the child's development in this area:
- Is there anything about your relationship with your child that you feel is especially important to understand better or to work on?
- If you could think of one thing that would help make life easier with your child, what would it be?
- What have you tried so far that seems to help *[Complete with needs identified above, e.g., What have you tried so far that seems to get your child to smile?]*
- Are family or friends nearby that you feel you can call on to help with the extra demands and stresses of having a young child (with special needs, if applicable)?

Sample *Functional* Outcome Statements which may be generated by the Family

[Will be dependent upon identified individual child and family needs and should incorporate objectives and activities from other domains]
My child will:
- Look at me when I smile and talk to him;
- Feel safe and secure in our relationship;
- Be happy;
- Do things on his own without always needing me to hold him;
- Not cry for so long when I come back from leaving him with a baby-sitter.

I will have a better understanding of and be able to help my child when:
- He gets upset if I leave;
- He gets upset when he sees strangers.

Transactional Assessment

May assess through observation and interview.

Assessment of the Child's Environment

1. Supportive:
[Environments that support or facilitate development in this area]
The child's caregiving environments usually:
- Are safe to explore;
- Are interesting and "invite" the child to explore;
- Provide consistent primary caregivers;
- Provide fairly consistent and predictable routines.

2. Compromising:
The child's caregiving environments are frequently:
- Unsafe;
- Unpredictable, e.g., no steady caregivers, lack of routines;
- Overly restrictive, i.e., do not allow the child to explore; e.g., too much time is spent in a crib or playpen.

Assessment of Caregiver Interactions with the Child

1. Supportive:

[Interactions that support or facilitate a secure attachment and independence]

The child's caregivers usually:

• Are available to comfort and nurture the child;

• Provide predictable routines;

• Are able to read and respond sensitively to the child's unique communicative signals and cues which request comfort, closeness, protection, reassurance and independence;

• Admire and encourage the child's autonomous behaviors and are tolerant of the child's assertive behaviors;

• Smile, touch, look at, and talk to their child with warmth and sensitivity;

• Act as a "secure base" as the child becomes mobile, e.g., keep in verbal and visual range; provide reassuring looks and hugs;

• Balance their protective interaction with "letting go" interactions as the child becomes more independent;

• Hold and comfort child when he is upset or afraid;

• Are empathetic about the child's separation anxieties.

B. Compromising

The child's caregivers frequently:

• Ignore, misinterpret and/or respond inappropriately to the child's bids for closeness, attention, and protection;

• Are unavailable or do not try to comfort the child;

• Avoid holding or interacting with the child;

• Overprotect, punish, or restrict the child's autonomous behaviors;

• Are over-stimulating, intrusive to the child's state and moods;

• Are hostile, distant, ignoring, abusive or neglecting to the child

[Important note: Caregivers may have difficulty providing supportive interactions because the child is or has a history of being medically fragile or because the child is a poor interactor. An invested parent may be exhausted, try too hard, worry about "rocking the boat" when the child is quiet, or may be overprotective because of the child's current or past medical condition. Consequently, interactions can appear compromising]

Identifying and Interpreting Needs for Intervention

If the child displays persistent and significant delays or atypical behaviors in this strand, especially if more so than in cognitive or motor development, he may be having difficulty in establishing a secure attachment.

This may be due to a primary socioemotional-communicative disorder, or it may be a symptom of difficulty in establishing trust and security in his caregiving relationship. *Consult with an infant mental health therapist regarding interventions and further evaluations.*

However, before targeting the caregiving relationship or socioemotional disorder as the primary or only need for intervention, consider other areas of the child's development and experiences that can influence or interfere with the development of a secure attachment. These may include:

• Sensory or regulatory disorders or difficult temperament: the child may be over- or underreactive to the environment and interactions, causing irritability, gaze aversion, extreme fearfulness, low affect, etc.;

• Motor impairment, motor delays, atypical tone: the child may not have the mobility skills needed to practice moving away from his parent to explore and practice independence; the child may have unclear, more subtle, weaker or distorted cues and signals; smiles may be weak or distorted;

• Visual impairment: child may have unclear or more subtle cues and signals to caregivers; child may be more fearful to leave parent to explore unknown territory; smiles may be weaker; child may appear rejecting when he stiffens or startles to unexpected approaches; child cannot rely on caregiver's eye contact or facial expressions for feedback and social engagement;

• Cognitive delays in the areas of object (people) permanence and/or goal-directed behaviors and understanding of cause and effect;

• Medically fragile: the child may be in pain, have undergone extreme stress and trauma, and/or have experienced long separations from parent;

• Transient benign stressful situations that are likely to resolve; e.g., child is tired, hungry, ill; parent has recently returned to work; new baby at home; recent move.

Assessment Adaptations   (Examples)

- Sensory or regulatory disorders: refer to Regulatory/Sensory Organization (0.0); *involve a pediatric therapist with experience in sensory integration in the assessment to adapt procedures and help plan interventions;*
- Motor impairment: *consult with a pediatric occupational or physical therapist for appropriate positioning and handling techniques and to identify possible adaptive strategies* that help the child practice physically moving away from the parent. Observe the child closely for the unique, subtle or alternative signaling systems he may be using;
- Visual impairment: if observations do not occur in the child's home, allow ample time for the child to explore the observation area/playroom and toys with his parent. Facilitators and parents should use frequent verbal, tactile and other auditory cues that help the child prepare for and recognize when they are leaving, moving to another area of the room and approaching him. Adapt or modify the following items:

  #5.04 "Establishes eye contact" - look for other differential attachment responses such as special hand or other subtle bodily movements; becoming quiet or still; change in breathing pattern.

  #5.17 "Recognizes parent visually" - substitute recognizing caregiver visually with smell or touch. Look for unique differential responses as described above in #5.04.

  #5.21 "Lifts arms to parent" - unless the child has specifically been taught to raise his arms up vertically, he probably will not do this spontaneously. Credit other bodily responses that the parents are able to interpret as meaning the child is requesting to be picked up.

  #5.36 "Explores environment enthusiastically" - may be typically delayed; child may need extra encouragement and motivation.

  #5.85 "Separates easily in familiar surroundings" - separation anxiety may normally continue.

- Transient benign stressful situations: reassess on multiple occasions as stressful situation resolves.

General Assessment Procedures & Processes   (apply to all items in this Strand)

1. *Reminder:* **the age ranges listed represent the age range within which these behaviors** *typically* **emerge.** The listed age range does *not* mean that the behavior begins and ends within that time frame.

   a. Although some behaviors are integrated and/or replaced by different behaviors, many continue throughout toddlerhood. For example, separation anxiety (#5.25) may typically continue for more than 2 years. Thus if a child is 18 months and displays separation anxiety, he should not be reported to be displaying behaviors at the 6-10 month level.

   b. Two items in this strand continue to be key indications of a secure attachment and should thus continue to be assessed *at and beyond* the expected age range of emergence:
   #5.04 "Establishes eye contact" (0-2 mo.)
   #5.36 "Explores environment enthusiastically..." (9-12 mo.)

2. **Structure of assessment:** assessment should occur through multiple observations in multiple settings of parent-infant interactions during play, dressing, feeding, diapering. Assessment can occur while assessing other areas of development as well as through sensitive parent interview.

3. **Cultural/family diversity:** some cultures and families will have different values and belief systems related to discipline, who the primary caregivers and decision makers in the family are, age expectations for independence, and the role of eye contact or avoiding direct eye contact as a sign of respect. These values and beliefs can be elicited through sensitive family interview (see parent questions above) and observations of the family. *Developmental expectations and interventions for the child should be adjusted accordingly.*

4. **Descriptive reporting** versus identifying age ranges:

   a. With many infants and toddlers, it will be more useful and appropriate to describe the child's attachment and separation behaviors rather than assign age levels. Rationale:

   (1). If a child displays atypical or extreme attachment behaviors, it may not be appropriate to assign development age levels since these behaviors <u>may not be appropriate at any age.</u>

   (2). There is an imaginary gap in this strand for children who are 15-24 months. There are no new attachment behaviors on any of the strands that emerge during this age range. Instead earlier behaviors typically continue and become more refined, practiced or evident. Thus, if a child is 18-24 months old, and

General Assessment Procedures & Processes (continued)

displays typical behaviors up to the 12-15 month age range, this does not mean the child is delayed at the 12-15 month range.

(3). Some children may not display all typical behaviors, or may not display them in the expected age of emergence because of individual, environmental or cultural differences. For example, a 9-month-old child who is accustomed to and has had safe, positive experiences with multiple caregivers and caregiving environments may not display stranger or separation anxiety. If the child appears safe and comfortable in his relationship with his parents, it would not be appropriate to report that he is delayed.

(4). Age levels are not useful for families in understanding their child's behaviors. Descriptions of the child behaviors that are typical can provide parents with an expanded view of their child's behavior that can help them "reframe" what may have been perceived as "bad" or "difficult" behaviors.

b. Descriptive statements with clinical and family interpretation can thus be more useful for reporting, determining strengths and needs, and intervention planning than assigning specific age levels. Examples:

(1). Case Example: a 12-month-old who displays many typical behaviors for his age range:

"Johnny displays many behaviors that are typical for a child his age related to attachment and separation issues. He appeared initially hesitant to one of the therapists he had not met and reached for his parent but was easily consoled when she held him. Johnny was interested in moving off his mother's lap to explore a toy but periodically looked to make sure she was still there. When his mother left the room for a few minutes, he cried briefly, watched the door, and stopped playing with a toy. Upon her return he cried and approached her but was quickly consoled with a brief hug and resumed his play with a toy."

(2). Case Example: a 12-month-old child who does not display behaviors typical for a child at any age range on the strands.

"Michael appears to be having difficulty

dealing with issues related to attachment and separation. His foster mother reports that he typically resists being held and frequently bangs his head against her while arching his back. He becomes upset, however, when she puts him down. He sat next to her holding on to her skirt during most of the session. He would not move away from her to play with toys that are reported as favorites but did engage in play if the toy was brought to him. His foster mother reports that when she leaves him he usually cries until he falls asleep. Upon her return he resumes crying and does not calm down for at least 10 minutes. Sometimes it takes him an hour to "recover."

(3). Case Example: a 20-month-old child who displays typical behaviors expected at her age, but on the strands, she would at first glance "ceil out" at the 12-15 month level.

"Sally displays many stage expected behaviors that reflect her secure attachment and continuing strive for independence. She freely explored our playroom and various toys, periodically turning to see if her father was still present and watching her. She was also willing and eager to try unfamiliar materials and equipment, with some verbal reassurance from her dad. Sally demonstrated many signs of learning and enjoying independence. After becoming comfortable in our playroom, Sally attempted self-direction in many activities, resisting adult help. For example, she refused help in figuring out how to use a switch toy, preferring to try to figure it out herself."

+ - A Credit Notes:

+   child displays typical behaviors as defined.

-    child does not display behavior.

A   child does display behavior, but the behavior is predominantly extreme.

O   circle the credit - or +, if:
  a. the environment or caregiver interactions compromise the child's secure attachment behavior;
  b. caregivers are having difficulty understanding or dealing with the child's behaviors.

N/A not appropriate due to child's disability.

Assessment Materials

Not applicable. This strand is assessed in the context of general observation and interview.

5.01 Enjoys and needs a great deal of physical contact and tactile stimulation 0-3

Definition: The child needs and seeks close and frequent contacts, such as touching and holding, from responsive caregivers. He may cry, vocalize, look toward, and/or smile to establish this contact.

Parent Questions: Does your child usually like to be touched and held? When do you usually hold him? (may ask further, e.g., during feeding, when child cries, to play, just for fun?)

Example Observation Opportunities: Provide ample opportunities for parent to hold and interact with the child during the observation period. Be sure to give parent "permission" to pick up or touch the child whenever he seems to need the parent. May also observe if child calms down when fussy, if parent picks him up or strokes him. If the parent does not spontaneously touch or pick up the child during the observation period, determine through sensitive questioning if the parent avoids close contact because the child becomes fussy when held.

Credit: (see also Credit Notes in this strand's preface)
- \+   child is beginning to give clear signals to his parent when he wants physical contact (e.g., fusses, looks toward, or smiles) and sometimes shows he enjoys the contact by looking, vocalizing, becoming alert or calm, and/or molding when held.
- \-   child does <u>not</u> display cues that attract parental contact and/or usually cries, arches, fusses excessively, typically pulls away, or shows no reaction and does not seem to notice that he is being touched (refer to 0.0 - Regulatory/Sensory Organization).
- A   child needs constant holding (refer to 0.0 - Regulatory/Sensory Organization).
- O   circle any credit if caregivers avoid or provide minimal touching or holding; or have difficulty identifying positions and tactile contact that is pleasurable for the child.

5.04 Establishes eye contact   0-2

Definition: The child usually enjoys looking into the eyes of others who look at him at a comfortable distance, a few seconds at a time. He may divert his gaze when he's tired, upset or over-stimulated, but should not consistently resist eye-to-eye contact.

Parent Questions: Does your child seem to really look at you when you are looking at him? Are there times when it seems hard to get him to look at you?

Example Observation Opportunities: May observe when child is content, and parent and the facilitators (on different occasions) are holding, feeding, talking to or playing with the child. It may be helpful to observe and note which naturally occurring interactions effectively elicit the child's eye contact, e.g., facial expression, distance, high-pitched voice. If eye contact is sporadic or more difficult to achieve, adjust your position and interactions to observe if eye contact is more easily established and note accordingly; e.g., dim lights, hold in upright position, or reduce interactions by only looking and smiling at child rather than holding, talking and looking.

Credit: (see also Credit Notes in this strand's preface)
- \+   it is usually easy to establish eye contact with the child for at least few seconds at a time.
- \-   child usually turns away or averts gaze, or eye contact is difficult or rarely established.
- A   in older child, displays extreme vigilance, i.e., always watches adult with wide-eyed, fearful expression.
- O   circle any credit if caregivers provide minimal eye contact, over-stimulate, or, do not interpret or respond to child's eye contact as a signal for interaction.

5.06 Draws attention to self when in distress   0-3

Definition: The child cries or fusses to elicit the attention and approach of a caregiver. During the first 2 months, his cries for attention are indiscriminate for any adult.

Parent Questions: How does your baby try to get your attention?

Example Observation Opportunities: Anytime child is awake and not receiving direct attention.

Credit: (see also Credit Notes in this strand's preface)
- \+   cries or fusses effectively to attract his caregiver's attention.
- \-   child rarely cries or fusses for attention even under stressful situations (e.g., wet diaper, hungry) or signals are weak and difficult to read.
- A   always cries excessively and demands constant holding.
- O   circle any credit if caregiver does not respond to child's bids for attention and/or interprets child's cries as "mean" or "bad."

1.18   Awakens or quiets to parent's voice   3-6

Definition: The child displays special preferential responses when he hears his parent's voice. For example, he may "still," quiet, turn to find, calm when upset, or may transition from sleep to awake more easily upon hearing his caregiver's soothing voice.

Parent Questions: Are there things you do or say when your child is fussy that seem to help him calm or feel better?

Example Observation Opportunities: Observe child's responses when he cannot see but hears his parent's voice; when parent talks to the child to gain attention or to play; and when the child fusses or awakens from a nap.

Credit: (see also Credit Notes in this strand's preface)
- \+   displays several instances of preferential responses to his parent's voice as defined.
- \-   usually does not respond differentially to parent's voice.
- A   usually responds in a negative way to or is rarely soothed by parent's verbal interactions.
- O   circle any credit if caregivers have difficulty recognizing, interpreting or responding to child's preferential responses, or provide minimal sensitive verbal interactions with child.

5.11   Socializes with strangers/anyone   3-5

Definition: At this stage, the child typically has not developed stranger anxiety and will thus usually socialize with any friendly person. Some infants may be slower to warm up or more cautious and need a brief warm-up period. The child may socialize by smiling, vocalizing, and/or enjoy a game such as "Pat-a-cake" or "Peek-a-boo."

Parent Questions: How does your child react to new people?

Example Observation Opportunities: If the child is not familiar with you, allow a few minutes warm-up period with his parent and/or a familiar toy before interacting. Then initiate a short phrase or game that parents report the child enjoys. Allow the more cautious baby to remain on the parent's lap.

Credit: (see also Credit Notes in this strand's preface)
- \+   socializes typically, by report or observation, with most people who approach sensitively; he more readily and frequently smiles at his caregivers.
- \-   is usually disinterested in people and turns away or displays a "flat" affect, even with ample warm-up time and if held by parent.
- A   always smiles readily to friendly strangers but averts gaze and/or rarely smiles to caregiver.

5.10   Discriminates strangers   3-6

Definition: The child discriminates familiar caregivers from unfamiliar people. Although he readily smiles to loved ones, when he sees a stranger he may initially "freeze up," stare, quiet, or refuse to smile.

Parent Questions: Does your child act differently when he meets someone new? In what way?

Example Observation Opportunities: Observe the child's expressions when initially meeting the child and when other staff enter the room.

Credit: (see also Credit Notes in this strand's preface)
- \+   acts differently when he initially meets a new person; e.g., he may delay a smile to a stranger (although he readily smiles to his parent), stare or become somber and quiet.
- \-   does not react to strangers any differently than he responds to parents.
- A   clings to all adults even when they are strangers.

(may also credit #5.20 "Displays stranger anxiety" if child displays overt anxiety)

5.17   Recognizes parent visually   4-8

Definition: The child shows differentiated and preferential responses when he sees his primary caregiver. He may smile more, excite, reach for, watch parent move around room, make postural shifts, vocalize and/or fuss when he sees his parent to initiate or maintain his caregiver's attention and closeness.

Example Observation Opportunities: May observe anytime when parent reenters child's visual field, e.g., returning from disposing a diaper, warming a bottle, getting a toy. May also observe when parent and facilitator are both near child. Observe if child displays different and more varied or intense responses to the parent than you or others in the room.

Credit: (see also Credit Notes in this strand's preface)
- \+   displays several instances of preferential/pleasurable responses as defined when he sees his parent.
- \-   child's expression or emotional response rarely changes upon seeing parent.
- A   usually responds in a negative way, e.g., averts gaze, fusses.
- O   circle any credit if parent reports difficulty recognizing, interpreting or responding to child's preferential responses.

5.21   Lifts arms to parent   *5-9*

Definition: The child puts his arms out to his parents (and other trusted caregivers) to signal that he wants to be held, picked up, comforted, or "rescued" from an unfamiliar or strange situation, e.g., if a stranger approaches child.

Parent Questions: Does your child let you know when he wants you to pick him up, e.g., out of his crib, playpen or high chair? How does he do this?

Example Observation Opportunities: Observe when child wants to get out of any situation that may occur during observation period, e.g., if he wants another parent to hold him, if he wants parent to "save him" when another approaches or tries to pick him up, when he wants to leave a situation or position, when parent starts to leave or enters room, when child is stressed.

Credit: (see also Credit Notes in this strand's preface)
+   lifts his arms (or some other preferential gesture) to his parents to indicate he wants to be picked up, comforted, rescued, etc.
-   child does not look toward, lift arms, or otherwise gesture to his parents for comfort when distressed.
A   insists on being held all the time or cries easily when not being held.
O   circle any credit if parents have difficulty interpreting or responding to child's gestural requests for comfort.

(also in Strand 2-4A "Communicating with Others: Gesturally")

5.22   Explores adult features   *5-7*

Definition: The child is curious about and seems to "study" his parent's face. He may begin to touch, poke, probe, and/or pat his parent's face and hair to explore. The child is learning that his primary attachment figure is a separate person from himself.

Parent Questions: Does your child like to touch or poke at your face? *If so,* What does he do? Why do you think he likes to do that?

Example Observation Opportunities: May be observed during any close face-to-face contact between parent and child when child is content, e.g., during feeding, after a diaper change, before assessment.

Credit: (see also Credit Notes in this strand's preface)
+   purposefully touches, pats, pokes and visually studies parent's facial features to explore.
A   (after 12 months) prolonged staring at or touching of faces without real social intent.
O   circle any credit if caregivers interpret child's exploration as being difficult or mean, e.g., if he accidentally scratches or pulls hair, or if caregiver avoids close comfortable face-to-face contact.

(may also credit in Strand 5-2 "Development of Self")

5.20   Displays stranger anxiety   *5-8*

Definition: As the child begins to learn that he is separate from his parent, stranger anxiety may emerge. The child may actively resist, reject, reach for or move to his parent, or cry if an unfamiliar person approaches or even looks at him. The parent can usually reassure and console the child with holding, touching or verbal reassurance, if the stranger maintains his distance and is introduced gradually. *[If the child is fatigued, ill or hungry, his anxiety responses may be more intense. Frequent or long hospitalizations or other situations perceived by the infant as traumatic may also cause more exaggerated or prolonged stranger anxiety responses]*

Parent Questions: Does your child usually get upset when he sees new or unfamiliar people? *If so,* how can you tell? About how long has he been doing this? Why do you think he acts this way? Does anything seem to help when he gets upset when he sees strangers? *[If child reportedly does not get upset - probe if child has already been through this stage]*

Example Observation Opportunities: May observe when child initially meets you or other staff who enter the observation setting.

Credit: (see also Credit Notes in this strand's preface)
+   child is observed or reported to display any signs of stranger anxiety as defined.
-   child rarely or never displays anxiety when a stranger approaches.
A   evidences extreme and prolonged anxiety responses even when held and reassured by parent, and stranger maintains a safe distance; takes more than 15 minutes to recover from anxiety (in a safe environment); or clings to any adult without discriminating primary caregivers.
O   circle any credit if caregivers usually interpret child's responses to strangers as "bad" or "mean," punishes child for negative responses; does not try to console or reassure child or request help in dealing with child's anxiety.
N/A if appropriately not present, e.g., child has already reportedly gone through this stage; child is used to meeting a variety of trusting strangers.

5.25 Shows anxiety over separation from parent *6-10*

Definition: Beginning anywhere between 6-10 months and extending through toddlerhood, children typically demonstrate anxiety and distress when separated even for brief periods from a primary caregiver. This anxiety is related to the child's feelings of strong dependence on his caregiver for security and his feeling unprotected when separated. For many children, separation anxiety peaks at about 18 months and then gradually declines.

A child's signs of anxiety frequently include one or more of the following: refusal to explore the environment or toys that he otherwise would have explored in his parent's presence; crying; searching; diminished activity level; low-keyed somber mood, going to sleep. Upon the parent's reunion after a short separation, the child who has developed a secure attachment generally shows signs of a fairly quick "recovery," e.g., promptly smiles to greet, shows a toy, moves close to parent, stops crying.

The degree, intensity, and duration of these behaviors vary with each child, age, experiences with prior separations, and with the circumstances of separation.

Important notes:

1. Infants who have experienced early out-of-home sensitive care on a daily basis may have become accustomed to repeated separations and reunions with their parents. They may evidence minimal distress at separation and a more nonchalant response on their return.

2. If the child is fatigued, ill or hungry, his anxiety responses may be more intense. Frequent or long hospitalizations, change in primary caregivers, or other situations perceived by the infant as traumatic may also cause more exaggerated or prolonged separation anxiety responses.

Parent Questions: How does your child react when you leave him to go to the store or to work? Why do you think he acts like that? How is that for you? What have you tried to deal with his distress when you need to leave? How does your child react to seeing you after you come back from a separation?

Example Observation Opportunities: Observe child's responses when his parent leaves or moves away from child to, e.g., warm a bottle, retrieve coats, get a diaper, go to restroom.

Credit: (see also Credit Notes in this strand's preface)

+   displays typical signs of distress as defined when separated from his parent.
-    child usually does not look or change his behavior when parent leaves or returns.
A   if child usually displays prolonged, avoidant, angry or ambivalent responses when parent returns from a brief separation, e.g., continues to cry, cling, hit, whine, hit, ignore, turn or move away from parent.
O   circle any credit if parent requests support and anticipatory guidance during this stage, or misinterprets child's anxiety as "bad" or "mean."
N/A   if appropriately not present, e.g., child is developmentally over 12 months, appears to enjoy a secure and satisfying relationship with an attachment figure and is accustomed to repeated frequent separations.

5.31 Lets only parent meet his needs 8-12

Definition: The child, during this stage, often displays a strong preference toward his primary caregiver to provide his basic needs, even when other caring adults are present, e.g., to feed, dress, change and comfort him. If his caregiver is not present, however, he may accept caregiving from others.

Parent Questions: Does it seem as if your child only wants you to feed, bathe, or change him even when other family members are around? *If yes*, Can you give me some examples? How do you handle this? Why do you think he acts this way?

Example Observation Opportunities: May observe if other family members are present and offer to help with a caregiving activity and child refuses or moves toward primary attachment figure.

Credit: (see also Credit Notes in this strand's preface)

+   sometimes refuses caregiving from adults other than a parent if that parent is present.
-    usually does not make requests preferentially to parent to satisfy needs.
A   always demands constant attention and cannot tolerate being alone even briefly; has tantrums or "falls apart" if his demands are not met immediately.
O   circle any credit if parents find this troublesome and request anticipatory guidance and support.
N/A   if not observed or reported but child does enjoy parental help.

5.36 Explores environment enthusiastically- safety precautions important 9-12

Definition: The child enjoys and is comfortable investigating new environments in the presence of a trusted caregiver as a "secure base." As he explores new territory, he periodically checks on his caregiver's whereabouts, sometimes needing some physical or verbal reassurance. If the child is hungry, tired or ill, he may be less interested in exploring the environment.

[The child's willingness and interest in exploring new environments develop out of his increased cognitive and motor abilities, as well as his strive for independence that originates from the security he feels in a secure attachment with his primary caregiver. Since children at this stage are highly interested in exploration and unaware of many unsafe situations and material, adult supervision and safety precautions are critical]

Example Observation Opportunities: May observe child's interest and eagerness to explore over several occasions when the child is feeling comfortable in the environment and his parent is within visual range. Observe the child's willingness to explore and the parent's interactions that support his exploration.

Credit: (see also Credit Notes in this strand's preface)
+ comfortably moves away from his primary caregiver to explore new and interesting environments but also periodically checks in with parent, e.g., looking to see that parent is still there, showing or pointing to an object, going to parent for a brief touch or hug.
- frequently withdraws from exploring new toys or environments in the presence of his parent (may become clingy, angry, inconsolable).
A has tendency to run off and explore strange environments with no apparent concern for the whereabouts of his caregiver; or prefers self-stimulating activities, e.g., pre-occupation with specific objects without including caregivers.
N/A if child's disability prevents him from exploring environment. See adaptations in this strand's preface.
O circle any credit if parent usually prevents child from exploring; and/or if safe environments are not frequently available for child to explore; or parent does not keep eye on child or offer reassurance when child seeks it.

5.37 Likes to be in constant sight and hearing of adult 12-13

Definition: The child usually wants his primary caregiver to be within his sight or hearing range. At this stage, the child needs his parent as a "secure base" from which he can feel safe to play or explore. This item is very similar to #5.36, and typically peaks through 18-24 months.

Parent Questions: Does your child seem to follow you around a lot at home? *If so,* Any thought on why he does this?

Example Observation Opportunities: May observe anytime throughout observation period, especially when the child moves to a new area of the room or explores a new toy.

Credit: (see also Credit Notes in this strand's preface)
+ frequently follows parent around or periodically checks to make sure parent is nearby.
- frequently wanders aimlessly without regard for parent; may be destructive and get hurt.
A rarely takes his eyes off his parent and does not explore the environment or toys; is afraid to leave parent's lap; wants to be picked up constantly; if over 18 months, always needs more than parent's verbal or facial reassurance when playing across a room, e.g., goes to parent for physical contact every few minutes; or never attempts to engage parent in a joint activity or an interesting environmental event.
O circle any credit if parent reports these behaviors as troublesome or if parent punishes or prevents child from maintaining proximity.

5.41 Attempts self-direction; resists adult control 12-15

Definition: During this stage, which continues through toddlerhood, the child begins to become self-assertive as he strives to be independent. He wants to determine his own activities and do things for himself. He may thus resist adult help, even if he knows he can't do a good job, e.g., wanting to feed himself, dress himself, figure out how a toy works. He also wants to make his own decisions about things, e.g., what toys to play with, which foods he'll eat, which rules he'll comply with. Resisting parent control is another sign of the child's emerging sense of autonomy and independence arising from the development of trust from a secure attachment.

Parent Questions: Does your child sometimes want to do things for himself and refuse your help? Can you give me some examples? How do you handle this?

Example Observation Opportunities: May observe when parent tries to help child with something; e.g., child pushes adult hand away when parent tries to help him with his cup or a toy. May also observe

Attempts self-direction; resists adult control   (continued)

when child tries to overrule an adult decision; e.g., adult tries to engage child in one toy, but he refuses and takes another.

Credit: (see also Credit Notes in this strand's preface)

+   sometimes attempts self-direction and resists adult control, e.g., wants to feed self; choose which toys to play with; ignores adult's "no."

-    never asserts himself; is excessively dependent on caregivers to do things he is capable of; does not persist in accomplishing a goal.

A   rarely or never uses parent as a helping resource even when faced with a difficult task.

O   circle any credit if caregiver has difficulty understanding or supporting child's needs for self-direction, punishes child for being independent and/or does not allow child to make choices.

5.69   Displays dependent behavior; clings/whines   24-30

Definition: The child's behavior at this stage, which may begin around 18 months, can appear paradoxical - one moment he may push his parent away and the next moment he may cling and whine for his parent, demanding constant attention. The child's dependency needs may intensify because his new-found independence and mobility skills make him feel more vulnerable and unprotected.

Parent Questions: Has your child seemed to become more clingy or whiny lately, even when he is in a familiar place and is feeling okay? *If yes,* Can you give me some examples? About how often does he act like that? Do you have any ideas why he does? Is this troublesome for you?

Example Observation Opportunities: May observe child's clinging and whining behavior anytime.

Credit: (see also Credit Notes in this strand's preface)

+   displays periodic bouts of clinging, whining, demands for attention, verbalizes "want Mommy," etc. But he is still able to exercise his independence and move away from parent to explore toys and the environment.

A   is excessively dependent or hostile, e.g., rarely takes his eyes off his parent; does not explore environment or toys independently; is afraid to leave parent's lap; wants to be picked up constantly; has tantrums easily if his demands are not responded to immediately; and/or if his dependent behavior reflects hostility or anger (e.g., hits or bites parent).

O   circle any credit if caregiver misinterprets and responds to typical dependent behavior as "mean" or "bad;" pushes child away.

N/A if not present; anticipatory guidance item.

5.68   Feels strongly possessive of loved ones   24-36

Definition: During the first 2 years, the child's primary concern related to his attachment relationship, is knowing his parent's whereabouts. During the second year, he becomes more concerned about maintaining his parent's approval and love. He thus may become more possessive of loved ones and become jealous when attention is given to others.

Parent Questions: Does your child seem to get upset, whine or become clingy when you are talking to or being affectionate with other people? Feeding the new baby? *If so,* Do you have any thoughts on why he acts like this?

Example Observation Opportunities: May observe when parent is involved in conversation with other adults or interacting with other children.

Credit: (see also Credit Notes in this strand's preface)

+   any behaviors which reflect child's possessiveness of his parents; e.g., he may verbalize "my Mommy!" or "talk only to me"; try to sit on parent's lap or pull on parent when parent is feeding new baby or talking to another person; want to drink only out of his parent's glass or only eat if he sits next to his parent; get hurt, "act out," whine, withdraw, etc., when parents are being affectionate with each other or other family members.

A   child's possessiveness is usually extreme e.g., child "falls apart," has tantrums; interferes with child's interest in exploring his environment.

O   circle any credit if parents find this troublesome and/or punish child for possessive behaviors; rarely provides child reassurances of love.

5.85   Separates easily from parent in familiar surroundings   30-36

Definition: By about 3 years, the child feels secure enough in his relationship with his parents that he can separate from them fairly easily, trusting that they will return. This trust arises from his repeated experiences of separation and reunion. Children who are shy or who have had traumatic separations or experiences, or who have had very few separation experiences may still demonstrate separa-

Separates easily from parent in familiar surroundings   (continued)

tion anxiety.

Parent Questions: Do you leave your child with someone else at least once a week to work, shop or go out? Do you use a regular child care provider? How does your child react when you leave?...when you return? *[If child continues to display significant anxiety, may explore through sensitive interview child's history of trauma, e.g., hospitalizations, history of extended separations, how parent handles separations]*

Example Observation Opportunities: May observe if child is in familiar setting with familiar people (e.g., if you have been with child on many occasions and parent leaves child to go to rest room, make a phone call, etc.).

Credit: (see also Credit Notes in this strand's preface)
+   typically displays only minimal or no separation anxiety (e.g., withdrawal, crying, refusal to play) when his parent leaves him in familiar surroundings with familiar, trusted people and is happy when parent returns.
-   child continues to display significant separation anxiety (refer to #5.25) in familiar surroundings with sensitive and familiar people.
A   rarely acknowledges parent's return with pleasure (refer to #5.25 for additional atypical responses that may persist).

5.86 | ## Shows independence; runs ahead of parent outdoors, refuses to have hand held   30-36

Definition: The child practices his independence by sometimes refusing to engage in earlier dependent behaviors, such as holding his parent's hand and running ahead of adults. He is able to realize and act on his urge for independence as learns he has an autonomous will and has internalized a secure emotional base.

Parent Questions: How does your child show you he wants to be independent? Does he ever want to run away from you or refuse to have his hand held when you are going for a walk or are shopping?

Example Observation Opportunities: May be observed when child goes outside to play or when leaving the observation setting. It may be useful to observe parent's willingness to allow child to move about freely if a safe outdoor playground is available.

Credit: (see also Credit Notes in this strand's preface)
+   by report or observation, child displays any behavior indicative of his urge to show his independence and move away from his parent.
-   child rarely shows interest in leaving parent's side or lap.
A   is overly aggressive in his independence, e.g., hits parents, never complies;
O   circle any credit if parent does not allow child to move out of sight even when environment is safe to do so; overly restricts child.

6.75 | ## Insists on doing things independently   30+

Definition: This item is similar to #5.86 "Shows independence; runs ahead of parent outdoors." The child is practicing his growing sense of autonomy by resisting adult help during daily activities, such as mealtimes, dressing, and figuring out how to make a toy work. This is further evidence of his strive for independence enabled by a secure attachment and internalized secure emotional base.

Parent Questions: Does your child prefer to do things for himself rather than letting you help him? Can you give me some examples?

Example Observation Opportunities: May observe when child resists adult help during snack time (e.g., he wants to open his pack of crackers, pour his own juice); when he enters or leaves the assessment setting if he wants to put on his own coat; during gross motor play when he refuses help on the small slide; during toy play when he refuses help with a toy. Also observe parent's willingness to support child's independence by allowing child to refuse help, not stepping in too quickly as he tries things for himself, praising child's attempts, even if unsuccessful.

Credit: (see also Credit Notes in this strand's preface)
+   displays his interest in independence verbally; e.g., "I do it!" "No," and/or gesturally, e.g., by pushing an adult away but complies with most reasonable limits.
-   passive; does not try new tasks independently.
A   child's independent behaviors usually reflect hostility; e.g., child aggressively "fights" with parent, hits, bites, kicks; never complies; breaks things; resistant to most parental limits.
O   circle any credit if caregivers do not set consistent limits or set limits that are developmentally inappropriate, e.g., too restricting or over-controlling; and/or, caregivers punish child for independent behaviors, encourages child to remain dependent.

5-2 DEVELOPMENT OF SELF AND SELF-ESTEEM

1.11	2-3	Inspects own hands
1.17	3-5	Plays with own hands, feet, fingers, toes
5.16	3-5.5	Makes approach movements to mirror
5.22	5-7	Explores adult features
2.16	5-7	Looks and vocalizes to own name
5.23	5.5-8.5	Smiles at mirror image
5.24	6-9	Distinguishes self as separate from *parent*
5.28	6-9	Responds playfully to mirror
5.30	7-12	Shows like/dislike for certain people, objects, places
5.39	12-15	Displays independent behavior; is difficult to discipline - the "no" stage
5.47	12-18	Shows toy preferences
5.50	12-18	Enjoys being center of attention in family group
1.77	12-18	Recognizes several people in addition to immediate family
1.90	15-16	Identifies self in mirror
2.52	18-24	Uses own name to refer to self
5.62	18-24	Experiences a strong sense of self-importance
1.110	19-24	Recognizes self in photograph
2.66	24-30	Uses "self-centered" pronouns
5.81	24-30	Values own property; uses word "mine"
5.82	24-30	Takes pride in clothing
5.83	24-30	Becoming aware of sex differences
5.65	24-36	Distinguishes self as a separate person; contrasts self with others
1.138	26-33	Knows own sex and sex of others
5.94	30-36	Takes pride in own achievements; resists help

Family Friendly Interpretation of Strand Concepts, Assessment, & Purpose

These behaviors relate to your child's developing sense of himself as a separate and important person. At first, infants do not realize they are separate from their parents or the environment. They experience their parents as an extension of themselves rather than understanding that they are distinct and separate people. As a child becomes more aware of his surroundings and discovers that he can make things happen, he begins to learn that he is a separate and important person. For example, when your child smiles and you smile back, or he shakes a rattle and his rattle makes a sound, he is learning that he can make things happen.

As a child discovers his separateness, he will also begin to develop his own likes and dislikes, to realize his own gender, and to figure out his role in the family. Sometimes a child may seem as if he is selfish or spoiled. This is because as he develops a strong sense of self-importance, he thinks that he is the center of the universe and everyone and everything should belong to him! Actually, this is a good sign because it shows he is feeling important and good about himself. When a child is in the "no" or "me" stage, he is showing us that he is learning the boundaries and power of his separateness.

Developing a positive self-esteem is an important part of your child's growing awareness of his separateness. A child develops a positive self-esteem from others who show the child that he is important and unique. He also develops a positive sense of self as he learns that he is able to do things successfully for himself.

Professional FYI

This strand is strongly inter-related with and dependent upon Strand 5-1 "Attachment and Separation." The development of a positive sense of self relies heavily on the child's development of a secure attachment.

Parent Questions   (General Examples - see Skills for specific questions)

To help identify the child's unique strengths and needs related to this developmental area:
General:
- Can you think of some of the ways that you show your child you love him and think he is special?
- What are some of the things you feel your child does really well?
- Are there some things your child can do that he seems really proud of?

Developmentally specific (Many specific questions are also included in each skill item procedure):
- Has your child seemed to discover and explore his own body parts, for example have you seen him play with his feet or toes?
- Has your child ever seen himself in a mirror? *If so, How does he react?*
[Note: some cultural systems believe that a child should not look into a mirror before a certain age or it could be harmful]
- Are there certain toys, people or places that your

child really seems to like more than others? *If so, How does he show you?*

To help identify family resources, priorities and concerns related to the child's development in this area:
- How do your other children feel about (child's name)?
- If you could think of one thing that would make life go a little easier with your child, what would that be?
- What kinds of advice have you been given about "how to raise a happy child?" How does that fit with what you believe?
- Can you think of some things that you feel would be okay to let your child begin to make his own decisions about? *[Provide examples as needed, e.g., whether he wants to play with his ball or look at his book, whether he wants to drink out of his blue cup or his orange cup]*
- What are some of the things your family does that you think help your child feel he is a very important part of the family?

Sample *Functional* Outcome Statements which may be generated by the Family

[Will be dependent upon identified individual child and family needs and should incorporate objectives and activities from other domains]
Our child will:

- Feel good about himself;
- Be happy;
- Feel important;
- Begin to understand that each person is different.

Transactional Assessment

May assess through observation and interview.

Assessment of the Child's Environment

NOTE: Also refer to the transactional assessment under Strand 5-1, "Attachment and Separation." All items in that strand are also applicable to this strand. The following are additional areas of environmental and interactional assessment.

1. Supportive:
[Environments that support/facilitate development in this area]
- The child has some things that he can learn belong only to him, e.g., a certain set of toys, his own room, or his special place in a room.

Assessment of Caregiver Interactions with the Child

1. Supportive:
[Interactions that support/facilitate the child's positive sense of self as lovable and competent. The caregivers are able to identify positive aspects of their child and view their child as a separate individual]
The child's caregivers:
- Are able to support their child's efforts to physically move away from them while reassuring him that they are still available;
- Let the child make developmentally appropriate choices;
- Allow and respect their child's preferences and dislikes when possible;
- Frequently make positive comments about their child;
- Let him sometimes be the center of attention and "show off;"

- Figure out ways to help their child be successful at the new skills he is learning.

2. Compromising:
[Interactions that may restrict, compromise, inhibit or be unsupportive of the child's positive sense of self]
The child's caregivers frequently:
- Make negative statements about their child;
- Overly control the child's activities, e.g., physically intrusive on the child's attempts to accomplish a task;
- Undermine their child's efforts to accomplish a task;
- Make verbal or physical threats to the child;
- Project their own thoughts and feelings onto their child rather than taking their child's point of view.

Identifying and Interpreting Needs for Intervention

If a child does not display any, or only a few, typical behaviors expected at his developmental age, he may be <u>having difficulty with developing a sense of self as a separate and important person.</u> *Consult with an infant mental health therapist regarding interventions and further evaluations.*

<u>However</u>, before targeting social-emotional development as the primary area of need for intervention, consider, rule out or adapt for other causes that can contribute to or interfere with a true assessment of the child's positive sense of self. These may include:

- <u>Motor impairment, motor delays, atypical tone</u>: the child may not have the motor skills needed to explore his parent's face or his own body; may have limited opportunities to practice moving away from his parent to

explore and experience independence; may have unclear, more subtle, weaker or distorted cues and signals of individual preferences;

- <u>Visual impairment</u>: the child may be more fearful to leave his parent to explore unknown territory; he also does not have the visual cues that help him define separateness and individual differences;

- <u>Cultural differences</u>: some cultures and families will have different values and belief systems related to the role of the child in the family and expectations for independence. Some cultures may also believe that a child should not look into a mirror before a certain age as it can cause bad luck or harm.

Assessment Adaptations   (Examples)

[Also refer to adaptations in Strand 5-1 that are also applicable] Be sure to note any adaptations needed to credit and help plan intervention.

- <u>Visually impaired</u>: omit skills related to identifying self in a mirror or photograph, i.e., #5.16, #5.23, #5.28, #1.90, #1.110. The child may be delayed in skill #5.38, "Becoming aware of sex differences" and #1.138 "Knows own sex and sex of others," as he does not have the early visual experiences which infants and toddlers rely heavily upon to differentiate gender.

- <u>Motor impaired</u>: *consult with a therapist for opti-*

mal positioning that enables the child to explore his own body and his parent's face, e.g., skills #1.11, #1.17, #5.22; use adaptive materials and equipment which help the child be as independent as possible; pay special attention to more subtle or distorted facial and vocal cues.

- <u>Speech delay</u>: some items require speech, e.g., #5.52 "uses own name to refer to self," #2.66, "Uses 'self-centered' pronouns," and #5.81 "Values own property;" uses word "mine". May adapt by accepting sign language or gestures that child uses.

General Assessment Procedures & Processes   (apply to all items in this Strand)

1. **Descriptive Reporting** versus identifying age ranges: With many infants and toddlers, it will be more useful and appropriate to describe the child's behaviors that reflect his growing sense of self and self-esteem, instead of assigning age levels. *Age levels are not useful for families in understanding their child's sense of self.* Descriptions of the child behaviors that are typical can provide parents with an expanded view of their child's behavior; this can help them "reframe" what may have been perceived as "bad" or "difficult" behaviors.

2. **Describe the assessment behavior and example observation opportunities and invite family members** to help observe and/or assess.

3. **Cultural/family diversity:** always consider family values and beliefs through sensitive family interviews (see Parent Questions

above) and observations. Developmental assessment, and the expectations and interventions for the child should be adjusted accordingly, e.g., do *not* test items related to a mirror if family beliefs dictate; expect different degrees of dependence.

`+ - A` Credit Notes:

+   displays typical behaviors as defined.

-    does not display behavior.

+/-   appears to be an emerging behavior; not consistently displayed.

· A   atypical: the behavior is present but it is extreme; interferes with daily living and interactions with others.

N/A   not appropriate to assess or plan for due to disability or family beliefs.

O   circle any credit if:
  – caregiver interactions compromise the child's positive sense of self;
  – caregivers are having difficulty understanding or dealing with the child's autonomous behaviors.

Note any adaptations used to credit.

Inspects own hands   2-3

Definition: The child sometimes brings one or both hands into view to watch and explore the movements he can make with his hands and fingers. When the child inspects his hands, he is developing an awareness of his body and that his hands are part of him. The child may inspect his hands for up to a minute, several times a day, but should easily "break out of it" to look at a new person or interesting object.

Parent Questions: Have you noticed your child watching his hands as he waves or wiggles them in front of his face? When do you see him do this? About how often?

Example Eliciting Situations: Hand-watching usually occurs at this age when a child is alone and content lying on his back in a quiet environment. May observe anytime during observation period if setting is conducive.

Credit: (see also Credit Notes in this strand's preface)
- \+   if under 5 months and child sometimes watches movements of his own hands, even briefly; stops looking when another activity is introduced.
- A   if over 5 months and spends a significant amount of time hand-watching, or prefers hand-watching to interacting with people.

(may also credit #1.11 in Strand 1-4C "Cause and Effect" and Strand 4-3 "Reach/Approach")

 ### Plays with own hands, feet, fingers, toes   3-5

Definition: The child enjoys exploring and playing with his hands and feet. He may clasp his hands together, finger one hand with the other, and if at 5-6 months in motor skills, reach for his feet to play with his toes. He is becoming aware that his hands, fingers, feet and toes are part of his body and that he can control their movements.

Example Observation Opportunities: <u>Incidental</u> - may be observed when child is quietly at play during a break or before others interact with him, e.g., after a diaper change when still lying on his back. <u>Structured</u> - if not observed incidentally, attract child's attention to his feet by playing a brief version of "This Little Piggy," or by nibbling on his toes. Pause to observe if the child maintains interest in his feet. This may be observed while the child is in supine or held flexed in a cradled position.

Credit: (see also Credit Notes in this strand's preface)
- \+   sometimes plays with his hands and feet in an exploratory manner as defined. This should be more than simply looking at them.

Makes approach movements to mirror   3-5.5

Definition: When the child sees his reflection in a mirror, he acknowledges it by staring intently, brightening, wiggling, or reaching toward it with his head, body, or hands. At this stage, he does not recognize the reflection as himself.

Example Observation Opportunities: <u>Incidental</u> - may be observed if child has a crib or playpen mirror and is playing alone; or when parent is holding the child and incidentally pauses for him to look in a mirror. <u>Structured</u> - when the child is in prone or supported sitting, position a mirror (playpen, safety mirror) in front of him within easy reach so only his image is available. Initially attract his attention (if needed) by tapping on the mirror and calling his name, pausing to allow his response. Allow about 1 minute for the child to build up his response

Credit: (see also Credit Notes in this strand's preface)
- \+   displays any signs of interest or approach movements toward his reflection as defined.

Explores adult features   5-7

Definition: The child is curious about and seems to "study" his caregiver's face. He may begin to touch, poke, probe, and/or pat another's face and hair to explore. The child is learning that his primary attachment figure is a separate person from himself.

Parent Questions: Does your child like to touch or poke at your face? *If so,* What does he do?...Why do you think he likes to do that?

Example Observation Opportunities: May be observed during any close face-to-face contact between parent and child when child is content, e.g., during feeding, after a diaper change, before assessment.

Credit: (see also Credit Notes in this strand's preface)
- \+   purposefully touches, pats, pokes and visually studies parent's facial features to explore.
- O   if caregivers interpret child's exploration as being difficult or mean, e.g., if he accidentally scratches or pulls hair, or if caregivers avoid close comfortable face-to-face contact.

(also in Strand 5-1)

2.16 Looks and vocalizes to own name   5-7

Definition: The child knows his name. When he hears his name called, he usually looks toward the person who called him.

Parent Questions: Do you call your child by any other names? Which name is he called most? Does your child seem know his name when you call him? How can you tell?

Example Observation Opportunities: Incidental - may observe anytime during feeding, play, diapering. Observe when a familiar person calls the child's name when he is not already looking at the person. The key is to be sure that the child is turning to his name, not just the sound of a new voice. Structured - when the child is playing, ask his parent to call out an unfamiliar name. Then after a minute or so, have the parent call out the child's name.

Credit: (see also Credit Notes in this strand's preface)
+   usually differentially turns to or looks to the person who called his name or nickname. He does *not* have to vocalize for credit. May also credit other clear indicators of understanding; e.g., an older child may vocalize "huh" or purposely ignore and move in another direction to avoid doing something.

(also in Strand 2-1 "Understanding the meaning of words")

5.23 Smiles at mirror image   5.5-8.5

Definition: The child smiles when he sees his reflection in a mirror. In contrast to #5.16 "Makes approach movements to mirror," the child is beginning to recognize his reflection in the mirror as his own.

Example Observation Opportunities: Same as #5.16 "Makes approach movements to mirror."

Credit: (see also Credit Notes in this strand's preface)
+   smiles or brightens to his mirror image.

5.24 Distinguishes self as separate from *parent*   6-9

Definition: The child realizes he is a person who is separate from others and the environment. This realization is the culmination of many of the developmental skills (listed in HELP) during the first 6 months of life. For example, when he hits a toy and it moves, or smiles at an adult and the adult talks back, he learns he can have an effect on other people or things.

Example Observation Opportunities: May observe child's signs of separateness anytime during observation, e.g., child intently exploring others' facial features; touches an adult's hand to reactivate a toy which has stopped; displaying signs of stranger or separation anxiety, cooperating in simple reciprocal games, interest in physically moving away from his parent.

Credit: (see also Credit Notes in this strand's preface)
+   by clinical judgment. Refer to examples of representative behaviors listed under the assessment procedures to help credit.

5.28 Responds playfully to mirror   6-9

Definition: The child is continuing to learn that the image he sees in a mirror is his own. He may laugh, pat or reach toward the mirror, make faces, mouth the mirror, and/or vocalize to his image.

Example Observation Opportunities: Same as #5.16 "Makes approach movements to mirror."

Credit: (see also Credit Notes in this strand's preface)
+   makes any playful responses toward his image in the mirror as defined.

5.30 Shows like/dislike for certain people, objects, places   7-12

Definition: The child displays his growing individuality as he displays preferences for certain people, objects and places. His preferences are often based upon his perception and memory of his experiences.

Parent Questions: Does your child seem to like certain foods more than others? Does he refuse to get near certain people? (probe for characteristics, e.g., unfamiliar people, men with beards.) What are your child's favorite toys? Does he seem to like certain places more than others; for example, does he like to sit in his highchair but dislike his car seat? What are some of the ways your child shows you he likes or dislikes different people, places or things?

Example Observation Opportunities: May observe at snack time when child refuses certain foods or drinks but finishes or gestures more for others; during play, when child tosses away or ignores some toys but plays with or explores others; during interactions, with others when he shows his toy to one

Shows like/dislike for certain people, objects, places   (continued)

adult but not another, or changes his proximity.

Credit: (see also Credit Notes in this strand's preface)

+   displays differentiated behaviors which indicate likes and dislikes for certain people, places and things. Examples: he may display his preferences for people by interacting positively with them, his preferences for objects by playing with them or selecting them more frequently, and his preferences for places by smiling when he enters the room and feeling free to explore. He may display his dislikes with any kind of negative behavior. Note characteristics of child's preferences and dislikes to help plan interventions.

-    usually passive, showing no particular preferences in toys or people.

O   circle any credit if caregivers have difficulty interpreting child's likes and dislikes.

Displays independent behavior; is difficult to discipline - the "no" stage 12-15

Definition: The child frequently says "no" as he experiences a growing sense of autonomy, separateness, and power. He may say "no" verbally or with bodily responses, e.g., running the other way, pushing things away, shaking his head, as well as sometimes actually verbalizing "no." He may also, however, sometimes say or gesture "no" when he really means "yes," just to exert his power.

Parent Questions: Sometimes this is referred to as the "no" stage because it seems like every time you ask the toddler to do something he seems to purposefully refuse or do the opposite! Have you noticed if your child has started acting like this? Can you give me one or two examples? How did you handle that? Why do you think he acts like that?

Example Observation Opportunities: May observe anytime child is given a suggestion to try or do something.

Credit: (see also Credit Notes in this strand's preface)

+   displays some independent "no" behaviors as defined.

A   negative behaviors dominate child's behavior and interfere with relationships; or overly compliant, i.e., never displays signs of independence and always complies with adult, appearing depressed.

O   circle any credit if caregivers have difficulty understanding and responding effectively to the child's negative behaviors, or do not provide clear, consistent and developmentally appropriate limits and rules.

Shows toy preferences   12-18

Definition: The child displays preferences for certain toys; e.g., he may prefer to play with dolls rather than cars or blocks. At this stage, he may also develop a special attachment to a favorite doll, stuffed animal, blanket, or car, insisting that he take it wherever he goes.

Parent Questions: Does your child have certain toys he seems to like more than others? *If so, how can you tell? [Probe which type of toys child prefers, e.g., certain textures, colors, toys with wheels, books, etc.]* Does your child have a favorite toy or object that he seems to always want to take with him when he goes out? *[If so, probe parents understanding or support of this]*

Example Observation Opportunities: May be observed if child brings a certain toy to the assessment; and/or during free play when a variety of toys are available to choose from and child ignores some toys and maintains interest in others.

Credit: (see also Credit Notes in this strand's preface)

+   displays a preference for one or two toys more than others; may be demonstrated by choosing a certain toy when several are available or holding on to certain toys.

A   perseverates on only one toy or object, or aspect of a toy, to the exclusion of all others; seems to "tune out" while engaged in the object; e.g., plays only with toys which spin; repeatedly "picks" lint.

O   circle any credit if caregivers have difficulty interpreting child's likes and dislikes; expects child to have same preferences as parent; or have difficulty understanding child's need for a special attachment object if present.

5.50 Enjoys being center of attention in family group 12-18

Definition: As the child's sense of self as a separate and important person becomes more established, he enjoys being the center of attention within his family. He may act silly, imitate the behavior of a family member, play a game, or perform a new skill to attract and maintain the center of attention, even though he is more reserved or shy around others. This is a stage when he tests out his role, worth, and power in the family. If he is not getting the attention he needs, he may purposefully misbehave or become whiny and clingy.

Parent Questions: Are there times during the day when several members of your family are together, for example, at mealtime or at the end of the work day? Sometimes children at your child's age like to be the center of attention. Does your child seem do things to get everyone's attention? *If so, probe for example behaviors and whether the family enjoys this or interprets his attention-getting behaviors as troublesome.*

Example Observation Opportunities: This may be a difficult item to observe unless observations occur when child is with more than one family member and you are either out of sight (e.g., behind an observation window) or the child is very familiar with you.

Credit: (see also Credit Notes in this strand's preface)
- + parent reports any positive attention-getting behaviors, such as acting silly, playing a game, or performing a new skill while watching family members reactions.
- A demands constant attention; only means of attracting attention is aggressive e.g., biting, hitting, whining, or tantrums.
- O circle any credit if caregivers interpret child's attention-getting behaviors as being spoiled or mean, and/or do not praise or admire child.

1.77 Recognizes several people in addition to immediate family 12-18

Definition: The child recognizes people beyond his immediate family, with whom he has had significant contact, e.g., daycare providers, neighbors, relatives who live outside of the home. This is another example of the child's continuing awareness of himself as separate from others.

Parent Questions: Who are the people your child seems to know best besides the people who live at home? How can you tell when he recognizes someone other than his family, for example, when his grandma comes to visit, how does he show you he recognizes her?

Example Observation Opportunities: May observe if observing child in multiple environments and if other people who the child has met happen to be present; e.g., at home if a friend drops by; at daycare when his teachers approach him, or if you have been involved with this child on several occasions.

Credit: (see also Credit Notes in this strand's preface)
- + looks or points to a few other people, not in immediate family, when their name is called, or readily interacts with them without stranger anxiety.

1.90 Identifies self in mirror 15-16

Definition: The child recognizes and reacts positively to his reflection in the mirror. *[Note: One reference (Lewis & Brooks-Gunn, 1979) reported that only 25 percent of the normally developing babies they studied recognized themselves in the mirror at 18 months, whereas 75 percent recognized themselves by 24 months. Our experience, however, as well as other literature (Caplan & Caplan, 1977), reports this to occur by the 15-16-month age range]*

Parent Questions: Does your child seem to recognize himself in a mirror? How can you tell?

Example Observation Opportunities: <u>Incidental</u> - when child is playing in front of a mirror, playfully ask "Where's (child's name)?" <u>Structured</u> - try to place a tissue on the child's head or a sticker on his nose without his noticing. Then place a mirror in front of him to observe if he immediately touches, removes or tries to remove the tissue or sticker when he sees himself in the mirror.

Credit: (see also Credit Notes in this strand's preface)
- + identifies self in a mirror by pointing toward reflection when asked, or if he removes a tissue or sticker from his head or face when he sees it in the mirror; he should display some positive affective responses, such as smiling.
- A recognizes self in mirror but <u>always</u> responds with a neutral or negative affect, not due to atypical muscle tone.

2.52 Uses own name to refer to self   18-24

Definition: The child knows and sometimes refers to himself by his first name. The name he uses may be an approximation or "nickname." Some children say their names spontaneously to label possessions e.g., "Johnny's ball," but others may only do so when specifically asked. This is another example of his continuing growth of identity and separateness.

Parent Questions: What names do you and others usually call your child? Does your child say his own name? *[If he is called by various names]* What name does he usually say when referring to himself? Can you think of an example when you have heard him say his own name?

Example Observation Opportunities: <u>Incidental</u> - ask "Who's there?" when talking on play telephones and/or when the child is hiding during a game; ask "Who's that?" when looking in a mirror or at a picture of the child. <u>Structured</u> - introduce yourself and others in the room, then ask the child his name. This can also be done in a game-like fashion naming a few dolls, stuffed animals or pictures of family members.

Credit: (see also Credit Notes in this strand's preface)

+   sometimes uses his own name to refer to himself.

(also in Strand 2-3)

5.62 Experiences a strong sense of self-importance   18-24

Definition: This is commonly referred to as the "me" stage. The child generally feels he is the center of the universe and that all other things and people revolve around him. He may grab someone else's things, and expect others to give him everything he wants when he wants it, including their undivided attention. If the child is not delayed in expressive speech, he incorporates much use of "self-" related language, e.g., saying his own name, and "me" frequently.

Parent Questions: After describing the "me" stage with parents, explore if they have noticed any similar behaviors in their child. Parents may also describe their child as spoiled during the interview. If so, explore the types of behaviors they are referring to.

Example Observation Opportunities May be observed anytime during observation period, especially if an adult, for example, serves someone else first during snack time, or gives another child a toy.

Credit: (see also Credit Notes in this strand's preface)

+   by clinical judgment if child displays behaviors typical of the "me" stage as defined.

O   may circle credit to target for anticipatory guidance if parents find these behaviors troublesome.

1.110 Recognizes self in photograph   19-24

Definition: The child can recognize himself in a recent photograph.

Parent Questions: Has your child ever seen pictures of himself at this age? Does he seem to recognize himself in the picture? How can you tell?

Example Observation Opportunities: Take an instant full-length picture of the child at the beginning of the assessment or ask the parent to bring a recent photo, if available. Later, place his picture with a picture of another child and ask him to point to, touch or pick up his picture, as you say his name. This may also be observed at home if parents have a family album. The parent can sit with the child and let him point to familiar pictures of people the parent names.

Credit: (see also Credit Notes in this strand's preface)

+   points to or says his name to the correct picture of himself when at least two pictures are available.

2.66 Uses "self-centered" pronouns   24-30

Definition: As the child's cognitive and language development expands, he uses self-centered pronouns such as "me," "you" and "mine," to further establish his identity, separateness, and boundaries.

Parent Questions: Have you ever heard your child say "me" to refer to himself? Can you think of an example?" Have you heard him say, "you,"… "mine?"

Example Observation Opportunities: May observe when child is e.g., giving parent a directive, e.g., "You get it;" responding to "Who wants a cookie?" "Whose car is this?" or saying "mine" when someone starts to take one of his toys.

Credit: (see also Credit Notes in this strand's preface)

+   uses self-centered pronouns frequently during interactions with others, e.g., "me," "you," and "mine". He may say them singly or in a multi-word phrase; usage does not need to be grammatically correct.

(also in Strand 2-3)

5.81   Values own property; uses word "mine"   24-30

Definition: The child is learning the boundaries and power of his separateness as he begins to develop a sense of ownership. For example, he knows which clothes, toys and pets are his and confirms his "ownership" by frequently saying "mine."

Parent Questions: Are there certain things at home that belong only to your child, such as certain toys, a certain bed, or a special cup? Does your child say the word "mine!" yet? Can you think of an example when he said "mine?"

Example Observation Opportunities: May be observed incidentally when child is showing someone one of his toys, or if someone begins to play with or take one of his things.

Credit: (see also Credit Notes in this strand's preface)

+   displays sense of ownership by saying "mine."

5.82   Takes pride in clothing   24-30

Definition: The child likes receiving compliments about his clothing and may sometimes seek compliments by, for example, showing you his new pair of shoes.

Parent Questions: Does your child ever seem to show off what he is wearing to others? How does he do this?

Example Observation Opportunities: When the child enters, or after he is comfortable in the assessment setting, make a complimentary remark about his clothing; e.g., comment about the picture on his shirt, his nice shoes, or his special belt.

Credit: (see also Credit Notes in this strand's preface)

+   smiles and points to his clothes or otherwise indicates his pride when receiving a compliment; or shows a clothing item to another in anticipation of a compliment.

5.83   Becoming aware of sex differences   24-30

Definition: The child's developing self-concept includes changes in body concept and gender identification. He develops a greater awareness of anatomical differences and of his genitalia.

Parent Questions: Does your child seem to know the difference between boys and girls or men and women? Does he seem to know that he is a boy? How can you tell? Children frequently begin to explore their body parts, including their genitals at this age. Have you noticed if your child has begun to do this?

Example Observation Opportunities: <u>Incidental</u> - may observe while looking at books and during doll play using dolls which have clear gender differences. Periodically ask the child to show you the girl, boy, man and/or lady pictures or dolls. This may also be observed if the child spontaneously labels people or pictures as boys, girls, etc. <u>Structured</u> - if the child, by report or observation, can say "boy" and "girl," ask, "Is that a boy or a girl" at an appropriate time, e.g., when looking at books and talking about boys and girls. Then point to another child or picture of a child of the opposite gender and ask if the child is a boy or a girl.

Credit: (see also Credit Notes in this strand's preface)

+   displays awareness of gender differences by pointing to boys and girls on request; he does not need to always respond correctly; at this age he may continue to make errors.

5.65 **Distinguishes self as a separate person; contrasts self with others   24-36**

Definition: The child, at this stage, has a better defined self-concept and has developed a good understanding that he and his body are separate and different from his parents and the rest of the world. He is learning about individual differences and realizes that he looks and can act differently than others. He is also beginning to understand needs of other people, and if he is not speech delayed, he may use adjectives to describe others, e.g., "red hair."

Parent Questions: Have you noticed if your child seems to be more concerned lately about getting little cuts or bruises? Does he seem more modest, e.g., not wanting to undress in front of anyone? Does he get overly upset if he sees a broken doll or an injured person?

Credit: (see also Credit Notes in this strand's preface)

+ displays a variety of behaviors that show he is aware of individual differences and has established himself as a separate person, e.g., making comments about his own or another's appearance; getting more upset about a painless cut or bruise; questioning why he can't do things others can if, for example, he is physically disabled; exerting his power to say "no" to others, even when he does not mean it; acting modest; being able to separate fairly easily from his parents; using self-identity words (me, mine, you); showing concern if another is hurt.

1.138 **Knows own sex or sex of others   26-33**

Definition: The child knows if he is a boy or girl and then learns to discriminate the gender of other children as boys or girls.

Example Observation Opportunities: If the child, by report or observation, can say "boy" and "girl," then ask, "Are you a boy or a girl?" e.g., during play when looking in a mirror; while looking at books and talking about boys and girls. Then point to another child or picture of a child of the opposite gender and ask if that child is a boy or girl. If the child cannot verbalize, ask, "Are you a boy (or girl, depending upon the child's gender)?" If he indicates "yes," also ask if he is the opposite sex to make sure he is not indicating "yes" to any question. Repeat this procedure, pointing to other children in the room or in storybooks.

Credit: (see also Credit Notes in this strand's preface)

+ always responds correctly when asked if he is a boy or a girl, and indicates for at least one other child of opposite gender if they are a boy or a girl.

5.94 **Takes pride in own achievements; resists help   30-36**

Definition: As the child's positive self-concept and sense of self as a separate and important person becomes established, he is able to take pride in his own achievements and independence. He takes pride in things, such as figuring out how a toy works, helping to carry something while shopping or accomplishing a self help task. The child's positive self-esteem and ability to take pride in his accomplishments is derived from his history and memory of receiving praise and encouragement from others. He feels competent enough to resist help from others.

Parent Questions: Can you think of some things that your child can do that he seems to be proud of? How does he show you he feels proud?

Example Observation Opportunities: May be observed throughout observation period as child interacts with new and/or challenging tasks. For example, does the child prefer challenging toys to easy ones; does he try to overcome obstacles independently; when faced a problem, does he try to figure it out himself and then clap or smile with his accomplishments; does he call his successful accomplishments to the attention of others?

Credit: (see also Credit Notes in this strand's preface)

+ by clinical judgment if child demonstrates several instances of being proud or pleased with himself, such as smiling, clapping etc., when accomplishing a task; he does not always need excessive encouragement or praise from others but may sometimes act like he expects some type of acknowledging praise.

5-3 EXPRESSION OF EMOTIONS AND FEELINGS

2.02	0-1	Cries when hungry or uncomfortable
5.03	0-1.5	Smiles reflexively
5.07	1.5-4	Responds with smile when socially approached
2.06	1.5-4	Laughs
2.10	2.5-5.5	Squeals
5.13	3-6	Vocalizes attitudes - pleasure and displeasure
1.39	6-7	Responds to facial expressions
5.29	6-18	May show fear and insecurity with previously accepted situations
5.42	12-18	Displays frequent tantrum behaviors
5.51	14-15.5	Hugs and kisses parents
5.53	18-24	Expresses affection
5.54	18-24	Shows jealousy at attention given to others, especially other family members
5.55	18-24	Shows a wide variety of emotions: fear, anger, sympathy, modesty, embarrassment, anxiety, joy
5.57	18-24	Feels easily frustrated
5.63	22-24	Attempts to comfort others in distress
5.74	24-30	Frustration tantrums peak
5.77	24-30	Dramatizes using a doll
5.79	24-30	Fatigues easily
5.84	24-30	May develop sudden fears, especially of large animals
5.87	30-36	Demonstrates extreme emotional shifts and paradoxical responses

Family Friendly Interpretation of Strand Concepts, Assessment, & Purpose

The behaviors in this strand help us understand what kinds of feelings and emotions your child may be experiencing, and how he is learning to express and deal with them. For example, we will be exploring how your child lets us know when he is feeling happy, sad, frustrated, lonely or angry. As adults, we have a wide range of feelings and emotions and have learned to deal with them in a variety of ways. For example, when we are upset we may cry or try to do something that helps us feel better, such as talking to a friend, taking a walk or perhaps reading a good book.

Young children also experience a variety of emotions but do not have as many ways to understand, express or cope with them. At first, infants can only express their upset feelings by crying. Later, they may express upset feelings by biting, throwing, or having a tantrum. As a child has more experience in dealing with his emotions, he may express some of his feelings by talking or playing with dolls. Although your child may not always know the name of his "feeling," he knows that different feelings exist and will express them in his own unique way.

Professional FYI

The child's emotions develop and evolve within the context of caregiver-child interactions and the safety of relationships. It is with in this context that the child learns to imitate expressing emotions and learns which emotional expressions are acceptable. The child's ability to express and successfully cope with a range of emotions is thus strongly dependent upon the preceding social-emotional strands related to the development of a secure attachment and positive sense of self.

This strand is also highly dependent upon the child's physiological and maturational capacities to self-regulate and organize sensory information (refer to Strand 0.0 "Regulatory/Sensory Organization").

Parent Questions   (General Examples - see Skills for specific questions)

To help identify the child's unique strengths and needs related to this developmental area:

- What are some of the things you've noticed about they way your child expresses his feelings?
- Have you noticed if there seem to be times when your child has difficulty letting you know how he feels?
- What are some of the ways your child lets you

know he is feeling good? ... happy?... upset? ...jealous?...angry?...frustrated?...ashamed?

- Is today a typical day for your child? Is he tired? When did he last eat? Has he been sick?
- Are there any other important things about how your child expresses his feelings or emotions which you think are important but we have not discussed?

Parent Questions   (continued)

To help identify family resources, priorities and concerns related to the child's development in this area:

- Can you tell me a little about how the people in your family usually express their feelings?
- What advice have you been given about the way children should behave? How does that fit with what you believe?
- How do you let your child know when you are angry about something? ...sad ?...upset? ...happy?...pleased?...etc.
- Is there anything about the way your child expresses his feelings that you are concerned about or would like help dealing with?
- Are there times when you wish you could figure out better ways to deal with some of your child's behaviors?
- What have you tried so far that seems to help your child (e.g., stop biting)?
- What have you tried so far that does not seem to help?
- Who are the people you feel you can talk to or call on to help with the extra demands and stresses of having a young child (with special needs, if applicable)?

[Note: these are general open-ended examples to choose from. These questions build upon prior questions in social-emotional domain. Specific behavior related questions are included in the procedure of most items]

Sample *Functional* Outcome Statements which may be generated by the Family

[Will be dependent upon identified individual child and family needs and should incorporate objectives and activities from other domains]

My child will:
- Stop having so many tantrums;
- Laugh and smile when we play;
- Let me know how he is feeling.

We will:
- Know what behaviors to expect at different developmental stages;
- Be able to deal effectively with our child's tantrums;
- Know ways to help our child express how he is feeling.

Transactional Assessment

May assess through observation and interview.

Assessment of Caregiver Interactions with the Child

1. Supportive:
[Example interactions which support/facilitate the child's healthy emotional expressions]
The child's caregivers usually:
- Allow and/or encourage the child to express a wide range of emotions and feelings;
- Are able to empathize with how the child is feeling;
- Help the child express his angry or frustrated feelings without hurting himself or others;
- Interpret and respond positively to the child's expressions of affection;
- Express much verbal and physical affection;
- Are available to comfort the child;
- Provide predictable routines;
- Are able to read and respond sensitively to all of the child's feelings;
- Provide predictable emotions and interactions.

2. Compromising:
[Example interactions which may restrict, compromise, or inhibit the child's healthy emotional expressions]
The child's caregivers frequently:
- Ignore or punish the child's expressions of feelings and emotions;
- Misinterpret the child's feelings and emotional expressions;
- Project their own feelings rather than empathizing with the child's feelings;
- Provide unpredictable emotional responses;
- Do not express verbal or physical affection, or are "pseudo-affectionate," e.g., jabs, pokes or teases child in a manner that is irritating to the child.

Identifying and Interpreting Needs for Intervention

If a child is delayed or displays extreme behaviors in this area, he may be having difficulty with <u>experiencing and expressing his emotions and feelings</u>. This may be related to problems associated with the development of a secure attachment or positive sense of self. *Consult with an infant mental health therapist regarding interventions and further evaluations.*

However, before targeting social-emotional issues as the primary area for intervention, consider, rule out, adapt or target interventions for other causes that interfere with or may contribute to difficult in expressing emotions. These may include:

• <u>Regulatory/sensory organization difficulties</u>: the child may display extreme emotional shifts and responses (underreactive and/or overreactive) due to constitutional or physiological differences. Refer to the "Regulatory/Sensory Organization" strand and a therapist who is experienced in sensory integration principles;

• <u>Motor impairment, motor delays, atypical tone</u>: the child may have unclear, more subtle, weaker or distorted cues and emotional responses; smiles may be weak or distorted;

• <u>Medically fragile</u>: the child may be in pain or heavily medicated;

• <u>Transient benign stressful situations</u> that are likely to resolve, e.g., child is overtired, hungry, ill, on medications which affect his behavior or is shy in new settings; parent has recently returned to work; new baby at home; recent move;

• <u>Allergies, food or chemical sensitivities</u> that may affect behavior and emotional responses;

• <u>Cultural diversity</u>: various cultures and families will have different values and belief systems regarding how feelings and emotions should be expressed.

• Significant <u>language delay</u> or <u>communication disorder</u>: emotional expressions may be more extreme due to frustration.

Assessment Adaptations   (Examples)

[Note any adaptations needed to credit and help plan interventions]

• <u>Visually impaired</u>: observe child's responses when he is in his familiar environment, with familiar trusted people using familiar materials. Most items can be assessed while observing the child from afar. The child may normally react to new or unexpected tactile and movement experiences with more extreme emotional responses.

• <u>Regulatory/sensory organization</u> difficulties: *consult with a therapist who is trained in sensory organization principles.* For the young infant, it may be helpful to swaddle him or provide rhythmic vertical rocking to help him become focused and organized. The older toddler may benefit from vestibular activities and a highly structured environment.

• <u>Transient benign stressful situations</u>: reassess on multiple occasions as stressful situation resolves.

• <u>Motor impairment</u>: pay special attention to the child's more subtle, distorted or weaker emotional responses. *Consult with a therapist to adapt positioning of the child and assessment materials* so that the child can be as independent as possible.

• <u>Language/communication disorder</u>: consult with a speech-language therapist for further evaluation and planning, using augmentative communication techniques if appropriate.

General Assessment Procedures & Processes (apply to all items in this Strand)

1. Descriptive reporting versus Identifying age ranges: Identifying specific age ranges at which certain emotions and feelings begin is difficult. Many of these emotional stages overlap and continue. With many infants and toddlers, it will be more useful and appropriate to describe the child's behaviors which reflect his current range of emotions and feelings instead of assigning age levels. Descriptions of the child's behaviors that are typical can provide parents with an expanded view of their child's behavior that can help them "reframe" what may have been perceived as "bad" or "difficult" behaviors.

2. **It is *important to assess behaviors at and below the child's current developmental level*** to ensure that earlier critical behaviors continue, e.g., although the child is 2 years old, we would still expect that smiling, laughing and expressing affection are still an important part of his emotional capacities.

3. **When observing the child's expressions of emotions and feelings it is important to observe, consider and note the following:**
   a. The context in which they occur, e.g., with whom and with what toys or activities does the child express pleasure, frustration, anger?
   b. The amount of stimulation needed to elicit the emotion; e.g., does the child need lots of social interaction to elicit a smile or laughter, or does he smile easily?
   c. The intensity, range, and duration of the response; e.g., does the child quickly escalate between joy and anger? Is he able to recover from his tantrums fairly quickly or does he remain disorganized and upset for more than 20 minutes?
   d. The amount of external support to help the child modulate his emotions; e.g.,

can he remain organized when frustrated or does he fall apart? Does he need to be physically removed from the situation when he becomes aggressive; can he self-calm or does he need to be rocked, held, etc.?
   e. Is the child able to experience and display a wide range of emotions rather than only responding in one predominant or restricted manner?

4. **Describe the assessment item and example observations opportunities and invite family members to help observe and/or assess.** Be aware of family values and beliefs related to expression of emotions. These values and beliefs can be elicited through sensitive family interview (see Parent Questions above) and observations of the family. Assessment and interventions for the child should be adjusted accordingly.

+ - A Credit Notes:
+ child displays typical emotional expressions as defined.
- child does not display behavior by report or observation.
A child <u>does</u> display emotional response, but the response is usually extreme, labile, or prolonged and interferes with the child's daily living or social relationships.
O circle the credit if:
  – caregiver interactions are not supportive or empathetic to the child's emotional expressions;
  – caregivers request support in understanding or dealing with the child's behaviors.

Note any adaptations used to credit.

Assessment Materials

Culturally sensitive dramatic play materials for older toddler, e.g., dolls, cars.

2.02 Cries when hungry or uncomfortable   0-1

Definition: The child's primary means for expressing discomfort is crying. Crying at this stage is reflexive in nature and may be difficult to interpret as the crying undifferentiated.
Credit: (see also Credit Notes in this strand's preface)
+ cries when distressed or uncomfortable.
A cries most of the time; takes more than 20 minutes to console, or rarely/weakly expresses distress.
O circle any credit if caregivers ignore child's cries.

5.03 Smiles reflexively   0-1.5

Definition: First smiles are typically brief, infrequent, and not discriminate to a specific person or interaction. *Note: The literature differs whether these smiles are true, or reflexive. It does not matter. Regardless of their nature, first smiles are an important elicitor of social interactions from others.*
Credit: (see also Credit Notes in this strand's preface)
+ any observation or report of brief smiles.

5.07 Responds with smile when socially approached   1.5-4

Definition: The child smiles purposefully and easily to express pleasure and enjoyment in response to a social interaction from others. At this stage, he may smile as readily to strangers as he does with caregivers.

Parent Questions: What kinds of things do you do that seem to make your child smile? Does your child smile easily or does it seem like you need to "work at it" to get him to smile?

Example Observation Opportunities: May observe whenever child is content and someone engages in a pleasant verbal or smiling interaction during play, feeding, diaper changing. High-pitched inflectional vocalizations, animated facial expressions, and gentle tummy strokes are usually potent elicitors of smiles.

Credit: (see also Credit Notes in this strand's preface)
+   smiles easily when others talk and smile to him.
A   always averts gaze, arches back, turns away, has depressed expression (not due to atypical muscle tone).
O   circle any credit if caregivers have difficulty identifying interactions that elicit their child's smiles.

2.06 Laughs   1.5-4

Definition: The child laughs or chuckles out loud to express delight in response to a pleasurable interaction.

Parent Questions: Does your child laugh out loud? About how often? What kind of things seem to make him laugh?

Example Observation Opportunities: When the child is content and alert, invite the parent to try doing one of the things that usually makes the child laugh. If the child does not laugh at this time, assure the parent that it's okay if he doesn't; you can credit by report.

Credit: (see also Credit Notes in this strand's preface)
+   usually laughs or chuckles to fun interactions every day. The laugh should be more than pleasurable vocal sounds.
A   always averts gaze, arches back, turns away, has depressed or vacant expression (not due to atypical muscle tone).

2.10 Squeals   2.5-5.5

Definition: The child squeals to express delight, happiness, or excitement. Squeals are loud, sudden bursts of vowel sounds.

Parent Questions: Have you ever heard your child squeal? When does he seem to do this? What do you think he's trying to say with his squealing?

Example Observation Opportunities: May observe when child is engaged in games, such as playing "I'm gonna get you!" tummy tickling, or playfully moving him up in the air when he is held securely.

Credit: (see also Credit Notes in this strand's preface)
+   sometimes squeals to express delight or excitement during solitary or playful interactions.

5.13 Vocalizes attitudes - pleasure and displeasure   3-6

Definition: During the first 6 months, primary emotions emerge and can be observed. The child is able to experience and express a wide range of emotions, such as pleasure, anger, interest, sadness, excitement, surprise, and love. The way he expresses feelings and emotions is no longer limited to laughing or crying. The child can now express varied emotions through changes in his vocalizations and facial and bodily expressions; e.g., he may chortle, squeal, grunt, whimper, coo, babble, smack his lips, frown, look surprised, and cuddle.

Parent Questions: What types of sounds and facial expressions does your child use to let you know he's happy?...upset?...mad?...frustrated?

Example Observation Opportunities: May observe whenever when child is enjoying himself, upset, frustrated, etc.

Credit: (see also Credit Notes in this strand's preface)
+   frequently expresses a variety of emotions and feelings beyond laughing or crying.
A   "flat" affect or irritable state predominates even during pleasant events and interactions; or when distressed typically requires holding, and it takes more than 15 minutes for child to "recover"; escalates quickly from laughing to screaming.
O   may circle any credit to target for anticipatory guidance if parent has difficulty interpreting or responding to child's varied emotional expressions.

1.39 ## Responds to facial expressions   6-7

Definition: The child is beginning to "read" and respond to others' facial expressions. He changes his behavior or his own facial expression according to the expressions he perceives. For example, the child may frown, pout, become still, cry or turn away in response to seeing an adult's angry expression; he may smile, laugh or babble in response to seeing a smiling or silly expression.

Parent Questions: Does it seem like your child can understand when you are happy, sad, or angry, just by looking at your facial expression? How can you tell? Can you give me an example?

Example Observation Opportunities: May observe anytime child watches an adult's facial expression when the adult does not vocalize; e.g., when approaching a new toy or food, the child continues if an adult smiles or nods; is more cautious or inhibited if the adult ignores or displays a worried expression; becomes sad or somber if child sees an adult look worried, sad, or cry.

Credit: (see also Credit Notes in this strand's preface)
+ displays several different emotional expressions that mirror or are appropriate to the facial expression of another; is able to "recover" when mildly distressed by watching interesting or empathetic facial expressions of person who is soothing him.

5.29 ## May show fear and insecurity with previously accepted situations   6-18

Definition: The child may cry, scream, and reach for his parent when he is afraid or presented with something he perceives as dangerous. He is developing feelings of fear and insecurity because he is beginning to realize that he is a separate person who is dependent and vulnerable in his environment. Common fears that may extend into toddlerhood include: animals, bath tub, hair-washing, vacuum cleaners, dark places, things that break. Fears are generally short-lived but new fears may arise as old ones are resolved. The child usually recovers fairly quickly when frightened if he is consoled and reassured by his primary caregiver.

Parent Questions: Do certain things such as animals or the dark seem to frighten your child? Do you have any thoughts about why he is afraid of these things? Are these new fears? Does anything seem to help?

Credit: (see also Credit Notes in this strand's preface)
+ reportedly has one or a few typical childhood fears that have not lasted more than a few months.
A displays extreme and prolonged fearful reactions; cannot be consoled, distracted or reassured by caregiver; fears interfere with daily activities.
O may circle to target for anticipatory guidance if caregivers interpret their child's fears as being bad, or are interested in ways to deal with their child's.
N/A does not, by report or observation, have any noticeable fears; this item is for anticipatory guidance; not an item to teach.

5.42 ## Displays frequent tantrum behaviors   12-18

Definition: Tantrums may typically emerge during this age range. The type, degree, frequency, and intensity of tantrums varies between and within each child, dependent upon the child's personality, health, stage of development, precipitating cause, and adult response. Tantrum behaviors typically include outbursts of two or more behaviors: screaming, crying, head banging, falling to the floor, kicking, breath holding.

Parent Questions: Does your child ever have temper tantrums or "fall out"? What does he do during a tantrum? About how often? About how long does it last? What do you do? When does he have tantrums? Can you usually figure out what caused it? What do you typically do when this happens? Are there certain things that seem to help? After a tantrum, is he able to forget about it and go back to playing or on to another activity?

Example Observation Opportunities: May observe if child is incidentally faced with a frustrating task, is not allowed to engage in something he wants, or has something taken away against his will.

Credit: (see also Credit Notes in this strand's preface)
+ displays typical temper tantrums (as defined), but they do not interfere with daily family functioning; the child can use other methods to express negative feelings such as banging on the door to go out, or yelling.
A tantrums are the primary means for expressing emotions; they are frequent, prolonged, and occur with little provocation, i.e., typically more than five or six per day lasting beyond 10 minutes; has great difficulty "recovering" from the tantrum and becoming organized, taking more than 10 minutes.
O circle any credit if caregivers are interested in learning techniques to minimize and effectively manage tantrums, and/or reinforce tantrums.
N/A if the child never or rarely displays tantrums but is still able to express anger or frustration.

5.51 Hugs and kisses parents   14-15.5

Definition: The child expresses affection for primary caregivers by sometimes hugging and kissing them.

Example Observation Opportunities: Observe how caregivers express their affection to the child during the observation period, since this will influence how the child learns to express his affection. For example, do caregivers spontaneously hug and kiss child when he is distressed or has accomplished a special task?

Credit: (see also Credit Notes in this strand's preface)
+ enjoys hugging and kissing primary caregivers; child may initiate the hugs and kisses or this may be in response to the caregiver's hugs and kisses. May also credit if child displays affectionate expressions other than hugging or kissing, see #5.53 below.

5.53 Expresses affection   18-24

Definition: The child displays a range of affectionate responses with others he cares about. His affectionate responses typically imitate the type of affection to which he is exposed.

Parent Questions: How does your child show that he is feeling loving or affectionate to other people, pets or his favorite dolls or stuffed animals?

Example Observation Opportunities: May be observed when child interacts with adults, other children, pets, dolls and stuffed animals. Also observe how caregivers express their affection to the child during the observation period, since this will influence how the child learns to express his affection.

Credit: (see also Credit Notes in this strand's preface)
+ displays a range of affectionate behaviors with significant others, e.g., patting, hugging, special looks, resting his head, offering a toy, holding hands.

5.54 Shows jealousy at attention given to others, especially other family members   18-24

Definition: The child experiences and expresses feelings of jealousy when he must share the attentions and love of family members with others. He may express these feelings through negative or regressive behaviors, e.g., whining, hitting, becoming clingy, reverting to baby-talk, but he is learning to deal with them through imitation (e.g., he may hug his doll or go to the person and seek the same attention).

Parent Questions: Does your child ever seem to act jealous? How can you tell? What does he seem to feel jealous about?

Example Observation Opportunities: May observe when caregiver gives attention to another person anytime during the observation period (also note if there is a new baby at home, or other new family member, e.g., a step-parent.)

Credit: (see also Credit Notes in this strand's preface)
+ displays any signs of jealousy as defined.
A displays excessive jealousy which has continued for more than a few months; falls apart; clings constantly; cannot be reassured.
O circle any credit if caregivers are have difficulty interpreting and/or responding sensitively to child's feelings.
N/A not reported or observed. This item is for anticipatory guidance.

5.55 Shows a wide variety of emotions: fear, anger, sympathy, modesty, guilt, embarrassment, anxiety, joy 18-24

Definition: The child experiences and expresses, with greater control, a wider range of emotions and feelings: fear, anger, sympathy, modesty, guilt, embarrassment, anxiety, joy. His emotions and feelings are primarily related to dependency, love and security issues. He may express them in varying degrees during play, when trying to meet his basic needs, and when interacting with others.

At this stage, the child begins to connect his emotions with behavior and thus is beginning to have better control over them. He is beginning to express his feelings in more complex ways rather than only relying on concrete methods such as hitting or having a tantrum. For example, he may express anger by using words such as "bad," "mad," "no," or by acting angry with his doll.

Parent Questions: Review various emotions typical at his age with parents and probe for their recognition and understanding of each as it may relate to their child; e.g., does your child ever seem to feel embarrassed (afraid, angry, etc.)? Can you give me an example of what may make him feel this way? What does he do that lets you know he feels this way? What do you do when he acts like that? Have you ever seen him express his feelings with his dolls or stuffed animals? Can you give me some examples?

Example Observation Opportunities: May observe throughout observation period as child interacts with others and is engaged in dramatic play with dolls, animals, cars, etc.

Credit: (see also Credit Notes in this strand's preface)

+ expresses a variety and different degrees of emotions which are not limited to concrete behaviors in all situations (laughing, hitting, biting, tantrums), e.g., nurturing a doll or stuffed animal; appearing joyful during play and pleasant interactions, verbalizing emotional needs or feelings (e.g., "hug me," "mad"); patting others or dolls when distressed; "crashing" cars or blocks together when angry; going to parent when feeling guilty, anxious, or embarrassed.

- emotional expression limited in all situations to concrete behaviors, e.g., hitting, biting, tantrums, smiling.

A limited to concrete expressions and does not display varying degrees or any sense of control, e.g., only screams intensely; one emotion quickly escalates to another.

O circle any credit if caregivers are having difficulty interpreting or responding sensitively to their child's range of emotions.

5.57 Feels easily frustrated 18-24

Definition: The child feels easily frustrated by his own inabilities and limits imposed on him from the environment. He may feel frustrated when he is unable to master a task, communicate a desire, have what he wants, or when he cannot understand why things are as they appear. He frequently wants to do more than he is capable of or allowed to do and does not have adequate language to express his thoughts and feelings. He thus gets easily frustrated by his own inabilities and by adult limits.

When frustrated a child may have a tantrum, throw down a toy, move away from the situation, or vocalize anger. If a child is tired or not feeling well, his frustration may be more frequent or intense.

Parent Questions: What seems to frustrate your child? Why do you think that frustrates him? What does he do when he's frustrated? How do you respond when he acts like this?

Example Observation Opportunities: May observe when child needs to wait for something, is playing with a challenging toy, or has something removed.

Credit: (see also Credit Notes in this strand's preface)

+ displays typical signs of frustration as defined but is able to recover and move on to another activity fairly easily. He should be able to handle some limits and levels of frustration without falling apart, e.g., explore one or two methods to make a toy work or get something he wants before getting frustrated, or be able to wait a few minutes before getting something he wants.

A frustration is apparent in most aspects of daily living; immediately falls apart without trying other strategies; is unable to recover within 10 minutes.

O circle any credit if the environment is overly restrictive or permissive; i.e., the child does not have developmentally appropriate play materials, is overly restricted in satisfying his curiosity and independence (e.g., spends much of his time in a playpen); has rules and developmental expectations which are too high or low for his developmental abilities (e.g., he is expected to sit still at the dinner table long after he is finished).

5.63 Attempts to comfort others in distress   22-24

Definition: The child is beginning to experience and express sympathetic feelings for others who are hurt or in distress. For example, he may try to comfort a crying child with a pat, hug or kiss. Or he may attempt to remove the cause of distress, e.g., he may remove a tricycle that has fallen over on a child or tell an adult when a peer or sibling is hurt.

Parent Questions: Have you noticed how your child reacts if he sees someone get hurt?

Example Observation Opportunities: May observe if someone accidentally gets hurt during the observation period, e.g., a pet, peer, sibling, or parent. Sympathetic behaviors may also be displayed during dramatic doll play. It can also be helpful to observe how caregivers respond to their child's distress, as this may reflect how the child responds to others; e.g., does the parent let him cry it out?...get angry?...wait a few minutes to see if he works it out on his own?...or usually offer immediate comfort?

Credit: (see also Credit Notes in this strand's preface)

- \+ any reported or observed example of trying to comfort another who is hurt or distressed, with positive intent.
- A always physically attacks or shows anger when another child is distressed.
- O circle any credit if caregivers punish or rarely comfort child when he is distressed.

5.74 Frustration tantrums peak   24-30

Definition: The number and intensity of tantrums may increase because of the many frustrations a young child experiences at this age. The child gets easily frustrated and may throw a tantrum when he cannot master a task, communicate his desires, or have his way. Refer to #5.42, "Displays frequent temper tantrums," listed earlier in this strand for typical tantrum behaviors. At this stage, however, he can also deal with frustration in other ways besides tantrums. For example, he may go to an adult for help with a difficult task or may express his frustration through play or using language, e.g., he may argue with the adult or his doll or say "me mad" while stomping his feet.

Example Observation Opportunities: Same as #5.42.

Credit: (see also Credit Notes in this strand's preface)

- \+ displays typical temper tantrums, but they do not interfere with daily family functioning; can also use other methods to express negative or frustrating feelings, such requesting help with a difficult task, talking, or acting out frustration through dramatic or imaginary play, e.g., eats an imaginary cookie when parent refuses.
- A tantrums are the primary means for expressing emotions; they are frequent, prolonged, and occur with little provocation; i.e., typically more than five or six per day lasting beyond 10 minutes; the child has great difficulty "recovering" from the tantrum and becoming organized afterwards.
- O circle any credit if caregivers are interested in learning techniques to minimize and effectively manage tantrums, or caregivers reinforce tantrums.

N/A never or rarely displays tantrums but is still able to express anger or frustration.

5.77 Dramatizes using a doll   24-30

Definition: The child is able to express emotional ideas through dramatic play with dolls. Early emotional themes expressed during doll play often center around love and nurturing (e.g., feeding, hugging, diapering), and anger or aggression (e.g., yelling, hitting, pointing finger at doll). The child interacts with the doll as if the doll has senses, i.e., as if the doll can see and hear.

Example Observation Opportunities: Give the child one or two dolls and doll play objects e.g., brush, a cup and spoon, two wash cloths, safe hand mirror, shoe box, small bowl of water. Invite him to play with the doll and join in by following his lead, but do not always demonstrate or suggest how to play with the objects.

Credit: (see also Credit Notes in this strand's preface)

- \+ doll play includes a variety of emotional themes, e.g., love, anger, protest.
- A exclusive and pervasive emotional themes of anger, rage, or unhappiness when playing with dolls.

(also in Strand 1-1)

5.79 ## Fatigues easily   24-30

Definition: A child can typically handle only a certain amount of an exciting or emotional activity before falling apart or becoming fatigued. Some children fatigue after an hour; others after 15-20 minutes. When fatigued, the child may become excessively whiny, clingy, aggressive, and irritable, and be more vulnerable to tantrums.

Parent Questions: About how long can your child seem to handle an exciting activity, such as going to a birthday party or play group, before getting tired or cranky?

Example Observation Opportunities: May observe child's behavior which is caused by fatigue if the assessment lasts beyond 30 minutes. If the observation period is expected to last more than 30 minutes, be sure to alternate unstructured and exciting periods with calm, relaxed and structured activities.

Credit: (see also Credit Notes in this strand's preface)
+   appears fatigued or displays cranky behaviors after extended periods of play or excitement.
A   cranky, whiny or aggressive behavior predominates throughout the day for no apparent reason; always falls apart quickly with even milder activities.
O   circle any credit if caregivers have difficulty recognizing the precipitant of cranky behaviors.
N/A if not reported or observed. This item is for anticipatory guidance.

5.84 ## May develop sudden fears, especially of large animals   24-30

Definition: Fear is an emotion which may become more prominent during this stage. Common fears may include large animals, fear of monsters, the dark, thunderstorms, and things that break. The fears a child expresses are typically a sign of his ability to interpret events and use ideas. He may, for example, be fearful of things that break because he thinks that if they can break so can he; he may be afraid of the dark because he imagines that things such as animals or monsters may appear.

Parent Questions: Do certain things, such as animals or the dark, seem to frighten your child? About how long has he been fearful of that? Do you have any thoughts on why he may be afraid of these things? Does anything seem to help?

Credit: (see also Credit Notes in this strand's preface)
+   reportedly has one or a few typical childhood fears that have not lasted more than a few months; is able to be reassured and may act out some of his fears through play.
A   displays extreme and prolonged fearful reactions lasting more than a few months; cannot be consoled, distracted or reassured by caregiver; fears interfere with daily activities.
O   circle any credit if caregivers interpret their child's fears as being bad or are interested in ways to deal with their child's fears.
N/A does not have any reported or noticeable fears; this item is for anticipatory guidance, not an item to teach.

5.87 ## Demonstrates extreme emotional shifts and paradoxical responses   30-36

Definition: The child may have many emotional "ups and downs". He may have some good days and some bad days, or have better periods of the day than during other times of the day. He may say one thing but mean another, or one day like one thing and the next day dislike it.

Parent Questions: This is a stage when children frequently have their share of emotional ups and downs, e.g., happy one moment and upset the next. Have you noticed any of these periods of ups and downs in your child? Can you give me an example? About how often does this occur? How is this for you and your family?

Credit: (see also Credit Notes in this strand's preface)
+   emotions are sometimes extreme and shift from one day or period to another, but he maintains some control and is able to recover easily; emotional shifts do not predominate child's overall daily behavior.
A   emotional shifts predominate overall behavior and interfere with family functioning; is not able to control or modulate expression of emotions; always needs external help from others to gain control.
O   circle any credit if caregivers have difficulty understanding or managing their child's fluctuating emotional responses.
N/A if these behaviors are not reported or observed. This item is for anticipatory guidance.

5-4 LEARNING RULES AND SOCIAL EXPECTATIONS

1.08	1.5-4	Shows anticipatory excitement
5.14	3-6	Becomes aware of strange situations
1.27	5-6.5	Distinguishes between friendly and angry voices
5.33	9-12	Tests parental reactions during feeding
5.34	9-12	Tests parental reactions at bedtime
1.55	9-12	Knows what "no" means and reacts
5.40	12-15	Acts impulsively, unable to recognize rules
1.67	12-15	Hands toy back to adult
5.43	12-18	Needs and expects rituals and routines
5.44	12-18	Begins to show a sense of humor–laughs at incongruities
5.48	12-15	Displays distractible behavior
5.49	12-18	Tends to be quite messy
5.56	18-24	Desires control of others–orders, fights, resists
1.115	21-24	Remembers where objects belong
1.122	24-27	Demonstrates awareness of class routines
5.67	24-30	Holds parent's hand outdoors
5.71	24-30	Says "no," but submits anyway
5.80	24-30	Dawdles and procrastinates
5.88	30+	Begins to obey and respect simple rules
5.91	30-36	Resists change; is extremely ritualistic
5.92	30-36	Experiences difficulty with transitions

Family Friendly Interpretation of Strand Concepts, Assessment, & Purpose

With experience, your child begins to learn some simple rules and develops his own set of social expectations; i.e., he learns what he can expect from his world and what the world expects of him. Young children begin to learn simple rules by watching how others, especially his parents, respond to the things he does. For example, if he hits or throws his food, and his parents say "no," he begins to learn that there are rules about hitting and throwing.

As children begin to learn rules, they need to test them to see if they always apply. For example, when a child is learning the rule, "don't throw food," he may continue to throw food on other occasions and with other people to see if the rule always applies. Sometimes children also

"break" rules because they have strong urges to be independent and are testing their power. It is also difficult for children to follow the rules they are learning because, at this age, they are very impulsive and can't always control their impulses. They don't ignore rules out of defiance, but do so because they do not have the understanding or inner controls to stop themselves.

A few basic limits and simple rules do, however, need to be established because young children are in the process of learning their boundaries. If a child had no limits and was allowed to act on every impulse, this would be very frightening to him because he does not have the inner control to help him act in acceptable ways.

Parent Questions   (General Examples - see Skills for specific questions)

To help identify the child's unique strengths and needs related to this developmental area:

- What kind of rules or limits do you have for your child at bedtime?...mealtime? ...during play?...about being messy?...regarding where he is allowed to play?
- Which rules does your child seem to follow the best?
- Which rules does your child seem to have the most difficulty learning?

To help identify family resources, priorities and concerns related to the child's development in this area:

- Are there any special routines that your child is used to at bedtime, e.g., kissing everyone

good night or having a story?...at mealtime, e.g., everyone eating together or sitting in a certain chair?...at bath time, e.g., usually given at a certain time or taking certain toys in the tub?
- Who are the people in your family who help decide the rules that your child should learn and follow?
- At what age are children expected to learn acceptable behaviors or (rules) in your family? *[Explore specifics related to the family rules parent has identified in previous questions]*
- Can you tell me a little about your family's beliefs regarding discipline or how to deal with children's misbehavior? How does that "fit" with what you believe?

Parent Questions   (continued)

- Who are the primary people who discipline your child?
- If you could think of one rule you wish your child would be able to follow, what would it be? What have you tried so far that seems to help?...that has not seemed to help?

Sample *Functional* Outcome Statements which may be generated by the Family

[Will be dependent upon identified individual child and family needs and should incorporate objectives and activities from other domains]

Our child will:
- Stay away from dangerous things such as the stove and basement steps;
- Stop throwing his food;
- Sit with us at the dinner table for at least half of mealtime;
- Do what he is suppose to;
- Go to bed without screaming.

We will:
- Have a better understanding of the rules we (can begin to) expect our child to follow;
- Be able to respond effectively when our child breaks a rule.

Transactional Assessment

May assess through observation and interview.

Assessment of the Child's Environment

1. Supportive:
[Example environments which support/facilitate development in this area]
The child's caregiving environments usually:
- Have spaces which are child-proofed for the child to freely explore;
- Have predictable rituals and routines.

2 Compromising:
[Example environments which may restrict, compromise, inhibit or be unsupportive toward development in this area]
The child's caregiving environments are frequently:
- Overly restrictive, e.g., exploration is prohibited because there are too many things which are dangerous or that the child could break;
- Chaotic without a sense of routine;
- Overly permissive, e.g., allows the child access to dangerous and fragile things.

Assessment of Caregiver Interactions with the Child

1. Supportive:
[Example interactions which support/facilitate child's development in this area]
The child's caregivers usually:
- Set rules and limits appropriate to the child's age;
- Let the child make developmentally appropriate choices during play and daily activities;
- Are available to comfort and nurture the child when he's feeling out of control;
- Provide predictable and age appropriate consequences when rules are not followed;
- Let the child know what he is allowed to do when he is told not to do something; e.g., showing and telling the child, "You cannot throw food, you can throw balls," "You cannot bite people, you can pat them."

2. Compromising:
[Example interactions which may restrict, compromise, inhibit or be unsupportive of the child's development in this area]
The child's caregivers frequently:
- Harshly punish their child when he breaks a rule;
- Set unclear, inconsistent or developmentally inappropriate rules and limits;
- Are overly permissive, setting few or no developmentally appropriate rules or limits;
- Provide inconsistent consequences;
- Over-control activities and interactions;
- Tease their child;
- Make blaming and negative statements to their child.

Identifying and Interpreting Needs for Intervention

If a child is significantly delayed or displays consistent atypical behaviors in this area, he may be having difficulty in <u>understanding or complying with limits, rules and other social expectations</u>.

However, before targeting social-emotional factors as the primary area of need for intervention, consider, rule out or adapt for, other causes that may contribute to difficulties in this area. These may include:

- <u>Lack of predictable experiences</u> with rules and limits;
- <u>Regulatory or sensory organization difficulties</u>: the child may display extreme emotional shifts and poor impulse control due to constitutional or physiological differences. *[Refer to the "Regulatory/Sensory Organization" strand and a therapist who is experienced in sensory integration principles]*

- <u>Cognitive delays,</u> especially in the area of learning cause and effect;
- <u>Motor impairment, motor delays, atypical tone</u>: the child may not have the mobility skills needed to comply with rules;
- <u>Language delays</u>: the child may not have developed language-mediated inhibitory controls;
- <u>Visual impairment:</u> the child does not have the visual experiences or cues which help him learn what to expect from his environment or to monitor others' responses to his behaviors;
- <u>Transient benign stressful situations</u> that are likely to resolve; e.g., child is tired, hungry, ill; parent has recently returned to work; new baby at home; recent move;
- <u>Cultural differences</u>: some cultures and families will have different values and belief systems related to rules, limits and discipline;
- <u>Allergies, food or chemical sensitivities</u> that may affect behavior and impulse control.

Assessment Adaptations   (Examples)

[Note any adaptations needed to credit and help plan interventions]

- <u>Regulatory/sensory organization</u> difficulties: *consult with a therapist who is trained in sensory organization principles.* The older toddler may benefit from vestibular activities and a highly structured environment.
- <u>Motor impairment</u>: pay special attention to the child's more subtle, distorted or weaker emotional responses. *Consult with a therapist to adapt positioning of the child and materials* so that the child can be as independent as possible.
- <u>Language delay</u>: consult with a speech-language

therapist regarding possible visual cues and augmentative communication techniques to enhance impulse control.

- <u>Visually impaired</u>: observe child's responses when he is in his familiar environment, with familiar, trusted people using familiar materials. Most items can be assessed while observing the child from afar. The child may normally react to new or unexpected tactile and movement experiences with more extreme emotional responses.
- <u>Transient benign stressful situations</u>: reassess on multiple occasions as stressful situation resolves.

General Assessment Procedures & Processes   (apply to all items in this Strand)

1. **When observing the child's responses to rules and limit setting, it is important to observe, consider and note the following**:
   a. The context in which the limit or rule is experienced;
   b. The amount of physical and verbal guidance and support needed to comply;
   c. Methods used by caregivers to help teach the child rules and limits.
2. **Describe each behavior and example opportunities that may elicit the behavior to family members.** Invite them to help observe and/or assess. Descriptions of the child's behaviors that are typical can provide parents with an expanded view of their child's behavior. This can help families "reframe" what may have been perceived as "bad," "mean," or "difficult" behaviors.

3. **Consider cultural diversity**: Various cultures and families will have different values and belief systems regarding rules, limits and discipline. These values and beliefs can be elicited through sensitive family interview (see parent questions above) and observations of the family. Expectations and interventions for the child should be adjusted accordingly.

+ - A **Credit Notes:**

+ child displays typical behaviors as defined.

- child does not display behavior by report or observation, and this is a behavior to encourage (in contrast to items provided for anticipatory guidance) but you would not want to teach or encourage; e.g., "Displays distractible behavior."

General Assessment Procedures & Processes (continued)

A child's response is usually extremely impulsive, labile, or prolonged and interferes with the child's daily living or social relationships.

N/A not observed or reported. This item is for anticipatory guidance and is not a behavior to teach.

O circle any credit if environment or interactions compromise or restrict child's optimal development in this area (refer to Transactional assessment above.)

Note any adaptations used to credit.

1.08 | **Shows anticipatory excitement   1.5-4**

Definition: The child is learning from his experiences that one familiar event leads to another. He displays anticipatory excitement when he recognizes a certain sight, sound, or smell, because he has learned to expect what comes next. For example, when he sees his bottle, he excitedly kicks in anticipation of being fed; or when he sees his mother's smile and open arms, he may smile and wave his arms in anticipation of being picked up.

Example Observation Opportunities: May observe when child hears approaching footsteps, sees his bottle or favorite toy, hears his parent's voice, or sees his parent lean over.

Credit: (see also Credit Notes in this strand's preface)

+   displays one or more signs of anticipatory excitement in response to a familiar stimulus, e.g., kicks, waves, smiles, becomes quiet, stills, arches back, squeals, breathes more rapidly.

5.14 | **Becomes aware of strange situations   3-6**

Definition: The child has developed a set of social expectations from his experiences with familiar people and places. When he sees someone or something that is different from his experiences, he may display an expression of surprise, intent look, or a grimace. For example, he may have a look of surprise or worry when he sees a person with a beard or glasses for the first time.

Example Observation Opportunities: May observe when child sees playroom or facilitator for the first time; when he sees a new toy, tastes or touches a new textured toy; hears an adult talk silly or make animal sounds for the first time; looks at an unfamiliar toy longer than a familiar toy.

Credit: (see also Credit Notes in this strand's preface)

+   child changes facial expression when confronted with a new experience.

1.27 | **Distinguishes between friendly and angry voices   5-6.5**

Definition: The child associates soothing and friendly voices with comfortable feelings and memories, and abrupt or angry voices with uncomfortable or frightening feelings and memories.

Parent Questions: Does your child seem to get upset if he hears yelling or scolding? Does he seem to smile more to some types of voices more than others?

Example Observation Opportunities: May observe child's responses if he hears scolding (directed to him or another), and when he hears friendly voices.

Credit: (see also Credit Notes in this strand's preface)

+   responds differently to friendly and negative voices, e.g., smiles to friendly high-pitched voice, and whimpers, grimaces or cries to loud angry voice.

5.33 | **Tests parental reactions during feeding   9-12**

Definition: The child is learning that there are certain mealtime "rules" that he should follow, e.g., no throwing or playing with food. He frequently tests these rules to make sure that they are really rules and to see if he has the power to change them. Examples of testing behaviors may include one or more of the following: throwing food, tossing his cup or spoon on the floor, refusing to eat, spitting food, or playing with his food.

Parent Questions: Sometimes at this stage, children seem to misbehave during mealtime; e.g., they play with their food instead of eating it! How is mealtime going with your child?

Example Observation Opportunities: May observe during snack or mealtime when parent is present.

Credit: (see also Credit Notes in this strand's preface)

+   displays any "testing" behaviors as defined.

O circle any credit if family reinforces behaviors; if family would like assistance with these behaviors, or if "testing" behaviors interfere with having adequate food intake.

N/A not observed or reported; anticipatory guidance item.

5.34 Tests parental reactions at bedtime 9-12

Definition: The child may use bedtime as a "testing ground" to test his limits and his power to get a reaction from his caregivers. He may scream, cry, refuse to lie down, throw his toys across the room and call for his parents helplessly. Separation anxieties and fear of the dark can also be a cause or intensify his reactions.

Parent Questions: Sometimes at this stage children seem to misbehave during bedtime with behaviors such as screaming, throwing things out of their cribs, or banging their heads. How are bedtimes at home going with your child?

Example Observation Opportunities: May observe if assessment is taking place at home and it becomes his nap time.

Credit: (see also Credit Notes in this strand's preface)
+ displays any "testing" behaviors as defined.
O circle any credit if family reinforces behaviors; or would like assistance with these behaviors.
N/A not observed or reported; anticipatory guidance item.

(also in Strand 6-4 "Grooming and Hygiene")

1.55 Knows what "no no" means and reacts 9-12

Definition: The child is learning to understand "no no" as meaning "stop what you are doing," or "stop what you are getting ready to do." He shows this by briefly stopping the activity he is engaged in, but will probably then continue. Some children may respond as though their feelings have been hurt and may actually cry. At this stage, his understanding of "no" is still very limited. To the child, "no" means "not this second," rather than "never." He also does not have the impulse control to hesitate more than briefly. The child may thus repeat the behavior within a few seconds of hearing "no" unless he is distracted to another activity. *[Note: Observe what terms caregivers use to tell their child "no." For example, a parent may say "Hey!" or "Uh-Uh!" Use these terms as the basis of assessing child's understanding of "no no."]*

Example Observation Opportunities: May observe child's responses if parent says "no" (or other similar term) e.g., when child starts to put nonedible in mouth; pulls hair; starts to throw toy; gets into parent's purse or diaper bag. *[Note: The unfamiliar professional should avoid saying "no" to the child. Instead, it is preferable to distract child to a new toy or activity in a "no" situation]*

Credit: (see also Credit Notes in this strand's preface)
+ usually inhibits or displays other signs as defined when adult says "no".
O circle any credit if caregivers overuse "no;" do not show child acceptable or alternative behaviors or do not set any limits even in dangerous situations.

(also in Strand 2-1 "Understanding the Meaning of Words")

5.40 Acts impulsively, unable to recognize rules 12-15

Definition: The child typically has poor control over his impulses at this age. Although he may understand a few simple rules, he does not always have the inner control to follow them. When breaking a "rule," he may briefly inhibit, but then often continues. He may begin to show a sense of guilt when caught at a wrongdoing.

Parent Questions: Do you have certain rules for your child, such as not playing in certain room or staying away from certain breakable items? Any others? Around this time children seem to begin to learn right from wrong, but don't have the inner controls to stop themselves from doing things they shouldn't. For example, parents may teach their child never to get into the drawer with important papers, but he does so anyway. Have you noticed if your child has started acting like this? Can you give me one or two examples? Does he seem to know he's broken a rule? How can you tell? How did you handle that? Why do you think he acts like that?

Example Observation Opportunities: May observe if the child inhibits briefly when told "no," but continues to try to do the "no" behavior, e.g., touching the stereo, parent's purse, TV. Observe his reactions when he is caught in a "no" behavior.

Credit: (see also Credit Notes in this strand's preface)
+ seems to understand a few simple rules and "no"; briefly inhibits but then continues; when "caught," he sometimes shows a sense of guilt by crying, bowing his head, puckering his lip or looking frightened.
A out of control most of the time; behavior interferes with daily functioning.
O circle any credit if caregivers do not have developmentally appropriate limits and rules.
N/A impulsive behavior is not observed or reported. Anticipatory guidance item.

1.67 **Hands toy back to adult   12-15**

Definition: The child is learning that he can rely upon adults as helpful resources to do things that he cannot. For example, when the action of a mechanical toy stops and the child wants it to continue, he may hand the toy back to the adult to restart the toy if he is unable to do so.

Example Observation Opportunities: Activate an interesting action toy which has a difficult switch or other mechanism that makes the toy move. When the toy stops, invite the child to play with it. Wait to see if he looks to his caregivers for help to restart the toy.

Credit: (see also Credit Notes in this strand's preface)

+   sometimes brings things to an adult when he needs help.

A   if older than 18 months, frequently takes adult hand to assist in tasks without eye contact.

(also in Strand 1-4C)

5.43 **Needs and expects rituals and routines   12-18**

Definition: The child begins to expect and demand consistency and routines during familiar daily activities, e.g., to have a certain cup and plate during mealtime; to always hear a certain story before bedtime; to always have a certain toy in the bathtub.

Parent Questions: Does your child have a typical sleep or nap time? When getting ready for sleep, are there certain things that usually occur, e.g., kissing people good night, rocking, looking at a book, getting a favorite stuffed animal? *[If yes]* Does your child seem to expect this to occur; e.g., if you don't get his stuffed animal, will he look for or request it? Does your child seem to expect this?...with mealtime?...bath time?

Credit: (see also Credit Notes in this strand's preface)

+   parent reports there are at least one or two consistent routines at home and that the child show signs of expecting them.

A   child has an excessive need for environmental sameness which interferes with daily activities, play or relationships, e.g., pervasive need to always line up his blocks in a certain way; have furnishings placed in an exact way.

5.44 **Begins to show a sense of humor - laughs at incongruities   12-18**

Definition: The child laughs at things that do not "fit" what he has learned to expect; e.g., he knows that dogs do not talk and laughs when he sees a talking dog on TV or when he sees a mechanical talking dog toy; he know bowls are for eating out of and laughs when he sees someone wearing one on their head as a hat.

Parent Questions: Can you think of any times when your child showed he is beginning to have a sense of humor?

Example Observation Opportunities: Playfully set up an incongruity; observe the child's responses; e.g., during dress up, put the wrong piece of clothing on your own or on the child's head as a hat; show him a funny battery-operated toy (e.g., a monkey beating a drum); put a hat on a dog; if the telephone rings, pick up your shoe and say, "Hello."

Credit: (see also Credit Notes in this strand's preface)

+   child recognizes social incongruities; laughs or expresses other signs of delight when people or objects behave in unexpected ways.

5.48 **Displays distractible behavior   12-15**

Definition: The child may shift his attention from toy or activity fairly quickly and have difficulty sitting still for more than a few minutes. He should, however, be able to engage in novel or favorite toys or activities for at least 5 minutes, several times a day.

Parent Questions: About how long do you think your child should be able to play with a toy or sit at a table during mealtime before wanting to do something else? How would you describe your child's attention span? Does he seem to be overly distractible to certain sights or sounds? Are there certain toys or activities that your child seems to be able to stay interested in for several minutes at a time?

Example Observation Opportunities: May observe anytime during toy play, fine motor activities, snack time and outdoor play. Observe during structured and unstructured periods.

Credit: (see also Credit Notes in this strand's preface)

+   displays some typical distractible behaviors (as defined) which do not interfere with development or daily functioning. *[Note the types of structures and activities that enhance the child's attention, as well as the activities or environmental settings that are distracting to the child to help in planning interventions]*

Displays distractible behavior   (continued)

A   is highly distractible in most settings; e.g., attention is fleeting; requires high degree of novelty and structure to focus on something even briefly; frequently "tunes out" during and activities and is then difficult to re-engage; typically becomes distracted by common environmental sights, sounds and details, which are not distracting to others. Refer to Strand 0.0, "Regulatory/Sensory Organization."

N/A not observed or reported. Anticipatory guidance item.

5.49   Tends to be quite messy   12-18

Definition: Children often do not have a sense of neatness or order at this stage. A child may make a mess with most things he gets involved in (e.g., feeding, washing, playing) without concern or understanding that he has made a mess.

Parent Questions: Does your child tend to be messy when he plays with his toys or feeds himself? Is he allowed to feed himself messy foods, such as pudding, cookies or bananas? Does he ever get upset if his hands or face are dirty? Does he refuse to touch certain messy things, such as pudding, play-dough, sand or dirt?

Example Observation Opportunities: May observe during snack or indoor or outdoor play.

Credit: (see also Credit Notes in this strand's preface)

+   seems generally unconcerned about making a mess.

A   child pulls away, cries or screams when he touches messy materials; constantly wipes hands or indicates he wants his hands to be wiped; or seems otherwise over-concerned with keeping himself and his environment neat. Refer to Strand 0.0 "Regulatory/Sensory Organization."

O   circle any credit if caregivers are overly concerned about the child becoming messy or making a mess.

5.56   Desires control of others – orders, fights, resists   18-24

Definition: The child may sometimes act "bossy" with others in an attempt to test limits and see if he can make his own "rules." He is driven by his strong urge to be independent and have power over others.

Example Observation Opportunities: May be observed, for example, during doll play when child acts "bossy" with dolls; during meal time when child refuses to follow rules; during play with a peer or adult and the child tries to direct exactly how he wants that person to participate.

Credit: (see also Credit Notes in this strand's preface)

+   sometimes orders others around; may sometimes be physically aggressive when adult tries to help him comply with simple rules and limits.

A   aggressive behavior predominates; hurts others or himself; child becomes physically aggressive when even mild limits or requests are made of him.

Remembers where objects belong   21-24

Definition: The child remembers where some familiar objects belong in the environment and sometimes helps put things away. Examples may include: putting his toys back on the shelf or in his toy box; putting his clothes in the hamper; putting some grocery items away; returning his shoes to his closet. He may need a reminder and enjoys praise.

Parent Questions: Is your child expected to help put his things away at home? Can you give me some examples? How is this going? Does he need help remembering where they should go?

Example Observation Opportunities: If the child is familiar with the environment or has watched where a toy came from, ask him to return a toy he has played with before going on to the next activity. Do not tell or gesture to him where it belongs, but rather ask, e.g., "Please put the toy back before snack."

Credit: (see also Credit Notes in this strand's preface)

+   remembers where at least two or three familiar items belong; returns them, tells, or gestures where they belong.

A   excessive need to have everything placed in an exact order or in exactly the same way.

1.122 | ## Demonstrates awareness of class routines 24-27

Definition: The child can anticipate the next classroom or daycare activity when given environmental or verbal cues; e.g., a certain song signals the end of circle time, a bell signals it is time to come in from outdoor play, he puts his lunch box in the "cubby" hole that has his picture. It may take a few weeks for the child to develop an awareness of and learn to comply with class routines.

Parent Questions: Does your child go to daycare, nursery school or other structured group settings? Do you know if there are certain routines or schedules that they consistently follow *[provide specific examples as needed]*? Has your child's teacher discussed how he is doing following routines (or have you observed him following routines in class)?

Example Observation Opportunities: If observations are conducted within the context of an ongoing early intervention or preschool program, may observe or interview with the child's primary teacher or therapist.

Credit: (see also Credit Notes in this strand's preface)
+ displays awareness of and usually complies with major routines, e.g., where to place his belongings; clean up after snack; going to the restroom after outdoor play; standing up after a song at the end of circle time.

5.67 | ## Holds parent's hand outdoors   24-30

Definition: The child understands and usually complies with an adult's rule to hold hands when walking in dangerous areas, such as near streets.

Example Observation Opportunities: May observe when going for a walk during outdoor play.

Credit: (see also Credit Notes in this strand's preface)
+ holds an adult's hand when walking in potentially dangerous areas out of doors.

5.71 | ## Says "no," but submits anyway   24-30

Definition: The "no" stage continues, but to a lesser degree. The child still strives to be independent and exert his power, but also wants to please adults. He is aware of "right and wrong" and responds to approval and disapproval. He thus may say "no," but without always using his earlier insistent tone, and then comply with the adult's request.

Parent Questions: Does your child sometimes seem to want to please you by doing what you ask of him? Can you give me some examples?

Example Observation Opportunities: May observe throughout observation period when child is asked to do something or given a direction, e.g., "Please throw your cup away" after snack time or "It's time to go to the potty," etc.

Credit: (see also Credit Notes in this strand's preface)
+ complies with (trusted) adult requests at least half the time even if he says "no."
O circle any credit if caregivers have difficulty giving clear directions or providing firm limits.

5.80 | ## Dawdles and procrastinates   24-30

Definition: The child may seem to purposefully take extra time to complete a task, respond to a request, or change activities. He may do this because he wants to continue what he is doing, does not want to do what is asked, is trying to avoid or delay the next activity, or simply to test parental limits.

Parent Questions: Sometimes children seem to dawdle or procrastinate at this age *[give specific examples such as getting dressed to go to daycare.]* Have you noticed if your child sometimes acts this way? Can you give an example? How did you handle that?

Example Observation Opportunities: May observe when child is avoiding the next activity or when he wants to continue with what he's doing, e.g., the child delays going to the potty by taking extra time to put his crayons away; the child delays leaving the playroom by continuing to help put things away after he's been told he's helped enough.

Credit: (see also Credit Notes in this strand's preface)
+ displays some purposeful "dawdling" type behaviors as defined.
A is usually sulky or hostile, rarely follows the expected activity without excessive external control.
N/A if not displayed or reported; this is an anticipatory guidance item.

5.88   Begins to obey and respect simple rules   30+

Definition: The child understands and often complies with simple rules related to respecting property and people, e.g., staying away from forbidden objects; not purposefully breaking things, not hurting others. He may tattle or tell on another child who "breaks a rule." He is also beginning to understand the concept of taking turns and can wait a few minutes for gratification. By this age, the child should have a good understanding of consequences and the effect of his behavior upon others.

Parent Questions: Can you give me some examples of the types of rules your child has at home and daycare? Does he usually follow these?

Example Observation Opportunities: May observe throughout observation period e.g., does child usually come when his parent calls him; put something back when asked?

Credit: (see also Credit Notes in this strand's preface)
+   generally tries to conform to developmentally appropriate rules related to respecting property and people; when he breaks a rule he may display signs of shame or guilt.
A   defiant behavior predominates throughout the day and has continued for several months; does not respond to consequences and displays no signs of shame or guilt.
O   circle any credit if caregivers are having difficulty setting developmentally appropriate rules and limits.

5.91   Resists change; is extremely ritualistic   30-36

Definition: Children need predictability and order in their day. Order and predictability helps them feel some control over their life as they deal with conflicts related to independence and autonomy. This need for predictability causes the young child to resist changes in his schedule or environment. For example, he may want to only eat with a certain fork or plate, refuse to try a new brand of cereal, become upset if his hair is cut or styled differently, become upset if he gets a new bed or changes rooms, or have difficulty sleeping if his night time routine is disrupted or incomplete.

Parent Questions: Interview caregivers about the child's typical schedule. Probe if there are certain rituals or routines he expects, using examples as needed. Inquire further about the child's reactions if routines are changed.

Credit: (see also Credit Notes in this strand's preface)
+   caregivers report that: (1.) there are several consistent routines and a fairly predictable schedule in the child's environments; (2.) the child notices when things are different.
A   displays an excessive need for environmental sameness that interferes with daily activities or development, e.g., pervasive need to always line up his blocks in a certain way, have furnishings placed in an exact way.
N/A if not reported or observed; this item is for anticipatory guidance.

5.92   Experiences difficulty with transitions   30-36

Definition: The child may have difficulty moving from one activity to other. He may whine, dawdle, and sometimes have tantrums or otherwise act out. The most difficult transitions at this age are often the transition from play to sleep, from outdoor play to coming inside, and from sleeping to awakening.

Parent Questions: Does your child seem to have difficulty changing activities, for example, coming indoors for dinner, getting ready for a bath after playing with toys, or moving from sleeping to waking up? Can you give me some examples of how he acts? How do you handle that?

Example Observation Opportunities: May observe when activities are changed during the observation period. Give the child a few minutes warning before changing activities and let him know what is coming next.

Credit: (see also Credit Notes in this strand's preface)
+   show some signs of having difficulty with transitions but is able to recover well after the transition is completed.
A   displays extreme difficulties during most transitions; usually "falls apart" and takes a long time to recover.
N/A if not reported or observed; this item is for anticipatory guidance.

5-5 SOCIAL INTERACTIONS AND PLAY

5.02	0-1	Regards face
5.04	0-2	Establishes eye contact
5.05	0-3	Molds and relaxes body when held; cuddles
5.07	1.5-4	Responds with smile when socially approached
5.09	3-5	Vocalizes in response to adult talk and smile
2.12	3.5-4.5	Laughs when head is covered with a cloth
5.12	3-8	Demands social attention
5.15	3-6	Enjoys social play
1.28	5-6	Hand regard no longer present
5.19	4-8	Repeats enjoyable activities
1.33	6-10	Plays "Peek-a-boo"
5.26	6-10	Cooperates in games
5.32	9-12	Extends toy to show others, not for release
2.30	11-12.5	Repeats sounds or gestures if laughed at
5.38	12-15	Gives toy to familiar adult spontaneously and upon request
5.46	12-15	Plays ball cooperatively
5.58	18-24	Interacts with peers using gestures
5.59	18-24	Engages in parallel play
5.64	23-24	Defends possessions
5.66	24-30	Displays shyness with strangers and in outside situations
5.72	24-30	Tends to be physically aggressive
5.70	24-36	Enjoys a wide range of relationships; meets more people
5.75	24-36	Relates best to one familiar adult at a time
5.76	24-36	Engages best in peer interaction with just one older child, not a sibling
5.78	24-36	Initiates own play, but requires supervision to carry out ideas
5.89	30-36	Tends to be dictatorial and demanding
5.90	30-36	Talks with a loud, urgent voice
5.93	30 +	Participates in circle games; plays interactive games

Family Friendly Interpretation of Strand Concepts, Assessment, & Purpose

We will be observing how your child is learning to socialize with others. This includes observing how he plays, interacts, and relates with other people, such as his parents, brothers, sisters, and other adults and young children.

Professional FYI

This strand, although related to Strand 1-1 "Development of Symbolic Play," focuses more on the child's social interchanges and relatedness with people. In contrast, the focus of Strand 1-1 is more on the child's interactions with inanimate objects and toys.

This strand builds upon all previous social-emotional strands, i.e., the development of a secure attachment, positive sense of self, and learning appropriate social expectations. If a child has demonstrated significant difficulties in those areas of social-emotional development, he is more likely to have difficulties in this strand.

Parent Questions   (General Examples - see Skills for specific questions)

To help identify the child's unique strengths and needs related to this developmental area:
- What do you think are the best ways and places to observe and understand your child's development in this area?
- Can you think of any special games that you or other family members enjoy playing with your child? *[Give a few of examples to ensure parent understands what we mean by "games;" e.g., "Pat-a-cake," tickle game, vocal games, knocking down tower; pay special attention to games which may be unique to each family and culture]*
- Can you tell me a little about your child's experiences being with other children around his age? Have you noticed how he plays with and enjoys being with other children?
- How would you describe your child's personality with other familiar people, e.g., shy and slower to warm up, or more outgoing and easy to engage?

Parent Questions   (continued)

- Does your child seem to act differently with you than with other people? *If so* Can you give me some examples?
- Are there any other important things I have not asked about the way your child socializes or plays with you or other people that you think are important?

To help identify family resources, priorities and concerns related to the child's development in this area:

- If you could think of one thing that would make playing with your child more enjoyable, what would that be?
- Is there anything about the way your child socializes with you, other adults or other children that you have concerns about or would like help dealing with?

Sample *Functional* Outcome Statements which may be generated by the Family

[Will be dependent upon identified individual child and family needs and should incorporate objectives and activities from other domains]

My child will:
- Enjoy playing with me;
- Have opportunities to be around other children;
- Play better with his older brother;

- Be able to stick up for himself when he plays with his friends.

We will:
- Learn games which are enjoyable for our child;
- Know of places nearby where our child can play with other children.

Transactional Assessment

May assess through observation and interview.

Assessment of the Child's Environment

1. Supportive:
[Example environments which support/facilitate development in this area]
The child's caregiving environments usually:
- Offer opportunities for the child to socialize with other people;

- Have small adult-to-child ratios;
- Have toys which promote interactions between children and opportunities for imaginative play;
- Value social play as an important part of the child's development.

Assessment of Caregiver Interactions with the Child

1. Supportive:
[Example interactions which support/facilitate child's development in this area]
When interacting and playing with the child, caregivers usually:
- Are in rhythm with their child's pace of interactions; i.e., take turns and give the child time to respond before continuing the interaction;
- Adjust their role in games so the child can be more active;
- Respond to the child's initiations to start a game or social interaction, e.g., child vocalizes and smiles, caregiver reciprocates and waits for another response;
- Play games which are developmentally appropriate and interesting to the child;
- Appear joyful and attentive during social interactions with the child;
- Follow the child's lead, cues and signals during social interactions.

2. Compromising:
[Interactions which may restrict, compromise, inhibit or be unsupportive of the child's development in this area]
The child's caregivers frequently:
- Are "out-of-sync" during social interactions with the child, e.g., too intense, fast-paced, not in tune with child's pacing or cues;
- Try to control the choice and duration of social games and interactions;
- Appear depressed or emotionally distant;
- Are hostile, ignoring, or abusive to the child.

Identifying and Interpreting Needs for Intervention

If a child is significantly delayed or displays consistent atypical behaviors in this area, he <u>may be having social-emotional difficulties in relating socially to others</u>.

<u>However</u>, before targeting social-emotional issues as the primary area of need for intervention, consider, rule out or adapt for, other causes that may contribute to and thus interfere with a true assessment of the child's capacities to interact and relate to people. These may include:

- <u>Lack of experience</u> with other children or adults who are sensitive partners during interactions. If the child has a history of extended hospitalizations or has a disability, he may be especially vulnerable to isolation and lack of opportunities to interact socially;

- <u>Motor impairment, motor delays, atypical tone</u>: the child may not have the mobility skills needed to play interactive games; the child may have unclear, more subtle, weaker or distorted cues and signals during interactions; e.g., smiles may be weaker or distorted, responses may be slower;

- <u>Visual impairment</u>: child may have unclear or more subtle cues and signals to caregivers; smiles may be delayed or distorted; facial expressions may not be as varied; child may appear rejecting when he stiffens or startles to unexpected approaches; child cannot rely on caregiver's eye contact or facial expressions for feedback and social engagement;

- <u>Cognitive and language delays</u>: especially in goal-directed behaviors, cause and effect and object (people) permanence;

- <u>Cultural differences</u>: some cultures and families will play different social games than, for example, in skill #1.33 "Peek-a-boo";

- <u>Regulatory/sensory organization difficulties</u>: the child may be overreactive or underreactive to the environment and interactions causing irritability, gaze aversion, extreme fearfulness, low affect, disorganized behavior;

- <u>Transient benign stressful situations</u> that are likely to resolve; e.g., child is shy in new settings, overtired, hungry, ill, on medications which affect his relatedness.

Assessment Adaptations   (Examples)

[Note any adaptations needed to credit and help plan interventions]

- <u>Motor impairment, motor delays, atypical tone</u>: *consult with a therapist to optimize the child's positions during social interactions*; allow extra response time for the child to "take a turn" in the interaction; pay special attention to more subtle or distorted vocal, bodily or facial expressions (e.g., weaker smiles due to hypotonia; arching back with a grimace when happy or excited due to hypertonia) which consistently signal the child's interactive intent.

- <u>Visual impairment</u>: observe when the child is with familiar people and in familiar environments; pay special attention to the ways the parent and child have adapted to each other, to "read" each other's cues; look for the child's more subtle cues of interaction, such as moving his hands instead of smiling or giving eye contact, or becoming still instead of increasing his activity to take a turn. Specific skill adaptations:
    - omit or adapt #5.02 "Regards face" and #5.04 "Establishes eye contact," e.g., may credit "stilling" or a specific hand movement as an indicator that the child is ready to interact with another.
    - replace items #2.12 "Laughs when head is cover with a cloth, and #1.33 "Plays Peek-a-boo" with sound and touch games, e.g., "I'm gonna get you," "This Little Piggy," and "Pat-a-cake."
    - omit #5.32 "Extends toy to show others" unless child has specifically been taught this.
    - omit or adapt #5.46 "Plays ball cooperatively," e.g., use a ball with a bell and use initial hand-over-hand modeling of the game;
    - omit #5.58 "Interacts with peer using gestures."

- <u>Cognitive and language delays</u>: use games and interactions that match the child's cognitive skills in the areas of cause and effect, symbolic play, and object permanence (e.g., substitute Pat-a-cake for Peek-a-boo if child is significantly delayed in object permanence.)

- <u>Regulatory/sensory organization difficulties</u>: if child is more passive and difficult to arouse, you may need to work harder to engage and get attention, e.g., with silly faces, firm touches, toys with more visual and auditory feedback. Respond to any of the child's signals, no matter how weakly he sends them. If the child is overreactive or hyper-excitable, active, and easily distracted, help him to first to relax and focus; e.g., begin by soothing with rocking, or using a calming voice or facial expression.

General Assessment Procedures & Processes   (apply to all items in this Strand)

1. **Try to elicit the child's optimal interactive responses.** Use of imitation, repetition and expansion may improve the quality and length of social interactions.

2. A transactional assessment is especially important when assessing the child's interactive behaviors because a child can usually only be as effective as his interactive partner. **Pay special attention to the caregivers' interactions which promote or restrict the child's interactive processes.** Refer to the "Transactional assessment" above.

3. To help in planning interventions, consider and make note of:
   – how much adult support the child needs to become engaged in and maintain the social interaction;
   – who initiates the interaction and how many "turns" can the child take before ending it;
   – what contexts promote and sustain interactions, e.g., which partners, which interactions, which toys?

4. **Describe the skill behavior and example opportunities to observe to family members and invite them to help observe and/or assess.**

5. **Consider cultural differences:** be sure to assess with culturally relevant social games which can be gleaned through sensitive parent interview (see parent questions above).

6. **Two items should always be assessed,** regardless of the child's developmental level or age: #5.04 "Establishes eye contact" and #5.07 "Responds with smile when socially approached."

+ - A   **Credit Notes:**

+   child usually displays social interaction behaviors as defined.

-   not observed or reported.

+/- appears to be an emerging behavior.

A   atypical or dysfunctional interaction interfering with social interchanges.

O   circle any credit if environment or interactions compromise or restrict child's optimal social interactive behaviors. (refer to Interactional assessment above.)

Note any adaptations used to credit.

 5.02   **Regards face**   **0-1**

Definition: The child shows interest in human faces by staring or looking at them.

Parent Questions: Have you noticed if your child seems to look at you? When have you noticed this? About how long does he seem to look at you?

Example Observation Opportunities: May observe when parent or facilitator's face is approximately 8-12 inches away from child's face, e.g., during feeding, holding, adult leaning over to greet, change diaper, etc. The adult may nod, smile or talk, or may remain quiet.

Credit: (see also Credit Notes in this strand's preface)
+   looks at faces several times a day; regard may be brief but there is some interest displayed.
(may also credit #5.04 if child easily establishes eye contact.)

 5.04   **Establishes eye contact**   **0-2**

Definition: The child usually enjoys looking (a few seconds at a time) into the eyes of others who look at him at a comfortable distance. He may divert his gaze when he's tired, upset or over-stimulated, but should not consistently resist eye-to-eye contact.

Parent Questions: Does your child seem to really look at you when you are looking at him? Are there times when it seems hard to get him to look at you?

Example Observation Opportunities: May observe when child is content and an adult is holding, feeding, talking to or playing with the child. Observe and note which interactions effectively elicit the child's eye contact, e.g., facial expression, distance, high-pitched voice. If eye contact is sporadic or more difficult to achieve, try adjusting your position and interactions; e.g., dim lights, hold in upright position, or reduce interactions by only looking and smiling at the child rather than holding, talking and looking simultaneously.

Credit: (see also Credit Notes in this strand's preface)
+   it is usually easy to establish eye contact with the child for at least few seconds at a time.
-   eye contact is difficult or rarely established.
A   always actively averts gaze, closes eyes; in older child, displays extreme vigilance; i.e., always watches adult with wide-eyed, fearful expression.
O   circle any credit if caregivers provide minimal eye contact, over-stimulate, do not interpret or respond to child's eye contact as a signal for interaction.
(also in Strand 5-1)

Molds and relaxes body when held; cuddles   0-3

Definition: When content, the child usually conforms or shapes his body to fit closely to an adult cuddling him.

Parent Questions: Does your child usually like to be held and cuddled? About how often do you think babies should be held?

Example Observation Opportunities: May observe whenever parent is holding child when both are relaxed and content, e.g., during feeding, parent interview, rest, play. If the child is easily stimulated, explore less stimulating handling techniques, e.g., do not rock, talk, or look excessively at child while holding.

Credit: (see also Credit Notes in this strand's preface)
+   can be characterized as "cuddly"; usually molds and relaxes body when held.
A   usually cries, fusses, arches, pulls away when held or, usually feels or appears limp or passive when held; does not mold or adjust posture to adult.
O   circle any credit if caregivers rarely hold or cuddle child, or have difficulty identifying interactions and positions for holding which are comfortable for caregiver and child.

(also in Strand 0.0 "Regulatory/Sensory Organization")

 Responds with smile when socially approached   1.5-4

Definition: The child smiles purposefully and easily to express pleasure and enjoyment in response to social interaction from others. At this stage, he may smile as readily to strangers as he does to caregivers.

Parent Questions: What kinds of things do you do that seem to make your child smile? Does your child smile easily or does it seem like you need to "work at it" to get him to smile?

Example Observation Opportunities: May observe anytime child is content and someone engages in a pleasant verbal or social interaction during play, feeding, diaper changing, e.g., smiling and/or vocalizing to child with high-pitched voice and animated facial expression; parent approaching child to pick up; stroking child's tummy while talking and smiling.

Credit: (see also Credit Notes in this strand's preface)
+   smiles easily when others talk and smile to child.
A   always averts gaze, turns away.
O   circle any credit if caregivers have difficulty identifying interactions that elicit their child's smiles.

(also in Strand 5-3)

 Vocalizes in response to adult talk and smile   3-5

Definition: The child vocalizes, coos, or makes other happy sounds when an adult smiles and talks to him. He is learning his role as a responder and partner in social interactions.

Parent Questions: Does your child ever seem to "talk" back to you when you talk to him? Can you give me an example?

Example Observation Opportunities: Incidental - a familiar caregiver may be more likely to elicit the child's vocalizations than an unfamiliar person. Observe at any quiet or break time during the observation session when parent and child are engaged in face-to-face interaction. Structured - if responsive vocalizations are not elicited spontaneously, ask parent to say a simple phrase (e.g., "Hi there...how are you doing?") and pause with an inviting smile for a few seconds while looking at the child. Or ask the parent to imitate any sounds child may make and wait for a response.

Credit: (see also Credit Notes in this strand's preface)
+   makes any sound as a way to "take a turn" and interact in response to an adult's interaction; continues to watch adult after making the vocalization.
O   circle any credit if caregivers rarely vocalize to child or do not respond to child's vocal response.

2.12 **Laughs when head is covered with a cloth** **3.5-4.5**

Definition: Some children enjoy the social interaction of the game "Peek-a-boo" with a trusted adult. If the child's face is briefly covered and then uncovered, he laughs. Some children do not typically laugh to this game at this stage.

Parent Questions: Have you or others ever played "Peek-a-boo" or another type hiding game with your child? How is that game played? Does your child seem to like it yet? How can your tell?

Example Observation Opportunities: Ask the parent to play a game of "Peek-a-boo" with the child in the way they play the game at home.

Credit: (see also Credit Notes in this strand's preface)

+ child laughs when his face has been covered and uncovered in a playful interaction.

N/A if item is not tested or reported because child has not had experience with this type of game or is upset by it.

5.12 **Demands social attention** **3-8**

Definition: The child is learning cause and effect in social relationships. When he wants social attention, he will purposefully act in some way to initiate an interaction; e.g., he may smile, look at, turn, twist, wiggle or shout to get someone's attention.

Parent Questions: Does your child let you know when he wants you to look at or play with him? How does he do this? *[May also ask parent what he/she thinks the child is doing when he is apparently trying to get his parent's attention during the session]*

Example Observation Opportunities: May observe when the child is not playing with a toy and not receiving attention from anyone, e.g., when parent is engaged in filling out forms or talking to other adults.

Credit: (see also Credit Notes in this strand's preface)

+ purposefully acts to attract attention or initiate a social interaction, e.g., looking, smiling, vocalizing, gesturing; does so for the purpose of social attention, not to relieve physical discomfort.

A always cries excessively and demands constant holding; or sits passively for long periods, or preoccupies self with self-stimulating activities.

O circle any credit if caregivers have difficulty interpreting or do not respond to child's bids for attention.

5.15 **Enjoys social play** **3-6**

Definition: The child enjoys interactive social "games" such as "Peek-a-boo," "Pat-a-cake," "This Little Piggy," "I'm gonna get you." At this stage the infant is more of a passive participant. and the adult takes a more active role. The child is learning to be a social responder, receiver or partner in play.

Parent Questions: Are there any special games your child seems to like, such as "Peek-a-boo," or bouncing on your knees?

Example Observation Opportunities: Invite the parent to play games with the child that he is familiar with when he's in a playful mood. Observe how easy or difficult it is to engage the child; e.g., does the parent need to use high arousal techniques, such as larger movements or higher voice variability, or does the child become over-stimulated quite easily?

Credit: (see also Credit Notes in this strand's preface)

+ displays signs of enjoyment and engagement when involved in a social interactive game; e.g., he may smile, squeal, try to continue the movement, display anticipatory excitement, and/or laugh; is able to remain engaged and focused for a few minutes.

A always turns away; appears distant and un-engaged with a flat or unresponsive affect.

O if parent has difficulty thinking of developmentally appropriate games or pacing the game to child's pace, attention, and cues.

1.28 **Hand regard no longer present** **5-6**

Definition: The child rarely or no longer engages in isolated hand-watching, e.g., watching intently while waving his hands in front of his face. He is more interested in observing and playing with others.

Parent Questions: Have you noticed if your child seems to like waving his hand in front of his eyes to watch? *If so* About how often do you see this? When do you see him do this (or give me an example of when he did this; e.g., where was he, what position, how long did it last, were other toys or people around)?

Example Observation Opportunities: May observe anytime during observation period, especially when

Hand regard no longer present   (continued)

no one is directly interacting with him.

Credit: (see also Credit Notes in this strand's preface)

+   does <u>not</u> watch hands waving in front of face for any significant amount of time; prefers interacting with people.

A   over 5 months and spends a significant amount of time hand-watching or prefers hand-watching to interacting with people.

5.19   ## Repeats enjoyable activities   4-8

Definition: The child repeats a gesture or movement to take a turn in a social interaction or game and to keep the interaction going, e.g., when adult claps hands in "Pat-a- cake" or bounces child on knees and then pauses, the child tries to clap his or the parent's hands for "Pat-a-cake," or wiggles to restart bouncing. At this stage, the child is also able to maintain or extend the "turn-taking" interaction with a sensitive partner, taking anywhere from five to ten turns. For example, after the child takes a turn with a gesture, the adult takes another turn by clapping again and then the child takes another turn by intentionally vocalizing, moving or gesturing, and so on for five to ten consecutive interchanges.

Parent Questions: Same as #5.15 above.

Example Observation Opportunities: Same as #5.15 above.

Credit: (see also Credit Notes in this strand's preface)

+   actively participates to take a turn; keeps the game or other social interchange going with a combination of gestures, movements, and vocalizations; is able to maintain the interaction by taking several turns as defined.

O   if caregivers have difficulty thinking of developmentally appropriate "games," or pacing and maintaining the game to child's pace, attention, and cues.

1.33   ## Plays "Peek-a-boo"   6-10

Definition: The child enjoys and actively participates in playing a turn-taking game such as "Peek-a-boo." He may participate by trying to remove the "hiding" hands or cloth, or by hiding his own face. He displays his enjoyment by responding with delight, e.g., happy facial expression, chuckle, squeal, laugh.

Parent Questions: Have you or other family members ever played a "Peek-a-boo" game with your child? How does he seem to like it? What does he usually do to help play the game?

Example Observation Opportunities: Ask the parent to play a game of "Peek-a-boo" with the child in the way they play the game at home. This may be played by covering the adult's or child's face according to child's preference. Observe the role the child plays in the game and how he tries to keep the game or interaction going.

Credit: (see also Credit Notes in this strand's preface)

+   enjoys and actively participates in "Peek-a-boo" game, e.g., pulls cloth, hides own face, vocalizes; can remain engaged in the game for several hidings.

-   pulls cloth off face only because it is irritating, <u>not</u> as a playful interaction.

5.26   ## Cooperates in games   6-10

Definition: The child takes an active role in simple interactive games with an adult and sometimes initiates the game.

Example Observation Opportunities: Ask the parent to play any games with the child the way they play them at home. If the parent has difficulty thinking of games or would prefer additional direction, suggest one or more of the following:

–   simple ball play: adult tosses ball to child and then waits for child to make a gesture to return it or takes it back in a playful manner, returning it again to the child;

–   "Peek-a-boo": (refer to #1.33 above);

–   "Pat-a-cake": saying "Pat-a-cake" and clapping or banging on the surface;

–   "So big": adult uses strong inflections, raises own or child's arms;

–   "Horsie": adult bounces child on knees.

Credit: (see also Credit Notes in this strand's preface)

+   participates in and tries to keep a game going; sometimes initiates a game by making the initial movement, vocalization or gesture (Examples of the child's active participation include: ball

Cooperates in games   (continued)

play – moving arms or legs in an attempt to toss ball back; "Peek-a-boo" – child hides own face or tries to pull off cover; "Pat-a-cake" – child claps own hands or pats adults hands; "So big" – child actively raise own arms; "Horsie" – child starts and/or maintains the game by bouncing his body when the adult is still).

O   circle any credit if caregivers cannot think of games to play which are enjoyable or over-control the game so child cannot actively participate.

5.32   Extends toy to show others, not for release   9-12

Definition: The child holds out a toy he finds interesting to communicate that he wants the person to whom he's showing it to look at, acknowledge, share, or explain it (but not take it away!) For example, "Yes, you have a ball."

Example Observation Opportunities: Incidental - may observe when child is given any novel or interesting object to play with during assessment period. Structured - invite the child to take an unfamiliar or interesting toy out of a box while his parent is seated nearby. Observe to see if child spontaneously "shows" his parent or other person nearby. Examples of objects include: plastic Slinky, Koosh™ ball, colorful squeak toy, crumpled tissue paper, doll, comb, book, cookie.

Credit: (see also Credit Notes in this strand's preface)

+   holds toy or other object of interest out to show; does so in an apparent attempt to initiate an interaction or socialize with another person; may also credit #5.38 if child also gives the object to the adult as a social gesture to share.

(also in Strand 2-4A "Communicating with Others–Gesturally")

2.30   Repeats sounds or gestures if laughed at   11-12.5

Definition: When the child makes an amusing vocalization or gesture, he repeats it when he sees he has elicited positive attention, such as appreciative laughter from others. This is another example of how the child is learning to initiate, be influenced by, and enjoy social interactions.

Example Observation Opportunities: Situations usually arise in which the child will spontaneously do something amusing, e.g., making an exaggerated grimace at the taste of a new food, tilting his head or wiggling his body to dance, making a "raspberry" sound. Also observe caregiver's responses to the child's antics.

Credit: (see also Credit Notes in this strand's preface)

+   repeats vocalizations, expressions, body movements or gestures when they are reinforced by another.

O   circle any credit if caregivers rarely notice, laugh at, nor appear to enjoy their child's cute gestures.

5.38   Gives toy to familiar adult spontaneously and upon request   12-15

Definition: The child gives a trusted adult a toy or other object to share (as something special) and to socialize. He may give it spontaneously or in response to an adult showing interest and asking to see or play with it together. *[Note: this skill differs from skill #5.32, "Extends toy to show others, not for release," in that the child has developed trust to know that the toy will be returned. If the child has siblings or playmates who regularly take toys away without returning them, he may be still hesitant to actually release the toy]*

Example Observation Opportunities: Observe when child is presented with new toys or objects which encourage interactions with another. These may include: book, bubbles, wind-up toy, ball.

Credit: (see also Credit Notes in this strand's preface)

+   gives an object to another for the purpose of sharing and initiating an interaction, not just because he does not want the toy; continues to look at the toy with the adult and may extend his hands to ask for it back.

-    gives toy but does not continue the social interchange; moves on to another activity.

(also in Strand 2-4A "Communicating with Others–Gesturally")

5.46 Plays ball cooperatively   12-15

Definition: The child participates in "give and take" games, such as tossing a ball back and forth, giving toys back and forth or building towers and knocking them down.

Example Observation Opportunities: Ask the parent to play any games with the child they way they play them at home. If the parent has difficulty thinking of games or would prefer additional direction, suggest one of the examples included in the above definition.

Credit: (see also Credit Notes in this strand's preface)
+ child participates in a turning-taking game taking many turns, e.g., moves body to repeatedly return a ball tossed to him; gives a series of toys to an adult each time the adult says "thank you!"; knocks down a tower of blocks each time adult builds one.

5.58 Interacts with peers using gestures   18-24

Definition: Although parallel play usually predominates at this age, the child does socially interact with peers. Since the child at this stage, however, does not have the social and verbal skills to effectively interact with peers, he communicates primarily through gestures. Many of these gestures are aggressive, such as pushing, pulling, or grabbing. He may use these gestures to communicate, for example, "That's my toy," "I want that," "Play with me," "Come here." He may also use less aggressive gestures of endearment and gestures to get attention or respond to another child's gesture, e.g., patting, hugging, waving, showing sympathy, shrugging shoulders, and pointing. Depending upon the child's verbal abilities, vocalizations may accompany gestures.

Parent Questions Does your child have opportunities to be around other children about his age? How do they play together? *[If needed, give examples of gestures children typically use to interact or probe]*

Example Observation Opportunities: If a playmate is available, observe instances of communicative interactions. Have toys available that invite interactions, e.g., ball, cars, dolls, sand or water play, rocking boat.

Credit: (see also Credit Notes in this strand's preface)
+ sometimes interacts with other peers, using a variety of gestures, some of which may be aggressive.
A only interacts with extreme aggression; usually hurting the other child; or appears oblivious to the presence of other children.

(also in Strand 2-4A "Communicating with Others–Gesturally")

5.59 Engages in parallel play   18-24

Definition: The child plays next to but not directly with another child while engaged in a similar activity. Although parallel play predominates, interactions between children are continuing to increase, e.g., via toy exchange and communicative gestures as discussed in item #5.58 above.

Parent Questions: Does your child have opportunities to play with other children who are about his age? About how often? Have you seen him play when he is with other children? Does he sit next to or near another child during play?

Example Observation Opportunities: May observe if one or more peers are present during the observation period. Provide materials and facilitate engaging the children in structured group activities, such as painting, playing with playdough, doll play, block play, play with cars. If children are not available, it will be helpful to interview the child's childcare provider or observe the child in other group settings in which he spends time, such as his play group or daycare setting.

Credit: (see also Credit Notes in this strand's preface)
+ parallel play predominates; child is clearly aware of other children and frequently observes them but there may be little turn-taking or cooperative interactions.

Defends possessions   23-24

Definition: The child's interactions with peers are dominated with ideas of taking or defending rather than giving or sharing. The child has also developed a good sense of ownership and displays an increase in possessiveness as he defends things he believes are his.

Parent Questions: How does your child react if one of his friends tries to take away a toy he is playing with?

Example Observation Opportunities: May observe when child is playing freely with other children.

Credit: (see also Credit Notes in this strand's preface)
- \+   defends possessions with peers and sometimes siblings by saying, "mine," "no," or by snatching things away, hiding them or holding on tightly; if these actions do not work, the child may become more aggressive; e.g., he may hit or bite another.
- A   only defends possessions by hurting others.
- O   circle any credit if caregivers hit (bite, etc.) child back to teach him not to act this way.

Displays shyness with strangers and in outside situations   24-30

Definition: Children may display varying degrees of shyness in new situations and with new people. They are usually able to warm up after developing a sense of safety and trust.

Parent Questions: How does your child react when he meets new people and he is not at home? *If reportedly shy or clingy,* About how long does it take him to warm up? What are some things that seem to make him feel more comfortable?

Example Observation Opportunities: Observe how child responds to you and other assessment staff if this is his first time meeting you or other assessment staff.

Credit: (see also Credit Notes in this strand's preface)
- \+   appears shy or slow to warm up, e.g., may refuse eye contact, suck fingers, hold on to parent.
- A   always overly frightened and anxious, even in safe places with parent; e.g., screams hysterically, throws up, hides; cannot be re-engaged after more than 20 minutes of sensitive interactions.

N/A not observed or reported; this item is for anticipatory guidance.

Tends to be physically aggressive   24-30

Definition: The child may sometimes hit, bite, push, take things, or throw to interact and assert himself to others.

Parent Questions: Sometimes at this stage, children become somewhat aggressive and sometimes hit, bite or push others. Have you noticed this with your child? Can you give me an example? Why do you think he acts this way? How do you respond?

Example Observation Opportunities: May observe when child is playing freely with other children and interacting with adults.

Credit: (see also Credit Notes in this strand's preface)
- \+ sometimes is physically aggressive in his interactions with others.
- A   aggressive behaviors dominate the child's interactions with himself and/or others, frequently breaks things, hurts other children, and/or bites or hits self, bangs head.

N/A if not observed or reported. This is not an item to teach.

5.70   Enjoys a wide range of relationships; meets more people   24-36

Definition: The child increases his curiosity and interest in meeting and interacting with other people beyond his family members.

Parent Questions: What are some of the activities and experiences your child participates in during the week where he has opportunities to meet other children and adults? How does he seem to get along with others?

Credit: (see also Credit Notes in this strand's preface)
- \+   by clinical judgment and parent report, child appears to be enjoying a variety of relationships with e.g., neighborhood children, children in daycare, teachers, family friends.
- A   shows no interest in meeting or interacting with people; appears unaware, withdrawn, "tuned-out"; depressed.
- O   circle any credit if the child has little or no positive opportunities to develop relationships with others.

5.75   Relates best to one familiar adult at a time   24-36

Definition: At this stage, many children feel overwhelmed, overstimulated and unable to relate to two adults at a time, even if both adults are his parents.

Parent Questions: Sometimes children at this age seem to get along better with just one adult at a time instead of having to relate to two adults. For example, some children like to play with just Mommy or just Daddy instead of playing with both parents at the same time. Have you noticed this happening with your child? Can you give me an example?

Credit: (see also Credit Notes in this strand's preface)

+   if child by report or clinical judgment seems to relate better with just one adult at a time. *[Note: This can have implications for conducting your assessment and interventions; e.g., if both parents attend, it may be helpful to hang back with one of the parents and have only one parent interact with the child at a time]*

N/A not observed or reported; this item is for anticipatory guidance.

5.76   Engages best in peer interaction with just one older child, not a sibling   24-36

Definition: After the second year, the child's interactions with other children include more communicative exchanges, especially when interacting with just one other child who is familiar and is slightly older than him. *[There has been some limited research that this is especially true for a child who has mild disabilities, i.e., pairing a child with mild disabilities with a slightly older child who does not have disabilities]*

Parent Questions: Who are the children your child seems to play with best ? Can you tell me a little about the way he plays with one of them?

Example Observation Opportunities: If possible, observe child playing with another child, e.g., in classroom or daycare setting; at home when neighbor comes over to play.

Credit: (see also Credit Notes in this strand's preface)

+   is able to play for at least 10 minutes with another child who may be a little older.

O   circle any credit if the child has little or no positive opportunities to develop relationships with children (disabled and non-disabled).

5.78   Initiates own play, but requires supervision to carry out ideas   24-36

Definition: During the third year, the child's play with peers becomes increasingly interactive. Play often includes initiating make-believe activities in which the children take on different roles and incorporate them in play, e.g., playing doctor or house. Although the child can initiate play, he still sometimes needs supervision to help negotiate conflicts or to figure out how to accomplish a difficult or more elaborate task, for example, to turn a table into a playhouse.

Example Observation Opportunities: Observe during a free play observation with one or two peers. Provide "props" and play materials which promote interactive and thematic play, e.g., soft playdough, small tin pan, blocks, pegs, doll; or, play doctor's bag with a stethoscope, BandAid, lotion; dress-up clothes; small wagon.

Credit: (see also Credit Notes in this strand's preface)

+   is able to initiate and maintain play activities with another child for at least 5-10 minutes with some adult supervision; interacts with simple turn-taking and some role-sharing; the child may have a different play agenda (e.g., one is playing doctor while another is playing birthday party), but is interacting verbally and/or gesturally; adults are needed to supervise conflicts, safety, and to help carry out a more elaborate idea.

5.89 Tends to be dictatorial and demanding   30-36

Definition: The child's interactions with adults and peers may sometimes appear to be dictatorial and demanding as he "orders" others to do things.

Example Observation Opportunities: May observe during any interactions with peers or adults.

Credit: (see also Credit Notes in this strand's preface)

+   sometimes "orders" others to do things; may act furious if they do not comply; can usually be distracted or humored out of it.

A   overly aggressive; e.g., needs total control of the environment and social interactions; cannot respond to rules and limits even though it's clear he understands them; is aggressive or destructive in play; may bite or kick others; purposefully break toys.

N/A if not reported or observed; for anticipatory guidance.

5.90 Talks with a loud, urgent voice   30-36

Definition: Many children at this age have difficulty modulating their voice tones and thus may seem to interact in a loud, urgent manner.

Example Observation Opportunities: May observe throughout assessment.

Credit: (see also Credit Notes in this strand's preface)

+   talks with a loud, urgent voice unintentionally.

N/A if not reported or observed; for anticipatory guidance.

5.93 Participates in circle games; plays interactive games   30+

Definition: The child enjoys and participates with peers in interactive games such as "Ring Around the Rosie," Tag," "Hide and Seek," "London Bridge."

Parent Questions: Tell me how your child plays with other children; e.g., what types of games they play, how he seems to get along with others?

Example Observation Opportunities: May observe child in familiar peer settings, e.g., daycare, preschool. May also interview child's parents, daycare provider and/or teacher.

Credit: (see also Credit Notes in this strand's preface)

+   usually interacts and plays well with two or three other peers in interactive games.

A   **overly aggressive:** e.g., needs total control of the game and does not follow simple game rules; frequently bites or hits peers; or **overly sensitive,** e.g., does well in one-to-one interactions, but becomes overwhelmed and falls apart in large groups or circle times; tends to shy away from new peers, distressed when others are nearby, such as sitting together during circle time; or **disengaged,** e.g., does not participate in interactive way; is withdrawn, "tuned-out;" may wander aimlessly; may be preoccupied with inner thoughts.

O   circle any credit if peer play environments are overly chaotic and unstructured.

(also in 0.0 "Regulatory/Sensory Organization")

6-1 ORAL MOTOR

6.01	0-1	Opens and closes mouth in response to food stimulus
6.02	1-5	Coordinates sucking, swallowing, and breathing
6.06	2-5	Suck and swallow reflex inhibited
6.08	3-6	Swallows strained or pureed foods
6.12	4-6	Rooting reflex inhibited
6.11	4-8.5	Uses tongue to move food in mouth
6.17	5-8	Mouths and *munches* solid foods
6.22	7-8	Bites and chews toys
6.19	*8-10*	Bites food voluntarily
6.20	6-12	Drinks from cup held for him
6.23	7-12	Drools less except when teething
6.24	8-13.5	Chews food with *coordinated movements*
6.44	18-24	Chews completely with rotary jaw movements

Family Friendly Interpretation of Strand Concepts, Assessment, & Purpose

We will be observing how your child is learning to use and coordinate his lips, tongue and jaw during feeding. Professionals often term this "oral motor development." Oral motor skills and development are important for feeding as well as speech development. These skills are also closely associated with and influenced by your child's overall motor development. For example, if your child tends to keep his head held back, he will have more difficulty moving food with his tongue and with swallowing.

Professional FYI

The italicized wording for skill #6.17 "Mouths and *munches* solid foods" and skill #6.24 "Chews food with *coordinated movements*" is an adaptation to the original HELP skill wording. These changes were made to more accurately define the chewing movements that typically emerge during these age ranges.

Parent Questions   (Examples)

To help identify the child's unique strengths and needs related to this developmental area:
• Can you tell me a little about how things are going with your child's feeding?
• What kinds of foods is your child eating?
• Do you have any questions or concerns about how your child drinks or eats?

[May probe further with the following questions as needed dependent upon child's age, apparent needs, and areas parent did not address in the general, open-ended questions]
• Has your child ever been tube fed?
• What types of food does your child eat? (probe for breakfast, lunch, dinner and how the food is prepared, e.g., commercial strained, blended, etc.)
• Who are the people who usually feed your child?
• Is he bottle- or breast-fed?
• How is he fed at home, e.g., in your lap, high-chair, propped on pillow?
• Do his lips seem to seal around the nipple fairly well or does it seem like a lot of milk drips out? What kind of nipples do you use?
• About how long does it take to feed your child?
• Does your child seem to have favorite foods?

(note texture, taste, temperature preferences)
• Does your child seem to dislike certain foods? (note texture, taste, temperature dislikes)
• Are there any other important aspects of your child's feeding or drinking that I have not asked that you feel are important for us to know?

[IMPORTANT: If the parent answers positively to any of the following questions, the child should be referred to a physician if this has not been evaluated. Intervention and assessment strategies will be dependent upon medical findings]
Does your child:
• Have any medical problems that you are aware of that could interfere with feeding?
• Have frequent respiratory or breathing problems?
• Cough or gag a lot during feeding?
• Ever vomit during or after feeding?
• Usually get extra fussy or irritable after he has eaten?
• Have any known or suspected food allergies or sensitivities? Does anyone in your family have food allergies?
• Has your child seen a doctor for any of these concerns?

Parent Questions (continued)

To help identify family resources, priorities and concerns related to the child's development in this area:
- What do you think would make feeding go better for you and your child?
- If you could think of one thing you would like to see improve with your child's feeding what would that be?

(If parent reports concerns or priorities)
- What have you tried so far?
- Has that seemed to work?
- Are you aware of community resources if you need help getting formula, milk, food, or special formulas for your child?
- Do you have a doctor or clinic you can go to help with feeding problems?
- Are there family or friends nearby who can help you with feeding your baby?
- Do you have a highchair (or adaptive seating)? Are you interested in having information about community resources to help get a highchair (or adaptive seating)?

Sample *Functional* Outcome Statements which may be generated by the Family

[Will be dependent upon identified individual child and family needs, and should incorporate objectives and activities from other domains]
My child:
- Won't fuss while I feed him a bottle;
- Will finish his bottle faster;
- Will gain weight;
- Will eat better;
- Will be able to eat solid foods.

Transactional Assessment

May assess through observation and interview.

Assessment of the Child's Environment

1. Supportive:
[Example environments which support/facilitate development in this area]
The child's feeding environment usually:
- Provides a predictable routine for feeding, e.g., times, places, consistent adult;
- Is safe, e.g., child is not left on couch or counter; highchair is secure; foods are prepared and stored safely;
- Is relaxed and interesting;
- Has appropriate feeding equipment to match the child's developmental stage, e.g., seating, appropriate sized spoons, cups, bottles.

2. Compromising:
[Environments which may restrict, compromise, inhibit or be unsupportive toward development in this area]
The child's feeding environments are frequently:
- Unsafe, e.g., highchair or seat is not secure; bottles are left out to spoil; foods are given that can cause choking;
- Unpredictable, e.g., no consistent adults who feed, no feeding routine or schedules;
- Chaotic, tense, and/or over-stimulating.

Assessment of Caregiver Interactions with the Child

1. Supportive:
[Example interactions which support/facilitate child's development in this area]
The child's caregivers usually:
- Are able to read and respond sensitively to the child's unique communicative signals and cues that request more food, signal he needs a break, or signal he is finished;
- Smile, touch, look at, and talk to their child with warmth and sensitivity during feeding if this does not over-stimulate the child;
- Allow the child to explore his food and support his attempts at independence;
- Try to determine and relieve the child's cause of distress during feeding;
- Position the child and themselves in comfortable developmentally appropriate positions (see appropriate position techniques below under "General child assessment procedures and processes," step 3).

2. Compromising:
[Example interactions which may restrict, compromise, inhibit or be unsupportive of the child's development in this area]
The child's caregivers frequently:
- Ignore, misinterpret and/or respond inappropriately to the child's signals that he is ready or not ready for more food, or is finished;
- Are doing other things while the child is feeding;
- Position the child in unsafe or uncomfortable feeding positions;
- Ignore or do not try to relieve child's distress if he becomes upset during feeding;
- Overly restrict their child's efforts to explore food or try to feed himself;
- Expect their child to eat better or more independently when he is developmentally not ready,

Assessment of Caregiver Interactions with the Child   (continued)

e.g., punishes child for spilling liquid while learning to drink from a cup; expects child to hold his own bottle when he is only a few months old.

[Important note: caregivers may have difficulty providing supportive interactions because the child is a

poor interactor; e.g., the child sends weak or confusing signals that he is ready to eat or has had enough. An invested parent may be exhausted, try too hard, or be overprotective during feeding, because of the child's current or past medical condition. Consequently interactions can appear compromising]

Identifying and Interpreting Needs for Intervention

If a child displays significant delays or atypical development in this area he may have <u>oral motor dysfunction</u> due to underlying neuromotor involvement, cranio-facial anomalies, such as clef palate, and/or structural abnormalities of the gastrointestinal, respiratory or cardiac systems.

    <u>However</u>, if these areas have been medically evaluated and ruled out, consider and, rule out or adapt for other causes that are <u>*not* related to neuromotor involvement, nerve damage, cranio-facial or structural abnormalities</u>. These may include:
- <u>Tactile sensitivities</u> or other sensory organization problems: the child may refuse, gag, or not chew certain food textures. Refer to

Strand 0.0 "Regulatory/Sensory Organization" and refer to a pediatric therapist with experience and training in sensory organization.
- <u>Infection</u> of gums, teeth, oral cavity.
- <u>Transient issues</u>; e.g., child is ill, irritable, not hungry during observation period.
- <u>Over-stimulating environment</u>
- <u>Emotional or behavioral issues</u>, e.g., if the child has a history of invasive procedures he may purposefully resist feeding; child is using feeding as a method to control his environment.
- Adult uses <u>inappropriate feeding techniques</u>, e.g., wrong nipple; props instead of holds; positions with head down; uses a spoon too big for child; force feeds.

Assessment Adaptations   (Examples)

- <u>Neuromotor, medical, or structural conditions</u>: it is critical to have medical supervision and to include a pediatric speech or occupational therapist trained in feeding involved in the assessment and planning process. Special equipment, positioning or handling techniques may be used during the assessment to optimize and facilitate feeding.
- <u>Visual impairment</u>:
  - Ask parents what routines they may use during feeding to help the child prepare for drinking and eating. For example,

they may help the child prepare for an approaching spoon, nipple, or cup by telling him what they are offering and by approaching him slowly e.g., help him touch the spoon, nipple, food, drink, or cup and pause at his lips to let him know the food is on its way.
- Use familiar positions, seating, foods, and utensils, preferably his own.
- Watch and wait for the child's unique cues that indicate he is ready for another bite.

General Assessment Procedures & Processes   (apply to all items in this Strand)

1. Feeding is a very personal area for caregivers and the child. **It is important to facilitate parents' feelings of competence during feeding**. Most of the assessment can occur by observing the parent feeding the child. After observation, direct assessment may occur with parental permission, if needed, to observe more specifically oral-motor movements, to assess areas not observed, or to implement and assess the effectiveness of special feeding techniques to help in programming.
2. **Assess in the child's natural feeding environments during a regular feeding time whenever possible.** This will provide a more comprehensive assessment, since you will be

able to see the types of utensils, foods, setting and seating used during feeding and will help the child and parent feel more comfortable. If a home-based assessment is not possible, try to schedule the appointment during one of the child's regular feeding times and ask the parent to bring in the child's utensils and foods if appropriate.
3. Good positioning is critical to ensure optimal responses during an oral-motor feeding assessment. **After initial assessment with the parent feeding the child, suggest adjusting the child's position**, if needed. If held, the infant's head should be higher than his hips, arms forward, head in slight flexion

General Assessment Procedures & Processes   (continued)

forward. If in a highchair, the child's back should be fairly straight, and hips, knees and ankles at 90-degree angles.

a. If the child does not have gross motor delays or atypical muscle tone, he should be seated as follows:

1 month – reclining at angle of less than 45 degrees;

3 months – supported semi-sitting position, reclining at an angle of 45 to 90 degrees;

7 months – sitting upright with back at a 90-degree angle, using external support-pillows, tray, person;

9 months – sitting upright with back at 90-degree angle, using a highchair for security;

18 months – sitting unsupported at family table in highchair or booster seat, or at a child-sized table and chair;

b. If the child has atypical muscle tone, refer to HELP at Home Appendix H, for adaptive positioning techniques.

4. **Be sure to seek medical consultation and contraindications for medically involved children.**

+ - A   Credit Notes:

+   **Present:** if child displays typical oral-motor skills, as defined.

-   Skill not present and not atypical.

+/-   Emerging; needs some facilitation.

A   Atypical: if child displays the skill but it is of poor or atypical quality, or inappropriately present for the child's age. In some of the skills atypical patterns specific to the skill are noted. However, if any of the following are observed for any skill item, they should be noted and the child should be referred for a comprehensive oral motor and feeding assessment:

– Strongly pushes head and neck backwards;

– Strongly lifts and holds shoulders up tightly toward his head;

– No contouring of the tongue, it remains thick rather than cupped when eating foods or liquid;

– Excessive gagging, choking;

– Persistent involuntary and strong forward pushing of the tongue, which appears thick;

– Strongly pulling back cheeks and lips; lips appear thin or pursed;

– Jaw thrusting, i.e., abnormally strong pushing of the jaw forward or pulling backward;

– Strongly and involuntarily biting down on spoon.

O   circle any credit if the environment or interactions interfere with optimal feeding. Some items give specific examples. However, in all items, the credit should be circled if the caregiver:

– Has difficulty positioning the child appropriately for feeding, (see # 3 above);

– Uses utensils that compromise feeding; e.g., spoon or cup is too large; nipple hole is too large or small;

– Presents spoon or bottle inappropriately; e.g., bottle is propped rather than held; spoon is pushed too far in mouth to cause gagging;

– Has difficulty pacing presentation of food or drink to child's readiness, e.g., puts more food or drink in child's mouth before he has swallowed previous food;

– Has difficulty adjusting the intensity of verbal and physical interactions to match the child's responses, e.g., talks, jiggles, rocks child to point of over-stimulation or remains distant, does not verbalize etc. when the child looks to caregiver;

– Has difficulty identifying, interpreting and/or responding to child's signals that he is ready for another bite, needs more time between bites, does not want any more food or drink;

– Has difficulty identifying developmentally appropriate foods or drinks.

Assessment Materials

Child's own spoon, bottle, cup, various familiar foods (dependent on level, noted for each item).

Opens and closes mouth in response to food stimulus   0-1

Definition: During the first few months the infant typically displays a rooting reflex. When this reflex is present, the child automatically turns his head and opens his mouth toward a stimulus touching his cheek or mouth area. This reflex should diminish by 4-6 months.

Example Observation Opportunities: Observe during typical feeding with caregiver. If the child does not incidentally display rooting, ask the parent to touch one side of the child's mouth with the nipple just prior to feeding (side closest to parent when held), or with a pacifier if non-feeding time. Do not stimulate both sides of the child's mouth at the same time.

Credit: (see also Credit Notes in this strand's preface)
+   if under 6 months displays typical rooting reflex as defined.
A   if over 6 months (8 months if breast-fed) and continues to display active rooting reflex.
O   circle any credit if caregiver usually over-stimulates rooting reflex, which may be perceived as "teasing by the infant."

 ### Coordinates sucking, swallowing, and breathing   1-5

Definition: The child effectively feeds from a nipple using rhythmical, up-down jaw movements. Jaw movements are coordinated with rhythmical forward-backward tongue movements and regular breathing. There is minimal cheek and lip activity and the tongue is cupped with loose approximation of the lips. This stage of sucking is termed "suckling."

Example Observation Opportunities: Observe feeding during typical feeding time when parent feeds child bottle, or if breast-fed, credit through parent interview.

Credit: (see also Credit Notes in this strand's preface)
+   sucking, swallowing and breathing appears rhythmic, and smooth. There may be some leakage of milk.
A   excessive chokes/coughs, loses a lot of liquid, needs to stop after almost every one or two sucks to breathe or swallow, has a weak suck, and/or displays irregular or labored breathing.
O   circle any credit if caregivers do not position child appropriately, or if the nipple size or hole is too large or too small.

 ### Suck and swallow reflex inhibited   2-5

Definition: During first 2 months the infant typically has a "suck and swallow" reflex; i.e., the mouth opens and sucking movements begin when light touch is applied to the corners or center parts of the lips. Sucking and swallowing at this stage should become voluntary.

Example Observation Opportunities: Same as #6.02 above.

Credit: (see also Credit Notes in this strand's preface)
+   sucking and swallowing appear voluntary; child is able to make several successive sucks before pausing to breath and swallow; some suck movements may occur with suckling; some coughing and choking may occur.

 ### Swallows strained or pureed foods   3-6

Definition: The child can swallow without gagging small amounts of strained baby food. At this stage he may use a suckling pattern of back and forward tongue movements, and thus may push some of the food back out with his tongue. Periodic minimal choking or gagging can occur. *[NOTE age range will vary dependent upon when child begins solids per physician]*

Example Observation Opportunities: Observe when parent presents food on small spoon. Use the child's spoon and a familiar food.

Credit: (see also Credit Notes in this strand's preface)
+   swallows at least half of the food presented on each small spoonful, using back-and-forth tongue movement.
N/A if child has not started solids.

Rooting reflex inhibited   4-6

Definition: When touched on the side of his mouth or cheek, the child does NOT automatically turn his head to source of stimulation. If breast-fed the rooting reflex may continue for a few more months.

Example Observation Opportunities: Same as #6.01 "Opens and closes mouth in response to food stimulus," earlier in this strand.

Credit: (see also Credit Notes in this strand's preface)
+   rooting reflex is not present; child does NOT automatically and strongly turn to nipple or source of stimulation.

Rooting reflex inhibited   (continued)

A if over 6 months (8 months if breast-fed) and child continues to display active rooting reflex.
O   circle any credit if caregiver frequently interrupts child's sucking by removing or jiggling the nipple.

6.11   ## Uses tongue to move food in mouth   4-8.5

Definition: The child uses up-and-down tongue and jaw movements as well as suckling (forward-backward) tongue movements to swallow food.

Example Observation Opportunities: Observe when parent presents food on small spoon to the center of child's mouth. Use a spoon and pureed food that the child is familiar with. Suggest to the parent to present and place the spoon in the child's mouth to see if he will use his upper lip to help remove the food. Observe the child's jaw, cheek, lip and tongue movements.

Credit: (see also Credit Notes in this strand's preface)
+   uses up-and-down tongue and jaw movements with some intermittent back-and-forth tongue movements; if over 8 months uses upper lip to help remove the food from the spoon.
-    continues to predominantly use back-and-forth tongue movements; if over 8 months, no upper lip activity; most of the food is pushed out by the tongue.
N/A if child has not started solids.

6.17   ## Mouths and munches solid foods   5-8

Definition: The child begins to "chew" a soft cookie using a munching pattern, i.e., by pushing his tongue against the roof of his mouth and gumming it with some up-and-down jaw movement. If a piece of cookie is placed on the side, between the biting surfaces of the gum, the tongue and jaw, he begins to show more lateralization, or movement to that side.

Example Observation Opportunities: Observe as the parent offers the child a baby cookie or graham cracker. The adult may need to assist the child in his effort to bite off a piece. Observe how he moves the piece around in his mouth. If lateralization is not observed, place a small piece of food toward the child's side on the molar area of his gums to observe tongue lateralization.

Credit: (see also Credit Notes in this strand's preface)
+   displays some up-and-down chewing-like motions as defined, and some side-to-side movement of jaw and tongue if a piece of cookie is on the molar area of his gum.
A   strongly closes jaw; strongly and involuntarily pushes tongue forward with no chewing motions.

6.22   ## Bites and chews toys   7-8

Definition: The child practices his biting and releasing pattern when biting toys, fingers, teething ring and harder cookies.

Example Observation Opportunities: May observe when child is playing with small toys, e.g., teethers, rubber squeak toys, or when he is given a teething biscuit..

Credit: (see also Credit Notes in this strand's preface)
+   bites or chews toys, or teething biscuit.
-    only sucking/licking is observed.
A   strongly and involuntarily bites or clamps down on toy; avoids mouthing any toys or teething biscuit.
O   circle any credit if caregivers punish or prevent child from mouthing toys, or if safe toys are not available for child to mouth.

6.19   ## Bites food voluntarily   *8-10*

Definition: Voluntary and more purposeful biting replaces the earlier phasic or bite reflex (i.e., when the child automatically bites when his gums or teeth are touched) with soft solids. The child purposefully controls and positions his jaw on the food to bite off a piece for chewing. Controlled voluntary biting with hard solids may not emerge until 12-13 months.

Example Observation Opportunities: May observe when child is eating a soft solid during feeding or snack time. Offer the child soft solids, such as graham cracker, saltine crackers, banana.

Credit: (see also Credit Notes in this strand's preface)
+   controlled voluntary biting is used with soft solids.
-    sucks or licks food.
A   forceful tense biting pattern; child has difficulty grading or releasing his bite.

6.20 **Drinks from cup held for him   6-12**

Definition: The child drinks a few sips from child-sized open plastic cup held by an adult. From 6 to 9 or 10 months, the child uses a suckling pattern to drink the liquid, i.e., large up-down or forward - backward jaw movements with little lip or cheek activity, with tongue protruding under the cup. After 9 or 10 months the child attempts to use his tongue and lower lip to stabilize the cup. The child's lips may be open while swallowing and he may lose some of the drink.

Example Observation Opportunities: <u>Incidental</u> - Observe parent offering the child a drink from a cup using the child's typical cup if available. Observe position of cup, amount of liquid, adequacy of cup for child, and effectiveness of parent and child positioning. If cup drinking is ineffectual, try the following more structured assessment if parent is comfortable with trying something different or identifies this as an area of need. <u>Structured facilitation</u> - demonstrate to the parent, presenting a cup on your own, the parent's or a doll's lips, noting how the cup is placed on the lower lip rather than teeth or gums. Also demonstrate tipping the cup rather than having to tip head, and allowing several seconds between sips. Ask the parent to try this with the child. Use a clear child-sized cup to monitor the flow of liquid. Do not use a "sipper" cup for assessment.

<u>**Credit:**</u> (see also Credit Notes in this strand's preface)

+   **at 6-9 months** if the child swallows a few sips of liquid using a suckling pattern as defined.

+   **at 10-12 months** if child uses his bottom lip to help stabilize the cup.

+/- needed structured facilitation.

-    if child sticks tongue in cup or otherwise can not seem to figure out how to consume the liquid.

O   circle any credit if child has not had experiences with a cup, or if parent has difficulty with cup presentation, positioning or selecting appropriate cups.

6.23 **Drools less except when teething   7-12**

Definition: The child rarely drools except when teething or congested. Some foods may stimulate drooling, and he may drool during feeding, but *not* immediately before or after feeding.

Example Observation Opportunities: Observe during feeding and play activities. Note if the child usually maintains a closed mouth posture. Use parent report if the child is congested or teething. May also notice if child's shirt is wet from drooling to help determine excessiveness. If child drools, record circumstances, e.g., during fine motor activities, prior to feeding, after feeding etc.

Credit: (see also Credit Notes in this strand's preface)

+   usually does not drool.

(also in Strand 0.0 "Regulatory/Sensory Organization")

6.24 **Chews food with coordinated movements   8-13.5**

Definition: The child chews soft-textured food with coordinated tongue, jaw and lip movements. He begins to vary the speed and height of up-and-down jaw movements and moves his tongue from the center of his mouth to either side to assist in the moving and chewing of food. His lips become more active in chewing, especially the upper lip. He begins to draw in his upper or lower lip to help remove food from a spoon.

Example Observation Opportunities: Use textured food the child is familiar with, e.g., mashed bananas, cookie or cracker.

Credit: (see also Credit Notes in this strand's preface)

+   uses up-down jaw movements of varied speed and height with textured foods; moves food to side of mouth with tongue and actively uses upper lip.

-    munching pattern continues as in #6.17 earlier in this strand; pushes much food out.

6.44 **Chews completely with rotary jaw movements   18-24**

Definition: The child uses diagonal rotary jaw movements to chew food and circular rotary movements when transferring food from one side of his mouth to the other. His tongue should not protrude, even in difficult food transfers.

Example Observation Opportunities: Observe when child is eating solids he enjoys and is familiar with, e.g., bite-sized pieces of chicken or fish; dry cereal, apple slices, firm crackers or cookies.

Credit: (see also Credit Notes in this strand's preface)

+   chews food effectively using rotary jaw movements; can close lips to keep food from falling out.

6-2 DRESSING

6.29	10.5-12	Cooperates with dressing by extending arm or leg
6.40	15-16.5	Removes hat
6.39	15-18	Removes socks
6.41	16.5-18.5	Places hat on head
6.46	18-24	Removes shoes when laces undone
6.47	18-21	Unzips, zips large zipper
6.57	21-30	Puts shoes on with assistance
6.64	24-26	Pulls pants down with assistance
6.65	24-25	Unbuttons large buttons
6.70	26-32	Undresses with assistance
6.71	26-28	Pulls pants up with assistance
6.72	28-32	Dresses self with assistance
6.81	30-36	Buttons large buttons
6.92	32 +	Dresses with supervision, requires assistance with fastenings

Family Friendly Interpretation of Strand Concepts, Assessment, & Purpose

We will be assessing how your child is learning to dress and undress himself. Dressing skills rely heavily upon your child's motor development and awareness of the relationship of different body parts to each other. For example, opening and closing fasteners, such as buttons, ties and zippers requires good eye-hand coordination, hand-grasping skills and the ability to coordinate both hands together to accomplish a task. During dressing the child also has to move his body in various ways, such as lifting his foot to slip it into a shoe, raising and then moving his arms to pull down a shirt, or stooping down to pull up his pants.

These movements depend upon good motor control, balance, and awareness of his body in space. Being able to imitate body movements and following simple directions are also an important part of learning independent dressing, because children learn how to dress from watching and listening to the people who help teach him. Finally, a child also needs to be interested in and motivated to become more independent. Some children are eager to become independent in dressing, whereas others enjoy or prefer to have others help them.

Parent Questions   (Examples)

To help identify the child's unique strengths and needs related to this developmental area:
- Can you tell me a little about how your child may have started to show an interest in learning how to dress or undress himself?
- Can he take off any clothing, such as his hat or shoes? Does he need any help?
- Has he started to try to help dress himself yet, such as pulling up his pants after you have helped put them on over his feet?

To help identify family resources, priorities and concerns related to the child's development in this area:
- Are you interested in your child is becoming more independent with dressing at this time?
- Who helps your child get dressed in the morning? ...get undressed at bedtime?
- Are there certain times that are better than others to let your child practice learning dressing skills?

Sample *Functional* Outcome Statements which may be generated by the Family

[Will be dependent upon identified individual child and family needs, and should incorporate objectives and activities from other domains]
My child will..
- Be more cooperative during dressing;

- Be able to pull his pants up-and-down independently to use the potty;
- Undress himself if we help him with the fasteners.

Transactional Assessment

May assess through observation and interview.

Assessment of Caregiver Interactions with the Child

1. Supportive:
[Example interactions which support/facilitate child's development in this area]
The child's caregivers sometimes:
• Help teach their child independent dressing skills through simple verbal instruction,

demonstration, and physical prompting;
• Encourage their child's independence through praise and by offering only as much help as he needs and by allowing ample opportunities and time for practice.

Identifying and Interpreting Needs for Intervention

If a child is significantly delayed in this area, he may be having difficulty with underlying <u>motor, motor planning, and body awareness skills</u> needed for independent dressing.

    <u>However</u>, before targeting these issues as the primary areas of need for intervention, consider and rule out other causes for delays in this area. These may include:
• <u>Parents are not interested in encouraging independent dressing</u> at this time; it is easier and

quicker to dress him due to tight scheduling demands on the family;
• <u>The child is does not want to be independent</u>; e.g., there may be a new baby in the house and he wants his parents to continue to provide a lot of attention to him;
• <u>The child's clothing is often too difficult to master</u>, e.g., many fasteners, small zippers and buttons.

Assessment Adaptations   (Examples)

[Note any adaptations needed to credit and help plan interventions]
• <u>Motor impairment:</u>
  – Adapt items and criteria to accommodate the child's motor abilities and any adaptive clothing he may have, e.g., if the child has a poor grasp and cannot manipulate a zipper or buttons, credit if the child can pull a larger ring-tab placed on the zipper tab, or open Velcro fasteners.
  – Some items may be inappropriate to fully assess due to severe motor impairments. These should be marked N/A.
  – Consult with a pediatric occupational or physical therapist regarding positioning and clothing adaptations that can optimize the child's independence during dressing for curriculum planning, e.g., dressing in side-lying, adaptations to clothing.

• <u>Sensory organization, motor planning problems:</u> be patient for the child's "best" performance before crediting. Give the child extra practice, time, repetition and simple concrete verbal and hand-over-hand directions. Help the family identify types of clothing and clothing material that is least offensive if the child is hypersensitive to touch, e.g., removing clothing tags, wearing short sleeves, avoiding stiffer material. Consult with a pediatric therapist with experience in sensory integration for individualized assessment and intervention techniques.
• <u>Visual impairment:</u> if the child has not had specific training in dressing using hand-over-hand modeling, he may have a normal delay since dressing skills rely heavily upon vision. Use clear verbal directions and orient the child to the clothing items, e.g., front, back, top, labels, seams, etc.

General Assessment Procedures & Processes   (apply to all items in this Strand)

1. Many developmental skills and behaviors from other developmental domains **can be naturally assessed while observing dressing skills**, e.g.:
  – <u>Regulatory/sensory organization</u>: may observe if the child seems extra sensitive to clothing touching his skin; has difficulty planning or sequencing movements required in dressing;
  – <u>Cognition and language</u>: may observe if the

child can follow simple directions related to retrieving his clothes, identifying names of clothing, ability to associate clothing with events, e.g., selecting a raincoat when it is raining; identifying and naming body parts;
  – <u>Gross motor</u>: may observe if child can stoop to help pick up clothes, has balance reactions in standing as he lifts his foot to slip it in a shoe;

General Assessment Procedures & Processes (continued)

– Fine motor: may observe grasp, bilateral and manipulative skills, motor planning skills;
– Social-Emotional: may observe degree of interest in doing things independently, pride in accomplishing tasks, how he handles frustration, and how he uses adults as resources.

2. **Observing dressing skills can occur unobtrusively as natural dressing and undressing activities occur during the course of the assessment,** e.g., taking coat off when entering room, putting coat on when leaving, removing and putting on shoes and sock before and after sandbox play, removing and putting back on a shirt before painting, pulling down and pulling up pants when

going to the toilet; putting on hats, gloves etc., during dramatic or dress-up play.

3. **Items that are not observed incidentally in the observations can be assessed through parent interview and report.**

+ - A Credit Notes:
+ child usually displays skill or behavior as defined during play and daily activities by observation or caregiver report.
- not observed or reported.
+/- appears to be an emerging skill, e.g., learned with prompting during assessment.
O circle any credit if clothing or interactions compromise or restrict child's optimal skills, in this area.

Note any adaptations used to credit.

Assessment Materials

Child's typical clothing.

6.29 Cooperates with dressing by extending arm or leg   10.5-12

Definition: The child is usually cooperative during dressing, sitting fairly still and helping by moving his arms or legs appropriately. He may: put his arms out spontaneously or on request to help his caregiver put on or take off his shirt and jacket; put his legs out to help put on or take off his pants, shoes and socks; push his arm through the sleeve to dress or pull it out with help to undress; pull his leg through the pant leg.

Example Observation Opportunities: After giving the child a simple verbal direction with gestures, e.g., "Let's take off your coat," pause to see if he spontaneously raises or moves his arms to help. Proceed to remove the item, continuing to request his help; e.g., when his coat is halfway off, ask, "pull your arm out." Praise any sign of participation. May also try when taking off a bib after snack time or his shoes and socks before evaluating his motor development. Repeat procedure when the child is putting the items back on.

Credit: (see also Credit Notes in this strand's preface)
+   cooperates in any way as defined by moving his arms or legs for any clothing item.

6.40 Removes hat   15-16.5

Definition: The child can take off a loose-fitting hat independently if it does not have a chin clasp or tie.
Example Observation Opportunities: May observe if child is wearing a hat into the assessment session, or during pretend play, provide the child with various hats (e.g., fireman's hat, baseball cap) and a mirror to play dress-up. Help him put the hat on if needed.
Credit: (see also Credit Notes in this strand's preface)
+   independently pulls off a hat.

6.39 Removes socks   15-18

Definition: The child can take off his socks independently. He may need some help if his socks are snug or are knee-high.
Example Observation Opportunities: After the child's shoes are removed, ask him to take off his socks so he can let his doll or teddy bear try them on. Demonstrate taking socks off yourself or a doll, if needed.
Credit: (see also Credit Notes in this strand's preface)
+   takes off short, loose-fitting socks independently.

Places hat on head   16.5-18.5

Definition: The child can put on a hat independently.
Example Observation Opportunities: May observe if child is wearing a hat as he leaves the assessment session, or during pretend play, provide the child with various hats (e.g., fireman's hat, baseball cap) and a mirror to play dress-up.
Credit: (see also Credit Notes in this strand's preface)
+   puts on a loose-fitting hat independently. He may put it on backwards.

 Removes shoes when laces undone   18-24

Definition: The child can take off his shoes, but may need help loosening laces. High-topped shoes or boots may need to be pulled slightly off his heel.
Example Observation Opportunities: Offer the child a pair of adult shoes to during dress-up play, requesting that he take off his own in order to put them on.
Credit: (see also Credit Notes in this strand's preface)
+   takes shoes off independently if they are not high tops. Laces can be loosened for him.

 Unzips, zips large zipper   18-21

Definition: The child can unzip and zip heavy duty larger zippers that have large tabs. Learning to unzip usually precedes learning to zip.
Example Observation Opportunities: May observe when child enters or leaves the assessment if he is wearing a coat with a large zipper, during dress-up play, and/or trying the zipper on a purse, diaper bag or zipper bag. Hold the base of the zipper taut and attach a key ring or ribbon to the tab, if needed. Invite the child to try zipping and unzipping with request and demonstration, as needed.
Credit: (see also Credit Notes in this strand's preface)
+   zips and unzips large zippers; adult may help hold the zipper taut and the zipper tab can be adapted.

 Puts shoes on with assistance   21-30

Definition: The child can put his shoes on independently but needs adult help with fasteners, ties, and high-top shoes. He will also need help putting shoes on the correct foot.
Example Observation Opportunities: If opportunities arise when the child needs to put his shoes back on (e.g., after a gross motor evaluation, dress-up play), loosen laces or other fasteners and pull the shoe tongue out of the child's shoes. Give him one shoe at a time, gesturing which foot it goes on. Let him know what will happen after he puts his shoes on, e.g., snack time, going outside, etc.
Credit: (see also Credit Notes in this strand's preface)
+   puts low-top shoes on independently with adult help for fasteners and discriminating left and right.

 Pulls pants down with assistance   24-26

Definition: The child can pull his pants or shorts down to undress but may need help with fasteners and pushing them down over his hips if tight-fitting.
Example Observation Opportunities: If opportunities arise that the child needs to take off or pull down his pants (e.g., to go to the toilet, to change soiled clothes), open any fasteners and invite him to take them off, offering assistance at his hips if needed. After the pants are to his knees, let him sit on a stool or the floor to complete the process.
Credit: (see also Credit Notes in this strand's preface)
+   removes loose-fitting pants and shorts independently; may have some assistance as defined.

6.65   Unbuttons large buttons   24-25

Definition: The child uses his fingers to manipulate and unbutton large, flat buttons. The buttons should be at least 1 inch in diameter and have button holes that are a bit larger than the button.

Example Observation Opportunities: During doll play show the child a large doll or stuffed animal that has a jacket or shirt with two or three large buttons. Unbutton one of the buttons and then ask the child to unbutton the rest so that he can give the doll a bath or put on new clothes. May also observe if child has opportunities to remove his own clothing that have large easily accessible buttons, e.g., on the front of his sweater or coat.

Credit: (see also Credit Notes in this strand's preface)
  +   unbuttons at least two buttons using his fingers to manipulate the button and button hole.
  -   unbuttons by pulling the clothing sides apart.

6.70   Undresses with assistance   26-32

Definition: The child can take off most clothing items, jacket, shirt, pants, shoes, socks, and underwear. He may continue to need assistance with fasteners and pullover shirts with narrow necks. He may need some reminders regarding the sequence of undressing, e.g., take off your shoes before taking off your pants.

Example Observation Opportunities: Probe through parent interview what clothing items the child can remove, how he removes them and the type of adult assistance offered. Opportunities may arise to observe removal of some items during the assessment session, e.g., if the child needs to change soiled clothes, goes to the toilet, removes his coat on arrival, takes off dress-up clothing.

Credit: (see also Credit Notes in this strand's preface)
  +   can remove most clothing items with some sequencing directions and help with fasteners and narrow necked pull-over shirts as defined.

6.71   Pulls pants up with assistance   26-28

Definition: The child can put on his loose-fitting slacks and shorts. He may do so by sitting on the floor, on a stool or in standing leaning against something for support, depending on his gross motor and balance abilities. He may need help recognizing front and back, pulling them over his feet and hips, and fastening them.

Example Observation Opportunities: Probe through parent interview if child can put on his own pants, the type of pants he can put on, how he puts them on and the type of adult assistance offered. Opportunities may arise to observe the child putting on his own pants during the assessment session, e.g., if the child needs to change soiled clothes or goes to the toilet.

Credit: (see also Credit Notes in this strand's preface)
  +   puts on loose-fitting slacks with some assistance as defined.
  +/- can put on shorts but not slacks.

6.72   Dresses self with assistance   28-32

Definition: The child is able to dress and undress himself with several simple clothing items, e.g., hat, shoes, socks, pants, underwear, shirt, jacket, coat. Some assistance is needed with fasteners and to discriminate right and left feet and fronts and backs of clothing.

Example Observation Opportunities: Probe through parent interview what clothing items child can put on and take off, the type of clothing items he is most successful with, the type of adult assistance provided, and the process the child uses; e.g., when putting on his shirt, is the shirt laid out in front of him whereby he puts his arms through and flips the shirt over his head? Does he need to sit down when putting on his clothing? Opportunities may arise to observe the child dressing during the assessment session, e.g., during dress-up or if the child needs to change soiled clothes after water play or playing outdoors.

Credit: (see also Credit Notes in this strand's preface)
  +   can independently take off all his clothes and put on at least four clothing items with minimal assistance as defined.

6.81 ## Buttons large buttons   30-36

Definition: The child is able to button at least three large buttons on his clothes during dressing. The buttons should be at least 1 inch in diameter and have button holes that are a little larger than the button.

Example Observation Opportunities: During doll play show the child a large doll or stuffed animal that has a jacket or shirt with a few large buttons unbuttoned. Button one of the buttons and then ask the child to button the rest. May also observe if child has opportunities to put on his own clothing that has large easily accessible buttons, e.g., on the front of his sweater or coat.

Credit: (see also Credit Notes in this strand's preface)

+   buttons at least three large buttons using his fingers to manipulate the button and buttonhole effectively. The buttons do not have to be buttoned in the correct order to their matching holes to credit.

6.92 ## Dresses with supervision, requires assistance with fastenings   32 and above

Definition: This is an extension of item #6.72 "Dresses self with assistance." The child can now put on more difficult clothing items, such as pull-over shirts with snug neck openings, coats, and dresses. Supervision is needed to help discriminate left and right shoes and fronts and backs of some clothing that are not easily identifiable. The child should be able to zip large zippers and button buttons, but may need adult assistance with difficult fasteners, plastic zippers, small buttons or snaps and shoelaces.

Example Observation Opportunities: Same as #6.72

Credit: (see also Credit Notes in this strand's preface)

+   independently puts on at least five clothing items with minimal assistance as defined.

6-3 INDEPENDENT FEEDING

6.07	2-4	Brings hand to mouth
6.09	3-5	Brings hand to mouth with toy or object
6.10	3.5-4.5	Recognizes bottle visually
6.13	4-5	Pats bottle
6.16	4.5-5.5	Places both hands on bottle
6.18	5.5-9	Holds own bottle
6.21	6.5-8.5	Feeds self a cracker
6.25	9-12	Finger feeds self
6.26	9-12	Holds spoon
6.30	12-18	May refuse foods - appetite decreases
6.31	12-15	Brings spoon to mouth - turns spoon over
6.32	12-18	Holds and drinks from cup with some spilling
6.33	12-15.5	Holds cup handle
6.38	15-24	Scoops food, feeds self with spoon with some spilling
6.42	18-19	Gives empty dish to adult
6.43	18-23	Distinguishes between edible and inedible objects
6.45	18-24	Gives up bottle
6.50	19-23	Plays with food
6.54	20-30	Holds small cup in one hand
6.58	23-25	May have definite food preferences
6.59	23-25	Unwraps food
6.63	24-30	Holds spoon in fingers - palm up
6.74	29.5-31.5	May reject many foods
6.77	30-36	Pours liquid from small container
6.78	30-36	Uses fork
6.79	30-36	Uses napkin
6.85	31 +	Serves self at table with little spilling

Family Friendly Interpretation of Strand Concepts, Assessment, & Purpose

We will be observing how your child is learning to feed himself during snack and mealtimes. Independent feeding relies heavily upon motor skills. For example, children need to be able to pick up small things with their fingertips before they can finger feed. Learning to be independent with a spoon requires even finer coordination, as the child needs to figure out how to hold the spoon, scoop with it, and bring it to his mouth without turning it completely over. In addition to motor skills, children also need to be interested and motivated in being independent. Some children are eager to try to learn to feed themselves, while others prefer the comfort of remaining more dependent.

Parent Questions   (Examples)

To help identify the child's unique strengths and needs related to this developmental area:
[Also include questions from Strand 6-1, "Oral motor development"]

- How is mealtime going at home with your child?
- Are there some things during feeding that your child is learning how to do himself, such as holding his own bottle or drinking from a cup?
- Are there certain cups or spoons that he uses to try to feed himself?
- What are some of the types of foods that he enjoys most? How about drinks?
- What foods, cups and utensils do you think we should use in our assessment?
- Has your child tried any of the foods *[name specific foods]* I've also brought to try? Would it be okay to try some of these foods ?

To help identify family resources, priorities and concerns related to the child's development in this area:

- What advice have you been given about when to introduce different foods?...when to start using a cup?...when to wean from a bottle? How does that fit with your beliefs?
- At what age are children usually expected to drink from a cup in your family? *[May repeat with giving up the bottle, eating independently with a spoon, learning table manners]*
- What would you like to see your child be able to do more independently during feeding? What have you tried so far that has seemed to help?...that has not seemed to help?

Sample *Functional* Outcome Statements which may be generated by the Family

[Will be dependent upon identified individual child and family needs, and should incorporate objectives and activities from other domains]
My child will:

- Finger feed himself for at least half his meal;
- Hold his own bottle;
- Give up his bottle;
- Be able to use a spoon independently.

Transactional Assessment

May assess through observation and interview.

Assessment of the Child's Environment

1. Supportive:
[Example environments which support/facilitate development in this area]
The child's feeding environment usually:
- Is safe, e.g., child is not left on couch or counter; highchair is secure; foods are prepared and stored safely;
- Is relaxed and interesting;
- Has appropriate feeding equipment to match child's developmental stage, e.g., seating, appropriately sized spoons, cups, bottles.

Assessment of Caregiver Interactions with the Child

1. Supportive:
[Example interactions which support/facilitate child's development in this area]
The child's caregivers usually:
- Allow the child to explore his food and support his attempts at independence;
- Expose child to new foods but let the child make choices;
- Let the child decide how fast and how much to eat;
- Position the child in comfortable and developmentally appropriate positions that promote independence (see appropriate position techniques below under "General child assessment procedures and processes," step 3.);
- Expect and allow for typical messes during mealtime.

2. Compromising:
[Example interactions which may restrict, compromise, inhibit or be unsupportive of the child's development in this area]
The child's caregivers frequently:
- Expect their child to be more independent during feeding than he is developmentally ready for, e.g., try to make child hold his own bottle at 2 months; harshly discipline for typical messes;
- Introduce solids before child is ready;
- Pressure their child to eat, by rewarding or punishing;
- Are overly concerned about spills and messes.

Identifying and Interpreting Needs for Intervention

If a child is significantly delayed in this area he may be having difficulty in <u>coordinating or planning the fine and gross motor skills need for independent feeding</u>.

    <u>However</u>, before targeting this as the primary area of need for intervention, consider, rule out, or adapt for other causes that may interfere with a true assessment of the child's <u>self-feeding abilities</u>. These may include:
- <u>Tactile sensitivities</u>: the child may refuse to finger feed or to eat certain textures;
- <u>Emotional or behavioral issues</u>: e.g., the child may want to remain dependent due to a recent trauma (e.g., new baby in house; parents going back to work); have a history of tube feeding or other medical procedures which influence current feeding behaviors (e.g., child wants to have control over his world and establishes this through refusing to eat, being extra picky, etc.);
- <u>Experiential</u>: the child has not had experiences in self-feeding. Respect family and cultural diversity. Become aware of the family values and beliefs related to achieving independence as well as the types of foods offered to the child. Some families may value and encourage independence early whereas others may expect their children to remain more dependent. These values and beliefs can be elicited through sensitive family interview (see parent questions above) and observations of the family. Expectations, assessment, and interventions for the child should be adjusted accordingly;
- <u>Assessment setting</u>: the child may not be hungry, may not like the food or utensils used, may not like to eat in new settings.

Assessment Adaptations   (Examples)

[Note any adaptations needed to credit and help plan interventions]

- Tactile sensitivities: use foods and textures that the child tolerates; firm foods with consistent textures may be better tolerated than soft or gooey foods or foods with lumpy textures; consult with an occupational therapist trained in sensory organization to help in planning desensitization techniques.

- Motor impaired:
  - Assess and credit using any adaptive equipment and special positioning that has been prescribed for the child. If this is the child's first assessment, consult with a pediatric therapist to adapt feeding positions and utensils as needed to ensure stability and optimize oral motor control and independence during assessment and interventions, e.g., using cups with lids, dycem to stabilize bowels, adaptive spoons.
  - A child with severe motor impairments may not develop reaching or grasping skills needed for independent feeding. Mark

N/A for items that may be inappropriate to assess, and replace items when appropriate with more functional self-feeding skills using adaptive utensils, e.g., using an adaptive or built-up spoon; replacing cup drinking with drinking from a straw.

- Visually impaired:
  - Many skills may be somewhat delayed unless specific hand-over-hand teaching has been provided.
  - Observe feeding in the child's natural environment whenever possible. It will be important to use foods and utensils that are familiar to the child. The child may be defensive to new food textures or forms. Orient the child to the various placements of food, cup, and utensils.
  - Encourage him to place his finger in the cup to identify the amount of liquid as you tell him what it is.
  - Use a scoop dish and encourage the child to feel the food with one hand while holding the spoon in his other, as you name the foods.

General Assessment Procedures & Processes   (apply to all items in this Strand)

1. Snack and mealtimes **provide excellent opportunities to observe many developmental skills and behaviors from other developmental domains**, e.g.:
   - Oral motor skills: may observe biting, chewing, lip closure during cup drinking etc.;
   - Regulatory/sensory organization: may observe if the child seems extra sensitive to touching or eating certain textures; has difficulty planning or sequencing movements required in eating;
   - Cognition and language: may observe if the child can follow simple directions related to eating, identify or say names of foods, drinks, utensils; communicates when he wants more or has had enough, understands concepts, such as "take <u>one</u> cookie," or "take the <u>little</u> spoon," etc.;
   - Gross motor: may observe child's sitting skills, ability to climb into and sit in a chair;
   - Fine motor: may observe child's reach, grasp, bilateral and manipulative skills as he reaches for and picks up small pieces of food, holds a spoon, etc.;
   - Social-Emotional; may observe degree of interest in doing things independently, pride in accomplishing tasks, how he handles frustration, and how he uses adults as resources.

2. **Assess in the child's natural feeding environments during a regular feeding time when-**

ever possible. This will provide a more comprehensive assessment since you will be able to see the types of utensils, foods, setting and seating used during feeding and will help the child and parent feel more comfortable. If a home-based assessment is not possible, schedule the appointment during a feeding time and ask the parent to bring in the child's utensils and favorite foods if appropriate.

3. It is critical to **have a pediatric therapist, trained in feeding, involved in the feeding assessment process if the child has neuro-motor, structural or physiological abnormalities.** Special equipment, positioning or handling techniques may be used during the assessment to optimize and facilitate independent feeding, but should be noted to qualify any credits. *Be sure to seek medical consultation and contraindications for medically involved children.*

4. **Good positioning is important to optimize the child's independence.** If in a highchair, or at a table, the child's back should be fairly straight, and hips, knees and ankles at 90-degree angles.
   a. If the child does not have gross motor delays or atypical muscle tone he should be seated as follows:
      bottle feeding - supported semi-sitting position, reclining at an angle of 45 to 90 degrees;
      7 months - sitting upright with back at a

General Assessment Procedures & Processes (continued)

90-degree angle, using external support-pillows, tray, person;

9 months - sitting upright with back at 90-degree angle, using a highchair for security;

18 months - sitting unsupported at family table in highchair or booster seat, or at a child-sized table and chair.

b. If the child has atypical muscle tone refer to *HELP at Home* Appendix H, for adaptive positioning techniques.

5. **Expect and plan for a mess!** Use bibs, and place paper or plastic on the floor as needed.

6. If this is one of the child's first self-feeding experiences, **allow extra practice and note when crediting.** Be sure to obtain parent permission before trying something new.

7. **Describe the skill and eliciting procedures to family members and invite them to help observe and/or assess.**

+ - A Credit Notes:

+ child usually displays skill or behavior as defined during feeding by parent report or observation.

- not observed or reported.

+/- appears to be an emerging skill.

N/A due to family preference, or child's disability or medical condition; also for items using a bottle if child does not use a bottle.

O circle any credit if environment or interactions compromise or restrict child's independent feeding skills.

Note any adaptations used to credit.

 Assessment Materials

Child's own spoon, bottle, cup, various familiar foods (dependent on level, noted for each item).

 Brings hand to mouth   2-4

Definition: The child brings one or both hands to his mouth to explore or play. Hand-to-mouth movements help the child prepare for later finger feeding.

Example Observation Opportunities

May observe anytime or by parent report.

Credit: (see also Credit Notes in this strand's preface)

+ can easily bring one or both hands to his mouth in supine and prone.

O circle any credit if caregivers perceive this behavior as "bad."

 Brings hand to mouth with toy or object   3-5

Definition: The child can bring a toy he is holding to his mouth to explore, using one or both hands. Hand-to-mouth movements help the child prepare for later independent finger and spoon feeding.

Example Observation Opportunities: May observe anytime child is holding small toy, such as a rattle, teether, small block. May be in supine, prone, supported sitting.

Credit: (see also Credit Notes in this strand's preface)

+ uses one or both hands to mouth toys.

O circle any credit if caregivers perceive this behavior as "bad."

6.10 **Recognizes bottle visually   3.5-4.5**

Definition: The child recognizes his bottle when he sees it and displays anticipatory excitement. He may smile, excite, vocalize, initiate sucking motions, kick or wave his legs and arms.

Example Observation Opportunities: Observe child's expression and movements before he is fed as his parent shows him his bottle.

Credit: (see also Credit Notes in this strand's preface)

+ displays signs of anticipatory excitement as defined. He should not already be displaying these signs before the bottle is shown.

(may also credit #1.08 "Shows anticipatory excitement," in Strand 5-4)

6.13 Pats bottle   4-5

Definition: The child periodically pats his bottle with one or both hands when he is fed by an adult.

Example Observation Opportunities: May observe during feeding or by parent report. Be sure the child is positioned with his arms forward.

Credit: (see also Credit Notes in this strand's preface)
+   sometimes pats bottle with one or both hands.
O   circle any credit if caregivers usually do not position child with arms forward.

6.16 Places both hands on bottle   4.5-5.5

Definition: The child spontaneously, or with initial prompting, periodically places both hands on a bottle held for him during feeding.

Parent Questions: Does your child sometimes put his hands on his bottle while you are feeding him? Does he use both hands at the same time? About how long does he keep his hands there?

Example Observation Opportunities: May observe incidentally during feeding.

Credit: (see also Credit Notes in this strand's preface)
+   places <u>both</u> hands on his bottle (or on top of parents hands holding bottle) for a few seconds. This should be more than just a brief pat, but the child does not have to control or support the weight of the bottle.

(also in Strand 4-5 "Bilateral and Midline skills")

6.18 Holds own bottle   5.5-9

Definition: The child holds and drinks from his own bottle without help

Example Observation Opportunities: May observe as occasion arises or by parent report. The bottle should be plastic. Note the type of bottle.

Credit: (see also Credit Notes in this strand's preface)
+   independently holds and drinks effectively from bottle; can usually tilt the bottle as needed to obtain liquid.

6.21 Feeds self a cracker   6.5-8.5

Definition: The child holds, bites and munches a soft cookie or cracker.

Example Observation Opportunities: Observe the child eating a soft cookie or graham cracker. Monitor closely, because at this stage the child can not grade the amount of cookie he is biting off or may stuff his mouth.

Credit: (see also Credit Notes in this strand's preface)
+   holds and munches on a soft cookie or cracker; not simply licking or sucking on it.

6.25 Finger feeds self   9-12

Definition: The child finger feeds a variety of foods.

Example Observation Opportunities: Provide a few pieces of familiar, bite-sized pieces of food, e.g., green beans, fresh fruits, diced chicken, cubes of cheese.

Credit: (see also Credit Notes in this strand's preface)
+   finger feeds at least half of each meal.

(also in Strand 0.0 "Regulatory/Sensory Organization")

6.26 Holds spoon   9-12

Definition: At this stage the child holds and shows interest in the spoon, but he may treat it more as a toy than a feeding utensil, e.g., for holding, banging or mouthing. If food happens to stick to spoon during this, he may get some to his mouth.

Example Observation Opportunities: Give the child a spoon to hold during feeding or play.

Credit: (see also Credit Notes in this strand's preface)
+   holds spoon in any manner and shows interest in the things he can do with it.

6.30 ## May refuse foods - appetite decreases   12-18

Definition: The child may sometimes refuse certain foods or entire meals throughout toddlerhood. This is because the child's growth rate often slows during this period, and the child is developing food preferences, as well as learning that he can exert control over feeding.

Example Observation Opportunities: May elicit through parent interview. Encourage caregivers to chart actual food intake during a three-day period if concerned about nutritional intake or if weight gain is a concern.

Credit: (see also Credit Notes in this strand's preface)
+ sometimes refuses foods or eats less, not due to tactile sensitivity or illness.
N/A **if** no apparent change in appetite.

6.31 ## Brings spoon to mouth - turns spoon over   12-15

Definition: The child can bring a filled spoon to his mouth. But since he usually cannot rotate his wrist efficiently at this stage he is likely to turn the spoon over as he brings it to his mouth.

Example Observation Opportunities: Encourage the child to feed himself after a small amount of favorite sticky food (e.g., pudding, mashed potatoes) is placed on the spoon. Allow plenty of practice if this is the child's first experience.

Credit: (see also Credit Notes in this strand's preface)
+ brings filled spoon to mouth; he should obtain some food if it does not fall off en route.

6.32 ## Holds and drinks from cup with some spilling   12-18

Definition: The child can independently drink from a cup. The degree of success depends upon the type of cup, liquid, and amount of practice the child has had with a cup. At this stage he may not have enough oral motor control to stabilize his jaw and control the flow of liquid and thus he may lose some.

Example Observation Opportunities: Use a small plastic cup that is one-third filled with a preferred liquid. Do not use a "sipper" cup.

Credit: (see also Credit Notes in this strand's preface)
+ independently lifts, drinks from, and then returns the cup to the table; there may be some spilling.

6.33 ## Holds cup handle   12-15.5

Definition: The child can hold a child's cup by one or two handles.

Example Observation Opportunities: Use a small plastic cup with one or two handles that is one-third filled with a preferred liquid. Do not use a "sipper" cup.

Credit: (see also Credit Notes in this strand's preface)
+ has good hand and finger control to hold the handle(s) of a cup and to drink.
N/A if child does not use a cup with handles.

6.38 ## Scoops food, feeds self with spoon with some spilling   15-24

Definition: The child can scoop food on his spoon to feed himself. At this stage he has lateral (side-to-side) wrist movements that help him scoop the food from the bowl and bring it to his mouth. However, he may bring the spoon to his mouth with his palm facing down, which causes some spilling.

Example Observation Opportunities: Provide a bowl half-filled with a favorite sticky food which can adhere to the spoon, e.g., mashed potatoes, mashed bananas or pudding. Give the child a spoon, but do not fill it for him. Help him stabilize the bowl if needed.

Credit: (see also Credit Notes in this strand's preface)
+ scoops and eats independently with a spoon using semi-solid foods; some spilling may occur.

6.42 ## Gives empty dish to adult   18-19

Definition: The child helps during mealtime by giving his dish to an adult to request more food or when finished.

Example Observation Opportunities: May observe after child is finished eating or wants more food as in #6.38 above.

Credit: (see also Credit Notes in this strand's preface)
+ gives empty dish to adult as a helping gesture.

6.43 Distinguishes between edible and inedible objects   18-23

Definition: The child does not put familiar inedible objects in his mouth. He may still experiment, however, with tasting inedible things that appear to be appetizing, e.g., Play Doh™, medicines, etc. Thus, toxic materials must always be kept out of reach.

Example Observational Opportunities: May observe as child plays with toys and other assessment materials, or assess through parent report.

Credit: (see also Credit Notes in this strand's preface)

+ usually does not attempt to taste or eat familiar, inedible substances.

6.45 Gives up bottle   18-24

Definition: The child no longer drinks from a bottle or breast. Note: weaning typically varies over a wide age range, dependent upon the family preferences and physician recommendations. Doctors and dentists often recommend weaning from a bottle after a year.

Example Observation Opportunities: Identify through parent interview. Note if child has resumed bottle drinking after giving it up secondary to a significant event, e.g., new sibling; hospitalization.

Credit: (see also Credit Notes in this strand's preface)

+ no longer drinks from a bottle or breast.

6.50 Plays with food   19-23

Definition: The child may play with his food by dabbing his fingers in it, smearing or mashing it, and throwing it. This should not be excessive.

Example Observation Opportunities: May observe during feeding or elicit through parent report. Note if certain foods or adult responses precipitate this for anticipatory guidance.

Credit: (see also Credit Notes in this strand's preface)

+ displays some food play during mealtime.

N/A if not present, this is not an item to teach.

O circle the credit if food play is excessive, or if caregivers request tips to help minimize food play.

6.54 Holds small cup in one hand   20-30

Definition: The child can drink well from a small cup using one hand. At this stage there is little or no spilling as the child has greater self-help abilities and more precise lip control and jaw stability

Example Observation Opportunities: May observe during snack or mealtime. Use a small easy-to-grasp cup, half-filled, using a favorite drink.

Credit: (see also Credit Notes in this strand's preface)

+ drinks well independently from a cup, holding it in one hand, usually with no spilling.

6.58 May have definite food preferences   23-25

Definition: The child may have definite food likes and dislikes that may change from day to day. In addition to adamantly refusing some foods, there may times when he will only eat certain foods to the exclusion of all others.

Example Observation Opportunities: Elicit through parent interview after explaining this typical behavior as defined.

Credit: (see also Credit Notes in this strand's preface)

+ has some definite food preferences.

N/A if none are reported. *This is not an item to teach.*

O circle the credit if family finds this troublesome and is interested in further guidance to ensure good nutrition.

6.59 Unwraps food   23-25

Definition: The child can remove wrappers from food as well as remove peels from some fruits.

Example Observation Opportunities: During snack time, offer foods in wrappers, such as crackers, cheese, or a fruit roll. Also offer fruit, such as a banana or a tangerine. Begin the peeling process before offering it to the child.

Credit: (see also Credit Notes in this strand's preface)

+ unwraps simple wrappers from food and can peel a banana or tangerine; may need help with initial tearing of cellophane or peeling of fruit.

6.63 Holds spoon in fingers - palm up   24-30

Definition: The child holds and feeds himself well with a spoon. He can scoop food with a spoon and then rotate his wrist to bring it to his mouth in a palm-up position.

Example Observation Opportunities: May be observed during snack or mealtime when child eats food requiring a spoon, e.g., cereal, pudding, vegetables.

Credit: (see also Credit Notes in this strand's preface)

+   scoops food with a spoon and usually rotates his wrist to a palm-up position as he brings it to his mouth.

6.74 May reject many foods   29.5-31.5

Definition: The child may refuse to eat certain foods as his preferences become more definitive.

Example Observation Opportunities: Elicit through parent interview.

Credit: (see also Credit Notes in this strand's preface)

+   refuses to eat certain foods; may be related to taste, texture or appearance; observe if there is a pattern.

N/A if not reported. *This is not an item to teach.*

O   circle any credit if family finds this troublesome and is interested in further guidance to ensure good nutrition.

6.77 Pours liquid from small container   30-36

Definition: The child can pour a drink from a small pitcher or other container, judging the correct amount to pour.

Example Observation Opportunities: During a "tea party," snack or mealtime, provide a small plastic pitcher that has a handle and is half-full. Invite the child to pour himself or others a drink.

Credit: (see also Credit Notes in this strand's preface)

+   independently pours from a small pitcher with little or no spilling.

6.78 Uses fork   30-36

Definition: The child can use a fork to eat.

Example Observation Opportunities: Use a child's fork or small salad fork. Provide bite-sized easy-to-pierce foods during snack or mealtime, e.g., sliced cooked carrot, soft cubed meat/chicken, fruits. Demonstrate using a fork, if needed.

Credit: (see also Credit Notes in this strand's preface)

+   sometimes uses a fork to eat; independently stabs food with fork.

6.79 Uses napkin   30-36

Definition: The child wipes his hands and face with a napkin.

Example Observation Opportunities: Observe during snack or mealtime.

Credit: (see also Credit Notes in this strand's preface)

+   sometimes uses a napkin to wipe hands or face; may be on request and with demonstration.

6.85 Serves self at table with little spilling   31+

Definition: The child serves himself foods he can take with his hands and some foods using a serving spoon or piercing with a fork.

Example Observation Opportunities: May observe during mealtimes or elicit through parent report.

Credit: (see also Credit Notes in this strand's preface)

+   serves self finger foods, such as rolls or sandwiches, and serves self with a spoon or fork when appropriate to take, e.g., a slice of meat, rice, or vegetables. He may have some spilling and have difficulty judging the correct quantity.

6-4 SLEEP PATTERNS AND BEHAVIORS

6.03	1-3	Sleeps nights four-ten hour intervals
6.05	1-3	Naps frequently
6.14	4-8	Sleeps nights ten-twelve hours with night awakening
6.15	4-8	Naps two-three times each day one-four hours
6.27	9-12	Sleeps nights twelve-fourteen hours
6.28	9-12	Naps once or twice each day one-four hours, may refuse morning nap
5.34	9-12	Tests parental reactions at bedtime
6.36	13-18	Sleeps nights ten-twelve hours
6.37	13-18	Naps once in afternoon one-three hours
6.53	19-31	Delays sleeping by demanding things
6.89	31 +	Sleeps ten-fifteen hours daily
6.90	31 +	May awaken, crying from dreams
6.91	31 +	May eliminate naps

Family Friendly Interpretation of Strand Concepts, Assessment, & Purpose

Although young child may have similar sleep patterns and behaviors at different stages of development, these are only general guidelines. Sleep patterns vary greatly from child to child, depending upon each child's individual sleep needs, biological make up and family routines. Illness, stress, being in unfamiliar surroundings, having a new routine, and sometimes certain foods or medications can influence sleep patterns and behaviors.

Parent Questions   (Examples)

To help identify the child's unique strengths and needs related to this developmental area:
[General open-ended questions]
- Can you tell me a little about your child's typical sleep patterns? Does this "fit" fairly well with your family's routine?
- What's it like getting him to go to sleep; for example, does he seem to fall asleep fairly quickly or do you need to do certain things to help him fall asleep?
- Where does your child usually sleep? How is this working out?

[More specific questions as needed, especially if sleep problems are expressed]
- Is your child sleeping through the night?
- If he wakes up at night, how long does it take for him to go back to sleep? What happens when he wakes up? (e.g., fed, changed, plays by self, cries back to sleep).
- How difficult is it for him to fall asleep? Does he wake up easily?
- Does your child go to sleep before you put him in his bed or do you put him in his crib while he's still awake?
- What activity occurs before your child's naptime?...bedtime at night? (e.g., feeding, playing).

- Does your child have a typical bedtime routine, e.g., bath and/or a story before bed, taking a special blanket or toy to bed, taking a bottle?
- Does your child use a night-light?
- Does your child have his own room? Is it fairly quiet?
- Is your child on any medications?
- Does your child ever seem to have nightmares? How can you tell?

To help identify family resources, priorities and concerns related to the child's development in this area:
- Are you able to get enough sleep? Does anyone else help if your child wakes up in the middle of the night?
- Do you have some family or friends nearby who can help out?

[If parent reports sleep problems and is interested in information or help]
- How long has this been a problem? What do you think might be causing this?
- What kinds of things have you tried so far? Do any of these things seem to help?
- What advice have you been given about how to help your child go to sleep better? How does that "fit" with your beliefs?

Sample *Functional* Outcome Statements which may be generated by the Family

[Will be dependent upon identified individual child and family needs, and should incorporate objectives and activities from other domains]
We will:
• Have some ideas to help our child sleep fall asleep on his own;

• Learn techniques to help him sleep in his own bed;
• Be able to get some sleep!

Our child will:
• Fall asleep without being rocked;
• Fall asleep without screaming for an hour;
• Sleep through the night.

Transactional Assessment

May assess through observation and interview.

Assessment of the Child's Environment

1. Supportive:
[Example environments which support/facilitate development in this area]
The child's sleep environments:
• Are consistent and fairly quiet; e.g., child has own crib, room;
• Are safe, e.g., safe bed, within hearing distance of family, no dangerous objects or toys in bed;
• Have a quiet, consistent place for the child to sleep;

• Have a night light and a safe "attachment" object, e.g., special stuffed animal, blanket.

2. Compromising:
[Environments which may restrict, compromise, inhibit or be unsupportive toward development in this area]
• The child's sleep environments are frequently inconsistent, unsafe, and/or over-stimulating.

Assessment of Caregiver Interactions with the Child

1. Supportive:
[Example interactions which support/facilitate child's development in this area]

The child's caregivers usually:
• Provide consistent bedtime routines;
• Avoid reinforcing bedtime "testing" behaviors.

Identifying and Interpreting Needs for Intervention

If a child <u>is demonstrating significant sleep problems,</u> these may be related to underlying:
• <u>Physiological or regulatory-sensory organization problems</u>, e.g., neurological disorders, pain or illness, medication, poor homeostasis, colicky;
• <u>Emotional issues</u>; e.g., child may be experiencing trauma, such as a new baby in house; parent going back to work; new environment;

• <u>Behavioral;</u> e.g., certain sleep habits have been reinforced, may be going through a typical developmental stage.

If a child does not have sleep problems, this area may still be targeted for intervention for anticipatory guidance purposes if parents are interested in ideas to prevent problems or prepare for typical sleep patterns and behaviors.

General Assessment Procedures & Processes (apply to all items in this Strand)

1. Assessment for all items in this strand will **generally occur through parent report.** *In contrast to other strands in this manual, specific assessment procedures and credit criteria are not included]*
2. **These items are primarily for anticipatory guidance; reporting of age levels is typically unnecessary; for reporting purposes, descriptions of the child's sleep patterns will be more appropriate.**

+ - A Credit Notes:

(by parent report):
    +   child's sleep patterns generally fall within description of item; does not need extensive external support to fall asleep.
    -   does not display this sleep pattern but

not atypical.
A atypical: extreme sleep problems or deviations; e.g., child rarely sleeps more than 20 minutes at a time; takes more than 20 minutes to fall asleep and/or needs extensive external support to help; or, child sleeps excessively.
N/A child does not display this sleep behavior, but it is not considered atypical; e.g., child does not nap after a certain age; does not appear to have nightmares; does not have "testing" behaviors.
O circle any credit if environment or interactions compromise or restrict child's optimal sleep patterns, or if family requests guidance in this area.

6.03 ## Sleeps nights four-ten hour intervals   1-3

Definition: After the first few weeks of getting adjusted to the environment, infants generally sleep in 4- to 10-hour intervals at night. Many infants combine two of their 4 hour sleep cycles during the night by the second or third month and sleep through the night.

6.05 ## Naps frequently   1-3

Definition: The frequency and duration of naps vary with each infant. One infant may take a 20-minute nap every 2 hours and another infant may take a 2-hour nap in the morning and another one in the afternoon. During the first few months many infants take four or five short naps per day. At this stage the infant can typically nap most anywhere without being overly disturbed by sound or activity.

6.14 ## Sleeps nights ten-twelve hours with night awakening   4-8

Definition: The child's sleep patterns become more regular and compatible with family sleep times, typically 10 to 12 hours per night. Many infants continue to wake up briefly for a diaper change or just to fuss or play for a few minutes and then resume sleep. If a child has slept through the night, he may begin to wake up during this period. This may be related to teething or separation anxiety that can emerge during this period.

6.15 ## Naps two-three times each day one-four hours   4-8

Definition: Many infants who took frequent short naps during the first three months begin to combine them into longer naps. At this stage a 2-hour morning nap and a 1- to 3-hour afternoon nap is common.

6.27 ## Sleeps nights twelve-fourteen hours   9-12

Definition: Sleep patterns by this age should be fairly regular. Nighttime sleep may average 12 to 14 hours with periodic brief awakenings.
(also in Strand 0.0, "Regulatory/Sensory Organization")

6.28 ## Naps once or twice each day one-four hours, may refuse morning nap   9-12

Definition: The child may not require morning naps. If this is refused, an earlier afternoon nap ranging from 1 to 4 hours is often suitable.

5.34 ## Tests parental reactions at bedtime   9-12

Definition: The child is learning that his caregivers have certain bedtime "rules," e.g., time to stop playing and time to lie down. He may use bedtime as a "testing ground" to test these rules, his limits and power to get a reaction from his caregivers. He may scream, cry, refuse to lie down, throw his toys across the room and call for his parents helplessly. Separation anxieties and fear of the dark can also be a cause or intensify his reactions.
(also in Strand 5-4, "Learning Rules and Expectations")

6.36 ## Sleeps nights ten-twelve hours   13-18

Definition: Children often reduce their nighttime sleep during the second year to 10 to 12 hours per night.

6.37 ## Naps once in afternoon one-three hours   13-18

Definition: Morning naps are typically rare.

6.53 | **Delays sleeping by demanding things   19-31**

Definition: The child may try to delay going to bed at night or nap time by asking his caregivers for things, e.g., for just one more kiss, one more story, or one more drink. At this stage, children generally require less sleep and have more difficulty falling asleep even when they are tired. Sometimes it is because they are too busy to sleep and don't want to miss anything.

6.89 | **Sleeps ten-fifteen hours daily   31+**

Definition: The child typically sleeps through the night, averaging 10 to 15 hours.

6.90 | **May awaken, crying from dreams   31+**

Definition: Nightmares are common and normal at this age and do not usually indicate emotional problems. Crying which is precipitated by a nightmare is usually different from typical crying or whining, as it has a very distressed and fearful sound.

6.91 | **May eliminate naps   31+**

Definition: Most children stop needing naps except on a particularly stressful or active day. Many still benefit from a quiet rest period.

Special Note:
The American Academy of Pediatrics recommends that healthy babies be placed on their back for sleeping in order to reduce the incidence of Sudden Infant Death Syndrome (SIDS). However, the Academy states that *certain* babies should still be placed on their stomach (prone) for sleep: *For premature infants with respiratory distress, for infants with symptoms of gastroesophageal reflux (spitting up), or with certain upper airway anomalies, and perhaps for some other reasons, prone may well be the position of choice.*
• While a baby is in the NICU, **the baby's nurse or doctor should specify which position is best for the baby when sleeping.**
• When a baby is taken home, **parents should ask their baby's nurse or doctor which position is best for the baby when sleeping at home.**
Once home, all babies should spend some time playing on their stomach during *awake* times (unless instructed otherwise by a doctor).

6-5 GROOMING AND HYGIENE

6.51	19-24	Washes and dries hands partially
6.66	24-30	Washes hands
6.67	24 +	Brushes teeth with assistance
6.73	*24-31*	Wipes nose with assistance
6.82	30-36	Dries hands
6.83	30 +	Helps with bathing self
6.93	32-34	Blows nose with assistance

Family Friendly Interpretation of Strand Concepts, Assessment, & Purpose

We will be observing how your child is learning to participate in self-care activities, such as washing and drying his hands, and brushing his teeth. Although toddlers and preschoolers usually need adults to help them do a complete job, many children become interested in learning how to do these things because of their urge to be independent.

Parent Questions   (Examples)

To help identify the child's unique strengths and needs related to this developmental area:
There are several ways children begin to participate and learn how to wash their own hands, e.g., helping to turn the faucets on and off, reaching for and replacing the soap, rubbing their own hands together, rinsing, and drying with a towel.

- Has your child started to try any of these things yet?
- Does your child seem ready or interested in becoming more independent in washing?
- What part of the washing process does he seem to do the best?...need the most help?
- How about during bath time...are there ways your child tries to help wash himself?

There are several ways children begin to participate in and learn how to brush their own teeth, e.g., helping put paste on the toothbrush, holding the brush, brushing their teeth partially, rinsing the toothbrush, and rinsing their mouth.

- Has your child started to try brushing his own teeth yet?
- Does he seem ready or interested in learning to brush his teeth?
- What part of the tooth-brushing process does he seem to do best?...need the most help?
- Does your child seem unusually sensitive to having his face washed or teeth brushed?

To help identify family resources, priorities and concerns related to the child's development in this area:
- Do you think this is a good time for your child to become more independent with washing up and brushing his teeth?
- Are there certain times that are better than others to let him practice washing up and brushing his teeth?
- Are there places at home or daycare that have sinks your child can reach? What type of faucets do you have, e.g., one rotating handle or two separate faucets for hot and cold?
- Have you thought of some ways to help protect him from the hot water faucet?

Sample *Functional* Outcome Statements which may be generated by the Family

[Will be dependent upon identified individual child and family needs, and should incorporate objectives and activities from other domains]
My child will be able to:
- Wash and dry his own hands;
- Brush his own teeth;
- Wipe his nose.

We will have a bath seat for our child to use during bathing.

Transactional Assessment

May assess through observation and interview.

Assessment of the Child's Environment

1. Supportive:
[Example environments which support/facilitate development in this area]
The child's caregiving environments:
• Have some general routines for washing and bathing, e.g., hand-washing before and after meals; bath time before bed; brushing teeth before bed;
• Have an accessible sink, soap and towel, e.g., step stool, small towel within reach;
• Are safe for independent washing, e.g., step stool is sturdy; hot water or faucet has been adjusted to prevent burns.

Assessment of Caregiver Interactions with the Child

1. Supportive:
[Example interactions which support/facilitate child's development in this area]
The child's caregivers:
• Let their child practice washing and brushing his teeth;
• Make positive comments about their child's attempts to wash and brush teeth;
• Make positive comments about their child's appearance after washing;
• Make simple comments about how cleanliness is important to health;
• Demonstrate and give clear directions when teaching their child self-care activities;
• Are available to provide extra help and direction without always taking over;
• Always supervise their child closely while bathing;
• Respect and try to adapt for any sensitivities or fears the child may have related to having his face washed or bathing in a tub.

2. Compromising:
[Example interactions which may restrict, compromise, inhibit or be unsupportive of the child's development in this area]
The child's caregivers frequently:
• Make negative comments about the child's incomplete washing attempts;
• Leave the child unattended in the tub.

Identifying and Interpreting Needs for Intervention

If a child is significantly delayed in this area he may be having difficulty in the <u>underlying motor (including oral motor) and cognitive skills</u> needed for independent self-care skills.

However, before targeting underlying motor or cognitive development as the primary area for intervention, consider and, rule out, or adapt for other issues <u>that may interfere with early independent self-care skills</u>. These may include:
• <u>Hypersensitive to touch</u>, e.g., child is very upset by having his face touched; is upset by the texture of soap; and/or is orally defensive and becomes upset with having a toothbrush in his mouth;
• <u>Difficulty with motor planning</u> needed to follow the sequence of steps in the washing process;
• <u>Tooth or gum infections or cavities;</u>
• <u>Lack of experience;</u>
• <u>Typical childhood fear</u> of the bath tub.

Assessment Adaptations   (Examples)

[Note any adaptations needed to credit and help plan interventions]
• <u>Hypersensitivity to touch:</u>
  – Allow the child to control all aspects of washing, which is often less offensive than adult-directed washing; if an adult needs to help to complete the job, try letting the child continue to hold the toothbrush or the washcloth while helping him via a hand-over-hand method.
  – Let the child explore and play with wash cloths, toothbrushes and bars of soap at his own pace to let him get used to the materials before assessing independent grooming skills.
  – Experiment with different textures of soap (e.g., small, dry, hard bar versus lotion-type or soft bar), and wash cloths as well as different types of toothbrushes.
  – Consult with a pediatric therapist who is experienced in sensory integration for individualized assessment and intervention techniques and material suggestions.
• <u>Difficulty with motor planning</u>: give the child extra practice, time, demonstration, repetition and simple concrete verbal and hand-over-hand directions when assessing grooming skills which require sequenced steps.
• <u>Visually impaired</u>: assess in the child's natural environment, using familiar grooming aids which are kept in predictable locations at the

Assessment Adaptations   (continued)

sink. Emphasize how the child's hands, face, and nose feel clean after washing and wiping.

- Motor impairment: if child is not ambulatory, let him use a plastic bowl/mirror or disposable wash-ups. Consult with a therapist to identify positions and adaptive toothbrushes to optimize independence, e.g., built-up handle or electric toothbrush. Jaw control may be provided if recommended while assessing tooth-brushing skills; be sure the child is positioned with his head bent slightly forward to prevent gagging. Liquid soap may be easier than a bar of soap for children with poor grasp. Consult with an occupational or speech therapist for tooth-brushing adaptations if the child has oral motor dysfunction.

General Assessment Procedures & Processes   (apply to all items in this Strand)

1. **Describe the skill and eliciting procedures to family members and invite them to help observe and/or assess.** Provide anticipatory guidance that children are not expected to do a complete or thorough job at this stage.

+ - A   Credit Notes:

+   child usually displays skill by observation or report.

-   not observed or reported.

+/-   appears to be an emerging skill, e.g., appeared to learn during the assessment.

O   circle any credit if environment or interactions compromise or restrict child's optimal skills, in this area.

Note any adaptations used to credit.

Assessment Materials

Small bar of soap, children's toothbrush, hand towel, accessible sink.

Washes and dries hands partially   19-24

Definition: The child participates in washing his hands with soap by rubbing his hands and drying them with a towel. He may need help with turning the faucet on and off, simple directions or reminders to take the soap, rub, rinse, etc., and he may not do a complete or thorough job.

Example Observational Opportunities: May elicit through parent interview or observe when child washes up before and after snack or mealtime, after playing outside, or after painting activities. Observe at low sink or using a sturdy step stool. Monitor and help regulate faucets. Provide demonstration and simple direction, as needed.

Credit: (see also Credit Notes in this strand's preface)

+   actively participates in hand washing; rubs hands with soap and attempts drying.

Washes hands   24-30

Definition: The child independently completes the steps involved in washing his own hands, i.e., turning the faucets on and off, using the soap, rinsing and drying. He may still not do a thorough job, and will need supervision regulating the faucets.

Example Observational Opportunities: Same as #6.51.

Credit: (see also Credit Notes in this strand's preface)

+   independently completes steps in washing process, i.e., turning on faucets if not tight, using soap, rubbing hands, rinsing and drying; hands should be mostly free of soap and may or may not be completely clean; he may need help regulating the faucets (i.e., making sure water is not too hot, and flow of water is appropriate) and in doing a thorough job in cleaning and drying.

Brushes teeth with assistance   24+

Definition: The child brushes his teeth partially after an adult puts the paste on the brush.

Example Observational Opportunities: May elicit through parent interview or observation when brushing teeth after snack or mealtime. Provide or have parent provide a small toothbrush with soft bristles. Put a dab of paste on the brush, as the child holds the brush and helps squeeze the paste, if interested. Demonstrate and provide verbal directions and encouragement as needed.

Credit: (see also Credit Notes in this strand's preface)

+   usually participates in brushing teeth; may participate by only brushing a few times; the adult needs to do the real cleaning.

6.73 | Wipes nose with assistance   *24-31*

Definition: The child wipes a runny nose on request if given a tissue. He may need help to do a complete job.
Example Observation Opportunities: May elicit through parent interview, or observe if the occasion arises during observation period.
Credit: (see also Credit Notes in this strand's preface)
+   usually wipes a runny nose at least partially if given a tissue.

6.82 | Dries hands   **30-36**

Definition: The child dries his own hands well with a towel after washing. He does so without adult direction or assistance.
Example Observation Opportunities: May elicit through parent interview or observe when child washes up before and after snack or mealtime, after playing outside, or after painting activities. Have a hand towel readily available. May make a comment, if needed, such as, "Oops! You need to dry your hands."
Credit: (see also Credit Notes in this strand's preface)
+   usually dries hands adequately after washing without adult help.

6.83 | Helps with bathing self   **30+**

Definition: The child washes body parts he can easily reach using a wash cloth or soapy hands when taking a bath under adult supervision and direction.
Example Observation Opportunities: May elicit through parent interview. If the child is physically disabled, it can be helpful for a physical or occupational therapist to observe child's bathing to assess if special adaptations can be helpful to caregivers or to help child be more independent, such as special bath seating or lifting techniques for caregivers.
Credit: (see also Credit Notes in this strand's preface)
+   actively participates in bathing process by washing some body parts.

6.93 | Blows nose with assistance   **32-34**

Definition: The child can blow his nose independently and may resist adult assistance. He may need a reminder to wipe completely or throw his tissue away.
Example Observation Opportunities: May elicit through parent interview, or observe if the occasion arises during observation period.
Credit: (see also Credit Notes in this strand's preface)
+   usually blows own nose fairly effectively.

6-6 TOILETING

6.34	12-18	Shows bladder and bowel control pattern
6.35	12-18	Indicates discomfort over soiled pants verbally or by gesture
6.48	18-24	Sits on potty chair or on adaptive seat on toilet with assistance
6.49	18-24	May be toilet regulated by adult
6.52	19-24	Anticipates need to eliminate - uses same word for both functions
6.68	24-36	Anticipates need to eliminate in time
6.69	24-36	Uses toilet with assistance - has daytime control
6.84	30-36	Distinguishes between urination and bowel movements
6.87	31 +	Verbalizes need to use toilet - has occasional accidents
6.88	31 +	Takes responsibility for toileting; requires assistance in wiping

Family Friendly Interpretation of Strand Concepts, Assessment, & Purpose

There are no exact timetables for determining when to start toilet training. In general, children should be at least 18 months old developmentally in cognitive and social development before they are ready to begin the process but usually do not have the physical control to regulate themselves until they are about 2 years old. Children typically have "accidents" for the first year after training begins because they still have difficulty recognizing when their bladders are full.

Professional FYI

The age levels for toileting skills may vary greatly depending upon when caregivers initiate toilet training.

Parent Questions   (General Examples - see Skills for specific questions)

To help identify the child's unique strengths and needs related to this developmental area:
- Can you tell when your child wets or soils his diaper? How does he let you know?
- Have you started any toilet training with your child?

[If so]
- How is it going? What are some of the things you've done to start training him; for example, does he use a potty chair and are there certain times you always take him to the potty? About how long does he sit on the potty? What happens if he doesn't go on the potty after several minutes?
- Does your child recognize or use any words to mean urination or bowel movement?

To help identify family resources, priorities and

concerns related to the child's development in this area:
- Sometimes children have more difficulty with toilet training when they are experiencing stress or changes in their life, such as moving to a new home or having a new baby at home. Are there any potential stressful events that have happened recently or that you anticipate happening in the near future that may interfere with toilet training?
- About how old do you think your child should be when he can be expected to be fully toilet trained?
- What advice have you been given about toilet training? How does that fit with what you believe?
- Is this a good time for your child and family to work on toilet training?

Sample *Functional* Outcome Statements which may be generated by the Family

[Will be dependent upon identified individual child and family needs, and should incorporate objectives and activities from other domains]

My child will:
- Stay dry all day;
- Be toilet trained.

Transactional Assessment

May assess through observation and interview.

Assessment of the Child's Environment

1. Supportive:
[Example environments which support/facilitate development in this area]
The child's caregiving environments:
• **P**rovide general basic predictable daily routines;
• Have a safe, secure and comfortable potty chair or adaptive toilet seat.

2. Compromising:
[Environments which may restrict, compromise, inhibit or be unsupportive toward development in this area]
The child's caregiving environments are:
• Currently undergoing stressful or changing events, e.g., parental divorce or other parental separation, new sibling, move, new childcare provider.

Assessment of Caregiver Interactions with the Child

1. Supportive:
[Example interactions which support/facilitate child's development in this area]
The child's caregivers usually:
• Wait until the child is developmentally ready before introducing toilet training;
• Give opportunities for the child to become acquainted with the potty or toilet seat before initiating toilet training;
• Avoid keeping their child on the potty for more than 5 minutes;
• Introduce toilet training with a calm, matter of fact, cheerful approach.

2. Compromising:
[Example interactions which may restrict, compromise, inhibit or be unsupportive of the child's development in this area]
The child's caregivers:
• Begin toilet training before the child is developmentally ready;
• Punish, shame, or make negative comments when the child has accidents or does not eliminate when put on the potty.

Identifying and Interpreting Needs for Intervention

If a child is significantly delayed in toilet training, not due to delays in other areas of development, he may have <u>underlying behavioral or emotional needs</u>.

However, before targeting this as the primary need for intervention, consider and, rule out, or adapt for other causes <u>that may contribute to delays in toilet training</u>. These may include:

• <u>Family or cultural diversity</u>, i.e., family does not encourage toilet training until a later age, due to culture or other priorities at this time;
• <u>Medical conditions or disabilities</u> which interfere with bowel and bladder control, e.g., spina bifida, neurological disorders, medications, frequent bladder infections.

Assessment Adaptations   (Examples)

[Note any adaptations needed to credit and help plan interventions]
• <u>Motor impaired:</u> if the child is not ambulatory, adapt #6.88 "Takes responsibility for toileting..." with a therapist to identify alternative goals that maximize the child's independence.

• <u>Medical conditions or disabilities</u> that interfere with bowel and bladder control: Discuss toilet training expectations with the child's physician and family; mark N/A for appropriate items.

General Assessment Procedures & Processes   (apply to all items in this Strand)

1. **Most items in this strand are assessed through parent interview but may be observed if natural toileting situations arise**, e.g., after snack time, going to the toilet if the child is familiar and comfortable with you.

+ - A Credit Notes:

+   child usually displays skill or behavior as

defined by parent report or observation.
-    not observed or reported.
+/- appears to be an emerging skill.
N/A not appropriate to assess due to medical condition or disability.
O   circle any credit if environment or interactions compromise or restrict child's optimal skills, in this area.
Note any adaptations used to credit.

Assessment Materials

Potty chair or adaptive toilet seat that the child is familiar with.

6.34   Shows bladder and bowel control pattern   12-18

Definition: Elimination is still automatic and not voluntary but a pattern is usually established around this time. The frequency of urination decreases and the child can remain dry for 1- to 2-hour intervals. Bowel movements may occur at predictable time, often after meals.

Example Observational Opportunities: Elicit through parent interview.

Credit: (see also Credit Notes in this strand's preface)

+ diaper remains dry for 1- to 2-hour intervals, and caregivers can often predict when their child has bowel movements.

6.35   Indicates discomfort over soiled pants verbally or by gesture   12-18

Definition: The child is aware of wetting and soiling his pants and feels uncomfortable. He may display one or more signs of awareness and discomfort: hiding his face, showing his wet pants, fussing, trying to take off pants; becoming very still, grimacing or straining, verbalizing his word for a bowel movement or urination.

Example Observational Opportunities: May observe signs of discomfort during observation period or elicit through parent interview.

Credit: (see also Credit Notes in this strand's preface)

+ usually displays one or more signs of discomfort as defined.

6.48   Sits on potty chair or on adaptive seat on toilet with assistance   18-24

Definition: The child is able to sit comfortably on a potty chair or toilet with a child's seat if an adult places him on the seat and remains nearby.

Parent Questions: Have you started to toilet train your child yet? Do you use a potty or the regular toilet? How much help does your child need to sit on it? Do he seem to mind sitting on it? About how long does he sit there? Does he let you know when he's ready to get off or do you take him off at a certain time?

Example Observational Opportunities: May observe if parent takes child to potty during observation period.

Credit: (see also Credit Notes in this strand's preface)

+ sits comfortably on a potty or adaptive seat on a toilet for at least a minute at a time without resisting or acting fearful. An adult may lead him to the potty or help him up to the toilet and helps him undress. He may or may not actually eliminate.

6.49   May be toilet regulated by adult   18-24

Definition: The child uses a toilet about half the time if an adult is the one who takes primary responsibility for "catching" him at the right time. He is not truly toilet trained at this stage and often does not indicate his need to go.

Parent Questions: Same as #6.48, plus, How long have you been toilet training your child? About how often do you take him? How is that going? What happens if he does not do anything after sitting on the toilet/potty?."

Credit: (see also Credit Notes in this strand's preface)

+ is successful about half the time if caregivers take him to toilet.

6.52   Anticipates need to eliminate - uses same word for both functions   19-24

Definition: The child has an awareness of when he needs to urinate or have a bowel movement. Sometimes he verbalizes, e.g., "potty," "doo doo," "pee pee" but may not always use the correct word.

Parent Questions: Do you use any terms to name your child's bowel movements or urination? Does your child use any of these terms? Does he ever use them to let you know he needs to toilet?

Example Observational Opportunities: May observe if child verbalizes his need to toilet during observation period. If not observing at home, show the child where the toilet is at the beginning of the assessment, inviting him to let you or his parent know it whenever he wishes to use it.

Anticipates need to eliminate - uses same word for both functions (continued)

Credit: (see also Credit Notes in this strand's preface)
+ sometimes indicates in advance need to use the toilet. He may indicate with a term meaning urination and/or bowel movement but may use the same word to indicate either. He may still have many accidents.

6.68 Anticipates need to eliminate in time 24-36

Definition: The child usually knows and indicates to others in advance when he needs to eliminate. He may verbalize or gesture his need and has few accidents unless deeply involved in play.
Parent Questions: How does your child let you know when he needs to toilet? About how many accidents per day or week does your child have?
Example Observational Opportunities: If not observing at home, show the child where the toilet is at the beginning of the assessment, inviting him to use it whenever he wishes.
Credit: (see also Credit Notes in this strand's preface)
+ usually indicates need to use the toilet in advance.

6.69 Uses toilet with assistance - has daytime control 24-36

Definition: The child is well on the way to being toilet trained. He rarely has accidents during the day, and is fairly independent on the toilet, only needing assistance with clothing and wiping.
Example Observational Opportunities: If not observing at home, show the child where the toilet is at the beginning of the assessment, inviting him to use it whenever he wishes. Ask the parent to let him be as independent as he can in all aspects of the toileting process before offering assistance.
Credit: (see also Credit Notes in this strand's preface)
+ child rarely (less than once or twice per week) has daytime accidents.

6.84 Distinguishes between urination and bowel movements 30-36

Definition: The child can distinguish between bladder and bowel movements. He may do so before or after toileting.
Example Observational Opportunities: May elicit by parent interview.
Credit: (see also Credit Notes in this strand's preface)
+ names urination and bowel moments correctly.

6.87 Verbalizes need to use toilet - has occasional accidents 31+

Definition: The child verbalizes his need to use the toilet with familiar adults; he may have occasional accidents when he is feeling anxious, not near a toilet, or involved deeply in play.
Parent Questions: How do you know when your child needs to use the toilet? Does he still have any accidents? About how often? Can you give me an example of when he had an accident; e.g., where was he, what was he doing?
Example Observational Opportunities: If not observing at home, show the child where the toilet is at the beginning of the assessment, inviting him to let you or his parent know anytime he may wish to use it.
Credit: (see also Credit Notes in this strand's preface)
+ tells or gestures to familiar adults his need to use the toilet; he rarely has (less than once a week) accidents.

6.88 Takes responsibility for toileting; requires assistance in wiping 31+

Definition: The child takes primary responsibility for his own toileting. He anticipates and goes to the bathroom on his own, undresses and dresses, takes some toilet paper, tries to wipe, and can flush the toilet. He may still need help taking the correct amount of toilet paper, doing an adequate job wiping, and fastening some clothing.
Parent Questions: Does your child usually go to the toilet on his own? In what ways do you still need to help? *Or,* Does he need any help with things like wiping or getting the right amount of paper?
Example Observational Opportunities: If not observing at home, show the child where the toilet is at the beginning of the assessment, inviting him to let you or his parent know anytime he may wish to use it. Ask the parent to let him be as independent as he can in all aspects of the toileting process before offering assistance.
Credit: (see also Credit Notes in this strand's preface)
+ usually takes most of the responsibility for toileting as defined.

6-7 HOUSEHOLD INDEPENDENCE/RESPONSIBILITY

5.45	12-18	Enjoys imitating adult behavior; responds well to the introduction of new tasks
1.103	18-24	Explores cabinets and drawers
6.55	21-23	Opens doors by turning knob
6.56	21-23	Helps with simple household tasks
6.61	24-26	Handles fragile items carefully
6.62	24-29.5	Helps put things away
5.73	24-30	Enjoys experimenting with adult activities
6.60	24-30	Understands and stays away from common dangers - stairs, glass, strange animals
6.76	30-36	Knows proper place for own things
6.80	30 +	Hangs clothing on hook
6.86	31 +	Shows interest in setting table

Family Friendly Interpretation of Strand Concepts, Assessment, & Purpose

We will be observing how your child is learning to help with simple chores around home, such as putting away his own toys. We will also be asking you questions related to how independent your child is around home without needing constant supervision or help, e.g., staying away from dangerous areas, such as a hot stove or steep stairs.

Parent Questions   (General Examples - see Skills for specific questions)

To help identify the child's unique strengths and needs related to this developmental area:

• Are there certain chores or responsibilities that your child is learning, such as helping to wipe up his messes or putting away a few toys?

• Are you comfortable letting your child move about your home without your constant supervision?

To help identify family resources, priorities and concerns related to the child's development in this area:

• If you could think of one thing that you wish your child would be more responsible about, what would that be?

Sample *Functional* Outcome Statements which may be generated by the Family

[Will be dependent upon identified individual child and family needs, and should incorporate objectives and activities from other domains]
My child will:
• Stay away from animals he does not know;

• Stay away from my garden tools;
• Help put his dirty clothes in the basket;
• Hold our kitten gently;
• Help put his toys away.

Transactional Assessment

May assess through observation and interview.

Assessment of the Child's Environment

1. Supportive:
[Example environments which support/facilitate development in this area]
The child's caregiving environments usually:

• Have spaces which are child-proofed for the child to freely explore;
• Have child-sized materials that promote independence, e.g., low hooks to hang clothing; toy boxes and low shelves to put toys.

Assessment of Caregiver Interactions with the Child

1. Supportive:
[Example interactions which support/facilitate child's development in this area]
The child's caregivers usually:
- Teach the child simple responsibilities appropriate to his developmental skills;
- Provide adequate child-proofing so the child has the freedom to safely explore and help out at home;
- Make positive comments and praise their child when he helps out around home or is extra careful with fragile items.

2. Compromising:
[Example interactions which may restrict, compromise, inhibit or be unsupportive of the child's development in this area]
The child's caregivers frequently:
- Harshly punish their child when he breaks a rule or does not help out;
- Set unclear, inconsistent or developmentally inappropriate rules and limits;
- Are overly permissive, setting few or no rules or limits.

Identifying and Interpreting Needs for Intervention

If a child is significantly delayed in this area, this may be <u>due to delays in other areas of development</u> or due to inexperience if his caregivers have <u>not encouraged responsibilities or independence.</u>

Assessment Adaptations   (Examples)

[Note any adaptations needed to credit and help plan interventions]
- <u>Motor impairment:</u> adapt items for assessment and planning with a pediatric occupational or physical therapist to accommodate the child's level of motor independence;

- <u>Visually impaired:</u> include a professional who specializes in mobility training in curriculum planning for adaptations to optimize the child's independence in his caregiving environments and in the community.

General Assessment Procedures & Processes   (apply to all items in this Strand)

+ - A Credit Notes:

+   child usually displays skill or behavior as defined during play and daily activities by observation or parent report.

-    not observed or reported.

+/-   appears to be an emerging skill; child learned during observation period with prompting.

N/A not appropriate to assess or plan for due to disability or parent preference.

O   circle any credit if environment or interactions compromise or restrict child's optimal skills in this area.

Note any adaptations used to credit.

5.45   **Enjoys imitating adult behavior; responds well to the introduction of new tasks**   **12-18**

Definition: The child watches and tries to copy the actions of older siblings and adults during daily activities. Examples of early imitation activities may include simple actions, such as wiping his highchair tray, wiping his face, feeding others or stirring in a cup. Later he becomes interested in imitating using adult "tools," e.g., keys, wallets, pens, screwdrivers, lipstick. Imitation is typically brief and only an approximation of the actual behavior.

Parent Questions: Have you seen your child try to copy some of the things he sees others do related to household chores or grooming, e.g., wiping his tray with a napkin, trying to brush his own teeth, pulling weeds, picking up trash? Can you think of any other examples?

Example Observational Opportunities: During snack or mealtime preparation, give the child an extra spoon to help; after mealtime give him an extra sponge to help wipe the table; during dress-up give him a brush to brush his hair when you are brushing yours.

Credit: (see also Credit Notes in this strand's preface)
+   watches with interest others performing simple household or grooming activities and tries to imitate at least two; imitation may be brief or inaccurate.

1.103 Explores cabinets and drawers 18-24

Definition: The child moves about and explores his environment without an adult. He enjoys investigating what is inside drawers, cabinets, boxes and closets.

Parent Questions: Is your child allowed to explore and move about the house without constant supervision? What kinds of things does he do when he is "on is own"? Does he like to explore and get into things such as your drawers or the kitchen cabinets?

Example Observational Opportunities: May observe if during free play child independently explores cabinets and drawers.

Credit: (see also Credit Notes in this strand's preface)

+ likes to explore cabinets, drawers, closets etc. by taking items out of the drawer or cabinet, and/or simply opening them without much play. He does not need adult encouragement to do so.

6.55 Opens doors by turning knob 21-23

Definition: The child increases his independence at home as he learns the problem-solving and motor skills needed to open doors using door knobs.

Parent Questions: When your child is going about the house independently, can he open closed doors? How does he do that? Are there some rooms that are off limits for him? How do you keep him from entering?

Example Observational Opportunities: May observe if accessible doors are available and the child independently opens it upon entering or leaving the observation setting.

Credit: (see also Credit Notes in this strand's preface)

+ can open accessible doors by turning door knobs; he may need help with heavy doors.

(also in Strand 1-4B "Means-Ends")

6.56 Helps with simple household tasks 21-23

Definition: The child helps an adult with simple household chores, such as sweeping, mopping, dusting, vacuuming, shoveling, raking, putting a few groceries away, watering plants, folding washcloths, cleaning up spills with sponge.

Example Observational Opportunities: Invite the child to "help" during the observation period, e.g., give him an extra sponge to wipe the table after snack time or messy activities; let him have a turn to stir the pudding; let him help collect and throw away trash.

Credit: (see also Credit Notes in this strand's preface)

+ actively participates in helping an adult with two or three simple household chores as defined. His "help" may not be perfect or complete and may last only a few minutes.

6.61 Handles fragile items carefully 24-26

Definition: The child can generally carry or handle fragile or breakable items without breaking or throwing them although accidents may still occur.

Parent Questions: Is your child sometimes allowed to carry fragile or breakable things, such as a pet, flowers, or a glass? How does he do with this?

Example Observational Opportunities: During snack invite the child to help carry his drink to the table; during painting activities let him carry a half-full jar of paint to the easel; during dress-up let him play with jewelry.

Credit: (see also Credit Notes in this strand's preface)

+ usually handles and respects breakable items with care, e.g., movements are slower, gentler and/or more deliberate.

6.62 **Helps put things away   24-29.5**

Definition: The child frequently helps put things away during daily activities with some adult encouragement and praise. Examples may include: putting his toys back on the shelf or in his toy box; putting his clothes in the hamper; putting some grocery items away; returning his shoes to his closet.

Parent Questions: Does your child help put things away at home, for example, his clothes or his toys? Does he usually help put things away every day?

Example Observational Opportunities: If the child is familiar with the environment or has watched where a toy or other materials came from, ask him to return the item before going on to the next activity, e.g., putting toys back on the shelf, his jacket in the coat room, paints back to the paint corner, snack items back to the kitchen corner. Do not tell or gesture to him where it belongs, but rather ask, for example, "Please put the toy back before snack."

Credit: (see also Credit Notes in this strand's preface)

+   helps put at least two or three things away every day as part of his routine. He should not be expected to put an activity or toy away in which he is involved and does not always comply on request.

5.73 **Enjoys experimenting with adult activities   24-30**

Definition: The child enjoys trying out adult roles and activities, e.g., gardening, dusting, sweeping, running errands, trying to put his own bed in order, feeding a pet.

Example Observational Opportunities: Give the child household "tools" to help clean up; during outdoor play, let him help plant seeds in a garden or help wash playground equipment.

Credit: (see also Credit Notes in this strand's preface)

+   actively enjoys and participates in many adult chores.

6.60 **Understands and stays away from common dangers - stairs, glass, strange animals   24-30**

Definition: The child has learned about basic dangers, such as fire, steep stairs, broken glass, streets and unfamiliar animals. He usually stays away from them and can safely play without constant close supervision in his home and fenced yard.

Parent Questions: Does your child seem to understand what things are dangerous? Can you give me some examples? How can you tell he knows they are dangerous? Do you feel you can let your child play around home or in your yard without your having to constantly watch him?

Credit: (see also Credit Notes in this strand's preface)

+   understands several dangerous situations and/or materials and typically does not go near them.

6.76 **Knows proper place for own things   30-36**

Definition: The child knows where most of his possessions are typically kept. He thus takes responsibility for independently putting them away or getting them when he wants them, e.g., that his cereal belongs in a certain cabinet; that his blocks belong in a box and his books on the shelf; his shoes belong in the closet and his socks in the drawer; his bath toys belong in the bathroom; his dirty clothes belong in the hamper.

Parent Questions: Explore with parents the types of responsibilities the child has and does independently during daily activities related to his own belongings. Be specific with questions such as, "During dressing, does you child get his own shoes from the closet? Pants from his drawer?"

Example Observational Opportunities: During daycare or classroom observations may observe when child puts away or retrieves his belongings, e.g., his lunch box in his cubby, his coat on his hook.

Credit: (see also Credit Notes in this strand's preface)

+   typically takes responsibility every day for putting away and retrieving several of his own belongings.

6.80   Hangs clothing on hook   30+

Definition: If available the child can hang his clothing on a low hook or child's clothes tree.

Parent Questions: Does your child have a low clothing hook or clothes tree at home or daycare to hang clothes on? Does he do so?

Example Observational Opportunities: If observing in a classroom or playroom setting, invite the child to hang his coat up on low hook. May also observe during dress-up play if a small clothes tree is available.

Credit: (see also Credit Notes in this strand's preface)

+   hangs up coat, robe, other clothing on a hook as part of his daily routine responsibility. This may be on request.

N/A If low clothing hooks or a child-sized clothes tree is not available.

6.86   Shows interest in setting table   31+

Definition: The child enjoys helping an adult set the table for mealtimes. He may help fold and put out napkins; set condiments out (salt, ketchup, etc.), place utensils (not in correct order), and wipe the table.

Example Observation Opportunities: Invite the child to help set the table during a pretend tea party with dolls or during snack or mealtime.

Credit: (see also Credit Notes in this strand's preface)

+   helps set table in any way.

REFERENCES

Adelson, E., & Fraiberg, S. (1976) *Sensory deficit and motor development in infants blind from birth*. In Z.S. Jastnzembska (Ed.), The Effects of Blindness and Other Impairments on Early Development. New York: American Foundation for the Blind.

Alexander, R. (1982) Early feeding, sound production, and pre-linguistic/cognitive development and their relationship to gross-motor and fine-motor development. Working document. Wauwatosa, Wisconsin: Curative Rehabilitation Center, .

Alexander, R. (1990) *Oral-Motor and Respiratory-Phonatory Assessment*. In E.D. Gibbs & D.M. Teti (Eds.) Interdisciplinary Assessment of Infants. Baltimore, MD.: Paul H. Brookes

Anderson, P.P. , & Fenichel, E.S. (1989) Serving Culturally Diverse Families of Infants and Toddlers with Disabilities .Washington, D.C.: National Center for Clinical Infant Programs.

Ayres, A.J. (1979) Sensory Integration and the Child.Western Psychological Services. L.A.

Bagnato, S.J., Neisworth, Munson, S.M. (1989) Linking Developmental Assessment and Early Intervention: Curriculum-Based Prescriptions (2nd. Ed.) Rockville, MD: Aspen

Bangs, T.E. Checklist of Learning and Language Behavior (1986) Allen, Texas: DLM

Barnard, K.E., (1987) Nursing Child Assessment Satelite Training, Learning Resource Manuel (Revised). Seattle, WA: University of Washington.

Barnes, Crutchfield, Heriza (1977) *Reflex Evaluation*, from The Neurophysiolgical Basis of Patient Treatment, II, Morgantown, WV: Stokesville Pub. Co.

Bayley, N. (1969) Bayley Scales of Infant Development, New York: Psychological Corporation

Beckwith, L. (1990) *Adaptive and maladaptive parenting-Implications for intervention*. In S.J.Meisels & J.P. Shonkoff (Eds.) Handbook of Early Childhood Intervention. Chambridge, MA: Chambridge University Press.

Berry, M.F.(1969) Language Disorders of Children. New York: Appleton-Century-Crofts.

Blackman, J.A. (Ed.) (1984) Medical Aspects of Developmental Disabilities in Children Birth to Three. Rockville, MD: Aspen

Bloom, L., & Lahey, M. (1978). Language Development and Language Disorders. New York: John Wiley & Sons

Boehme, R. (1988) Improving Upper Body Control. Tucson, AZ.: Therapy Skill Builders.

Bond, L.A., Creasey, G.L. and Abrams, C.L. (1990) *Play Assessment, Reflecting and Promoting Cognitive Competence*.In E.D. Gibbs & D.M. Teti (Eds) Interdisciplinary Assessment of Infants. Baltimore, MD.: Paul H. Brookes

Bradley, R., & Caldwell, B. (1976) *Early home environment and changes in mental text performance in children from 6 to 36 months*. Developmental Psychology, 12, 93-97.

Butterworth, G. (1981). *The origins of auditory-visual proprioception in human development*. In R.D. Walk & H.L. Picks (Eds.), Intersensory Perception and Sensory Integration. New York: Plenum Press.

Bzoch, K.R., & League, R. (1978) Receptive Expressive Emergent Language Scale. Austin, TX:Pro-Ed.

Caplan, F. & Caplan, T. (1973) The First Twelve Months of Life. New York: Grosset & Dunlap.

Caplan, F. & Caplan, T. (1979) The Second Twelve Months of Life. New York: Grosset & Dunlap.

Casby, M.W. (1992) *Symbolic play: Development and assessment considerations*. Infants and Young Children; 4(3):43-48.

Case-Smith, J. (1988) Posture and Fine Motor Assessment of Infants, Research Edition, Virginia Commonwealth University

Chandler, L., Andrews, M., & Swanson, M. (1980). The Movement Assessment of Infants: A Manual. Rolling Bay, WA: Infant Movement Research.

Chandler, L.S. (1990) *Neuromotor Assessment*. In E.D. Gibbs & D.M. Teti (Eds) Interdisciplinary Assessment of Infants. Baltimore, MD.: Paul H. Brookes

Church, J. (1978) *Techniques for the differential study of cognition in early childhood*. In L.J. Stone, H. T. Smith, L.B. Murphy (Eds) The Infant's First Year, The Competent Infant Series, New York: Basic Books.

Cicchetti, D., Wagner, S. (1990) *Alternative assessment strategies forthe evaluation of infants and toddlers: An organizational perspective*. In S.J.Meisels & J.P. Shonkoff (Eds.) Handbook of Early Childhood Intervention. Chambridge University Press.

Coley, I.L.(1978) Pediatric assessment of self-care activities. St.Louis: C.V. Mosby Company.

Coplan, J. (1983) Early Language Milestone Scale. Tulsa Oklahoma: Modern Education Corporation

Dunst, C.J. (1980) A Clinical and Educational Manual for use with the Uzgiris and Hunt Scales of Infant Psychological Development, College Pk, MD: University Park Press

Erhardt, R.P. (1982) Developmental Hand Dysfunction, Tucson, Az: Therapy Skill Builders

Federal Register/Vol. 58, No.145/July, 1993/Rules and Regulations, Part III, Department of Education, 34 CRF Part 303: "Early Intervention Program for Infants and Toddlers With Disabilities; Final Rule."

Ferrel, K.A., et. al., (1990) *Visually impaired infants research consortium (VIIRC): First year results.* Journal of Visual Impairment and Blindness, 84, 404-410.

Ferrell, K.A. & Raver, S.A. (1991) *Techniques for Infants and Toddlers with Visual Impairments.* In S. Raver, Strategies for Teaching At-Risk and Handicapped Infants and Toddlers. New York: Macmillan

Fewell, R.R.(1986) Play Assessment Scale, 5th Revsion, Unpublished manuscript. Seattle: University of Washington

Foley, G.M. (1990) *Protrait of the Arena Evaluation: Assessment in the Transdisciplinary Approach.* In E.D. Gibbs & D.M. Teti (Eds) Interdisciplinary Assessment of Infants. Baltimore, MD.: Paul H. Brookes

Folio, M.R., Dubose, R.F (1983) Peabody Developmental Motor Scales. Hingham, MA: Teaching Resources Corporation.

Fraiberg, S., Siegel, B.L., & Gibson, R. (1966). *The role of sound in the search behavior of a blind infant.* Psychoanalytic Study of the Child, 21, 327-57.

Frankenburg, W.K, and Dodds, J.B. (1969) Denver Developmental Screening Test. University of Colorado Medical Center.

Furuno, S. et. al. (1985) Hawaii Early Learning Profile (HELP) Activity Guide. Palo Alto: VORT Corporation

Garwood, S.G. and Fewell (1983) Educating Handicapped Infants. Rockville, MD.: Aspen

Gerson, L., (1991) *Developmental Challenges of the 24-36 month old.* In Developmental Dialogue, Newsletter of the Reginald S. Lourie Center for Infants & Young Children, III, (2)

Gilfoyle, E.M., Grady, A.P., Moore, J. C. (1981) Children Adapt Thorofare, N.J.: Charles B. Slack

Glover, E., Preminger, J.L. & Sanford, A.R. (1978) The Early Learning Accomplishment Profile for Developmentally Young Children Birth to 36 months. Winston-Salem, N.C.: Kaplan Press.

Greenspan, S, & Greenspan, N. (1986). First Feelings. New York: Penguin Books.

Greenspan, S.I.(1992) Infancy and Early Childhood, The practice of clinical assessment and intervention a with emotional and developmental challenges. Madison, Conn.: International Universities Press

Griffin, H.C. (1981). *Motor development in congenitally blind children.* Education of the Visually Handicapped, 12, 106-111.

Guitar, Barry, Dr., and Edward G. Conture, Dr. If You Think Your Child Is Stuttering. Stuttering Foundation of America, 1991-2006. 31 July 2006 http://www.stutteringhelp.org.

Hanson M.J., Lynch, E. W. (1989) Early Intervention Austin, Texas: PRO-ED.

Hasenstab, S.M. (1987) Language Learning and Otitis Media. Boston, MA.: College Hill Press.

Hedrick, D.L., Ratther, E.M., & Tobin, A.R. (1984). Sequenced Inventory of Communication Development, Revised. Seattle: University of Washington Press.

Hill, E.W. (1970). *The formation of concepts involved in body position in space.* Education of the Visually Handicapped, 2(4), 112-114.

Hoskins, T.A., & Squire, J.E. (1973) *Developmental Assessment: A Test for Gross Motor and Reflex Development.* Physical Therapy, 53, 117-126.

Johnson-Martin, N.M., et al, (1991) The Carolina Curriculum for Infants and Toddlers with Special Needs, Baltimore, MD: Paul H. Brookes.

Katzenstein, B. (1987) *Incidence of Balance Deficits in Hearing Impaired Children* in Physical Therapy Forum. VI (31)

Knobloch, H., et. al., (1980) The Revised Developmental Screening Inventory-1980, Houston, Tx.: Developmental Evaluation Materials.

Lieberman, A.F., *Attachment and exploration: The toddler's dilemma.* In Zero to Three, Bulletin of National Center for Clinical Infant Programs, V. XI. #3, Feb. 1991

Linder, T.W., (1990) Transdisciplinary Play-Based Assessment Baltimore, MD.: Paul H. Brookes

Long, T. M. & Raver, S.A. (1991) *Neuromotor Development in Infants and Toddlers.* In S. Raver, Strategies for Teaching At-Risk and Handicapped Infants and Toddlers. New York: Macmillan.

Main, M., George, C. (1985) *Responses of abused and disadvantaged toddlers to distress in agemates: A study in the day care setting.* Developmental Psychology, 21 (3), 407-412.

McGonigel, M.J., Kaufmann, R.K., & Johnson, B.H. (Eds.), (1991). Guidelines and Recommended Practices for the Individualized Family Service Plan, (2nd ed.). Bethesda, MD: Association for the Care of Children's Health.

McLean, J. E., Snyder-McLean, L.K., & Sack, S. (1982) A Transactional Approach to Early Language Training: A Mediated Program for Inservice Professionals. Columbus, OH: Charles Merrill.

Meisels, S.J., & Provence, S. (1989). Screening and Assessment: Guidelines for Identifying Young Disabled and Developmentally Vulnerable Children and their Families Washington, D.C.: National Center for Clinical Infant Programs.

Miller, J. (1981) Assessing Language Production in Children. Baltimore: University Park Press.

Morris, S., & Klein, M. (1987). Pre-feeding Skills. Tucson, AZ: Therapy Skill Builders.

Morris, S.E. (1982) Pre-Speech Assessment Scale. Clifton, NJ: J.A.Preston.

Murphy, L.B. ()1992. Sympathetic Behavior in Very Young Children. In Zero to Three, Bulletin of National Center for Clinical Infant Programs, XII.(4), 1-5.

Northern, J.L. & Downs, M.P. (1974) Hearing In Children. Baltimore, MD: William & Wilkins.

Parks, S., et. al. (1988) HELP....at Home. Palo Alto: VORT Corporation

Parks, S., et. al. (1984) HELP When the Parent is Handicapped. Palo Alto: VORT Corporation

Poisson, S.S. & DeGangi, G.A. (1991) Emotional and Sensory Processing Problems: Assessment and Treatment Approaches for Young Children and Their Families. Rockville, MD.: Reginald S. Lourie Center for Infants and Young Children

Project RHISE (1979). Manual for Administration of the Rockford Infant Developmental Evaluation Scales. Bensenville, ILL: Scholastic Testing Service.

Raver, S.A. (1991) Cognitive Development in Infants and Toddlers.In S. Raver, Strategies for Teaching At-Risk and Handicapped Infants and Toddlers. New York: Macmillan

Reuter, J. & Bickett, L. (1985) The Kent Infant Development Scale Manual, 2nd Edition. Kent, OH: Kent Developmental Metrics.

Rossetti, L. (1991) Social and Communication Development in Infancy. In S. Raver, Strategies for Teaching At-Risk and Handicapped Infants and Toddlers. New York: Macmillan

Roth, F.P. (1990) Early Language Assessment. In E.D. Gibbs & D.M. Teti (Eds) Interdisciplinary Assessment of Infants. Baltimore, MD.: Paul H. Brookes

Sacks, G.K, Young, E. C. (1982) An Assessment Tool: The Infant Scale of Communicative Intent. Update Pediatrics 7 (1).1-4

Samerof, A.J., Fiese, B.H., (1990) Transactional regulation and early intervention. In S.J. Meisels & J.P. Shonkoff (Eds.) Handbook of Early Childhood Intervention. Chambridge University Press.

Sass-Lehrer, M. (1991) Techniques for Infants and Toddlers with Hearing Impairments. In S. Raver, Strategies for Teaching At-Risk and Handicapped Infants and Toddlers. New York: Macmillan

Satter, E. The Feeding Relationship. (1992) In Zero to Three, Bulletin of National Center for Clinical Infant Programs XII (5)1-9.

Schafer, D.S. and Moersch, M.S. (Eds.) (1977) Developmental Programming for Infants and Young Children, Vol. I., Assessment and Application, Ann Arbor, MI: University of Michigan Press

Sensory Integration International (no specific author reported) (1991). A Parent's Guide to Understanding Sensory Integration. Torrance, CA.

Teti, D. & Nakagawa, M. (1990) Assessing attachment in infancy, the strange situation and alternate systems. In E.D. Gibbs & D.M. Teti (Eds) Interdisciplinary Assessment of Infants. Baltimore, MD.: Paul H. Brookes

Trembath, J. (1977) The Milani-Comparetti Motor Development Screening Test. Omaha: Meyer Children's Rehabilitation Institute, University of Nebraska Medical Center.

Uzgiris, I.C. and Hunt, J.M. (1975) Assessment in Infancy: Ordinal Scales of Psychological Development, Urbana, Ill.: University of Illinois Press. 1975.

United States Congress. U.S. Senate and House of Representatives . Individuals with Disabilities Education Improvement Act of 2004. 108th Cong., Public Law 108-446. 2004. 1 Aug. 2006 http://www.copyright.gov/legislation/pl108-446.html.

United States. National Institute of Child Health and Human Development. Safe Sleep for your Baby: (SIDS) Ten ways to reduce the risk of sudden infant death syndrome. Rockville: NIH, 2003. Back to Sleep Campaign. Nov. 2005. National Institute of Child Health and Human Development, Maternal and Child Health Bureau, American Academy of Pediatrics, SIDS Alliance/First Candle. 1 Aug. 2006 http://www.nichd.nih.gov/SIDS/reduce_infant_risk.htm.

Vincent, L..F., et. al. (1990) A behavioral-ecological approach to early intervention: Focus on cultural diversity. In S.J.Meisels & J.P. Shonkoff (Eds.) Handbook of Early Childhood Intervention. Chambridge University Press.

Vulpe, S. (1977). Vulpe Assessment Battery. Toronto: National Institute on Mental Retardation.

Wetherby, A.M. and Prizant, B.M. (1989) Communication and Symbolic Behavior Scales. Special Press, Inc., San Antonio, TX.

White, B. L. (1975) The First Three Years of Life, Prentice-Hall, Englewood Cliffs, N.J.

Winton, P.J., (1990) Working with Families in Early Intervention: An Interdisciplinary Preservice Curriculum, Carolina Institute for Research on Infant Personnel Preparation, Frank Porter Graham Child Development Center, University of North Carolina, Chapel Hill, NC.

Note: If a skill applies to more than one Strand, the skill is repeated in this Index for each Strand occurrence.

Skill ID	Strand	Page	Skill ID	Strand	Page	Skill ID	Strand	Page
2.16	5-2	296	2.76	2-3	114	3.39	3-6A	184
2.17	2-6	140	2.77	2-5	134	3.40	3-6A	186
2.18	2-4B	125	2.78	2-3	114	3.41	3-6A	185
2.19	2-4A	121	2.79	2-6	143	3.42	3-2	160
2.20	2-6	140	2.80	2-3	115	3.43	3-1	155
2.21	2-4B	126	2.81	2-4B	129	3.44	3-5	175
2.22	2-6	140	2.82	2-6	143	3.45	3-4	168
2.23	2-6	140	2.83	2-3	115	3.46	3-4	168
2.24	2-6	140	2.84	2-6	143	3.47	3-5	176
2.25	2-6	140	2.85	1-1	29	3.48	3-5	174
2.26	2-1A	95	2.86	2-5	135	3.49	3-5	174
2.27	2-4B	126	2.87	2-5	134	3.50	3-6A	187
2.28	2-6	141	2.88	2-4B	130	3.51	3-3	165
2.29	2-3	109	2.89	2-3	115	3.52	3-5	174
2.30	5-5	328	2.90	2-4B	130	3.53	3-5	175
2.31	2-6	141	2.91	2-7	147	3.54	3-5	175
2.32	2-6	141	2.92	2-3	115	3.55	3-6A	186
2.33	2-6	141	2.93	2-3	116	3.56	3-6A	186
2.34	2-6	141	2.94	1-7C	86	3.57	3-5	175
2.35	2-4B	126	2.95	2-5	135	3.58	3-5	176
2.36	2-5	132	2.96	2-4B	130	3.59	3-5	176
2.37	2-3	109	2.97	2-4B	130	3.60	3-4	169
2.38	2-4A	122	2.98	2-6	143	3.61	3-5	176
2.38	2-4B	127	2.99	2-3	116	3.62	3-6B	190
2.39	2-4A	122	2.100	2-3	116	3.63	3-5	177
2.40	2-3	110	3.01	3-6A	183	3.64	3-5	177
2.41	2-3	110	3.02	3-2	158	3.65	3-5	177
2.42	2-3	110	3.03	3-1	153	3.66	3-5	179
2.43	2-7	146	3.04	3-1	154	3.67	3-5	177
2.44	2-4B	127	3.05	3-1	153	3.68	3-4	169
2.45	2-3	111	3.06	3-6 B	189	3.69	3-5	178
2.46	2-4B	127	3.07	3-1	154	3.70	3-5	178
2.47	2-6	141	3.08	3-6B	189	3.71	3-4	169
2.48	2-6	142	3.09	3-1	154	3.72	3-5	178
2.49	2-4B	128	3.09	3-2	158	3.73	3-6A	187
2.50	2-3	111	3.10	3-5	73	3.74	3-5	178
2.51	2-6	142	3.11	3-2	158	3.75	3-5	179
2.52	2-3	111	3.12	3-6A	183	3.76	3-7B	199
2.52	5-2	299	3.13	3-6A	183	3.77	3-7F	211
2.53	2-6	142	3.14	3-2	158	3.78	3-5	179
2.54	2-5	133	3.15	3-1	154	3.79	3-5	179
2.55	2-7	146	3.16	3-1	154	3.80	3-7B	199
2.56	2-3	112	3.17	3-5	173	3.81	3-7B	200
2.57	2-5	133	3.18	3-6B	189	3.82	3-7A	195
2.58	2-3	112	3.19	3-6A	184	3.83	3-7A	195
2.59	2-4B	128	3.20	3-6B	190	3.84	3-7A	195
2.60	2-6	142	3.21	3-3	163	3.85	3-7F	212
2.61	2-3	112	3.22	3-3	163	3.86	3-7H	215
2.62	2-6	142	3.23	3-4	168	3.87	3-7B	200
2.63	2-5	133	3.24	3-6A	184	3.88	3-7F	212
2.64	2-7	147	3.25	3-6A	185	3.89	3-7A	196
2.65	2-6	142	3.26	3-1	155	3.90	3-7E	209
2.66	2-3	113	3.27	3-6B	190	3.91	3-7B	200
2.66	5-2	299	3.28	3-5	173	3.92	3-7B	200
2.67	2-5	134	3.29	3-3	164	3.93	3-7H	216
2.68	2-5	134	3.30	3-6A	185	3.94	3-7H	216
2.69	2-3	113	3.31	3-5	174	3.95	3-7D	206
2.70	2-3	113	3.32	3-3	164	3.96	3-7A	196
2.71	2-3	113	3.33	3-3	164	3.97	3-7F	212
2.72	2-4B	128	3.34	3-3	164	3.98	3-7G	213
2.73	2-4B	129	3.35	3-2	159	3.99	3-7B	200
2.74	2-4B	129	3.36	3-4	168	3.100	3-7D	206
2.75	2-1A	99	3.37	3-6B	190	3.101	3-7E	209
2.76	1-7B	82	3.38	3-5	173	3.102	3-7A	196

Note: If a skill applies to more than one Strand, the skill is repeated in this Index for each Strand occurrence.

Skill ID	Strand	Page	Skill ID	Strand	Page	Skill ID	Strand	Page
3.103	3-7A	196	4.20	4-4	240	4.79	4-6B	259
3.104	3-7A	197	4.21	4-5	246	4.80	4-7C	275
3.105	3-7H	216	4.22	4-2	228	4.81	4-7D	277
3.106	3-7E	209	4.23	3-2	159	4.82	4-6A	255
3.107	3-7C	203	4.23	4-5	246	4.83	4-6A	255
3.108	3-7C	207	4.24	4-1	224	4.84	4-4	242
3.109	3-7A	197	4.25	4-4	240	4.85	4-6D	266
3.110	3-7B	201	4.26	4-5	247	4.86	4-6A	255
3.111	3-7F	212	4.27	4-3	235	4.87	4-6B	259
3.112	3-7G	214	4.28	4-2	228	4.88	4-7D	277
3.113	3-7A	197	4.29	1-5	63	4.89	4-2	231
3.114	3-7E	209	4.29	4-3	235	4.90	4-7B	272
3.115	3-7E	209	4.30	4-2	228	4.91	4-6B	259
3.116	3-7C	204	4.31	4-1	224	4.92	4-6B	259
3.117	3-7C	204	4.32	4-1	224	4.93	4-7C	275
3.118	3-7B	201	4.33	4-4	240	5.01	0.0	7
3.119	3-7H	216	4.34	4-3	235	5.01	5-1	285
3.120	3-7H	217	4.35	4-5	247	5.02	5-5	324
3.121	3-7H	217	4.36	4-6A	253	5.03	5-3	305
3.122	3-7A	197	4.37	4-5	247	5.04	5-1	285
3.123	3-7E	210	4.38	4-4	240	5.04	5-5	324
3.124	3-7B	201	4.38	4-5	248	5.05	0.0	7
3.125	3-7C	204	4.39	1-1	25	5.05	5-5	325
3.126	3-7H	217	4.40	4-2	229	5.06	5-1	285
3.127	3-7B	201	4.41	4-4	241	5.07	5-3	306
3.128	3-7C	204	4.42	4-3	236	5.07	5-5	325
3.129	3-7C	204	4.43	4-2	229	5.08	0.0	10
3.130	3-7H	217	4.44	4-2	229	5.09	5-5	325
3.131	3-7E	210	4.45	4-2	229	5.10	5-1	286
3.132	3-7C	205	4.46	4-5	248	5.11	5-1	286
3.133	3-7C	205	4.47	4-7B	271	5.12	5-5	326
3.134	3-7C	205	4.48	1-5	64	5.13	5-3	306
3.135	3-7A	198	4.49	4-3	236	5.14	5-4	315
3.136	3-7A	198	4.50	4-4	241	5.15	0.0	11
3.137	3-7B	202	4.51	4-2	230	5.15	5-5	326
3.138	3-7H	217	4.52	4-2	230	5.16	5-2	295
3.139	3-7G	214	4.53	4-6A	253	5.17	5-1	286
3.140	3-7E	210	4.54	4-5	249	5.18	0.0	11
3.141	3-7D	207	4.55	4-2	230	5.19	5-5	327
3.142	3-7F	212	4.56	4-4	241	5.20	5-1	287
3.143	3-7C	205	4.57	4-3	236	5.21	2-4A	121
3.144	3-7B	202	4.58	4-6B	258	5.21	5-1	287
3.145	3-7B	202	4.59	4-6A	254	5.22	5-1	287
3.146	3-7B	202	4.60	1-5	65	5.22	5-2	295
4.01	4-1	222	4.60	4-4	242	5.23	5-2	296
4.02	4-5	246	4.61	1-5	66	5.24	5-2	296
4.03	4-1	222	4.61	4-6B	258	5.25	5-1	288
4.04	4-1	222	4.62	4-7B	272	5.26	5-5	327
4.05	4-1	223	4.63	4-2	231	5.27	3-2	160
4.06	4-1	223	4.64	1-4B	52	5.28	5-2	296
4.07	3-2	159	4.65	4-6A	254	5.29	5-3	307
4.07	4-5	246	4.66	1-5	67	5.30	5-2	296
4.08	4-3	234	4.67	4-4	242	5.31	5-1	288
4.09	4-1	223	4.68	4-5	249	5.32	2-4A	121
4.10	4-1	223	4.69	4-6B	259	5.32	5-5	328
4.11	4-1	224	4.70	4-7B	272	5.33	5-4	315
4.12	4-2	228	4.71	4-6A	254	5.34	5-4	316
4.13	4-4	239	4.72	4-6B	259	5.34	6-4	356
4.14	1-5	63	4.73	4-6A	254	5.35	1-1	26
4.15	4-4	239	4.74	4-7C	275	5.36	5-1	289
4.16	4-3	235	4.75	4-6A	255	5.37	5-1	289
4.17	4-1	223	4.76	4-6D	265	5.38	2-4A	122
4.18	4-1	224	4.77	4-6B	259	5.38	5-5	328
4.19	4-1	224	4.78	4-2	231	5.39	5-2	197

Note: If a skill applies to more than one Strand, the skill is repeated in this Index for each Strand occurrence.

Skill ID	Strand	Page
5.40	5-4	316
5.41	5-1	289
5.42	5-3	307
5.43	5-4	317
5.44	5-4	317
5.45	6-7	367
5.46	5-5	329
5.47	5-2	297
5.48	5-4	317
5.49	5-4	318
5.50	5-2	298
5.51	5-3	308
5.52a	1-1	27
5.52b	1-1	28
5.53	5-3	308
5.54	5-3	308
5.55	5-3	309
5.56	5-4	318
5.57	5-3	309
5.58	2-4A	123
5.58	5-5	329
5.59	5-5	329
5.60	0.0	15
5.61	0.0	16
5.62	5-2	299
5.63	5-3	310
5.64	5-5	330
5.65	5-2	301
5.66	5-5	330
5.67	5-4	319
5.68	5-1	290
5.69	5-1	290
5.70	5-5	330
5.71	5-4	319
5.72	5-5	330
5.73	6-7	369
5.74	5-3	310
5.75	5-5	331
5.76	5-5	331
5.77	1-1	28
5.77	5-3	310
5.78	5-5	331
5.79	5-3	311
5.80	5-4	319
5.81	5-2	300
5.82	5-2	300
5.83	5-2	300
5.84	5-3	311
5.85	5-1	290
5.86	5-1	291
5.87	5-3	311
5.88	5-4	320
5.89	5-5	332
5.90	5-5	332
5.91	5-4	320
5.92	5-4	320
5.93	0.0	18
5.93	5-5	332
5.94	5-2	301
6.01	6-1	337
6.02	6-1	337
6.03	6-4	356
6.04	0.0	9
6.05	6-4	356

Skill ID	Strand	Page
6.06	6-1	337
6.07	6-3	349
6.08	6-1	337
6.09	6-3	349
6.10	6-3	349
6.11	6-1	338
6.12	6-1	337
6.13	6-3	350
6.14	6-4	356
6.15	6-4	356
6.16	4-5	247
6.16	6-3	350
6.17	6-1	338
6.18	6-3	350
6.19	6-1	338
6.20	6-1	339
6.21	6-3	350
6.22	6-1	338
6.23	0.0	13
6.23	6-1	339
6.24	6-1	339
6.25	0.0	13
6.26	6-3	350
6.27	0.0	13
6.27	6-4	356
6.28	6-4	356
6.29	0.0	14
6.29	6-2	342
6.30	6-3	351
6.31	6-3	351
6.32	6-3	351
6.33	6-3	351
6.34	6-6	364
6.35	6-6	364
6.36	6-4	356
6.37	6-4	356
6.38	6-3	351
6.39	6-2	342
6.40	6-2	342
6.41	6-2	343
6.42	6-3	351
6.43	6-3	352
6.44	6-1	339
6.45	6-3	352
6.46	6-2	343
6.47	6-2	343
6.48	6-6	364
6.49	6-6	364
6.50	6-3	352
6.51	6-5	360
6.52	6-6	364
6.53	6-4	357
6.54	6-3	352
6.55	1-4B	53
6.55	6-7	368
6.56	6-7	368
6.57	6-2	343
6.58	6-3	352
6.59	6-3	352
6.60	6-7	369
6.61	0.0	16
6.61	6-7	368
6.62	6-7	369
6.63	6-3	353

Skill ID	Strand	Page
6.64	6-2	343
6.65	6-2	344
6.66	6-5	360
6.67	6-5	360
6.68	6-6	365
6.69	6-6	365
6.70	6-2	344
6.71	6-2	344
6.72	6-2	344
6.73	6-5	361
6.74	6-3	353
6.75	5-1	291
6.76	6-7	369
6.77	6-3	353
6.78	6-3	353
6.79	6-3	353
6.80	6-7	370
6.81	6-2	345
6.82	6-5	361
6.83	6-5	361
6.84	6-6	365
6.85	6-3	353
6.86	6-7	370
6.87	6-6	365
6.88	6-6	365
6.89	6-4	357
6.90	6-4	357
6.91	6-4	357
6.92	6-2	345
6.93	6-5	361

Note: If a skill applies to more than one Strand, the skill is repeated in this Index for each Strand occurrence.

HELP®– Hawaii Early Learning Profile®– 0-3 years

Supported by the *Inside HELP* Administration Manual, following are the other HELP components for comprehensive assessment, planning, intervention, and family support

HELP Family-Centered Interview Form
Simple 8-page booklet facilitates your family interview and assessment process – a listing of 80 key open-ended questions and prompts based on over 400 sample questions from *Inside HELP* – in a format you can use directly with parents. Helps you focus on family-centered priorities, concerns, and outcomes for more effective intervention.
No. 157. each.   **No. 157-B.** pkg of 25.

HELP Strands – Developmental Assessment Record/booklet.
This latest assessment form groups the 685 HELP skills into 58 "concept-based" Strands for easier assessment and planning. Helps you meet IDEA, Part C regulations – in conjunction with *Inside HELP*, you can identify a child's approximate level of development within and between domains and interpret why a child may be having difficulty in a specific strand. Makes for easier identification and selection of target skills. Provides columns for recording credit notes/dates/ observations. (8 1/2" x 11", 28 pages.)
No. 158. (bound version); **No. 158-B** (loose-leaf version)

HELP Charts — Visually track progress.
The Charts are a set of three different sheets that display 685 developmentally sequenced skills as a horizontal continuum for the six areas of Cognitive, Language, Gross Motor, Fine Motor, Social and Self-Help. Each sheet covers 2 areas/domains. The clear format makes it easy to identify current mastery of skills and to record and visually track progress. Ideal for communicating with and involving parents in their child's plan. (set of 3 sheets (11" x 28") fold to 8 1/2" x 11" for filing)
No. 150.

HELP Checklist — Assessment booklet.
Covers the same six developmental areas of Cognitive, Language, Gross Motor, Fine Motor, Social and Self-Help as the HELP Strands, but the format is different. The Checklist groups the 685 skills by area/domain and in age sequence with columns for recording assessment dates, progress information, and comments. The skills are listed by domain in skill # sequence, not necessarily in developmental sequence (see i.15-i.35). (20 pages)
No. 151.

HELP. . . at Home-2nd Edition (2006) — 535 pages of unique, reproducible, ready- to-use parent handouts to help you make parent involvement easy and effective! Saves time – Practical and convenient format offers a separate, reproducible activity sheet for each HELP skill – that you annotate, copy and handout directly to parents to facilitate their involvement. **Interdisciplinary and comprehensive** – Handouts for parents with children (developmentally) birth to three years, including disabled, delayed and at risk children. Provides thousands of activities in the six major developmental areas. **Written from the child's point of view** – Parents definitely prefer this unique approach. Written in warm, simple language. **Easily individualized** – With space for your notes.
No. 156.

HELP When the Parent has Disabilities
This comprehensive and unique resource offers thousands of activities and training techniques for **directly involving** *blind, deaf, physically disabled* and *mentally retarded parents* **in their child's cognitive, motor, social and language development**. The activities are cross-referenced to the 685 skills from HELP and offer special adaptations for parents. A valuable tool for meeting the requirements of IFSPs, it provides an effective basis for outreach to all parents and for offering comprehensive family support. (296 pages) **No. 153.**

HELP Activity Guide — Comprehensive Curriculum and Strategies.
Takes you easily beyond assessment to offer the important next step – practical, task-analyzed activities and intervention strategies indexed by the 685 HELP skills. With up to 10 activities/strategies per skill, this valuable resource includes definitions/criteria for each skill, illustrations and cross references to skills in other developmental areas, a glossary and lists of commercial materials. Essential and effective for planning intervention and preparing home plans. (208 pages)
No. 152.

TERMS:
- Orders from individuals must be prepaid.
- Orders from organizations must be pre-paid or accompanied by a purchase order.
- Foreign orders must be prepaid in *U.S. dollars* on a U.S. bank draft (includes Canada).
- Net 30; FOB Palo Alto.
- Prices are subject to change without notice.

SHIPPING/HANDLING:
All orders must pay shipping charges – including prepaid orders:
- U.S. Mail – 10% or a minimum of $7.00 - *whichever is greater*; [allow 2-3 weeks].
- U.S. UPS ground – 12% or a minimum of $8.50 - *whichever is greater*; [allow 1+ week].
- Foreign– Call or visit our web site.

VORT Corporation, PO Box 60132, Palo Alto, CA 94306

Check for latest pricing and information, and order at our website: www.vort.com